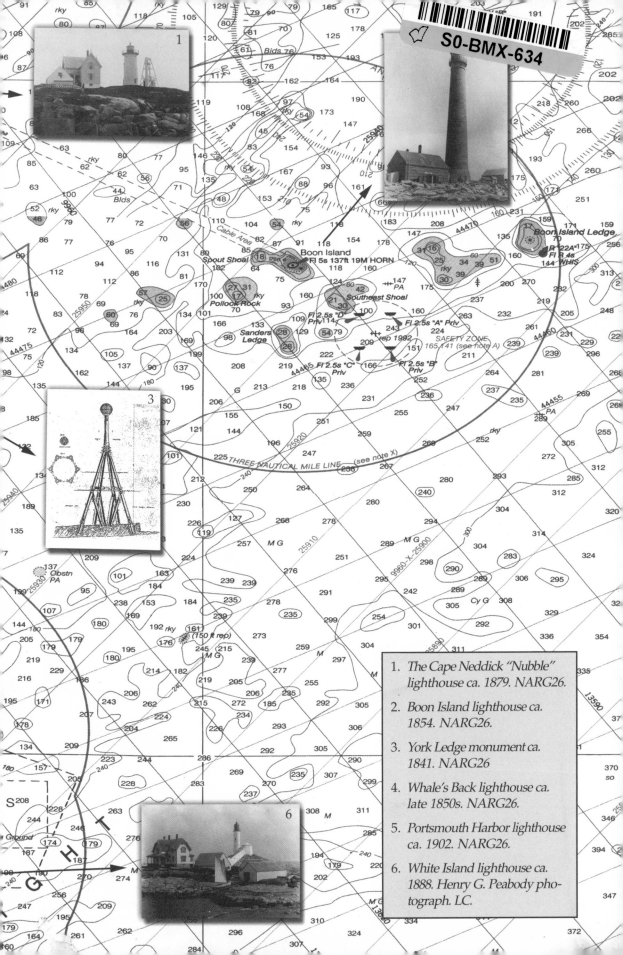

1. The Cape Neddick "Nubble" lighthouse ca. 1879. NARG26.

2. Boon Island lighthouse ca. 1854. NARG26.

3. York Ledge monument ca. 1841. NARG26

4. Whale's Back lighthouse ca. late 1850s. NARG26.

5. Portsmouth Harbor lighthouse ca. 1902. NARG26.

6. White Island lighthouse ca. 1888. Henry G. Peabody photograph. LC.

Friendly Edifices

*Piscataqua Lighthouses
and Other Aids to Navigation
1771-1939*

Perched on a small island and now owned by the Town of York, Maine, Nubble Light is one of America's most picturesque and photographed lighthouses. Photograph by Peter Randall.

Friendly Edifices

*Piscataqua Lighthouses
and Other Aids to Navigation
1771-1939*

by
Jane Molloy Porter

Published by

Peter E. Randall Publisher LLC

for the

The Portsmouth Marine Society
Portsmouth, New Hampshire
2006
Publication Thirty

Designed and produced by
Peter E. Randall Publisher LLC
Box 4726, Portsmouth, NH 03802
www.perpublisher.com

A publication of
The Portsmouth Marine Society
Box 147, Portsmouth, NH 03082

ISBN 10: 0-915819-36-8
ISBN 13: 978-0-915819-36-9

Library of Congress Cataloging-in-Publication Data

Porter, Jane Molloy.
  Friendly edifices : Piscataqua lighthouses and other aids to navigation
1771-1939 / by Jane Molloy Porter.
      p. cm.
  Includes bibliographical references and index.
  ISBN-13: 978-0-915819-36-2 (hardcover : alk. paper)
  1. Lighthouses--Piscataqua River Estuary (N.H. and Me.) 2. Piscataqua
River Estuary (N.H. and Me.)--History. I. Title.
  VK1024.N38P67 2006
  387.1'55097426--dc22
                                        2006010350

In memory of my mother and father and

for my family and friends

Other Portsmouth Marine Society Publications:

Contents

List of Abbreviations

KHNM	Kittery Historical and Naval Museum, Kittery, ME
LC	Library of Congress, Washington, DC
MM	Mariners' Museum, Newport News, VA
MLM	Maine Lighthouse Museum, Rockland, ME
MSM	Mystic Seaport Museum, Mystic, CT
NARG26	National Archives Record Group 26, Washington, DC; Suitland, MD; and Waltham, MA
NHDRMA	New Hampshire Division of Records Management and Archives, Concord, NH
NHHS	New Hampshire Historical Society, Concord, NH
OML	Osher Map Library, University of Southern Maine, Portland, ME
OYHS	Old York Historical Society, York, ME
PA	Portsmouth Athenaeum, Portsmouth, NH
PEM	Peabody Essex Museum, Salem, MA
PNS	Portsmouth Naval Shipyard
PPL	Portsmouth Public Library, Portsmouth, NH
PrC	Private Collection
SI	Smithsonian Institution, Washington, DC
SB	Strawbery Banke Museum, Portsmouth, NH

Acknowledgments

THE ORIGINAL IMPETUS FOR THIS BOOK dates back quite a while. It was a Maine Historic Preservation Commission conference on lighthouses held in Rockland, Maine in 1985, which I attended with my mother, Anne Molloy Howells. Richard Candee, who taught a historic preservation course I had taken at Boston University, was there and suggested that a book about the lighthouses around Portsmouth would be a good thing, and why didn't I see about writing one for the Portsmouth Marine Society? The proposal I sent to Joe Sawtelle and Peter Randall at the society was accepted, and I began to research the subject—about which I was intrigued but had very little knowledge.

Fortunately for me, my mother, a seasoned researcher and a wonderful writer whose fiction for young people includes *Celia's Lighthouse*, was inspired by the lighthouse conference to investigate lighthouses in Maine's Machias Bay. Together we learned the ins and outs of Record Group 26 at the National Archives in Washington and its satellite facility in Maryland, spent time at various libraries, and had a great time sharing finds about "our" lighthouses. Sadly, she died before writing the book she'd planned.

I've read a lot of books about lighthouses. Probably one of the most influential of those listed in the bibliography was F. Ross Holland Jr.'s *America's Lighthouses*, first published in 1972 with a corrected and expanded version appearing in 1988. Unlike many of the books published around the time of the 1989 bicentennial of the U. S. lighthouses, it contained not only information about specific lighthouses and their keepers but also the history of their administration and the technology involved. His bibliography pointed me to many primary and secondary sources. George Putnam, lighthouse commissioner 1910–1935, wrote well, and of course extremely knowledgeably, about lighthouses and lightships and carefully studied the history of American lighthouses. Robert W. Sterling, a newspaperman turned lighthouse keeper, published *Lighthouses of the Maine Coast* in 1935. Sterling knew personally many of the lighthouse keepers he wrote about and included a good deal of information about lighthouse and buoy tenders, district engineers, and other personnel who helped keep the lights and fog signals going during this period. Edward Rowe Snow began publishing his very popular books about lighthouses in the 1940s, and it is evident that he spent a lot of time with primary sources as well as with the lighthouse keepers he got to know well both as an author and as the "Flying Santa."

Work on this book, put on the shelf for quite a few years when I had a job, introduced me to many helpful librarians and archivists and fellow researchers. Of these, Richard E. Winslow III stands out. During his journeys through microfilmed Portsmouth newspapers at the Portsmouth Public Library, he kept an eye out for news items about lighthouses. Over the years Dick printed out hundreds and hundreds of them for me, at least quadrupling the number I found myself while peering at microfilm readers. Early on, the late Ray Brighton generously turned over to me his file on lighthouses and a copy of the fat, juicy 1852 report of the Light-House Board.

Many Portsmouth Athenæum friends and colleagues, past and present, gave me encouragement as well as assorted large and small pieces of information they'd come across. They helped me locate documents, books, and photographs at that dear place, and I thank them all: Lynn Aber, Michael Baenen, Rita Conant, Armistead Dennett, Robert Dishman, James Dolph, Ronan Donohoe, Carolyn Eastman, Rose Eppard, Tom Hardiman, Marcia Jebb, Susan Kinstedt, Kevin Shupe, Robin Silva, and Ursula Wright.

Carolyn Roy, Tara Webber, and Courtney MacLachlan at Strawbery Banke Museum helped with illustrative material, as did Nicole Luongo-Cloutier at the Portsmouth Public Library, Yolanda Theunissen of the Osher Map Library at the University of Southern Maine, Kirk Mohney of the Maine Historic Preservation Commission, Christine Michelini at the Peabody Essex Museum in Salem, and Louise Laplante at the Smith College Museum of Art. Virginia Spiller and Cynthia Young-Gomes at the

Old York Historical Society were extremely helpful, as was James Dolph at the Portsmouth Naval Shipyard and Wayne Mason at the Kittery Historical and Naval Museum. Ted Panayotoff of the Maine Lighthouse Museum in Rockland Maine, readily shared his extensive knowledge of that museum's holdings of objects and images, and Sandra Armentrout told me about Eliphalet Grover's "Logg" and the stringed instruments he made at Boon Island, now in the Old York Historical Society's collections. Nelson Lawry shared information about the "Muscovy" lanterns at Fort William and Mary and Michael Brodhead, U. S. Army Corps of Engineers historian, was cheerfully and speedily responsive to my queries about lighthouse engineers, as was Claudia Jew at the Mariner's Museum about lighthouse tenders. Joseph W. P. Frost is a hero for locating at the last minute the print of Whale's Back lighthouse in a storm, as is its kind owner for allowing Joe and Peter Narbonne to transport it to Peter Randall for photographing.

My thanks to Peter Hutt for responding to a query about the whereabouts of a Russell Cheney painting of the Nubble lighthouse, and to professors Lino Pertile, Master of Eliot House at Harvard University, and Kevin Van Anglen, Keeper of the F. O. Matthiessen Room, for expediting permission to photograph and publish the painting; thanks as well to Sue Weltman at Eliot House for her cheerful help. Thanks also to Jeremy D'Entremont for information about contemporary local lighthouse advocacy groups.

Over the years, I've had assistance, in person and in writing, from the staffs at the various National Archives facilities, the Library of Congress, the Smithsonian Institution, the Maritime Museum in Bath, Maine, the Maine Historical Society, the Maine Historic Preser-vation Commission, the Peabody Museum and the Essex Institute Museum (now combined as the Peabody Essex Museum), the Royal Ontario Historical Society in Canada, the New Castle Public Library, the Portsmouth Naval Shipyard archives, the Dimond Library at the University of New Hampshire, the New Hampshire State Archives, the U. S. Coast Guard Academy Library in New London, Connecticut, and the G. W. Blunt Library at the Mystic Seaport Museum.

My sister-in-law, Martha Molloy, very kindly put me up in her New York apartment when I visited a Coast Guard archive located at the time on Governor's Island.

For access to material about Herman Ingalls, I thank his granddaughter Prudence Heard, of Yarmouth, Maine, and Lois Ingalls

Sprague and Marjorie Sprague Pinkham of Starboard, in Machiasport, Maine. For sharing their knowledge of Edwin Hobbs, I am grateful to his grand-nephew, the late Stillman Hobbs, and his wife Helen, of Hampton.

Jonathan Hubbard generously permitted me to use his Childe Hassam watercolor for the cover of this book. Thanks as well to Jean Sawtelle, Celia Thaxter Hubbard, Pat Meyers, Peter Narbonne, Bolling Smith, Douglas and Karin Nelson, and Robert Chase for their kind permission to reproduce images in their possession.

I am grateful to the Coast Guard for arranging exciting transportation to two lighthouses in rigid-hull inflatable "Zodiacs." In 1988 Robert Tiner and Chris Wisinski Jr. took me to White Island and Tom Dutton and Diane Graham made sure I got safely to and from Boon Island.

Richard Candee gave very helpful advice on an early draft of the first chapters of the book, and Michael Baenen carefully read and tactfully edited the first seven chapters of a later draft. Doris Troy thoroughly edited a version for the Portsmouth Marine Society. Ed Stevens and Grace Peirce skillfully put images and text together and with good humor dealt with final corrections.

My thanks to Peter Randall for his extraordinary patience. It's just about twenty years now since I signed on to do this book, and he has not scolded or threatened me once. Much gratitude is due to Jean Sawtelle for the support of the writing and publishing of histories of our seacoast region that her husband Joe began back in 1982 when Peter published the first Portsmouth Marine Society volume.

Finally, I give heartfelt thanks to family and friends, who mercifully decided after about ten years to stop asking, "How's that book coming along?"

Jane Molloy Porter
Portsmouth,
New Hampshire
February 2006

I. Introduction

The life of the most experienced is more endangered
when he approaches the coast, than when exposed to
the tempests which agitate the mid-ocean.

—*The American Coast Pilot*, 1833

FOR MARINERS, these words are as true now as when they were written more than a century and a half ago, except that at the beginning of the twenty-first century, both the master of a six-hundred-foot-long tanker bound up the Piscataqua River for the power plant at Newington, New Hampshire, and the weekend captain of a twelve-foot outboard off on a fishing jaunt can take for granted an amazing array of aids to navigation by day or night.

A glance at the chart "Portsmouth Harbor: Cape Neddick to Isles of Shoals," reproduced on the end papers of this book, shows numbered, color-coded buoys, day marks, whistles, horns, lighthouses, floating lights, and paired range lights. The chart indicates the color and flashing or steady character of the lights, and the intervals at which fog signals sound. Countless depth soundings and indications of landforms and man-made landmarks help sailors establish their bearings. Also shown are river and harbor channels, deepened and widened by dredging and blasting operations, and breakwaters built to create safe anchorages. In addition, modern technology has produced ways to measure the water's depth and equipment for receiving signals to establish bearings from invisible sources like LORAN and Global Positioning Satellites, as well as ship-to-shore radios, cell phones, and ready access to government reports of impending storm conditions.

Commercial vessels and pleasure powerboats are now far less at the mercy of the winds and tidal currents that every master of a sailing vessel once had to take into account. Modern pleasure sailboats have deep, weighted false keels and hulls and sail rigs designed to make it possible to go to windward and change direction efficiently, unlike the cumbersome square-rigged sailing vessels of the past. These might be driven onto lee shores during onshore gales because they "mis-stayed" and were unable to come about in time to avert this dreaded event. And most modern sailboats are outfitted with auxiliary engines.

The stretch of the North Atlantic coast off Portsmouth is occasionally punctuated by rocky headlands. On the charts they are called heads, points, necks, or capes; their names, like Great Boar's Head and Raynes Neck, reflect their appearance or commemorate early landowners. Offshore are rock ledges and islets, many of which are underwater at most stages of the tide. The names of some recall the physical characteristics by which mariners identified them. Others memorialize the shipmasters or vessels that came to grief upon them. Much of this stretch of coast lies low and consists of sandy beaches, shallow coves, and salt marshes laced with meandering tidal creeks. Six miles out from Ragged Neck in Rye, New Hampshire, are the Isles of Shoals, a small archipelago of treeless islands and ledges. Seven miles off York, Maine, is the low-lying, boulder-strewn ledge called Boon Island, along with its satellite hazards, Boon Island Rock and Boon Island Ledge.

The mouth of the Piscataqua River forms the only major deep-water harbor along this portion of the coast. The river flows into the sea at the north edge of the seventeen-mile New Hampshire shoreline and marks the boundary between Maine and New Hampshire at the coast. It was described three hundred years ago by William Hubbard:

> The Piscataqua is a river of noat, which has been frequented ever since the country was first planted, by such as came this way for trafficke with the inhabitants, natives, and others, that have seated themselves in several plantations about the uppermost branches thereof. The channel is very swift and spacious, fit for vessels of great burden for the space of near twenty miles, where it divides itself into many considerable bays and small branches.[1]

Jeremy Belknap, writing a hundred years later, noted one of the major advantages of Portsmouth Harbor: It practically never freezes over. The reason for this is the rapidity of the current in the river. This tidal force was and is still one of the harbor's major drawbacks, however, especially in the main channel of the river between Pierce's and Seavey's Islands. Belknap wrote that there "the stream is contracted to a very narrow passage, and the tide is extremely rapid," but he noted that small vessels and boats could navigate the inner channels between these islands and both shores of the river. He also mentioned another entrance to the river, by way of Little Harbor on the south side of Great Island (now New Castle).[2]

On the southern side of the river between Great Island and the town of Portsmouth was the Pool, with water deep enough for the mast ships of the colonial era to lie at anchor, safely out of the tidal power and turbulence of the main channel. Belknap also wrote that the town of Portsmouth, two miles from the river's mouth, had water deep enough to anchor and dock the largest of the vessels of his time.[3]

Not far from the river's mouth on the north side, in Kittery, Maine, Pepperrell's Cove offers anchorage; and a mile and more upriver, narrow tidal creeks are navigable by small boats for a mile or so. At Dover Point, about six miles from the Piscataqua's mouth, the river branches and rebranches, flowing to Little and Great Bays and the towns of Exeter, New Market, Durham, Dover, and Somersworth, New Hampshire, and South Berwick, Maine, at the tidal heads of the Piscataqua's tributaries, as far as twenty river miles from the sea. Along the Maine shore, about six miles northeast of the entrance to the Piscataqua, is the tortuous entrance to York Harbor, the only other harbor in the area that could accommodate vessels of any size, and the winding York River.

After his voyage of 1614, Captain John Smith wrote that the charts and sailing directions he carried aboard his vessel for this stretch of coast "did me no more good, than so much waste paper, though they did cost me more."[4] Before there were adequate charts and printed sailing directions, masters of vessels feeling their way into anchorage in the waters around Portsmouth had to depend on the accumulated and shared experience of those who had come before. However, by 1760 at least, and probably much earlier, pilots were available to take over upriver navigation for vessels arriving at the mouth of the Piscataqua.[5] Shipmasters unfamiliar with these waters dispatched men in boats to scout for hazards and to gauge the water's depth with a lump of lead on the end of a line. When night came, the safe course was to anchor and

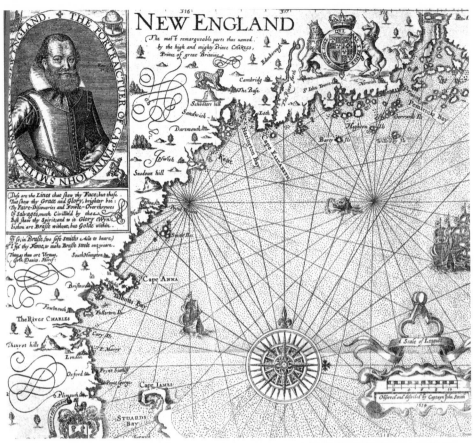

Captain John Smith, who named the Isles of Shoals for himself on this map, called contemporary charts and sailing directions for the New England coast "no more good than so much waste paper," but this early 17th century production cannot have been an especially useful guide for travel on land or sea. From John S. Jenness, The Isles of Shoals, An Historic Sketch.

wait for daybreak. In a strong onshore gale, hoisting anchor and sails and cruising offshore was the only way to avoid being driven onto a lee shore; however, during times of war or piracy, having to anchor or sail offshore to wait for daybreak or favorable winds increased the dangers of attack.

Until just before the Revolution, the intricacies and obstacles to navigation around and into the Port of Piscataqua, as Portsmouth's port was then called, were perhaps better shown on maps produced by land surveyors than on the nautical charts prepared by hydrographers. The "Map of Pascataway River in New England," produced in England by "I. S." (ca. 1660), gives a relatively detailed representation of the port and the hazards at its entrance.[6] But as late as 1703, the slapdash "A

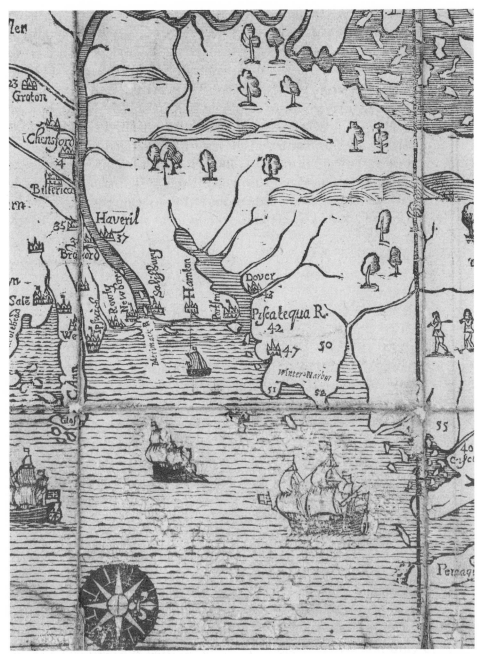

John Foster, considered the earliest engraver in the colonies, and the first printer in Boston, produced this "Map of New-England" for William Hubbard's A Narrative of the Troubles with the Indians in New-England *printed by Foster in 1677. The map was not intended as a navigational chart. It shows the "swift and spacious" Piscataqua River that Hubbard described in his slightly later history of New England.* Courtesy of the Osher Map Library, University of Southern Maine.

Chart of Ye Coast of New England, New York and Long Island," issued by Sellers and Price of London, perpetuated the inadequacies evident in most charts available before the end of the seventeenth century.[7]

London-born Captain Cyprian Southack (1662–1745), who emigrated to Boston in 1685, is considered the first American-based navigator to undertake surveys, many in the *Province Galley,* for charts of the northern part of the North American coast between Cape Cod and Nova Scotia. Southack had produced a chart of Boston Harbor by 1694. Military engineer Colonel William Romer, who in 1699 had produced a chart of New Castle Island that provided the first depth soundings for this area, recorded Southack's presence in the Piscataqua in a view of the fort at New Castle. The legend identifies the masts seen to the left of the flag as those of Southack's vessel. By 1719, Southack had produced a "draught of the sea coast and river of Piscataqua." Between 1729 and 1734, he published in the *New England Coasting Pilot* eight charts, heavily annotated with sailing directions, covering portions of the coast from Sandy Hook, New Jersey, to Nova Scotia.[8]

Southack's charts and notations in turn were used in various editions of the British publication *The English Pilot: The Fourth Book.* This was last published in 1794 and was widely consulted well into the next century. No copy of Southack's Piscataqua chart has been located, but a draft of it was presented to the New Hampshire General Assembly in 1719, perhaps with a view to having it produced at province expense. It apparently never was. Southack's knowledge of the coast was extensive and his notations helpful, but his cartographic techniques were unsophisticated. In the middle of the nineteenth century, one critic, sounding much like John Smith more than a hundred years earlier, wrote of one of Southack's productions that it was "one continued error" and "ought to be... destroyed if found among sea charts." [9]

A dozen years before the American Revolution, after the 1763 treaty finally ended sporadic French and Indian wars and confirmed England's acquisition of east Florida and Canada, British territorial possessions embraced the entire east coast of North America except for France's St. Pierre and Miquelon islands off the coast of Newfoundland. In the decade before the Revolution, the British government undertook state-of-the-art land and nautical surveys of the coasts of its North American holdings. In 1764, a surveyor general was appointed for the northern district of New England and another for the southern Atlantic coast.

New Castle, 1699. Attributed to William Romer (with north at the bottom) showing the first depth soundings for this part of the coast. PA.

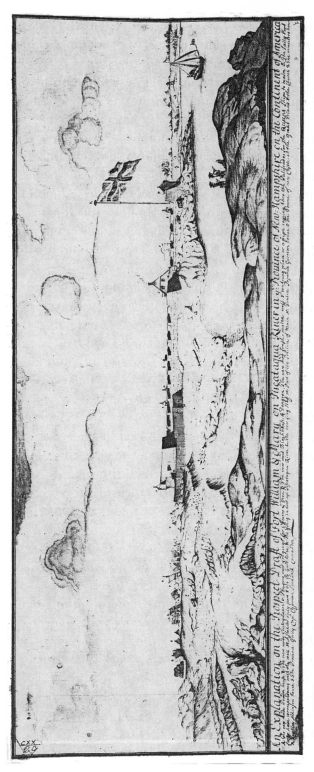

Fort William and Mary on the Piscataqua River, 1699. The legend indicates the presence of Captain Cyprian Southack's Province Galley. PA.

Opposite page: *Detail from "A Map of the Coast of New England, from Staten Island to the Island of Breton ...London, 1775, produced in 1744 from eight charts in Cyprian Southack's 1729-1733 New England Coasting Pilot. The many errors in Southack's productions were perpetuated in British publications as late as 1794 that were used well into the nineteenth century. Courtesy of the Osher Map Library, University of Southern Maine.*

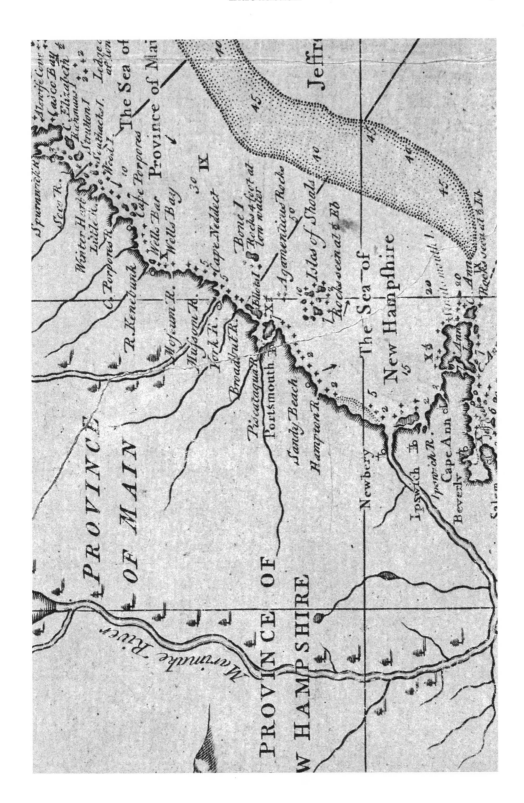

Assigned to the northern district was Captain Samuel Holland (1728–1801), who was simultaneously appointed surveyor general of the Province of Quebec. Holland had been active since 1756 in military reconnaissance, mapping, and engineering in America. He was born Samuel Jan Hollandt in Deventer in the Netherlands, possibly to parents who had emigrated from England, and was trained in the Dutch army before going to England in 1754. Under a 1755 act of Parliament permitting army commissions to foreign Protestants experienced as officers or engineers, Holland was one of about fifty German, Swiss, and Dutch officers commissioned for the 60th Royal American Regiment, and arrived in the colonies in 1756. Before his 1764 appointments, he had already surveyed the St. Lawrence Gulf and River. One of his assistants was Captain James Cook, whom Holland had taught the use of the plane table.[10]

Holland spent more than a dozen years on surveys in the Province of Quebec before turning his attention to the northern district of New England. By December 1770, Holland, with six deputy surveyors and their assistants working in different parts of this district, had set up

Captain Samuel Holland (1728-1801) and his surveying teams produced the most technically advanced charts of the northern American coast for the British government in the pre-Revolutionary era and were working in the Portsmouth area in the early 1770s. Prince Edward Island Public Records and Archives Office.

headquarters in Kittery, Maine, on the north side of the Piscataqua. In 1771, Holland and two, possibly three of his deputies appear on the Portsmouth tax rolls, and one of them, James Grant, is listed on the rolls in 1773, 1774, and 1775.[11] Holland and a deputy were to survey most of the coast of Maine and New Hampshire and south to Boston, with others taking on the southern part of his district. James Grant was in the Portsmouth area often through 1771 and most of 1772, according to the records of St. John's Masonic Lodge, and continued in the area as late as 1775. "Plan of Piscataqua Harbor, the Town of Portsmouth, & ..." bears Grant's name and is dated 1774.

The armed merchant vessel *Canceaux,* commanded by Henry Mowatt, provided transportation for Holland and his team as well as offshore soundings for the Maine and New Hampshire portion of the survey—as it had done for Holland in Canada since 1764.[12]

The work produced by Holland and his deputies resulted in a richly detailed record of roads, houses and property boundaries, as well as the coastline and its topography. Considering the magnitude of his assignments and the wilderness nature of much of the coastal terrain involved, Holland's accomplishments are evidence of outstanding organizational ability, technical proficiency, and stamina.

Contemporaneous with Holland's work was that of Joseph F. W. DesBarres (1721–1824.) Born in either France or Switzerland, DesBarres, like Holland, had emigrated to England by the early 1750s, and in the middle of the decade became an officer in the Royal American Regiment.[13] The commander of the British fleet in America, Sir Richard Spry, argued the strategic importance of adequate nautical charts. On his recommendation, in 1764 the Lords of Admiralty appointed DesBarres to conduct nautical surveys of the Nova Scotia coast. His surveys were still under way as late as 1775. Back in England on the eve of the American Revolution, DesBarres took on the assignment of providing charts for the Admiralty. He was given permission to use the surveys Holland had finished for the Board of Trade and those of Holland's counterpart for the southern portion of the American coast, William G. DeBrahm.

Over the next years, Des-Barres and his assistants produced some 250 engravings of charts and harbor views. These combined the coastal portions of the surveys and views produced by Holland and

Sir Richard Spry, Commander of the British Fleet in American, whose 1764 recommendation to the Lords of Admiralty was instrumental in the appointment of J. F. W. DesBarres to conduct nautical surveys of the Nova Scotia Coast. It was DesBarres who published Holland's surveys in the Atlantic Neptune *in various versions from 1777-1784. Portrait by John Smibert. PA.*

DeBrahm and their teams with his own work and were published by Des-
Barres as an atlas, the *Atlantic Neptune*. Charts in various combinations
and states of completion were gathered in editions published in England
between 1777 and 1784.[14]

DesBarres's charts are renowned for both their aesthetic qualities
and the marked technical improvements they represented. They were
of great strategic importance to the British during the Revolution,
though it is highly probable that some fell into the hands of the Revolutionary forces. After the war, American publishers used them either
in their original form or as the basis for amended versions. DesBarres,
Holland, and DeBrahm had employed the most up-to-date equipment

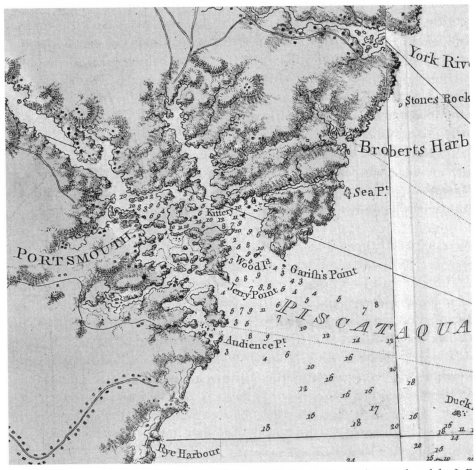

Detail from Atlantic Neptune *chart of Portsmouth Harbor, engraving produced for J. F.
W. DesBarres from the 1770s surveys by Holland and his team.* Courtesy of the Osher Map
Library, University of Southern Maine.

and techniques of their time, and for decades the *Atlantic Neptune* remained the best available source for charts of our coast.[15]

Early in the nineteenth century, the U.S. government made an abortive attempt to systematically survey the coasts, and the U.S. Navy produced a number of charts before the War of 1812. But the federal government did not effectively undertake coastal surveys until the 1830s, leaving the task in private hands. It was Edmund March Blunt (1770–1862), a native of Portsmouth early transplanted to Newburyport, Massachusetts, near the New Hampshire border, who began to fill the void with the 1797 publication of a single chart of the Georges Bank prepared by Captain George Pinkham. The previous year, Blunt had published the first edition of the *American Coast Pilot,* containing detailed sailing directions for the eastern seaboard prepared with the assistance of Captain Laurence Furlong. This, and the twenty revised editions of the *Pilot* published through 1867, provided information about bearings, tidal currents, hazards, and landmarks, and, as they were built, about lighthouses and other navigational aids. Small charts of individual harbors began to appear in the fifth edition (1806), some cribbed from the *Atlantic Neptune* and other sources. Blunt, whose publications by 1799 included Nathaniel Bowditch's *New American Practical Navigator,* moved his nautical publications business to New York in 1811. His sons, Edmund and George W., eventually joined him in this enterprise, and as hydrographers were also associated with the U. S. Coast Survey, first superintended by Ferdinand Hassler and then by Alexander Dallas Bache. The Blunts added new

Edmund March Blunt (1770-1862) started publishing the American Coast Pilot *in 1796, and with family members produced twenty-one editions of this valuable aid to mariners. The federal government took over publication of the* Pilot *around 1868. Beginning in the 1830s, the Blunts were persistent critics and advocates of reform of many aspects of the United States lighthouse system. MSM.*

THE
AMERICAN COAST PILOT:

CONTAINING

DIRECTIONS

FOR THE

PRINCIPAL HARBORS, CAPES, AND HEADLANDS,

ON THE

COASTS OF NORTH AND SOUTH AMERICA:

DESCRIBING THE

SOUNDINGS, BEARINGS OF THE LIGHTHOUSES AND BEACONS FROM
THE ROCKS, SHOALS, LEDGES, &c.

WITH THE PREVAILING

WINDS, SETTING OF THE CURRENTS, &c.

AND THE

LATITUDES AND LONGITUDES

OF THE

PRINCIPAL HARBORS AND CAPES;

TOGETHER WITH A

A TIDE TABLE.

BY EDMUND M. BLUNT.

FOURTEENTH EDITION, IMPROVED,
BY E. & G. W. BLUNT.

—⊗∞—

NEW YORK:

Title page of the fourteenth (1841) edition of Blunt's American Coast Pilot. *PA.*

charts to the *Coast Pilot*, many produced by themselves, as they became available.[16]

In the early 1840s, the U.S. Coast Survey under Bache accelerated the pace of government surveying. A preliminary chart of Portsmouth Harbor was available in the 1840s, but it was not until 1867 that the federal government took on responsibility for providing the detailed sailing directions the Blunts had published as a commercial venture in their *Coast Pilot*.[17]

However, even the best of the charts and sailing directions available during the colonial era could not have prevented situations like the one in which John Deane, master of the *Nottingham Galley,* found himself on his voyage from the British Isles in the fall of 1710. His intended destination was Boston. Delayed by a stormy crossing, Deane and his crew did not sight land until the eleventh of December, "and then, in a Quarter of an Hour, lost Sight of it again by the Fogs and hazy Weather, that had prevented their taking an Observation for 10 or 12 Days before; which with the unaccountable Currents here met with, so disconcerted their Reckoning, they could not, with Certainty, determine which Part of the Coast they had seen."[18] Peering into the darkness in alternating snow and rain, as the temperature hovered around freezing, Deane spotted breakers too late to avoid the rocks upon which they crashed. The *Galley* was smashed to pieces on ledges off Boon Island. Deane and his men managed to scramble onto the island itself. His account of their twenty-four days on this shelterless, boulder-strewn island makes hair-raising reading. Before they were rescued the men had no way to make a fire and barely any food until they resorted to cannibalizing a dead member of the crew.[19]

A lighthouse might have warned Captain Deane in time to avert this disaster. What is generally agreed to have been the first true lighthouse built in the British colonies of North America was constructed six years later, on Brewster's Island in Boston Harbor, but it would be a century before one was built on Boon Island.

There have been many histories of the early lighthouses in the Mediterranean basin and along the Atlantic coasts of Europe.[20] Of these European lighthouses, there are two, both built before the first lighthouse rose to mark a safe anchorage in the Piscataqua River in 1771, that exemplify two separate and sometimes conflicting influences on American lighthouse design and management.

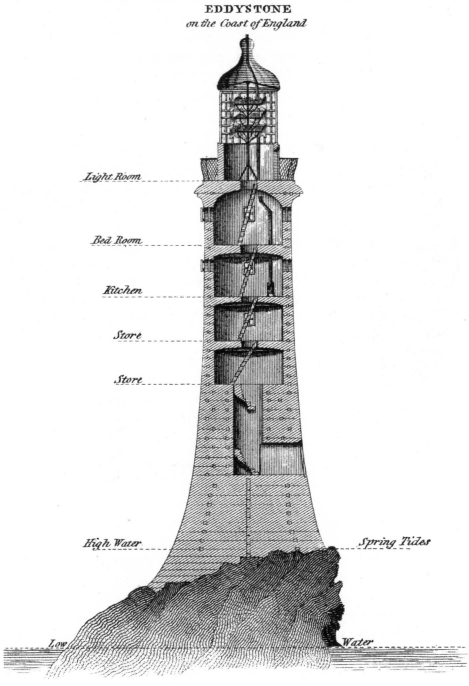

John Smeaton's Eddystone light. Edinburgh Encyclopaedia.

Of these, perhaps the better known is engineer John Smeaton's seventy-foot-high, unadorned lighthouse completed in 1756–9 on the difficult, wave-battered Eddystone Ledge twelve miles off the southern coast of England. It was the fourth lighthouse built at this site. Smeaton applied scientific principles to his design, but he also studied and learned much from the models and plans of each of the preceding structures: how tall his lighthouse should be to keep the lantern out of reach of storm seas, the need for improved ways to secure the structure to the ledge, and to create a mass of interlocking stones that could withstand the force of storm seas and fire (which had consumed the wooden cribwork of the previous lighthouse). This pragmatic approach, based on the experience gained from the failures of the previous structures at this site, to some extent characterized the first generation of lighthouse construction in America.[21]

The other is a French lighthouse. It was a monumental, architecturally embellished lighthouse on Cordouan Island, a challenging, sea-washed ledge off the mouth of the Gironde River. Built between 1584 and 1611, this structure included a vaulted, coffered chapel; a spire soared above the unglazed lantern where blazing oak fires provided the first light source. This lighthouse, still standing, was modified in 1790 with the addition of a more businesslike conical tower giving it a height of 216 feet above the rock. It was at the Cordouan lighthouse that the first of the Fresnel lenses, which revolutionized lighthouse illumination, was placed in 1823. The Cordouan lighthouse is symbolic of the French expertise in engineering and lighting technology, which in the mid-nineteenth century had enormous influence on reform of the U.S. lighthouse system.

Although lighted aids to navigation may very well have existed previously, one of the earliest known such aids in the British colonies of North America appears in 1673 petitions and bills submitted by citizens of Nantasket (now Hull), Massachusetts, to the General Court of the Massachusetts Bay Colony. They asked tax relief because of the material and labor they had spent to erect a stone *beacon* on Point Allerton, a prominent headland near the entrance to Boston Harbor, and payment for furnishing "fier bales of pitch and ocum" for this beacon.[22]

The word *beacon* has come to mean a lighted guide of some sort, but at that time it described an unlighted navigational marker, or daymark. The word is thought to derive from the German *Bake,* and its plural *Baken,* which first signified poles placed in shoal water to mark the channel of an estuary. Later beacons were land-based constructions

Plan of the French Cordouan Lighthouse at the mouth of the Gironde River, as it appeared in 1790 after additions to the structure that was begun in 1584.

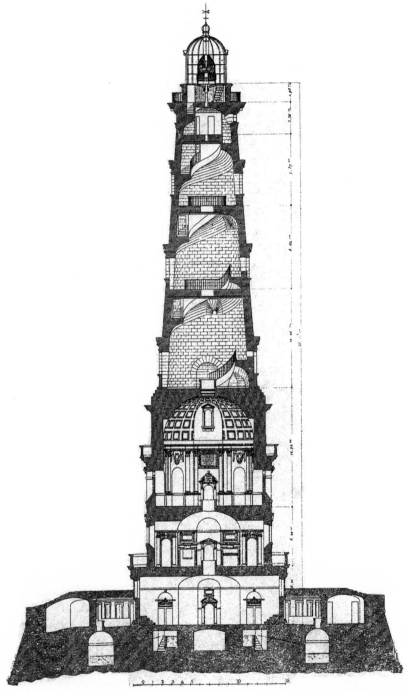

Cross-section of the Cordouan Lighthouse, showing the vaulted, coffered ceiling of the chapel below the later addition to the tower.

of wood, cairns of loosely piled stones, or even mortared stone towers serving as daytime navigational aids. The Point Allerton beacon probably served principally as a daymark, with the men lighting their bundles of pitch-soaked flax or hemp only during special circumstances like the arrival of a vessel sighted toward dark during rough weather and in need of guidance to reach a safe anchorage.[23]

The first true lighthouse—a man-made structure elevating a light source that was lit every night and was tended by someone paid to do the job—in English America was not built until sixty years before the American Revolution. It was the stone structure erected in 1716 on Brewster's Island at the entrance to Boston Harbor.

The Piscataqua region was settled in the 1620s, with an economy based on plentiful timber and the fisheries at the Isles of Shoals. Maritime activity in the Piscataqua River and its tributaries was significant from the middle of the seventeenth century onward, and shipbuilding was in evidence by then. It would not be surprising if bonfires had been lit on beaches and headlands to help navigation in the area by the end of the century, although no records of such activity have been found. And it is probable that when local sailors headed home before dark, they set their course with the help of strategically placed cairns of rocks or wooden poles; when aligned with prominent buildings or landmarks such as trees, hilltops and coastal promontories, they would mark a safe course into harbor.

There is evidence that lighting devices were used in the region by the early eighteenth century as a means of signaling enemy attack at night and the need to muster defensive forces. The English had fortified the northeastern tip of New Castle Island, which commanded the entrance to Portsmouth Harbor, by the mid-seventeenth century. In 1708, during Queen Anne's War, the military engineer Colonel William Romer recommended not only that the fort, then known as Fort William and Mary, have additional supplies of guns and powder, but also that it be supplied with "2 ordinary Muscovy lanterns and one extraordinary Muscovy lantern to hoist at the mast for a distress signal." A 1711 enumeration of equipment and supplies at the fort confirms the presence of not just two but "4 ordinary and 1 extraordinary Muscovy lanterns."[24]

The designation "Muscovy" seems to have been a corruption of the word *muscovite,* a crystalline mineral formation of glass-like, transparent layers that could be separated into sheets. Muscovite is a variety of mica that occurred naturally in Russia, and was used at one time in Siberia instead of window glass. Sheets of this mineral are said to have been used for windows of Russian war ships because they were less likely to shatter than panes of glass when guns were fired. Muscovite was discovered in Pennsylavania and used there and in New Jersey by Swedish settlers in the seventeenth century. The lanterns acquired for use at the fort were called "Muscovy lanterns" because they were fitted not with glass but with sheets of this mineral. Muscovy lanterns were probably requested because they were suited to withstand being banged around while hanging from a flagpole or mast, though it may have been because it was cheaper than glass. [25]

On April 21, 1721, the committee that audited the marine accounts of the New Hampshire Council and Assembly approved payment of the following bills:

> Robert Coats for Light-house and
> other work at Ye Fort..........£14:10:7
> ...also 20s to Robt Coates for his
> trouble about the lighthouse, as pr
> his acct..........................£1:1:0 [26]

No later reference to this structure has been found and it is not known what other work at the fort was included in Coats's bill. It is highly probable, given the amount of money involved, that the "lighthouse" was a shed of some sort to store the Muscovy lanterns and the fuel for them, rather than an early attempt to build a real lighthouse. It is possible, though not documented, that by then a lantern hoisted on a mast at the fort was used as a guide for vessels as well as to warn of attack. After all, the first lighthouse in the British colonies had been built just five years earlier on Brewster's Island to aid navigation into Boston Harbor, a fact surely not lost on the many masters of Piscataqua vessels who frequented that harbor. In any case, the use of a lantern on a mast was discontinued at some point after this, though the idea was revived nearly fifty years later by Governor John Wentworth as a cheap substitute for a real lighthouse.

By the beginning of the eighteenth century, the center of merchant shipping activity in Portsmouth had begun shifting away from the wharves off the shallow coves on the north side of New Castle Island upriver to the deeper waters off Portsmouth, where other wharves and warehouses were being built. In the 1720s and 1730s, there was continued growth of maritime commerce in the Port of Piscataqua; by

1743, 147 vessels averaging eighty-three tons' burden were making their way in and out of the port annually. By the next year in New England, Piscataqua shipbuilding would be second only to Boston's.[27]

In April 1742, the New Hampshire provincial government passed an ambitious "Christmas tree" act, approved by the Crown the following year, calling for the issuance of twenty-five thousand pounds. The money was earmarked to increase the income of the recently appointed royal governor, Benning Wentworth, and for capital improvements including a state house and repairs to Fort William and Mary. The act also provided for a lighthouse:

> Moreover Considering... the great Service which a light-House upon Odiorn's Point [so called] would be of to Vessels coming in or near this Harbour, the Great Difficulty the Trading part of His Majesty's good Subjects of this Province will be under in carrying on that Trade with Our Mother Country which is necessary to the very Subsistence of the People Here... For Building a Light house upon Odiorn's point so called and Maintaining Lights therein the Sum of One thousand Pounds.[28]

This, however, did not result in the building of a lighthouse on Odiorne's Point, or anywhere else. Odiorne's Point, in Rye, New Hampshire, is a rocky headland about a mile and a half south of the mouth of the Piscataqua, and is the easternmost point on the New Hampshire coast. For transatlantic vessels, a lighthouse on this eminence would have been a helpful guide to landfall. For coasting vessels, it would have been a useful reference point for the entrances not only to Portsmouth Harbor but also to Little Harbor. The latter is a small, shallow basin on the south side of New Castle Island that was the entrance for the small-draft vessels of the early colonial period to Sagamore Creek, where the first settlement of the Piscataqua region took place. Little Harbor also provided an alternative entrance to the Piscataqua River that let small vessels avoid the most turbulent stretch of the river by proceeding through the waters to the west of New Castle Island and using the small channel between Shapleigh and Pierce Islands and the Portsmouth mainland. However, as vessels grew in size and bridges were built, fewer could use the Little Harbor approach. According to an analysis of Piscataqua Naval Office Shipping List statistics, between 1694 and 1764 the numbers of vessels involved in Port of Piscataqua trade had quadrupled, and their capacity had grown six and a half times.[29]

Between October 1763 and October 1764, the Piscataqua Naval Office recorded entrances and clearances of 224 vessels. Still no lighthouse had been built to guide shipping into the port. Frustrated, "Sundry Merchants & others of Portsmouth and other Adjacent places Concerned in Trade" petitioned the Assembly on June 14, 1765. Referring to the Loan Act of 1742, the one hundred signatories, including half of the wealthiest and most influential men in Portsmouth, complained that "… if such a building was then Estimated of such Importance, to the Safety of Navigation & benefit of Trade it is much more so now by the Increase of both."[30] The Assembly appointed a committee of eight of the petitioners to "take a view of Odiorns Point & any other place which they may think more suitable to erect a Light house" and to prepare a plan, make an estimate of the construction cost and annual maintenance expense. They were then to "report to the General Assembly as soon as may be." No such report has been located, but a 1772 document notes vaguely that the money earmarked for a lighthouse in 1743 had been "applied to other uses." [31]

In spite of the petition, five more years passed before a lighthouse helped vessels come to safe anchorage in the harbor. It was John Wentworth (1727–1820), named in 1766 to replace his uncle Benning, who was responsible for the first lighthouse for the Port of Piscataqua.

Detail from the 1779 print "View of Piscataqua Lighthouse from Kitterie point" showing the lighthouse at Fort William and Mary. BM

II *The First Portsmouth Harbor Lighthouse*

*In examining the Treasury Accompts there appears,
a Sum appropriated for building a Light-house; but it
is insufficient for that purpose. Many valuable Lives
are annually lost, and much property destroyed for want
of Such a friendly Edifice.*

—John Wentworth, April 4, 1771, NHSP 7:279

GOVERNOR JOHN WENTWORTH gets the credit for the first light-house for Portsmouth Harbor, though there is evidence that improving navigation into the harbor was not high on his "to-do" list when he first became governor. Wentworth was a native of Portsmouth and the last royal governor of the province of New Hampshire, serving from 1766 until his flight from Fort William and Mary in August 1775.

Wentworth's family had gathered and held power and wealth in New Hampshire through a large part of the eighteenth century. His grandfather John Wentworth (1671–1730) was a shipmaster who became a merchant and was lieutenant governor early in the eighteenth century. His uncle, Benning Wentworth (1696–1770), was royal governor for twenty-five years, and his father, Mark Hunking Wentworth (1709–1785), was one of the richest men in Portsmouth. Much of the family's wealth came from control of the mast trade and the export of lumber. John Wentworth himself had learned about merchant shipping as a young man working for his father before going to England in 1763. The fortunes of the family depended a great deal upon maritime commerce, as, of course, did those of a large proportion of the population of Portsmouth. Ways to reduce risks to their vessels and cargoes would have been a natural concern, and Mark Hunking Wentworth was one of the Portsmouth merchants who signed the 1765 petition for a lighthouse.[1]

Yet in June 1767, when John Wentworth returned to Portsmouth as the new governor after four years in England, the building of a lighthouse was far from his mind. During his first years back in New Hampshire, the young governor devoted much attention to the development of the interior of the province. He successfully promoted the establishment of Dartmouth College, at the western edge of New Hampshire; road building; the division of the province into counties; and the provision of legal services for these counties. Within a year of his return from

John Wentworth (1737-1820) did not have the needs of navigation in Portsmouth Harbor foremost in his mind when he returned from a stay in England to become governor of the province of New Hampshire in 1767, but four years later he had constructed the first Portsmouth lighthouse. PA.

England, he also began to improve land he owned in Wolfeborough in the wilderness near Lake Winnepesaukee; in 1769, he started to build and furnish an ambitious mansion there.[2]

Pressure continued to mount for a lighthouse for Portsmouth Harbor. In December 1768, a Portsmouth-owned schooner laden with molasses was wrecked and its cargo lost on White Island (not one of the Isles of Shoals, but rather one of the numerous ledgy islets sprinkled in the waters southwest of Gerrish Island at the mouth of the Piscataqua River). The *New-Hampshire Gazette* commented sarcastically about the cause of the wreck: "It is to be hoped within 50 years more we will have a Light-House at the Entrance of this Harbour, which its more than probable would have saved this Vessel, and a number of others heretofore."[3]

PORTSMOUTH, Dec. 16.

Last Monday Night about ten Clock, Capt. Richard Keating, in a Schooner from Guadaloupe, lading with Molaſſes, was caſt-away on White-Iſland, within a Mile to the Eaſtward of the Entrance of this Harbour, the Wind being freſh, and very dark—Veſſel and Cargo intirely loſt ; reckon'd to be worth Six Thouſand Dollars—The Mens Lives are all ſaved—The Veſſel and Cargo was own'd here.

It is to be hop'd within 50 Years more we ſhall have a Light-Houſe at the Entrance of this Harbour, which its more than probable would have ſaved this Veſſel, and a number of others heretofore.

The Schooner Hawke, Joſeph Greenleaf Maſter, from Gaudalope, loaded with Molaſſes, was caſt aſhore laſt Saturday Night on Rye-Beach ; the Cargo is ſaved, but the Veſſell will not be got off again.

New-Hampshire Gazette, *16 December 1768.*

Wentworth, however, was so preoccupied with other concerns that he did not act for more than two years. Inadequate funds in the provincial coffers may have been responsible, but a lottery like one authorized by the General Court in 1768 to raise money to build a bridge over the Exeter River, or another, sponsored by Wentworth himself for Dartmouth College, could have raised the funds for a lighthouse. Lotteries had financed the building of both the 1764 Sandy Hook lighthouse for vessels making for New York Harbor and the 1767 Cape Henlopen Light for shipping entering Delaware Bay. It is evident that a lighthouse for Portsmouth Harbor was not a priority for Wentworth.[4]

Finally, on April 4, 1771, Wentworth delivered an extravagantly worded appeal in the council chamber for an altogether inadequate substitute at the Castle, as Fort William and Mary was called. He proposed a "Large and proper Lanthorn to be raised into the Head of the Mast which supports the Flagg Staff in the Castle—the Cost will not exceed thirty Dollars." Wentworth pointed out what had long seemed obvious to just about everyone else, that "many valuable Lives are annually lost, and much property destroyed for want of Such a friendly Edifice."[5]

Wentworth argued that levies of ninepence on each sloop and schooner and eighteen pence on all other vessels passing the fort would take care of the expense of maintaining the light; he would order the commanding officer at the fort, Captain John Cochran, to take care of the light free of charge. He went on:

"There can be no Officer, who would not willingly do this duty, free of other Reward, than wou'd result from the animating Glows of Humanity." Wentworth justified at length the initial outlay:

> When we reflect on the many distressful Losses that now fill
> our Sea Coast with Widows & Orphans; which would undoubt-
> edly have been in a great degree prevented, by Such an aid as
> herein earnestly requested; their Tears, their pitiable Com-
> plaints irresistably engage our Minds in So Salutary purposes;
> Every future expiring Cry of a drowning Mariner upon Our
> Coast will bitterly accuse the unfeeling Recusant, that denys
> and in effect wastes that Life, to save a paltry unblessed
> Shilling—I trust the Honble Assembly will therefore enable
> me to establish this Light, and that we shall participate with
> ev'ry Contributor, in the Blessings of our fellow Creatures
> whose Lives may thus be rescued from Death.[6]

Because the merchants and shipmasters of Portsmouth had wanted a lighthouse for decades, it is possible to imagine the derision, if not anger, that met the governor's proposal for a lantern on the flagpole at the fort instead of a real lighthouse. Nevertheless, eight days later, on April 12, a law was enacted for a "Large and Suitable Lanthorn" at Fort William and Mary. Governor Wentworth's suggested duties were approved.[7]

CHAP. XXVI.

An Act for establishing a Light

to be kept at Fort WILLIAM and MARY, for the Benefit of Veſſels arriving or being upon this Coaſt in the Night Time.

WHEREAS loſſes frequently happen of the lives and properties of perſons arriving and being upon the ſea coaſt of this province in the night time, for want of a proper light for their direction, and it is thought that a large and ſuitable lanthorn to be lighted and kept upon the top of the maſt that ſupports the flag ſtaff at the fort, might be a means of preſerving the lives and properties of many perſons :

BE IT therefore ENACTED, by the GOVERNOR, COUNCIL, and ASSEMBLY, That there ſhall be procured and kept at his majeſty's fort William and Mary, under the direction of the commander of ſaid fort, a large and ſuitable lanthorn to be lighted and raiſed each night into the top of the maſt that ſupports the flag-ſtaff, for the benefit of marriners, being on this coaſt in the night time. And that the expence of procuring and maintaining the ſame be once a year, or oftener ſettled, by the Governor, Council and Aſſembly, and paid out of the treaſury of this province. And that a duty of nine pence on all ſloops and ſchooners, of more than thirty tons burthen, and one ſhilling and ſix pence on other veſſels, be laid, levied and collected, by the commander of ſaid fort, every voyage they make, free of charge, to be paid on paſſing out by the fort, and that the ſame be paid, by him, to the treaſurer of this province, once a year or oftener, if required, to be laid out for the purpoſe aforeſaid, as the Governor, Council and Aſſembly ſhall order.

This act to continue and be in force for the term of three years, and no longer.

Acts and Laws of His Majesty's Province of New Hampshire, *printed by Daniel and Robert Fowle, 1771.* PA.

1 7 7 1.
NEW-HAMPSHIRE.
NOTICE is HEREBY Given,
to all Mariners, That on the Night of the
8th Day of June next, will be illuminated a

Light-House,

for the Benefit and Direction of Veffels,
bound into this Harbour : The Edifice is
now erecting, upon the Eaftermoft part
of Fort-Point (fo called) at the entrance of
Pifcataqua Harbour, and will be lighted
up every Night.
  The Printers of News-Papers, it is hoped
will publifh this Advertifement in their fe-
veral Papers, for the Information and
Benefit of Maritime Perfons, within the
Spheres of their refpective Circulations.
  Portfmouth, April 17, 1771.

New-Hampshire Gazette, *17 April 1771.*

Then, out of the blue, the next week's *New-Hampshire Gazette* carried a notice that a real lighthouse was "now erecting, upon the Eastermost part of Fort-Point," and would be lit on June 8.

Where did Wentworth find the money for this much more expensive project? And why did he go ahead without the formal approval of the council and assembly? The most likely explanation is that Wentworth had just received news from England that the House of Commons had voted to repay New Hampshire for expenses incurred during the French and Indian Wars. The amount, six thousand pounds, was about three times the normal "supply" provided the province.[8]

The old idea of a real lighthouse at Odiorne's Point had been abandoned, probably because the larger vessels of this period could enter and leave the river only by the main opening of the Piscataqua River, on the side of New Castle Island where the fort was located. Wentworth's expectation that the men garrisoned there would take care of the light *gratis* may have influenced his decision as well. Later events would prove the difficulty of combining a light station and a fort at the same location and disprove Wentworth's assumption that the fort's soldiers would maintain the light without extra pay.

The lighthouse was finished with surprising speed. It was first lit in early July 1771—less than three months from the announcement that it was "now erecting." By contrast, the lighthouse that replaced it early in the nineteenth century took two years and three months from authorization to completion. The delay then, in the early years of management of lighthouses by the federal government, was due in part to the requirement to obtain bids for the work, but another factor was "the unacquaintedness with this kind of architecture of our mechanics."[9]

No drawing, framing plan, or specifications for the first lighthouse, or a bill for their production, has been found. A plausible candidate for providing such a plan, or at least technical advice, is Captain Samuel Holland, surveyor general for the northern district of North America. Holland, trained in the country of his birth in military engineering, surveying, and cartography, was also an accomplished draftsman. As an engineer for the American Regiment, he oversaw the building of fortifications, houses, barns, and a mill in British Canada. He designed at least one structure in New Hampshire during his few years in the province.[10]

Holland was already known to Wentworth. By February 1770, one of his deputies, Thomas Wheeler, had prepared a plan of the Lake Winnepesaukee region of Wentworth's Wolfeborough estate. And by December 1770, Holland himself had set up headquarters for his coastal survey just across the river from Portsmouth in Kittery. Wentworth, pursuing his conviction that the development of the interior was crucial to the future of New Hampshire, late that month proposed to the General Assembly the hiring of Holland to "survey as much of the Province as can be done before the Season Permitts his surveying on the Sea Cost." This step was not actually taken until 1772 or later.[11] By the time the Portsmouth tax collectors made their rounds in 1771, Holland and his survey team had moved across the river; the tax list for that year shows Holland and his deputies James Grant and Thomas Wheeler and perhaps Charles Blaskowitz on the tax rolls.[12]

It is conceivable, of course, that Daniel Brewster, the housewright who was put in charge of the project, improvised the lighthouse structure, without help from Holland or anyone else. One of the windmills that had been built in the area might have served as a prototype for the wooden frame.[13]

Most major European lighthouses, and all but two of the existing American colonial lighthouses, were of masonry construction—logical because the fuel needed for the light source also was a threat to a wooden structure. But the lighthouse at the fort was to be of timber, like those at Brant Point on Nantucket Island and at Plymouth, both in Massachusetts.[14]

The decision must have been based on local building traditions. Wood, plentiful in the Piscataqua region, was the material of choice, convenience, and economy for domestic and commercial structures. Men who knew how to put together buildings and ships of wood were in good supply. With few exceptions, local masonry work was limited to brick chimneys and fieldstone foundations, perhaps because the lime needed to make adequate mortar had to be brought in from elsewhere. At this time, there were few, if any masons in the area with the expertise to build an entire structure like a lighthouse.[15] And Wentworth could pass a little business to his father, Mark Hunking Wentworth, who supplied much of the lumber.

Whatever the source of the know-how to plan the structure, men to do the work and to supply the necessary materials were mobilized swiftly. The contractor, Daniel Brewster, came from a family of builders. Born in 1735, he was the fifth son of Samuel Brewster, of Portsmouth, a housewright. Daniel's older brother, Samuel, was also a housewright. After their father's death in 1752, the younger Samuel was appointed guardian of brothers Daniel, David, and William. It is likely that he trained Daniel in the art of fashioning and fitting together heavy timbers for house frames. Daniel hired his brother David, who was a joiner, and David's journeyman, to work on the lighthouse.[16]

The bills submitted by craftsmen, laborers, tradesmen, and merchants to Daniel Brewster for lighthouse materials and work are preserved in the New Hampshire State Archives, along with Brewster's final summary bill for 395 pounds, fourteen shillings, and fourpence.[17]

Once Governor Wentworth set the project in motion, he apparently was not much involved with the construction process; in fact, he was probably in Wolfeborough during most of it. It is conceivable that he had

Detail of Noah Parker's December 1771 bill, with the word "consented" and the governor's initial at the bottom of the sheet. NHDRMA.

employed some of these men for work on buildings on his Wolfeborough property and was confident of their abilities.[18] Wentworth's initial, following the word *consented,* appears on only one of the bills submitted by the men who built the lighthouse. All the bills were presented to the New Hampshire House of Representatives for payment in December 1771; an adjusted payment to Brewster of 372 pounds, eleven shillings, and one penny was approved on January 9, 1772.[19]

The craftsmen's bills provide a fascinating glimpse of the work, although they leave unanswered questions as to the structural character of the lighthouse. The daily pay rates of the men, servants, and boys show the relative value of their skills a few years before the Revolution. Daniel Brewster himself worked for fifty-eight days on the job, at six shillings per day, while at the low end of the pay scale "sarvents" earned two shillings. Brewster's brother David and his "joynerman" worked a total of one hundred days on the job for five and four shillings a day, respectively. Daniel Davis worked at four shillings a day for thirty-two days of unspecified work.[20] Five years later, four of them, Noah Parker, Moses Noble, John Furnald (or Fernald), and Joseph Simes would be involved in the construction of the frigate *Raleigh* launched in the Piscataqua River for the Continental Congress.[21]

The lumber came from several sources. The governor's father furnished much of it. His bills, submitted in May, included a large mast twenty-four inches in diameter for the "Kink Post" (cost: five pounds), other spars for framing timbers, and white pine for sills, as well as five thousand twenty-penny nails. Thomas Bell, a New Castle merchant and selectman, provided spruce spars for joists, and Daniel Brewster himself charged the account for spruce spars and white oak timbers. Captain John Cochran supplied more oak. Special tools and hardware came from blacksmith Noah Parker: a stone auger, a "steelpointing crow," spikes, deck nails, wedges, braces, hinges, latches, staples, a maul, "priming wire & worm," and a "hoop for mast."[22]

The earliest bill was Moses Noble's. Dated "April, 1771," it was for twelve days' work at five shillings, and ten days at two shillings per day for each of his two servants. Noble was both a mast maker and a joiner. His role in the project is not entirely clear. He may have been hired to shape tall timbers in preparation for the work of the framers and joiners. The function of the large mast for the "Kink Post" is also unclear. An estimated seventy feet in length, it could have been a center post on which the structure was hung. A king post has also been

defined as a mast installed near a structure in progress to which a derrick boom is affixed for hoisting its components into place; the "hoop for
mast" provided by Noah Parker suggests that this may have been the
case, and that one of Noble's tasks was to install and rig—and perhaps
operate—such a hoisting device.[23] Blasting was required. John Payn,
who worked for a total of thirty-eight and a half days at four shillings
per day, was involved in a variety of tasks, including "blowing rocks,"
presumably to prepare the site, a rocky arm on the northeast end of
New Castle Island. It is also possible that blasting produced the stone
for the foundation. Captain Cochran's bill included a charge for twenty-one days for "Carring Stone for the foundation." The foundation was
accomplished by mid-May. Mortar presumably was used, though lime
does not appear on any of the bills. William Doak, a mason, worked fifteen days at four shillings per day. Helping lay the foundation for eight
days in May were William Caverly, more highly paid at five shillings,
and his "boy" at two shillings per day. These three workers boarded
with Captain Cochran at the fort during this time.[24]

While the foundation was being readied, Brewster's crew cut and fit
the components of the timber frame. This was probably done at a site
off New Castle Island. They were boarded by Captain Cochran at his
house within the walls of the fort for only a few days, and this must
have been when they assembled timbers that had been previously cut
and fitted elsewhere. An essential "perk" for workers during this era
was a daily ration of rum; Cochran's bill shows that during the course
of construction, he supplied a total of fifteen and quarter gallons at a
cost of three pounds, seventeen shillings.[25]

The bill of mariner John Briard, who worked for only two days, May
18 and 19, "raising the Light House" and "getting gaze," provides the
date when the components of the timber frame of the lighthouse were
raised on the site. Briard's daily rate of six shillings (as much as Daniel
Brewster was paid) suggests that he brought special expertise or equipment of some sort to the task. If a 1778 view by a French artist is accurate, the site, partly surrounded by water, would have posed problems
not usually confronted by housewrights. An early nineteenth century
description of the Eddystone lighthouse refers to "a tackle called a
guys" used to produce a sideways pull on vertically hoisted building
materials to guide them to the desired spot. Briard was a pilot, and perhaps he used his boat to procure such a guys (or "gaze," as is written on
his bill) from an upriver shipyard.[26]

The cordage needed to hoist the timbers of the frame into place was bought from merchant and shipbuilder George Boyd, except for one "Coyl" (perhaps of exceptional thickness or length) rented from Boyd for a generous fee of eighteen shillings and returned after the work was finished. Captain Cochran procured oxen, at twelve shillings, to "Raise the Frame," and for the occasion furnished "Sundry Liquors" at the cost of one pound, six shillings, and six pence. The bill of John Payn, who earlier had been involved in the blasting of rocks, also included "assisting to raise."[27]

Captain John Cochran's 12 December 1771 bill for expenses associated with the building of the lighthouse. NHDRMA.

Aside from shipping news, marriages, and deaths, practically the only local events reported by the *New-Hampshire Gazette* were freaks of weather and bizarre disasters. There was no news in the *Gazette* of the raising of the lighthouse frame—an event of such considerable drama and importance that many people must have been aware of it and turned out to watch, and maybe to help out.

The single most costly component of the lighthouse was the iron framework for the glazed lantern through which the light of the lamps would shine from the top of the wooden tower. This ironwork was produced by Noah Parker at a cost of 165 pounds, according to his bill dated simply "1771."[28] Noah Parker was a whitesmith, blacksmith, and gunsmith. According to a posthumous description, he was "an honest and upright mechanic, with a fair education" and "a large thinking brain." Probably working without a model or plan, he must have needed a good deal of his ingenuity and mechanical skills to create this wrought-iron lantern, with its grid of muntins into which small glass panes were inserted. This structure was about five feet high. Small-scale items like horseshoes, spikes, nails, and some of the tools Parker made for the project were about as complicated as ironworking got during this period, when the Crown rigidly controlled colonial manufacturing. Parker's lantern may well have been one of the more elaborate wrought-iron pieces made in the area by this date.[29]

Joseph Simes (who also charged for the labor of glazing the lantern), Mark H. Wentworth, and Thomas Martin among them supplied putty and 170 panes of eight-by-ten-inch glass, most likely of English manufacture. Wentworth also provided sheet lead and a bushel and a half of "Salt to put under the Lead on the Top of the house." This last referred to the platform or floor on top of the timber-framed tower on which the lantern rested. It would have been built with an opening, or scuttle, for access. The sheet lead was to furnish a barrier to keep the flammable fuel from soaking into the wooden platform and the timbers of the structure, and. the salt was to keep the planks of the platform from rotting. John Furnald, a copper- and tinsmith, supplied sheet copper for the domed roof of the lantern itself and "3 large copper lamps for seventeen pounds, three shillings, and sixpence.[30] No description of these first lamps has been found.

The lighthouse was not finished by the June 8 date optimistically projected in the April newspaper announcement. Captain Cochran, a Mason, hosted at the fort a meeting of St. John's Lodge on June 24. Whether the meeting was scheduled to celebrate the completion of some aspect of the lighthouse, or perhaps a trial lighting of the lamps is not known; no minutes of this meeting were recorded. Mark Hunking Wentworth's bill included a "Stock lock for the dore" on June 7. He delivered planking and shingles on June 26. Joseph Simes's bill for two coats of "White paint ground in Oyl," for putty, and for the labor of inserting glass panes into the lighthouse lantern was dated simply "July."[31]

Most utilitarian structures were left unpainted during this period, as were many houses. The two coats of paint indicate that this was considered a structure that should be protected from the elements; and the use of white, the most highly visible of the paints then available, is evidence that thought had been given to the potential use of the lighthouse as a daymark.

Only an estimate of the dimensions of the first Portsmouth lighthouse is possible. It was not as tall as the more than eighty-foot-tall lighthouse that replaced it in 1804. There are a few known eighteenth-century representations of this first lighthouse. As we know that the lantern placed on the tower was five feet eight inches high, it is possible to make a very rough estimate of its height at somewhat less than forty feet.[32]

Captain John Cochran was responsible for seeing that the light was lit and maintained. On December 18, 1771, he submitted a bill for eight pounds, six shillings for "attending the light since first lighting till date." Based on the one shilling per day Cochran paid a soldier

Copper compass card plate by Portsmouth navigational instrument maker William Hart, showing the Portsmouth Harbor lighthouse. PA.

for this job, the first lighting must have been on or about July 6, 1771, perhaps even before the planking, shingling, and painting were finished. The occasion would have offered a chance for Governor Wentworth to make political capital in his hometown port, but there is no evidence that he was on hand for the event.[33]

This was the tenth lighthouse built in the colonies that later became
the United States, and the first north of Boston; it was followed closely
by the twin lights on Thacher's Island off Cape Ann, Massachusetts, the
last lighthouses actually finished before the Revolution.[34]

On December 14, 1771, Governor Wentworth reported to the General Court, at the assembly's first sitting after approval of the "Lanthorn" raised on the flag staff he proposed in April, that this scheme
had been "impracticable." He had gone ahead to have a real lighthouse
built, since "the Necessity, Humanity and Advantage of a Building for
this purpose is universally known . . . already it hath been the acknowl-
edged means of preserving two Vessels and their men."[35]

Local pilots soon devised sailing directions for using the light for
guidance into the harbor "in order to render the same of more general
benefit and Utility to the Public." These directions were first published
in the *New-Hampshire Gazette* in February 1772.

There were many wrinkles to iron out during the first years of the
lighthouse. Light fees were raised twice to cover the cost of maintaining
the light, and Captain Cochran continually complained about how difficult it was to be reimbursed for his out-of-pocket expenses. The keeper's
duties were clarified and penalties established for dereliction of duty.

Fish oil fueled the three copper lamps of the lighthouse. John
Cochran's bill covering the period from June to December of 1771 shows
payments for a total of five barrels and nineteen gallons of fish oil, seven
pounds of wick yarn, portage, a stone jar, candles, a funnel and scissors,
all for a cost of seventeen pounds, eight shillings, and eightpence.[36]

Revenues collected from shipping for "light money" during the first
five months did not even cover the cost of supplies, let alone the shilling
a day for the soldier who tended the light. Cochran was owed more than
twelve pounds on December 18. In 1772, Joseph Simes came "sundry
times" to mend the lantern (probably to putty or to replace glass); mops,
brushes, soap, and oakum were acquired to clean it.[37]

Because the lighthouse cost more to maintain than expected, the
levies were raised and the schedule of fees refined in an act of January
1772. Masters of vessels of from fifteen to thirty tons (previously
exempt) could choose between paying an annual fee of six shillings or
paying one shilling for each entry into the port. The highest charge was
eight shillings per entry, for vessels of more than two hundred tons.
This act also required that the "person who shall be Appointed to be the
keeper of said light shall carefully Attend his duty at all Times in kin-
dling the Lights from the Sun-setting to Sun Rising and keeping the

Province of New-Hampſhire.

WHEREAS a LIGHT-HOUSE has been lately erected at the Expence of the ſaid Province, on Fort-Point, at the Entrance of the Harbour of Piſcataqua, for the greater Safety of all Ships and Veſſels trading thereto ; —In order to render the ſame of more general Benefit and Utility to the Public, the following Directions are publiſhed from a Survey made by Pilots experienced in Navigation into the ſaid Harbour.

"As the Light-Houſe is erected on "Fort-Point, we find it neceſſary that all "Ships or Veſſels coming from the Eaſt-"ward ſhould keep in twelve Fathom of "Water until the Light bears North, "North one-half Weſt, and North one "half Eaſt, Diſtance about three Miles, "and then bear away for the Light-Houſe, "keeping the Weſtern Shore on board, "and coming no nearer that Shore than "nine Fathom of Water, giving the Light "a proper Birth, and alſo ſtand over to "the North Shore, and anchor in nine "Fathom of Water, abreaſt of Sparhawk's "Point, ſo called ; — And all Ships or "Veſſels coming from the Southward, "are to obſerve the ſame Directions re-"ſpecting the Light as above, and keep "in nine Fathom of Water, on the Weſt-"ern Shore."

Portſmouth, February, 1772.

Sailing directions, with reference to the new lighthouse, were published in the New-Hampshire Gazette, *21 February 1772.*

same Sufficiently Supplied with Oil."[38] Apparently this had not been the case during the first few months of operation. During the next full year, Cochran paid for twenty-five barrels of oil and thirty and three-quarters pounds of wick yarn, indicating a higher rate of consumption and probably better maintenance of the light. The act provided for a fine of one hundred pounds (two-thirds of which would go to the Crown, and one-third to the informant) for dereliction of duty by the keeper.[39]

The 1772 act evidently considered John Cochran himself to be the keeper, rather than the soldier who actually tended the light. Born in Londonderry, New Hampshire, Cochran had moved to the seacoast and become a sailor and then a shipmaster. After his appointment as commandant, his wife and four children lived with him at the fort, along with a manservant and a maid. The names of the soldiers conscripted for fort duty are recorded on muster rolls, but we do not know which of them lit and maintained the lighthouse lamps. The lists for the years 1771–1773 show that tours of duty at the fort could range from less than two weeks to thirteen months; a number of different men probably tended the lamps during the four years the lighthouse was maintained by the provincial government.[40]

Governor Wentworth's promise of free maintenance of the lighthouse by the garrison at the fort had already proved hollow. Near the end of 1772, Cochran asked for and was given twenty pounds to reimburse his out-of-pocket expenses, "that the Light might not fail, before the meeting of the General Assembly."[41] To raise more money, light fees went up again in February 1773. Vessels of from fifteen to thirty tons burden continued to pay the same rate, but for those between fifty and one hundred tons the rate went to one shilling per entry. Those from one hundred to 150 tons paid double the previous levy, or eight shillings; any over 150 tons paid twelve shillings. For the first time, a salary for the keeper was authorized—twenty-four pounds per year.[42] Within less than half a year, Cochran was complaining again about the inadequate financing of the light and the slow pace of reimbursement: " . . . have Allway's been, and am now, in a Considerable Advance for the Light, and its not in my power to Continue and Keep up the light any longer, unless that your Excellency will be pleas'd to Order me a Supply of twenty pounds for that use, Otherwis shall be under the disagreeable Necessity of letting the light House stand useless."[43]

There is no record of a response to Cochran's request, or to another he made to the General Assembly in May 1774. He wrote then that the soldier who tended the light was paid a shilling a day, or more than eighteen pounds a year, above his annual soldier's wage of twenty-nine pounds, seven shillings. But no soldier could be found to tend the light at night for the amount allocated. Cochran felt sure that no one would take on the job unless he was also given an additional twenty pounds to "find his own Diett." An act passed the same month in effect increased fees substantially for vessels of more than thirty tons, providing for a levy of one and a half pence per ton, presumably to fund more attractive pay for the soldier who tended the light.[44]

Given the quantity of shipping in and out of the harbor during this period, higher pay should have been possible. According to customs records of exports in the last three months of 1774, sixty-four vessels cleared the harbor for the West Indies and three for southern Europe; many more shipped to England and the other North American English colonies and northern Europe.[45]

The export cargoes were similar in many ways to those of the previous century and included masts and spars; fish and fish oil; and boards, shingles, and barrel staves. But the chairs, tables, desks, cart wheels and tongues, oxbows, entire frames for houses, saddles, bridles, harnesses, bricks, and spermaceti candles aboard many of the vessels reflected the development of craftsmanship and manufacture to the limited extent allowed by British policies that were designed to preserve markets in the colonies for English manufactured goods. Exports of agricultural products previously imported included livestock of all kinds, grain, flour, bread, potatoes, onions, and beef. Most of the rum carried out of the harbor was domestic—perhaps distilled locally. Many of the vessels bound to the West Indies carried as cargo flat-bottomed "moses" boats used for loading sugar, and the horses and oxen needed for its production.[46]

The average capacity of the vessels leaving Portsmouth Harbor for the West Indies and southern Europe at this time was ninety-four tons. Forty-five of the sixty-seven vessels clearing in 1774 were Portsmouth-owned. But only twenty of these, however, were Piscataqua built—twelve of them brand-new ships of from one hundred thirty to two hundred tons. Local merchants and investors built the rest elsewhere, suggesting that Piscataqua shipbuilders were hard-pressed to keep up with the local demand. George Boyd wrote in 1773 that he alone had "seven sails of new ships on the stocks," and it has been estimated that the region was turning our fifty vessels per year, some destined for sale in England.[47]

Approval for higher pay for tending the light came in late spring 1774, but evidently none of the soldiers at the fort wanted the job. In the *New-Hampshire Gazette* for June 3, 1774, an advertisement appeared for "an able Man, for attending the LIGHT-HOUSE," at twenty-four pounds per year; anyone interested should apply immediately to either the secretary of the province or to Captain John Cochran at Fort William and Mary. It must have been difficult to find someone at this rate of pay. A similar ad appeared on November 25. Presumably someone, probably from the village of New Castle, agreed to do the job under Cochran's supervision.[48] But by the end of the year seeing that the light was maintained was far from Cochran's principal concern.

Governor Wentworth in the early years of his administration was adept at balancing the interests of New Hampshire colonials with those of the Crown, but British policies on taxation and the control of American commerce eventually overwhelmed him. New Hampshire's responses to the succession of taxes and trade restrictions passed by Parliament had been mild in comparison to reactions in Massachusetts and Rhode Island. But in the wake of the Tea Act of 1773 and the Boston Tea Party of that December, anti-British sentiment strength-

Whereas the General-Assembly of the Province of New-Hampshire has granted Twenty-four Pounds Proclamation Money, to pay an able Man for attending the LIGHT-HOUSE within said Province, for one Year— Whosoever is willing to undertake the same, may, by applying immediately at the Secretary's-Office, or to Capt. John Cockran's at Castle William & Mary, enter upon the Business.

Portsmouth, June 1, 1774.

Lighthouse help wanted ad, New-Hampshire Gazette, *3 June 1774.*

ened markedly in New Hampshire. Passage of the "Intolerable Acts" of March 1774, which included the closure of the Port of Boston as of June 1 to all but military supplies and essential food, heightened tensions. In June and September 1774 two mast ships entered Portsmouth Harbor with provocative cargoes of tea, and angry citizens prevented the landing of the tea and forced the ships out of the port.[49]

Virtually all the goodwill and support Wentworth had cultivated in the years since his appointment evaporated in the fall of 1774, when word reached Portsmouth of his quiet arrangements to send carpenters to Boston to help build barracks for General Thomas Gage's troops.[50]

None of the records and accounts of the events in the Port of Piscataqua prior to the Revolution, many of which focused on the fort, mentions the lighthouse. However, Captain John Cochran played a starring role of sorts in these events—not in his capacity as keeper of the light, but as commandant of Fort William and Mary and its tiny garrison. On December 13, 1774, Paul Revere rode into Portsmouth with news that British ships and soldiers were on their way to seize the guns and military stores at the fort. Over the next two days, the fort became the scene of one of the earliest open acts against a military installation of the British Crown.[51] In depositions taken shortly afterward for Governor Wentworth, Captain Cochran takes on a swashbuckling, almost comic-opera aura.

On December 14, an advance party of revolutionaries ambled into Cochran's house at the fort. Governor Wentworth had warned Cochran of impending problems; when the men came into the house, Cochran's wife, Sarah, smelled trouble and brought him a pair of pistols "well charged." Cochran ordered the intruders off the premises and had the six men of the garrison load the cannons and fix their small arms with bayonets against the attack he realized was coming. In a deposition, Cochran stated that he ordered his men "not to flinch on pain of Death but to defend the Fort to the last Extremity, telling them that the Instant I saw any Sign of Cowardice in either of them I would drive a Brace of Balls through his Body." When the attack came—from an estimated two hundred men, many of them known to the tiny, wildly outnumbered garrison at the fort—Cochran gave the order to fire the cannon at the men storming the walls from all sides, "but the men being in too much haste they had no Effect." Cochran and his men were soon overpowered; they were guarded while the crowd hauled down the flag and carried off about one hundred barrels of gunpowder.[52]

The next night, close to one thousand men came to the fort to take away more military stores. Cochran was reduced to repeating, like a refrain, that "they must not at their Peril Meddle with or take away anything belonging to the King," while the revolutionaries went about their business, hauling away sixteen cannon and other military stores.[53]

Wentworth had sent for help several days earlier, but the armed British sloop *Canceaux* did not enter the Piscataqua until December 17. Two days later the man-of-war *Scarborough* arrived, with from eighty to one hundred soldiers aboard. Tensions mounted over the next months, with *Scarborough* seizing vessels coming into the harbor with provisions.[54]

Governor Wentworth by this time was virtually a prisoner in his Portsmouth house. On June 13, 1775, he fled with his wife, infant son, and retinue out his back door and proceeded downriver to take refuge at the fort. It is not recorded how Cochran and family coped during the seventy days that Governor Wentworth and his party of twenty were at the fort. Wentworth and his immediate family most likely stayed in the commandant's house, which would have provided the best accommodations.

A "food war" ensued, with the British warships interfering with local fishermen and stopping all vessels entering and leaving the port. The people of New Castle retaliated by trying to keep provisions from reaching the warships and the governor's party at the fort. On August 24, 1775, Wentworth left Fort William and Mary for Boston aboard the *Scarborough*, along with the loyal Captain Cochran.[55]

Wentworth returned briefly to the area the next month and from the Isles of Shoals he sent word on September 21, 1775 that he was postponing the meeting of the General Assembly scheduled for the twenty-eighth, and then departed. He never returned to his native Portsmouth. Before he left the Shoals, his messenger came back to him with news about the house he had lived in at the fort: "It was rendered uninhabitable within a half an hour after my Departure by a Body of Men who had been lurking on the island near the fort, and carried off or destroyed the Doors, Windows, Chimnies and other Accommodations, together with the Platforms and Walls of the Fort."[56]

To prevent any further damage at the fort, the Committee of Safety voted the very day after Wentworth's departure to "Forbid any person or Persons from destroying the Buildings" there.[57]

There is no record of damage to the lighthouse during or immediately after the gunpowder raids, but it is unlikely that the light was maintained afterwards. In July 1775, the *Gazette* reported that Captain Barclay, of the *Scarborough,* had been stopping all shipping in and out of the harbor. The schooner *Ann* and its cargo of dried fish belonging to Captain Titus Salter was one of the vessels seized by the British warship. If the light had not already been extinguished, Wentworth would presumably have ordered it done by then, to make it more difficult for vessels to sneak in and out of the harbor at night.[58]

The Crown's control of the lighthouse and the fort essentially ended with the departure of Wentworth in August 1775. The *Canceaux* remained offshore until mid-October. It was one of the British warships that virtually destroyed Falmouth (now Portland), Maine, later that fall. Portsmouth escaped Falmouth's fate because of defensive measures taken after Wentworth left. The revolutionaries fortified and manned Pierce and Seavey's Islands, upriver, and Jerry's Point in New Castle, overlooking Little Harbor, and placed a log boom and a line of fireships across the Piscataqua from Pierce Island to Henderson's Point.[59]

Beginning in March 1776, the lighthouse played a role in Portsmouth defenses as a lookout post, even though the fort at New Castle was useless for defensive purposes. Captain Titus Salter, who had been involved in the preparation of the harbor defenses, was commandant of Fort Washington on Pierce Island. In response to orders from the Council and Representatives, Salter wrote them on March 14, 1776:

> I have posted a Guard on Fort point at New Castle with orders frequently to go up to the top of the Light House and Diligently to observe if any ships appear sailing toward this port, and on Discovery of the same to make me acquainted that I may transmit it without loss of time to your Honours.[60]

How long this guard was maintained is unknown. On September 18, 1776, New Hampshire's House of Representatives settled an outstanding account with Nathaniel Jordan, voting to pay him five pounds, six shillings, and sixpence still owed him "for taking care of the Light House." Whether Jordan was the man Salter posted is not at all clear. Given the fear that the British would act against Portsmouth as they had against Falmouth, it is unlikely that he was hired to maintain the light, which would have helped attackers. On the other hand, he may have been the civilian who tended the lighthouse from late in 1774 until it was extinguished sometime either before or immediately after Wentworth's departure in August 1775.[61]

After the Treaty of Paris officially ended the Revolutionary War, the New Hampshire General Assembly in April 1784 passed an act to reestablish the lighthouse "for the benefit of foreigners as Well as for the inhabitants of the united States." The lighthouse having gone without maintenance for nearly ten years, the selectmen of Portsmouth were directed to repair it "immediately." The state would appoint and pay a keeper, levying fees on vessels entering the port as follows:

> 30–50 tons........................3 shillings
> 50–100 tons.....................6 shillings
> 100–150 tons....................8 shillings
> 150 tons & over...............12 shillings

Foreign vessels were to pay triple these fees.[62]

The lighthouse was usable again by July. Portsmouth Selectman George Gaines, a joiner by trade, submitted bills totaling more than one hundred and three pounds for the necessary supplies and renovations—and ten gallons of rum for the workmen. Blacksmith Noah Parker (who by then was minister to the Universalists in Portsmouth) provided an iron door for the lighthouse, a shallow pan for the fish oil, and iron bars on which to place cotton wicks to provide the light in the lantern. John Simes presented a bill for setting thirty-two panes of glass, painting the ironwork of the lantern, and "painting Speaking Trumpet" for hailing vessels. Supply Clap's bill was for shingles, tar, rigging, tackle blocks, and the use of cordage. Jonathan Warner provided the necessary sheet lead, paint, and glass; Gaines himself furnished eight barrels of oil, cotton wick yarn, an hourglass, a "tin" gallon pot for carrying oil to the lamps, and bread, beef, port, and rum.[63]

As before the war, the commandant at the fort would supervise the lighthouse, with a soldier doing the actual maintenance. In July 1784, the council ordered Lieutenant Meshech Bell, a native of New Castle, to "enlist Six able bodied, effective men" to serve under him at the inactive fort, and to make sure that the trade and navigation laws were obeyed. He was, "in particular," to see that the lighthouse light was maintained.[64]

Bell chose Sergeant Elias Tarlton of New Castle to see to the lighthouse, at the prewar rate of two pounds per month, in addition to his soldier's pay. The lighthouse must have been relit on July 22, 1784, because New Hampshire's president and council in December approved Tarlton's pay from that date.[65]

Financing the lighthouse proved even more of a problem than before the Revolution. The shipping activity that funded the operation of the lighthouse had not regained its health after the war, whereas the cost of maintaining the light was constant regardless of how few vessels used the harbor. The General Assembly had to scrape the bottom of the barrel. An act that passed in November 1784 pointed out that many vessels came into the harbor to shelter without entering at the Naval Office upriver at Portsmouth and thus avoided paying a fee, although they got "as much benefit from the light." Henceforth, any vessel over fifteen tons burden passing the fort was to pay a fee, even if not entering at the office.[66]

George Gaines, as quartermaster of the militia, was authorized to supply oil and cotton wicks for the light through 1787, when he was replaced by Supply Clap, who also made additional repairs to the light and barracks. With the death of Captain Bell in September 1786, Captain Titus Salter took over the command at the fort, the keepership of the light, and the supervision of Sergeant Tarlton.[67]

In the year after the ratification of the Constitution in 1788, an act of Congress transferred to the federal government the supervision and the expense of operating the twelve functioning lighthouses in the United States and the four under construction at the time. The actual transfer of the lighthouse in Portsmouth Harbor would drag on for two more years.

Joseph Whipple (1737-1816) was the new United States government's first Collector of Customs for Portsmouth, a position he held 1789-1798 and 1801-1816. 1805 engraving by Charles Balthazar Julien Fevret de Saint-Memin. National Portrait Gallery, SI.

III *The Federal Government Takes Over*

*Herewith you have Copy of the Act for the establish-
ment and support of Lighthouses, Beacons, Buoys
and public Piers...you will perceive that it is made
the duty of the Secretary of the Treasury to provide
[for them] by Contracts to be approved by the President of the United States.*

—New Hampshire State Papers 18:812

JOSEPH WHIPPLE OF PORTSMOUTH, to whom this letter was written by Secretary of the Treasury Alexander Hamilton in early June 1790, penned a somewhat acid reply. Whipple, who had been appointed Collector of Customs for the Port of Portsmouth by President Washington the previous August, pointed out that "This Act was omitted to be enclosed with your letter... I conceive a knowledge of its contents essential to my understanding perfectly the business which is required by it."[1]

As the task of transforming the new federal government from concept to working reality moved slowly forward, snafus like the delay in forwarding a document were probably no more frequent than in the early twenty-first century. In July 1790 the act was amended to set a deadline of July 1791 for the states to cede their lighthouses to the federal government. A copy of the amended act establishing federal responsibility for lighthouses, beacons, buoys, and public piers finally reached Whipple later that month.[2]

This act was one of the earliest passed by Congress. (The first called for duties on imports and arranged for their collection at each port.) A remarkable document, it was the first by the United States to undertake the cost and maintenance of public works of any sort. The centralization of lighthouse administration it mandated, although far from perfectly managed over the next decades, preceded by three years the French establishment of a central bureau of lighthouses and beacons. In England, Trinity House, a mariner guild of medieval origin, controlled most English lighthouses, but as late as 1836 there were ten privately owned lighthouses, the last of which Trinity House bought at great cost only in 1841.[3]

Another notable feature of the American legislation was that it eliminated the direct user fees, or "light duties," that had financed the building and maintenance of lighthouses during the colonial and confederation periods. England and France continued to levy light duties well into the nineteenth century. In England, the fees levied by Trinity House had to pay not only for the lights but also for assistance to aged mariners and their widows and orphans. Fees collected for the proprietary lights lined their owners' pockets. Even when storms threatened their vessels, many shipmasters went to extraordinary lengths to avoid putting into a sheltering harbor where exorbitant light fees were charged—often with fatal results.[4]

The aid that Congress and the president gave to navigation in 1789 shows how crucial maritime commerce and its revenues were for the new nation. The duties on imported goods and the tonnage of vessels carrying them amounted to ninety-nine percent of the federal government's revenues until passage of the tax on whiskey in 1791.[5]

Joseph Whipple, U. S. Collector of Customs

Joseph Whipple and the fifty-eight other customs officers appointed by Washington were charged with collecting these duties. A collectorship was probably the most important local appointment by the executive branch during the formative years of the federal government. Early U.S. collectors of customs had more jobs to dispense than any other local federal appointees. For more than a century, before civil service regulations were enacted, they had considerable political clout. In a thriving port, this could be a lucrative post, as pay was based on a percentage of collections of duties on imports and of the costs of constructing aids to navigation. Whipple and the other collectors were key figures in the new revenue collection bureaucracy and were involved in setting precedents for the management of their responsibilities. Joseph Whipple and the customs collectors who followed him in Portsmouth played a major, if not always knowledgeable, part in the management of aids to navigation well into the nineteenth century.[6]

Joseph Whipple (1737–1816) was not Washington's first choice for the position. Perhaps two thirds of the president's first appointments came from the ranks of leading military men of the Revolutionary War or from other backgrounds that provided no preparation for these new positions. For the Portsmouth collectorship, Washington first chose Pearse Long, commander of the 1st New Hampshire Regiment, who had earlier taken part in the raids on Fort William and Mary. Long died, however, before he could take office.[7]

Joseph Whipple turned out to be a good replacement for Long. He was born in 1737 of a well-to-do seafaring family in Kittery. For a time he was partner in the Portsmouth business of his older brother William, a prosperous shipmaster who retired from the sea in 1759 to become a full-time merchant. Both men signed the unsuccessful 1765 petition for a lighthouse.[8]

In the early 1770s, perhaps heeding Governor Wentworth's exhortation to "go west," and taking advantage of land available to those who would settle the interior of New Hampshire, Joseph Whipple struck out on his own to develop wilderness lands in the western part of the state beyond the White Mountains. He amassed thousands of acres in Dartmouth (later renamed Jefferson), then part of Grafton County. There he built a house and eventually grist-and sawmills. By way of Crawford's Notch, he made annual arduous trips back to the seacoast for supplies and mail, and during the Revolution traveled back to the Piscataqua region to represent his thinly populated district in the legislature.[9]

In the meantime, his brother William was deeply involved in revolutionary politics as a signer of the Declaration of Independence and delegate to the Continental Congress from 1776 to 1779. In 1776, Joseph was the principal supplier of mast timber for the thirty-two-gun frigate *Raleigh* built for the Continental Navy by John Langdon in a Piscataqua River shipyard.[10]

After a couple of years as a colonel in the twenty-fifth state militia regiment, Whipple returned in 1786 to Portsmouth to become impost officer for New Hampshire. He continued his political influence in the western part of the state; along with several other seacoast men who settled and developed land there, he is credited with using his clout to influence votes crucial to the close New Hampshire vote to ratify the Constitution in 1788.[11]

Whipple's position as impost officer was good preparation for his later post as U.S. collector of customs. He and his thirty deputies had to collect duties on all goods imported into the state, by land or by sea. He soon learned that the habit of evading taxes under British rule was not easily altered, and wrote of "the adverse humour of every anti-revenue, anti-patriotic and selfish person who imported goods." Because he would "not suffer the Laws to be trampled upon & the Revenue deprived of its dues," he wrote that even when friends and fellow townsmen were involved, he had to enforce the new federal customs laws "at the risque & loss of their Friendship and good will."[12]

The first secretary of the treasury, Alexander Hamilton, depended on his customs collectors for information about economic conditions in their respective states. Whipple reported a post-Revolutionary decline in New Hampshire's maritime commerce and shipbuilding activity, which he attributed it to the "great losses sustained by our Merchants in the Late War (almost the total of their personal property)." According to Whipple (who may have exaggerated somewhat the quantity of pre-war shipbuilding), "The want of any regular establishments of trade or employment for ships has discouraged shipbuilding in this State. Formerly 30 to 40 Sail of vessels of 200 to 300 tons were built in a year."[13]

Whipple's customs house records show that in 1790 only seven small merchant vessels, averaging 121 tons apiece, were built along the Piscataqua River and its tributaries. The historian Jeremy Belknap wrote that the total number of vessels owned at the port in 1791 was eighty-three—only thirty-three of which were of one hundred tons or more. From 1790 to 1799, the number of vessels built yearly fluctuated wildly with the international situation, from a high of twenty-six in 1795 to a low of two in 1797. Over this period, the annual average of vessels built was fourteen—ships, brigs, barks, schooners and sloops— with an average only 165 tons burden.[14]

Whipple's report to Hamilton gives a picture of the nature of maritime commerce in Portsmouth in 1789:

New Hampshire Vessels trade 1st to the West Indies and other Settlements of the Dutch and French Nations with Lumber, some Fish and Beef, whence they return with the produce of those Settlements chiefly Mollases and Rum which they carry frequently to Carolina, Phila., or Boston for a market. 2 or 3 of these Voyages are performed in the year. 2nd They Proceed from the West Indies with the proceeds of their Lumber cargo for Virginia or Carolina where they are employed 8 to 10 Months. 3rd, they perform Voyages to England, Scotland, Ireland, and France with Lumber Cargoes, Some flaxseed and Pottash and return in Ballast or with salt. 4thly Some have gone in Ballast for Carolina and Virginia and Load with rice or Tobaco for Europe, but the preference given to British Vessels or the power of British Factors to engross tobaco and other produce of those States renders these Voyages uncertain and they are seldom attempted at present. [15]

Whipple, like other collectors, was reimbursed for the part of his job that included superintending the lighthouses. His compensation was based on a percentage of the money spent for keeping lit the single lighthouse in his bailiwick and for the construction of new navigational aids. For the year ending October 1, 1792, his earnings for this responsibility amounted to $3.17. Boston collector Benjamin Lincoln, with more lighthouses to superintend, received thirty-four dollars.[16] But collectors also received a percentage of duties. In 1792, Joseph Whipple received $820.39 and incurred expenses totaling $273.51, making his actual earnings $546.88. In larger, busier ports the collector's job could be a real plum, and the compensation is something of an index of the volume of commerce and the comparative prosperity of seaports. In New York, Philadelphia, and Boston a collector could clear a very comfortable income of more than four thousand dollars per year. Salem's collector fared better than Whipple did in 1792, with earnings of $1,007.[17]

Joseph Whipple was fired in 1798. Like Portsmouth leader and then U.S. Senator John Langdon, he had been a supporter of the Revolution and later of the Constitution and the federal system of government it created. By the mid-1790s, however, Langdon, Whipple, and many others in New Hampshire's only deepwater port had become partisans of Thomas Jefferson's Republicans. They heatedly opposed Jay's treaty with Great Britain, which did not explicitly prohibit seizure of American vessels and the impressment of their crews, and they were convinced it would destroy Portsmouth's chances for prosperity. By the mid-1790s, all but one of the men working for Whipple in the Portsmouth customs house supported Jefferson's position.[18]

After the election of President John Adams, Federalists led by Jeremiah Smith of Exeter waged war on the Portsmouth Jeffersonian Republicans. Whipple, like other customs collectors, controlled more

jobs in his state than any other local federal official. And regardless of how his earnings compared to those in other ports, his was considered the most potentially lucrative federal office in New Hampshire. Whipple was therefore a juicy political target for the Federalists. They labeled him a "violent Jacobin" partisan of the French Revolution and accused him of using his office to foment opposition to the government. Though Smith did not question his competence and honesty, Eliphalet Ladd accused Whipple of withholding customs collections from the Government—a charge never substantiated—and characterized him as "one of the most inveterate Jacobins in the United States." Captain

Eliphalet Ladd was one of Joseph Whipple's most vigorous detractors. Portrait at the Moffatt-Ladd House. Douglas Armsden photo.

Hopley Yeaton, of the Portsmouth revenue cutter *Scammel* was also attacked. He was called "intemperate," a "violent furious democrat," and "a tool of Whipple who is a tool of Langdon."[19]

In what has been called a "precedent-setting turnover," Thomas Martin, the Customs Surveyor and the one remaining Federalist in the customs house, was appointed collector; Hopley Yeaton was replaced as master of the *Scammel;* the naval officer at the customs house, Eleazer Russell, resigned; and some twenty employees of the customs house— weighers, gaugers, measurers, boatmen—were replaced with men of the proper political persuasion.[20] The only person who owed his job to Whipple who was not replaced was David Duncan, the keeper of the lighthouse at the fort. Duncan, an invalided veteran of the Revolutionary War, does not seem to have been politically minded. Furthermore, it is unlikely that anyone would have wanted the job; the pay was miserable and the living conditions terrible.

Thomas Martin had been surveyor since March of 1791. When he became collector, he moved the customs office from Eleazar Russell's store, near what was later a ferry landing, to space above Joseph Haven's store on Spring Hill. There, in addition to his duties as collector, he served as clerk of the Piscataqua Bridge Company and sold pepper and cassia. No records of his tenure as collector have been located.[21]

In a political housecleaning similar to the one that threw him out of office, and which would be repeated whenever another political party won the presidency, Joseph Whipple returned to his post as collector of customs with the election of Thomas Jefferson in 1801. He remained collector until his death in 1816.[22]

Whipple corresponded with his Treasury Department superior (alternately the Secretary of the Treasury and the Commissioner of Revenue) on many lighthouse issues and problems: inadequate lighting equipment, the need for housing near the lighthouse for the keeper, and patronage concerns. He supervised the building of a replacement light-house at the fort and the manufacture and placement of the first known floating aids to navigation for the Port of Portsmouth. His early advice that effective revenue collection required armed vessels contributed to the creation of the Revenue Marine, and three Portsmouth revenue cut-ters were built during his tenure.[23]

Joseph Whipple died on February 25, 1816, at the age of seventy-nine. He had served a total of twenty-two years under three presi-dents—Washington, Jefferson, and Madison. During these years he was involved not only in the creation of the federal customs, lighthouse, and Revenue Marine systems, but also in the turbulent maritime affairs of his period, including the embargo and the War of 1812, which so affect-ed the fortunes of Portsmouth. He experienced firsthand the politiciza-tion of federal government service that developed early in the history of the republic and influenced for many decades the management of lighthouses and the appointments of the men who tended them.

The Transfer of Portsmouth Harbor Light to the Federal Government

The lighthouse at the inactive Fort William and Mary, the eleven other functioning lighthouses in the United States, and the four under construction when Congress passed the act establishing federal respon-sibility for them were the nucleus of the federal lighthouse system. They became highly visible symbols of the new government. But first the legalities had to be taken care of. One of collector Whipple's early lighthouse chores was to oversee the transfer of the Portsmouth lighthouse from the state to the federal government.

Congress stipulated that the states maintain the lighthouses until they were formally ceded to the United States, with the government reimbursing the states for their expenses from the date of the federal enactment. The red tape must have been considerable during this transitional period. President Washington himself signed the early contracts for lightkeepers, which in turn had to be approved by the state legislatures.[24]

Through 1790 and into the summer of 1791, Whipple reported to Hamilton on the progress of the transfer of the lighthouse to the federal government.[25] New Hampshire was cautious and voted in January 1791 to have a survey made of the lighthouse site on New Castle Island and a plan drawn of the fort and lighthouse; Supply Clap was voted four pounds, one shilling, and ninepence to do this work. Finally, on February 14, 1791, an act ceded to the United States one and three quarters acres that included the grounds of the fort as well as the lighthouse. Because there was concern that criminals would use the federal property as a sanctuary, a proviso in the state's legislation gave New Hampshire the right to pursue and apprehend anyone escaping from the law officers of the state. Some states were even more wary than New Hampshire; the last transfer of a lighthouse to the federal government was not until 1795—well past the August 1791 deadline established by Congress.[26]

Lighthouse Problems: Lights, Housing, Patronage

The 1791 transfer of New Hampshire's sole lighthouse from state to federal jurisdiction brought few immediate changes in the way the Portsmouth light was run. Captain Titus Salter continued as keeper. His job, for an annual stipend of 175 pounds, was to maintain it either "by himself or some careful Person" and to make sure there was a supply of at least one hundrd gallons of "no other Oil than Spermaceti, or Hakes Oil... and Suitable Brushes for cleaning the Lanthorn." Salter, as commandant of the inactive fort, was also responsible for the military stores there and for making sure that a signal flag was hoisted when topsail vessels went by to let them know their arrival in the port had been observed. Sergeant Elias Tarlton, living outside the fort walls in the village of New Castle, retained the job of actually tending the lighthouse lamps.[27]

Titus Salter was keeper of Portsmouth Harbor light from 1784 until President Washington in 1793 ordered that the keeper live "on the spot where the lighthouse is," and that "he will not be permitted to employ a deputy to take care of the Light House..." From William Emery, The Salters of Portsmouth.

Sperm oil was being used at many other lighthouses, but fish oil still fueled the lamps in the Portsmouth lighthouse in the early 1790s. Whipple wrote that of the fish oils available locally, hake oil was superior, as it "was esteemed the freest from impure matter, less glutinous and yielding less smoke than any other." The local fishermen who supplied the fish livers for the oil were asked to separate the livers of the hake from those of other fish they caught. Quality control must have been uncertain. Who was to know, and who would have wanted to check up on, how carefully the fishermen sorted fish livers? As Whipple observed, it "depended upon the fidelity of the fishermen." [28]

Local shipmasters had seen brighter lights elsewhere. Whipple, stung by their complaints, in the fall of 1791 tried to achieve a more brilliant light by ordering the use of the more volatile sperm oil. Explaining to Alexander Hamilton an unusually large bill for replacement glass for the lantern, Whipple reported that it was needed because of "the oyl taking fire in the lantern and breaking the windows by which the building was in imminent danger of destruction."[29]

His account of this near disaster provides a description of the lighting apparatus installed in the lantern in 1784 to replace the three large copper lamps of pre-Revolutionary days:

> The vessel containing the oil is an open copper pan about 20 inches wide and 4 or 5 inches deep. This is suspended to a proper hight in the lantern, the wicks are rested on a plate or strip of Iron laying across the pan and sunk in the oil to the level of the surface of it. These being lighted as usual to the amount of 7 wicks on the suspending plate or strip of iron, it is supposed to effectually heat the irons and consequently the whole quantity of oil exposed on a surface of 400 square inches and 2 inches deep only.[30]

This system of illumination must have been the notorious "spider lamp." It may have produced better light than the lamps used in the colonial period, but spider lamps were infamously difficult. They produced acrid smoke, making it impossible for the person tending the light to stay long in the lantern, called for frequent trips to the top of the lighthouse to manage them, and required considerable effort to keep the glass of the lantern free of obscuring film from the smoke.[31]

In January 1793, Whipple asked for lamps in which sperm oil could be used to produce a brighter light. He mentioned reports by shipmasters that the sperm oil lamps in use at the Nantucket lighthouse were better than other types. Tench Coxe, who as the U.S. commissioner of revenue was then in charge of the lighthouse system, did not know anything about them, much to Whipple's frustration. He wrote, "I did conceive a minute description of every Lighthouse and the apparatus attached to them had been transmitted in conformity to circular directions." Whipple gave Coxe a detailed description of the four lamps used at Nantucket, each with three half-round spouts. Somewhat peevishly, he suggested that for fuller details, Coxe might talk to Mr. Peleg Coffin, the inventor of the apparatus, who was then serving in Congress as a representative from Massachusetts.[32]

By May 1793 Coxe had sent five lamps (though not of the Nantucket type that Whipple hoped for) along with ventilating pipes to help draw in fresh air and exhaust the spent air and smoke from the lantern. Only three of the new lamps would fit into the narrow lantern, but Whipple immediately sent to Boston's collector of customs, Benjamin Lincoln, for a supply of sperm oil. He crisply instructed Lincoln to make sure the barrels were tight. He wrote that oil put up in Boston had the reputation for becoming so thick in winter that three quarters of it could not be poured out of a barrel even when the top was taken off it, and insisted on the "best Winter strained Spermacite." He also asked Lincoln to "direct the coaster who receives the Oil to shake it into the hold of his Vessel immediately after it comes along side to prevent the effect of the sun on it." On July 8, Whipple reported on tests with vent pipes inserted through the floor and roof of the lantern and on the use of the new lamps and sperm oil.[33]

Coxe wrote to Whipple in 1797 that the lamps in Portsmouth were using an inordinate amount of cotton wicking. Whipple's long reply provides a description of the lamps then in use as well as evidence of the personal attention he gave to improve their effectiveness. He reported that three lamps, each with three "pipes," or spouts, were suspended in the lantern in a triangular arrangement. Wicks were lit in two of the three spouts in each lamp. In winter, a fourth lamp was set on the floor of the lantern and lit to provide heat below the other lamps to keep the oil warm enough to flow. He conducted experiments with the spare lamp, probably at the customs house. He tried out various thicknesses and lengths of cotton wicking in each of its three spouts to see how to produce the most effective light.[34] Whipple's conclusion was that the lightkeeper's "zeal to excel... led him into an erroneous profusion in the use of cotton." He continued with an astute critique of the state of lamp technology in the U.S. lighthouse system:

> I conceive that the construction of lamps, the size and manner of spiring or preparing the wick and the management of the whole is susceptible of further improvements—& that among the several keepers of Lighthouses... there may be some whose ingenuity... might produce some useful alterations—I have heard of mirrors or reflectors being applied to Lanterns & the fountain lamp I think would be an improvement.[35]

He apparently had heard from local shipmasters of the substantial improvements in the lighting apparatus by then being used in European lighthouses.

Whipple also struggled with the problem of housing for Sergeant Elias Tarlton, who had tended the light since 1784. The titular keeper, Captain Titus Salter, lived about two miles away on Salter Lane in Portsmouth, out of sight of the lighthouse. The house Captain Cochran had lived in at the fort before the Revolution was uninhabitable after being vandalized upon Governor Wentworth's departure in 1775. There was evidently no other housing remaining at the fort by the end of the war. Whipple tried without success in 1792 to get an appropriation of one hundred dollars to build a house for Tarlton, who had to walk several hundred yards from his house in New Castle outside the fort grounds. Maintenance of the light throughout the night must have been onerous, and Tarlton evidently neglected to check the light as regularly as he should have. In 1793, President Washington himself addressed the practice of delegating the actual tending of the Portsmouth lighthouse to an assistant, a practice that began in 1771, when Captain Cochran's soldiers did the work.

> The President thinks it proper that the Keeper of the Light House at Portsmouth be informed, that he must reside on the

spot where the Light House is, if he continues in that office,
and that he will not be permitted to employ a deputy to take
care of the Light House, unless upon some special occasion.

Washington also directed the keeper to make sure that the light
was maintained all night long.[36]

Because patronage was an early and continuing concern, both
Titus Salter and Elias Tarlton were offered the keepership; each
turned it down: Neither wanted it under Washington's conditions. With
a directive that the keeper had to live on the lighthouse premises but
no funds to build a house for him, Whipple was in a bind. On the ter-
mination of Salter's contract at the end of June 1793, he hired David
Duncan as a temporary keeper and arranged for him to live in an
abandoned barrack—"a miserable accommodation"—at the inactive
fort. In 1795, after military construction at the fort (but still without
funds for a keeper's house), Duncan and his family moved into the
newly built blockhouse there.[37]

When the fort was manned, Duncan had to move to rented rooms
in a house a quarter of a mile from the lighthouse, an arrangement
that must have made nighttime maintenance very difficult. After his
reappointment as collector, Whipple wrote in June 1802 that the
owners of the house needed the rooms and the keeper would soon be
without a place to live. That year, a decade after he first made the
request, Whipple was finally authorized to spend eight hundred dollars for a keeper's house.[38]

Buoys and Beacons

The act of Congress providing for federal support of lighthouses
included buoys and beacons. By the early 1790s, collectors of customs
were asked to report on existing aids to navigation and make proposals
for new ones. In the Delaware River, for example, in 1767 there were a
few buoys, some of which were actually small, anchored boats called
floating beacons, onto whose masts distinctive cages were placed to
identify their different locations. The word *beacon* now denotes a lighted navigational aid, but in Joseph Whipple's day, it usually designated
an unlit marker, built to serve as a daymark ashore, on a ledge, or, as
in the Delaware, on a boat. *Buoy*, however, was the period's usual term
for an anchored, unlit floating aid to navigation.[39]

It seems likely that a number of buoys would have been placed at some earlier time in the harbors of major ports like Boston, though documentation for them has not been located. Closer to Portsmouth, when the federal government took over aids to navigation, there were four buoys of some sort at the difficult entrance to the Merrimack River in Newburyport, Massachusetts. No buoys are recorded in the waters around Portsmouth during the colonial or confederation eras, although they may have existed.[40]

Phineas Merrill's 1806 map of New Castle identifies the highest point of land on the island as "Beacon Hill." No beacon at this site is indicated in the detailed charts of DesBarres's pre-Revolutionary *Atlantic Neptune.* It could have been a structure built as a daymark for masters of small vessels and fishing boats to align with some natural or man-made feature to guide them into the tricky entrance to Little Harbor. It seems possible, though no documentary evidence has been located, that in this case the word *beacon* referred to a Revolutionary War tower or pole of some sort where a lantern or basket of burning material could be raised to warn upriver forces of approaching enemy warships. No reference to it can be found in any editions of the *American Coast Pilot,* even though the name Beacon Hill appears as late as the 1854 preliminary edition of the U.S. Coast Survey chart of Portsmouth Harbor.[41]

Phineas Merrill's 1806 map of New Castle, showing "Beacon Hill." PA.

Collector Whipple consulted local seamen before enumerating sites for needed beacons and buoys in 1793. First on his "wish list" was a whitewashed stone beacon tower about thirty feet high on Boon Island, even though the island, located off the coast of what is now Maine, was under the jurisdiction of Massachusetts. Perhaps mindful of the 1710 wreck of the *Nottingham Galley,* Whipple suggested that such a beacon be sixteen feet in diameter at the base to provide a "cavity that would give shelter to such persons as may be cast on the island." He also proposed:

- For Sunken Rocks, a ledge in the river off Pierce Island about a mile upstream from the lighthouse, bare at low tides: a beacon of stone, cased with wood, or at the very least a buoy to mark the ledge;
- For Kitt's Rock, about 1 1/4 miles northeast of the lighthouse: a buoy to mark the southern edge of the jumble of ledges and rocks that formed a wedge of hazards off Gerrish Island at the entrance to the river;
- For Cod Rock, about a half mile east of the lighthouse: a buoy;
- For Pumpkins Island "opposite the town of Portsmouth, another beacon to keep vessels from grounding on it."[42]

By April 1794, an act of Congress authorized "two buoys in the harbour of Portsmouth," which the ever-scrupulous Whipple pointed out should have read "near the entrance or off the harbor" to include the most needed buoy sites at Kitt's Rock and Stileman's Rock. (The latter hazard may have been Cod Rock, possibly re-named since Whipple's list was prepared.)[43] A beacon on Sunken Rocks was authorized as well, but funding was inadequate.

Keeping within the three hundred dollars allowed for both sites, Whipple had two sets of solid, conical wooden buoys made so that there would be a backup buoy for each of these two locations. These buoys were constructed of large timbers bolted together and then shaped into the "form of a nun's buoy." Placement of the buoys at Kitt's and Stileman's Rocks would wait until warmer weather, Whipple wrote at the end of December 1794. He had already used one of the backup buoys as a marker for Sunken Rocks, however, as an experiment to see how it would withstand the extremely powerful tidal force of the river. He was afraid that if these buoys became waterlogged and heavy, they would break the chains holding them to the large stones that anchored them. He also ordered hollow ones made of staves by a cooper, evidently patterned after the type long in use in English and continental European waters. He abandoned this project when he decided the person with whom he contracted was not up to the task; he ended up having two more solid wood buoys made for Sunken Rocks.[44]

Revenue Cutters

Another of Joseph Whipple's early assignments as collector of customs was to recommend to the Secretary of the Treasury ways to ensure that no one avoided paying duties on imported goods. In October 1789, Whipple proposed a Portsmouth-built vessel to ply the waters between Cape Elizabeth, Maine, and Cape Cod, Massachusetts. Its crew would board and inspect coasting and fishing vessels coming from the eastward, to make sure goods were not smuggled in from the maritime provinces of British Canada. The collectors in Boston and Philadelphia made similar suggestions, and the U. S. Revenue Marine was established in 1790. Thus Whipple was directly involved in the creation of the ancestors of the present-day Coast Guard: the Lighthouse and Revenue Marine services. Until the middle of the nineteenth century, the revenue cutters of the U.S. had a role of sorts in supervising offshore aids to navigation.[45]

President George Washington spent several days in Portsmouth early in November 1789, an especially momentous event for the people who had been involved in the Revolution and the creation of the federal government. His visit included a trip on a barge propelled by white-clad oarsmen down the Piscataqua and past the fort and lighthouse. It would be surprising if the recently appointed collector of customs Joseph Whipple had not been aboard. The coxswain of the barge was Hopley Yeaton, who had seen war service as a junior officer aboard the Ports-mouth-built frigate *Raleigh*. Five months later, he became the first of ten revenue cutter commanders commissioned by Washington.[46]

Whipple negotiated with Alexander Hamilton the details of the construction and fitting out of Yeaton's command: a two-masted schooner of fifty-one tons, fifty-seven and three-fifths feet long "from the fore part of the bow to the after part of the stern," to be armed with four swivel guns. When the cutter first sailed out of Portsmouth Harbor on August

26, 1791, she bore the name *Ferret*—a name so descriptive of her projected function that it had already been given to a British Canadian government vessel. She was quickly renamed S*cammel* to commemorate Alexander Scammel, one of New Hampshire's fallen military heroes of the Revolution.[47]

In spite of the Neutrality Act of 1793, the British had seized hundreds of American ships and their cargoes, and after that year Whipple had required shipmasters to carry with them lists attesting to the U.S. citizenship of their crews. This did not prove effective in preventing their impressment. Frequent harassment and boarding of U. S. merchant ships by French privateers and the depredations of the Barbary pirates contributed to the depressed state of shipbuilding and mercantile enterprise in the Piscataqua region, as elsewhere in the United States. Even before the establishment of the U.S. Navy Department in 1798, the Treasury and War Departments planned to beef up the revenue cutter service for patrolling the coast with larger, faster vessels capable of carrying more guns and greatly expanded crews. In October 1797, Whipple recommended the sale of the *Scammel;* the contract for a replacement went in the spring of 1798 to James Hackett's shipyard. The new cutter, *Scammel II,* a two-masted schooner with square topsails on her fore and main masts, was launched in August 1798. At 187 tons and seventy-seven feet in length, *Scammel II* was fitted with fourteen guns, ten more than the first *Scammel* carried, and better suited for her purpose than her predecessor.[48]

Late in 1798, all U.S. Revenue Marine cutters were turned over to the newly created Navy Department for the duration of the Quasi-War with France—a precedent that was eventually formalized by law and followed in later wars. *Scammel II*, then commanded by Hopley Yeaton's replacement, John Adams, was at first assigned to the New England coast. The secretary of the Navy wrote Adams that his territory extended from Machias, Maine, to Cape Cod, where he and his crew of thirty were to "indulge in a spirit of Enterprize" to counter the depredations of the French. In December, along with three other revenue cutters, the *Scammel II* was sent to patrol Prince Rupert Bay, on the west coast of Dominica in the West Indies, where she captured the French war vessel *Felix.* The *Scammel II* did not return to Portsmouth, but was sold by the Navy in Baltimore in 1801. Another revenue cutter, the smaller *Governor Gilman,* with a keel fifty-eight feet long, a beam of twenty feet, and a draft of nine feet was also constructed in 1798 by

James Hackett in Portsmouth, but was sold only four years later. The *New Hampshire* was built in Portsmouth in 1802. No information as to her dimensions and armament has been located, but her price tag of only $3,325 reflected President Jefferson's opposition to maintaining a hefty military capability during peacetime. This vessel probably confined her patrolling to Portsmouth Harbor and its immediate environs and was sold in 1816. No record of a replacement has been located until 1829, when the Connecticut-built schooner *Hiram* was purchased for $1,635 and sailed to Portsmouth to become the revenue cutter *Portsmouth*.[49]

The cutters of the Revenue Marine provided crucial, if often uncertain, links between the Customs Collectors and offshore lighthouses. New Hampshire had no offshore lighthouse until 1820, but until that year, when Maine became a state, the District of Maine and its lighthouses and other aids to navigation were the responsibility of the Boston customs collector. The first revenue cutter *Massachusetts*, was launched only a month earlier than the first *Scammel*, was replaced by a second *Massachusetts* in 1798, and by a third *Massachusetts* in 1801 or 1802. The revenue cutter *Search* was built as a replacement

U. S. Revenue Cutter **MASSACHUSETTS**
Launched at Newburyport, Massachusetts, 1791

United States Revenue Cutter Massachusetts. *The cutter likely resembled* Scammel II, *launched in 1798. This 1969 postcard image is identified as the first (1791) vessel of this name, although the revenue cutter ensign shown on the foremast was not adopted until 1799, three years after the first* Massachusetts *was replaced by a sloop, a much smaller vessel.* AC.

in Newport, Rhode Island in 1815, at the same time as *Detector,* which was sent to Portland, Maine. These cutters, with the primary duty of intercepting smugglers, also carried the Boston collector or his deputies to the sites of Massachusetts's offshore navigational aids, including those in the District of Maine. In the Portsmouth area, a succession of two unlit daymarks, or monuments, followed by a light-house built in 1811 on Boon Island, remained under the jurisdiction of the collector in Boston until Maine achieved statehood. Thereafter, cutters based either in Portsmouth or Portland, and occasionally Boston served the lighthouses in the waters of this area.[50]

A New Lighthouse for Portsmouth Harbor

The Portsmouth lighthouse was not tall enough for its light to be seen from the ocean side of Friar's (now Gerrish) Island, on the Maine side of the entrance to the Piscataqua River. Much to Whipple's consternation, a petition to Congress for a taller lighthouse, which he claimed he had sought for two years, was surreptitiously circulated. He complained in a letter to his friend and political ally Senator John Langdon in January 1793 that he thought it had been done to make him look bad.[51]

In 1793 and 1794, Whipple consulted with Revenue Commissioner Tench Coxe about a replacement lighthouse. He suggested to Coxe a structure eighty-three feet high and discussed the pros and cons of various sites on the fort grounds. He himself preferred a spot near the existing light about forty feet eastward towards the main channel, instead of a site one hundred yards south, on Pollack Rock, which some of his advisers preferred because it more directly faced the harbor entrance. Whipple pointed out that this location would require a long causeway or bridge for access, as water surrounded the site at high tide. If the fort was re-activated, he wrote, it would be in the direct line of cannon fire "with the most important point for the defense of the harbour... [and] be exposed to great danger." He rejected suggestions for other sites nearer the mouth of the river. Gerrish Island would have given a higher elevation to a lighthouse, but no vessel could come nearer to it than a mile because of the dangerous rocks surrounding it. Whale's Back ledge, another possible site, was awash at half tide, and Wood Island would have presented problems of construction and access in bad weather. Of Odiorne's Point, another suggested site, Whipple said that although a

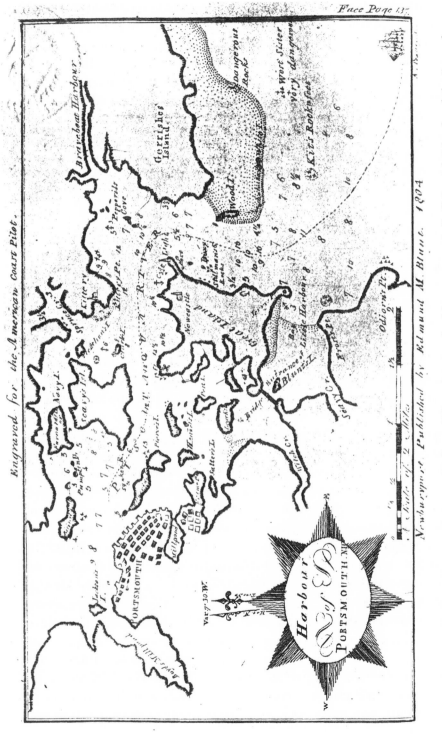

Chart of Portsmouth Harbor, from Blunt's 1804 Coast Pilot, showing the "dangerous rocks" off Gerrish Island and the "very danger-ous" West Sisters and indicating a safe course into Portsmouth. The chart also shows a bar near the entrance to Little Harbor, running from Frost's Point to New Castle. The only buoy labeled is the one marking Stielman's Rocks off New Castle.

light there would be visible far sooner by approaching vessels, a second light would be needed to direct them into the harbor itself.[52]

Whipple secured estimates for both stone and wooden lighthouses. Stone could be had by cannibalizing the walls of the old fort. However, if the fort was ever needed again this would be a false economy—much better to bring stone from Durham, twelve miles upriver. He wrote that if a masonry tower was built, he was sure that masons would have to be imported from other states "where building in stone has been in practice." He estimated a wooden lighthouse tower would cost only fifteen hundred dollars, less than half the expense of a masonry structure.[53]

Whipple obviously felt more comfortable with wood construction, in spite of the greater possibility of destruction by fire. (He calculated that the interest on the difference saved in building costs between wood and masonry could buy fire insurance and would pay for two coats of paint every eight years.) He pointed out that because of the "exhalations" of salt from the sea, wood did not rot. Whipple sent Coxe a drawing prepared by Mr. Clifford, "an ingenious and capable carpenter," for a wooden framework for a tower seventy-eight feet in height to the base of the lantern.[54]

To prove his point about the preservative effects of salt air, but perhaps scotching the chance for a new lighthouse of any description, Whipple wrote that "in the present building... there is not the least appearance of decay in the wood work within or without although it has stood upwards of 20 years and has not received such repeated coats of paint as would have been best for its preservation." Shortly thereafter, Whipple conceded that a new lighthouse could wait for "a more eligible period in the affairs of the Government."[55]

Though direct user fees no longer funded lighthouse expenses, as they had in the colonial and confederation periods, the customs duties collected in a particular port, and nationally, bore on federal allocations for aids to navigation. This was not an "eligible period" for lighthouse building, because the war between France and England was creating troubled times for shipping interests in the United States in general and the Port of Portsmouth in particular.

At the turn of the century, after the end of the 1791–1800 Quasi-War with France, shipping activity rebounded, and the Port of Portsmouth was again a candidate for consideration of its need for navigational aids. Two developments in the mid-1790s helped the maritime economy

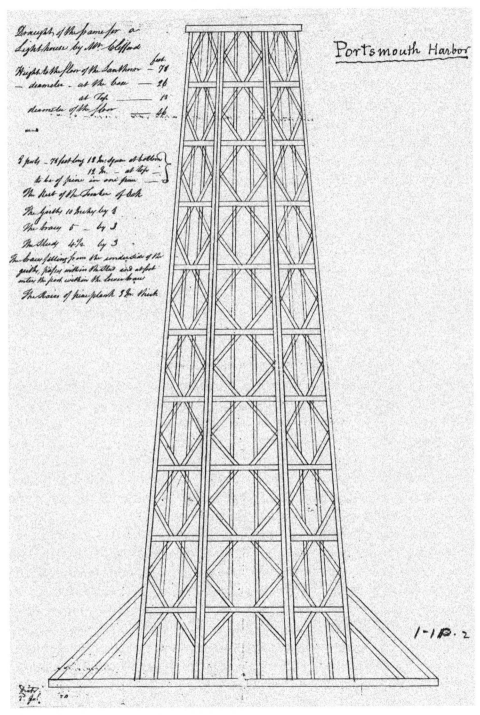

Mr. Clifford's frame for a lighthouse. NARG26.

of the region once international conflict had subsided. By 1795, the Piscataqua River at Fox Point in Dover was spanned by a timber bridge a half-mile long. A huge arched segment over the deepest section of the river, 244 feet long, let vessels pass underneath. The bridge opened up markets in developing inland communities north of the river, promising more business for merchants and owners of vessels bringing goods into the port. The next year, Portsmouth merchants, organized as the Proprietors of the Portsmouth Pier, built an important improvement along the waterfront—a pier 340 feet long and sixty-five feet wide, with shops and warehouses and even a hotel built on it. Early in 1799, the *New-Hampshire Gazette* reported that in the year between 1797 and 1798 the number of Piscataqua-built vessels had increased by one-third. [56]

After he was reappointed collector in 1802, one of Joseph Whipple's early assignments was to arrange for the building of a new, taller lighthouse at the fort. In April 1802, Congress appropriated four thousand dollars for this project, but it was not actually accomplished for over two years.[57]

It is noteworthy that Governor John Wentworth had been able to rush the first Portsmouth lighthouse to completion within three months of his decision to have it built, whereas this one took twenty-seven months from the time of the appropriation until its completion in July 1804. For one thing Whipple, unlike Wentworth, had to put out the job to bid. Probably more important, Whipple obviously did not have Wentworth's ready access to the engineering and technical know-how necessary to design such a specialized structure. The departure of the cadre of trained military engineers like Captain Samuel Holland at the outbreak of the Revolutionary War seems to have caused an engineering "brain drain." Whipple wrote in June 1802 to both Boston Collector Benjamin Lincoln and Revenue Commissioner William Miller of the Treasury Department asking for guidance. He was still uncomfortable with stone construction, expecting it would cost more than the appropriation would cover, and requested any drawings, models, or descriptions of lighthouses they could provide.[58]

Whipple was evidently armed with enough information by mid-August 1802 to place the following ad in the *New-Hampshire Gazette*:

> **WANTED**
>
> A quantity of stone for the foundation of a new Light-House, to be erected at Fort Point, (so called) at New Castle—Any persons

willing to contract for the delivery thereof, at said Fort Point, are requested to apply to this Office, where a particular description of the work may be obtained, and proposals received for the same.[59]

Two weeks later he placed another ad, this one soliciting bids for building a wooden lighthouse on Pollock Rock, "about 90 yards from the old Light-House." Whether he had changed his mind about the site or had been overruled is not known. The structure was to be octagonal, seventy-eight feet high to the base of the lantern and thirty feet in diameter at the base, tapering to twelve feet at the top. It was to be shingled and painted with three coats of white paint. Construction was to be completed by May 20, 1803.[60]

Whipple did not report on progress obtaining a building contract until April 1803: "The unacquaintedness with this kind of architecture of our Mechanics...led me to extend my notice & correspondence to every point on which a probability existed... " He ended up with five proposals, including one from Pittston, Maine—two hundred miles away—and another from men in Hingham, Massachusetts. All the bids came in over the appropriation. Some of the bidders may have been aware that local labor was scarce and costly, for Portsmouth was rebuilding in the wake of a fire that had devastated a large part of the commercial district in December 1802. Another five hundred dollars authorized by the Treasury put the bid of Benjamin Clark Gilman of Exeter within one hundred and fifty dollars of the appropriation, and he got the job.[61]

Gilman (1763–1835) was an innovative engineer and clockmaker, described by Whipple as a man "possessed of great mechanical ingenuity." He had been active in town as contractor for the Portsmouth Aqueduct, completed late in 1799, and was doubtless well known to Whipple, who was a director of the aqueduct company.[62]

The lighthouse contract, as finally written, called for a structure eight stories high and with a forty-foot diameter at its base—substantially greater than had been proposed in 1802. The images of Governor Wentworth's 1771 lighthouse, if accurate, show that it tapered only slightly from base to platform; the addition of ten feet to the base created a structure broader in its proportions than the earlier one. There is no evidence that the first lighthouse was unstable; the principal reasons for its replacement were simply that it was not tall enough to be seen over Friar's (Gerrish) Island and that its lantern was too small for the number of lamps needed to create an effective light.[63]

The contract also called for weighting down the base of the new structure with stones sandwiched between the sleepers bolted to the foundations and the sleepers of the first floor. These changes suggest anxiety that the new, taller structure would be more susceptible to wind. A wooden lighthouse at Brant's Point, Nantucket, in fact, was blown over in 1774.[64]

Allowance was made for a lantern of more generous dimensions than the one Noah Parker built for the first lighthouse. It was to be seven feet in diameter and seven feet high, not counting the roof. The lantern would rest on a copper-sheathed platform with an iron railing; a small iron stove would keep the sperm oil from congealing in winter. To stay within his forty-three-hundred-dollar contract, Gilman would omit paint for the sheathing shingles called for in the specifications. Whipple asked permission to use timbers from the old lighthouse, when it was taken down, along with leftover planks once intended for gun platforms at the fort, to build an elevated walkway to bridge the gully between the island and the lighthouse site, but this too was deferred.[65]

In mid-August 1803, Gilman placed the following ad that reflected his aqueduct-building work as well as his lighthouse contract:

> **WANTED**
> Immediately, a few good workmen at the House-Carpenter's Business, to assist in framing a Frame for Portsmouth Light-House, and a good Workman or two at the Stone-Laying Business,—also part of the timber for said Frame, and a quantity of small round timber for the aqueduct—The timber to be delivered at Exeter.[66]

No itemized bills survive to give the names of the craftsmen Gilman hired, although there is evidence that Portsmouth carpenter Nathaniel Marston worked on the lighthouse. Almost forty years later, a survey of northern New England lighthouses reported that the structure was "an excellent piece of carpentry," and would "bear favorable comparison with its more modern neighbors." [67]

"Good lamps of an approved model" were to be placed in the lantern; those from the old lighthouse lantern were possibly transferred to the new one. A scarcity of sheet copper for the lantern roof delayed the project, and the lighthouse was finally finished in late July 1804, fourteen months past the completion date originally established. Whipple took it upon himself to have paint applied to the shingles and to have built a three-hundred-foot long walkway and bridge to the lighthouse—a three-hundred and fifty dollar initiative for which he was taken to task by his superiors in Washington. He had hoped to be able to use some of the timbers from the old lighthouse for the walkway but wrote that "the wood materials on examination were found unsuitable," but that perhaps local fishermen might want to purchase the wood for repairing their fish houses. The old iron lantern with its copper dome Whipple suggested might be sold for use in a new lighthouse requiring a lantern of its size and would fetch more than if it were sold for scrap metal.[68]

The 1771 lighthouse remained standing for nearly a year and a half. The *New-Hampshire Gazette* carried this advertisement at the end of December 1805:

> To Be Sold at Auction
>
> On Tuesday the 7th of January next, at the office of Alex'r Ewen, in Water street, Portsmouth.
>
> The Wood Materials of the old Light House now standing on Fort-Point, to be taken down by the purchaser within 20 days from the day of sale, which will be at 12 o'clock.

No reports on the auction of the timber or the disposition of the old lantern have been found.[69]

The lighthouse was reduced in height in the mid-nineteenth century. Few pictures showing it at its original height are known. One is a conceptual rendition of the fort as it was supposed to have looked in 1790. But the lighthouse the artist drew looms up beyond the fort in the location of the 1804 (rather than the 1771) lighthouse. The artist seems to have been unaware that this was the second lighthouse at the fort, as was John Albee in the 1880s.[70] Another image is an 1872 painting by Thomas P. Moses based on his recollection of the original structure.

David Duncan, Keeper of Portsmouth Harbor Light, 1793-1820

The keepers of the lighthouse during the colonial period and after the Revolutionary War—Captain John Cochran, Lieutenant Meshech Bell, and Captain Titus Salter—had been sea captains or in military commands, or both. They supervised the work of the men who actually tended the lighthouse lamps, ordered and kept track of supplies, and

Copyright 1907, by David Urch   Used with his permission

FORT WILLIAM AND MARY (RENAMED FORT CONSTITUTION IN 1808)
AS IT APPEARED WHEN ATTACKED BY THE NEW HAMPSHIRE MINUTE MEN
(Issued by 175th Anniversary Committee of St. John's Lodge, No. 1, Portsmouth, N. H.)

Postcard issued in 1909 by the 175th Anniversary Committee of St. John's Lodge, No. 1. The lighthouse is identified as the first, 1771 structure. The position and height of the lighthouse relative to the fort strongly indicate that this was the second, 1804 lighthouse. PA

submitted their accounts for payment. President Washington's early 1793 directive that the lighthouse keeper live on the premises brought a different kind of keeper to the Portsmouth lighthouse.

Salter's contract terminated at the end of June, 1793, and on July 8 Whipple wrote to Tench Coxe that he had hired David Duncan, "a wounded pensioner of the United States, who is unable to perform hard labor," on a trial basis. Whipple wrote that unless the president objected, "I shall continue him as his fidelity serves." Mr. Duncan remained keeper for twenty-seven years.[71]

David Duncan had neither the habit of command nor a title that commanded respect. He had been a lowly corporal during the war. He was born around 1746 either in Scotland or of Scottish parents on the other side of the Piscataqua River in Kittery. It is thought that he worked as a carpenter on Forts Sullivan and Washington before enlisting at New Castle in 1776 in Pearse Long's 1st New Hampshire Regiment. Long and his regiment were ordered to Ticonderoga late in November, and there Duncan signed on with Zachariah Beal's company of the 3rd New Hampshire Continental Regiment, commanded by Alexander Scammel. Corporal Duncan was wounded at the second battle of Saratoga and returned to New Hampshire after recovering in military hospitals. With other invalided soldiers, he joined a company manning Piscataqua forts. At some point before 1782, he had signed aboard the privateer *Retaliation* under Captain Samuel Rice and was captured and held prisoner for several months in Plymouth, England. In a prisoner exchange he was sent home, unfit to do heavy physical work.[72]

Duncan's pay was fifteen dollars per month. The pay and the only available living accommodations—an abandoned barrack at the fort—were evidently inadequate for a more "eligible" person. Local tradition holds that Major Moses McFarland became keeper of the lighthouse at this time. Though he wanted to, and recommended him for the position, there is no evidence that Whipple hired McFarland. Like David Duncan, he was a disabled veteran of the war, but with a higher rank. McFarland was "a deserving officer in unfortunate circumstances," but Whipple considered three hundred dollars per year—ten dollars more per week than Duncan was paid—a suitable salary for the major, and enough to cover the cost of a paid assistant (needed perhaps because of McFarland's disability, perhaps because of his rank, or possibly because members of his family would not be expected to help him without pay). But only $180 per year was authorized, and no funds provided to build a suitable house. Duncan's sixteen-year-old son would help him, and would not be paid.[73]

Duncan, his wife Susannah, and their four children had a hard time of it. The new sperm oil lamps installed in 1793 needed "constant attention. The attendant almost lives in the lantern in the night," Whipple reported. The family lived in a "miserable" abandoned barrack that had been only partially cleared of military stores. Supply Clap, the commissary general, wrote to New Hampshire Governor Ichabod Bartlett on July 31, 1793, that he had "removed the stores from the barrack at the Fort, which belonged to the state. At Colonel Whipple's request I left a few articles sufficient to work two cannon if occasion should require... under the care of Mr. Duncan." Duncan had not only to share his living space with the equipment, but also to "prevent its being stole."[74]

Construction at the fort caused another disruption. French engineer Bechet Rochefontaine arrived in Portsmouth in the summer of 1794 to supervise the rebuilding of the fort. Expecting that the Duncans would be displaced from the barracks once a garrison arrived at the reconstructed fort, in 1795 Whipple made another unsuccessful plea for a lightkeeper's house. The manning of the fort was delayed, however, and in December Whipple obtained permission to use the new blockhouse as a keeper's house. This was a one-story structure with a hipped roof, "a neat finished brick building about 30 feet square consisting of two rooms in the front about 12 by 15 feet each and a guard room in back about 15 by 30 feet." Whipple warned, though, that the Duncans would have to vacate it when troops were stationed at the fort. [75]

There was, of course, no provision for automatic cost-of-living adjustments, and Whipple fought for a raise for Duncan during inflationary times. In May 1795 he wrote Tench Coxe, "The present price of Provisions are for Indian Corn 100 to 117 per bush, and fresh meats 8 to 10 cents per pound." He urged a raise for the keeper, who had to support a wife and four children, three of them too young to work. "I entreat your feeling attention to this object..." He had already given Duncan a chance to earn extra money by working on what he called a "brow," a sort of wooden bridge, to provide easier access to the lighthouse. Coxe was reluctant, and it was not until the very end of March 1796—almost a year later—that he informed Whipple he could pay Duncan an extra twenty dollars per year.[76]

The construction of the long-sought keeper's house in 1802 meant a shorter walk to the lighthouse, but when the new lighthouse was finished two years later, there were eight flights of stairs for keeper Duncan or his son to climb on each trip to tend the lamps. Joseph Whipple again urged a raise in pay, observing that elsewhere the rate of pay allowed by the government varied according to the height of a lighthouse. Moreover, Whipple argued, the Duncans had previously augmented their larder by raising vegetables, hens, and pigs; this was no longer possible after the reestablishment of the garrison at the fort. The soldiers felt free to help themselves to the Duncans' crops and livestock. Finally, Whipple pointed out that the location of the lighthouse denied Duncan the chance to earn extra money from "entertaining seafaring people"—a practice that must have added to the income of keepers of other lights.[77]

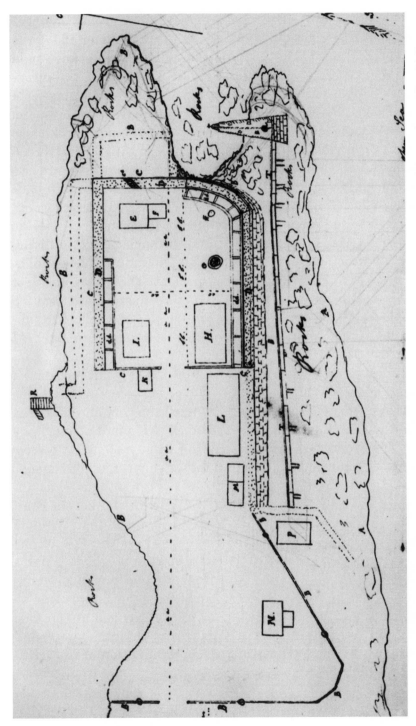

Map of Fort Constitution, attributed to Captain John Walbach, shows the blockhouse (E) where lighthouse keeper David Duncan and his family lived for a time; the 1802 keeper's house (P) at the location to which it was moved in 1809; the footbridge (T) to the lighthouse; and the lighthouse itself (Q). Also shown is the board fence (O) built in 1808 to separate the keeper's grounds from those reserved for the military.

The relationship between the soldiers at the fort and the Duncan family deteriorated over the next months. It is possible to imagine Duncan hobbling about and shaking an ineffectual stick at the soldiers as they helped themselves to his chickens and turnips. In September 1805, Whipple wrote to both Albert Gallatin, Secretary of the Treasury, and Henry Dearborn, Secretary of War, to report pilferage by the soldiers and "Disorder and abuse." He recommended construction of an eighty-foot-long post-and-board fence to define separate grounds for the keeper. As a result of this high-level deliberation, the Treasury eventually allowed about two hundred dollars for the fence, for which Whipple sent a bill to Gallatin in February 1808.[78]

The fort, renamed Fort Constitution by 1801, was rebuilt again in 1808, creating another conflict between the defensive and lighthouse establishments on the northeastern point of New Castle Island. The south wall of the expanded fort almost abutted the keeper's house, with the resulting "great inconvenience' that the "house has already received a considerable injury from discharging only two of the Guns." Whipple recommended that the house be moved to a site between four hundred and five hundred feet to the west; he considered a longer walk for the keeper to be a lesser evil than the gradual destruction of his house from the vibrations of the guns.[79]

The festivities of the Fourth of July 1809 included a gun salute from Fort Constitution. This ended in a catastrophe that probably hastened the release of an appropriation for moving the keeper's house away from the wall of the fort. It was described in the *New-Hampshire Gazette*:

> In the midst of the joy and hilarity of the 4th inst. between 4 and 5 o'clock, P. M. the following terrible disaster took place… Two chests of powder, and a number of loose cartridges which were placed near, took fire (supposed from the slow match) and in the explosion killed and wounded from 14 to 20 citizens and soldiers, besides doing much other essential damage. The quantity of powder exploded was between 3 and 400 weight… no blame whatever can be attached to Capt. Walbeck, commander of the fort. He directed an under officer to attend carefully to the firings of the afternoon, while he should enjoy himself with a few selected friends at his house, which was within the fort, and also within thirty feet of the explosion. Judge ye of the surprize of this excellent officer, when his

house was nearly blown up, with his guests and family with him!—The windows with part of the house bursting in, and everything breaking and crushing around them, so that there was scarcely a pane of glass, or an article that could be broken, but was dashed to atoms.

An article two days later reported that seven people had been killed and many more injured, including Captain Walbach's wife. There was no report of damage to the lighthouse keeper's house, and David Duncan and his family apparently were not injured. However, Whipple was soon negotiating the cost of moving and repairing Duncan's house. He also arranged for the construction of a tarred and graveled "composition" roof over the original cellar of the house, where the sperm oil for the lighthouse lamps would continue to be stored."[80]

The installation in 1812 of new, more complicated lighting equipment required more time-consuming maintenance. This, combined with continued inflation, brought yet another plea for a raise in pay, this time from Duncan himself: "westindies goods are nearly double, corn and most every other necessary of life greatly enhanced in price—with a numerious family dependent on me for support."[81]

A letter written in February 1820 by the fort's commandant, Colonel Walbach, to Timothy Upham, who had been appointed collector after Joseph Whipple died in 1816, attests to other problems. The aging Duncan had been sick, and Walbach suggested his immediate replacement—not because Duncan had not been a good, conscientious keeper, but because of family hangers-on. Walbach described them, Duncan's son "Samuel excepted," as "so wretched and infamous a set, as not to be trusted." Duncan is "so easy and weakminded," wrote Walbach, "that he never would be able to keep the families of his Brother and Sister from the house of the Lamp Lighter, on these limits, and thus I fear, we should only have an increase of the disorder and difficulties occasioned by this most abominable set of beings and out casts of society."[82]

The state of the keeper's house when Duncan was replaced suggests that he was unable to maintain it or even to request basic structural repairs, and that his relatives were unwilling to help him. Timothy Upham had been collector since 1817, but evidently had not paid much attention to the state of the keeper's house until he reported in 1820, "Windows and sashes are much broken, the doors off the hinges, the sills rotten, and part of the foundation has given away."[83]

Upham recommended Duncan's replacement, because of his "very advanced age, & great infirmities." He took Walbach's advice and recommended the appointment of Allan Porter of New Castle, a "sober, steady and industrious man," who had tended the light when Duncan was sick. Evidently Duncan's family was not even to be trusted to take care of the keeper and his wife. Upham made arrangements for Porter to see to Duncan's needs for the rest of his life, which ended in 1826.[84]

Duncan had been in charge of the light since 1793, when the federal government and its system of lighthouse management were both in their infancy. He had not prospered in the position: the sum total of his estate was a bureau, three chairs, one bed and a bedstead, and $44.64 in cash.[85]

IV   Boon Island Lighthouse and the Rise of Winslow Lewis

... the forlornest place that can be imagined.

—Celia Thaxter, *Among the Isles of Shoals,* 1873

UNTIL MAINE BECAME A STATE IN 1820, Boon Island, off the York coast, was in the Massachusetts District of Maine and therefore within the domain of the Boston collector of customs. In 1793, however, Portsmouth customs collector Joseph Whipple had judged an unlit beacon of whitewashed stone to mark this menace one of the most-needed aids to navigation in the waters around Portsmouth. A wooden beacon was finally built on Boon Island in 1799 and replaced by a stone structure in 1805.

Before the 1763 treaty with France, development of scattered coastal settlements in the District of Maine was stifled by the threat of French-inspired Indian raids. Even so, by the 1720s the depletion of forest resources in New Hampshire shifted the center of the mast trade to Falmouth (now Portland), with its generous, deepwater harbor in Casco Bay. By the 1770s, Falmouth had developed a maritime economy similar to that of Portsmouth.[1]

York, about seven miles due west of Boon Island, was one of a number of towns along the coast between Portsmouth and Falmouth whose small harbors could not accommodate the largest of vessels. Before the Revolution, however, York owned twenty to thirty small vessels active in the West Indies and coasting trades. Falmouth's growth was nipped in the bud by the British bombardment in the fall of 1775, and in fact the Revolutionary War put a stop to progress all along the Maine coast.[2] The decades after the War saw remarkable development in Portland, as Falmouth was called after 1786, and other ports farther east on the Maine coast, where many rivers and deep bays penetrated far into rich forestlands. Between 1794 and the outbreak of the War of 1812, the total tonnage of vessels registered in Maine tripled.[3]

The pace of lighthouse construction reflected the shipping activity along the Maine coast. The District of Maine had no lighthouses before the Revolution; by 1808, it could boast six. Five were built in an eastward progression, from Portland Head—begun in 1790 and finished in 1791, under the aegis of the federal government—to West Quoddy Head at the eastern extremity of the district. A sixth lighthouse, one of two built in 1808, was at Wood Island, at the entrance to the Saco River, twenty miles north of Boon Island.[4]

Boon Island, about fourteen miles from Portsmouth, was one of the places where the increasing numbers of vessels in the coasting trade, bound to or from ports in Maine or the Canadian maritime provinces, could come to terrible grief. No one who has read Captain John Deane's account of the 1710 wreck of the *Nottingham Galley* and the terrible ordeal of its survivors, or Kenneth Roberts's historical novel *Boon Island*—or who has set foot on the island, even on a sunny summer day in the early twenty-first century—can escape the impression that this desolate, low-lying island, treeless and strewn with boulders, is dangerous.[5]

According to one tradition, Boon Island received its name after the 1682 rescue of the crew of the pinky *Increase,* which was wrecked on one of the ledges near the island while on an April voyage between Plymouth, Massachusetts, and Pemaquid, Maine. The remains of the vessel with those aboard—three white men and an Indian named Asseomet—drifted onto the island itself. They lived for a month on shellfish and rainwater collected in depressions in the rocks. One day in May, they saw the smoke of an Indian ritual fire rising from the top of Mount Agamenticus to the west. The survivors of the wreck gathered a huge pile of driftwood and seaweed to make a smoky fire. The fire's smudgy billows were seen by the Indians on Agamenticus.

Thinking the smoke a response from the Great Spirit, the Indians rushed to Cape Neddick and pushed off in canoes for the island, where they found and rescued the castaways. According to this tale, the survivors named the island to honor their good fortune, the "boon" they had received. Another legend holds that the fishermen who lived in the area traditionally left a supply of food on the island as a "boon" for anyone shipwrecked there.[6]

Unlike the men of the *Increase,* those of the *Nottingham Galley,* when they were shipwrecked on Boon Island in December of 1710, had no means of making a fire, either to signal for help or to keep warm; if a "boon" of food had been left there, it had been swept away by the storm seas that periodically washed the island clean. Captain Deane, in his account, described the inhospitable island as "a mere Rock, without a Shovelful of Earth, and destitute of the Growth of a single Shrub; besides, so small and inconsiderable, as not to exceed 100 Yards in Length, and 50 in Breadth at high Water; and withal so craggy, as not to admit of their walking to keep themselves warm."[7]

There were other hazards in the vicinity. Captain Laurence Furlong, who wrote the sailing directions for the early editions of Blunt's *American Coast Pilot,* described Boon Island Ledge, lying about three miles east-southeast of the island itself, as "the worst ledge that I know on our Eastern shore." A mile north of the island were submerged ledges that Furlong, who had sailed this coast for forty years, discovered for himself for the first time in 1783. Between four and five miles inshore were York Ledge—about an acre in extent and uncovered at low tide—and the sunken ledges of the "Triangles."[8]

In April 1799, Congress passed an act for the building of a wooden beacon on Boon Island, with an appropriation of four hundred dollars. According to lighthouse historian Edward Rowe Snow, the effective impetus for its construction came from the Boston Marine Society, an organization of Boston shipmasters and an influential force in maritime affairs since pre-Revolutionary days. In 1797, after meeting with the society, Boston customs collector Benjamin Lincoln, who was responsible for lighthouses and aids to navigation in the District of Maine, came away convinced that a monument was needed on Boon Island. A petition from Maine residents, presented by Peleg Wadsworth of Portland, increased the pressure for such a marker. In 1799, Lincoln recommended building an octagonal wooden structure forty feet high and sixteen feet in diameter at the base, shingled and painted white to

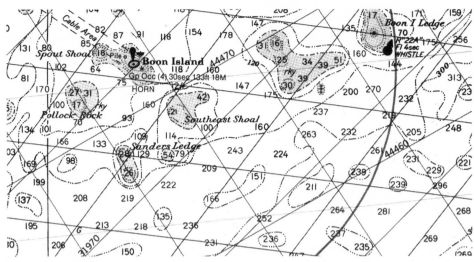

Detail of 1985 National Ocean Survey chart #13278, showing Boon Island and the hazards in its vicinity. The entrance to York Harbor is about seven miles to the West.

Detail showing Boon Island from "A Map of the Coast of New England, from Staten Island to the Island of Breton...London, 1775. Southack identified it as "Bone" Island; it's not known if this was how "Boon" was pronounced in those days or because the island was littered with bones of mariners wrecked there. Courtesy of the Osher Map Library, University of Southern Maine.

[N.B. I have passed this place several times, but never discovered the ledge till the year 1783, when being bound to the eastward, the wind took me from the westward, but the vessel having no more than steerage way, I hove over a line to catch a fish, and found I had 24 fathoms water, sandy bottom, and in a few minutes I had but 10 feet of water, and my vessel drawing nine : all that saved me from striking was, that the water being entirely smooth, the current set me to the eastward, and I got into 24 fathoms within the length of the vessel from where I sounded, and had but 10 feet.]

The worst ledge that I know on our eastern shore, is *Boon island ledge,* which bears East from *Boon island,* distant one league; and from *Agamenticus hill* it bears S.E. 5 or 6 leagues.—It is not safe for strangers to go very near this ledge, for several of the rocks are to be seen, long before low water.

Note in the 1804 edition of Blunt's American Coast Pilot *describing the hazards in the vicinity of Boon Island. The* Pilot *also referred to the wooden beacon built on the island in 1799.*

increase its visibility. Approval came rapidly, and in April, William Miller of the Treasury Department, instructed Lincoln to go ahead.[9]

There were delays: when seas were high, it was impossible to land men and building materials at the island. It took about three months to finish the work. According to Snow, Lincoln himself was present at the raising of the frame in July. The structure was described as a "high beacon, in the form of a light-house" in the 1804 edition of Blunt's *American Coast Pilot.*[10]

The wooden beacon stood barely five years before it was wrecked by a violent storm on October 9, 1804. The following summer a stone monument took its place. Snow writes that when the work was done Captain John Williams, of the revenue cutter *Massachusetts,* arrived to take off the workmen who had been deposited on the island. While ferrying the first three men from the island to the cutter, his boat capsized and the three men drowned. Williams, who could swim, managed to get to the *Massachusetts,* sailed ashore, bought a new boat, and sailed back out to the island to take the remaining workers off the island.[11]

The successive monuments on Boon Island were useful warnings of its dangers for daytime mariners and provided bearings for other hazards in the vicinity, but they did not serve the needs of vessels at night. In May and again in late December 1810, two vessels struck two of the hazards near Boon Island. The brig *Concord* of Kennebunk, blown off her course from Lisbon to Boston, lost her rudder after striking Boon Island Rock and managed to limp into Portsmouth Harbor.

The molasses-laden schooner *George*, commanded by Captain Frost, on her way to Portsmouth from Martinique, was less fortunate, and sank after striking rocks west of Boon Island. The crew was saved, but the citizens of York felt that it was high time for a lighthouse off their coast.[12]

On January 25, 1811, Richard Cutts, representative from York County, presented their petition to Congress for a lighthouse on Boon Island. Newburyport merchants added their weight to the lobbying effort; a petition from Moses Brown "and others" supported an act establishing the Boon Island light, as well as buoys at Edgartown Harbor, in Massachusetts; a stone column on Cape Elizabeth, Maine; and buoys in the harbor of Beverly, Massachusetts. In short order Boon Island was ceded to the United States and, by March 2, 1811, Congress had passed and President Madison had signed an act for building the lighthouse.[13]

By the end of March, Henry Dearborn, who had become collector for Boston, advertised a request for proposals to build an octagonal stone lighthouse and a stone keeper's house. The successful low bidders were Thomas Heath and Noah Porter, described in the Articles of Agreement signed on August 11 as "both of Boston... , yeomen." Both men were masons and in 1800 were listed on the membership roster of the Mechanics Association in Boston.[14]

The highest bid had been for fourteen thousand dollars, but for $2,377 Heath and Porter agreed to build a lighthouse of stone, octagonal in form, rising from a base eighteen feet in diameter to an unspecified height, with walls four feet thick sunk three feet below the surface, "or whatever greater depth may be sufficient to render the whole fabric perfectly secure." Above this they would build a twenty-five-foot-high tower with walls tapering from three feet in thickness at the bottom to two feet at the top, faced with hammer-dressed stone and fitted with three windows, each glazed with eight panes of ten-by-twelve-inch glass. The top of the tower was to be arched, with an opening, or scuttle, with a trap door into the lantern, and a stone, copper-covered cornice. The contract specified a floor of brick or stone at the entry level and a wooden stairway with a handrail and "substantial plank floors on the joist of each story." The platform for the lantern was to be constructed of "a sufficient number" of iron sleepers bedded into the stone of the tower and covered with layers of sheet iron, tar-soaked sheathing paper, and sheet copper.[15]

Heath and Porter were to furnish an octagonal iron lantern with a diameter of six feet six inches and a height of seven feet to the bottom of a copper-roofed dome to the height of three feet at the center. The lantern's eight iron posts were to extend six feet down into the stone tower walls. At the top of the lantern, iron rafters were to center on an iron hoop through which a copper vent pipe would extend through the roof to a ventilator ball, also of copper. This ball, to have a volume of forty gallons, would be turned by a large vane in order to keep its opening facing away from the wind and rain. The sashes for the lantern were to be of iron, with ten-by-twelve-inch glass "of the first quality." One sash was to be hinged, to open onto a platform around the lantern, fitted with a two-foot-high balustrade. Eight "dormant ventillators" and two lightning rods would be placed on the roof. Inside the lantern there would be an unspecified number of lamps hung on chains to raise and lower them, and a close stove with stovepipe. The lantern was to receive three coats of "good paint" of an unspecified color.[16]

The final agreement eliminated an "eclipser" called for in the request for proposals. This would have been a shield, probably of sheet metal, with a clockwork mechanism to rotate it around the lamps in the lantern. It was intended to create the distinctive "characteristic" produced by a light alternately concealed and revealed, distinguishing it from the steady beams of other lighthouses along the coast.

The need to differentiate the characteristics of light stations had been recognized in America at least as early as 1768, when a lighthouse was built in Plymouth, Massachusetts, with two light towers, one at each end of the keeper's house. In 1771, more widely separated twin light towers were built on Thacher's Island off Cape Ann. The two separate towers, each with its own lantern and lamps, were a costly solution to the problem, doubling the expense of construction and fuel and adding to the burdens of the lightkeeper. The first known eclipser was used in 1753 at the lighthouse in Uto, Sweden, and in 1791 one was placed in the French Cordouan lighthouse. Captain Furlong, in the first, 1796 edition of the *American Coast Pilot,* wrote that the lighthouse just completed on Seguin Island at the mouth of the Kennebec River in Maine was fitted with a "repeating light, so constituted to disappear once every minute and a half." The effect was doubtless achieved by the use of an eclipser. Another one of these devices was installed in the lantern of the Cape Cod light at the end of 1797. Why the eclipser was eliminated from the Boon Island lighthouse specifications has not been determined. It is possible that it was decided to install one instead at Wood Island, the next lighthouse to the east.[17]

Heath and Porter also agreed to build a keeper's house for $1,050. Their contract provided for a one-and-a-half-story house, thirty-four by seventeen feet, with eighteen-inch-thick walls of undressed stone, and with the following amenities: two windows with sixteen squares of seven-by-nine-inch glass for each of the two lower rooms; one similar window in each gable end of the attic; a brick center chimney to serve the fireplaces of the two downstairs rooms; and an oven for the kitchen. The downstairs rooms were to be plastered and white-washed, but not the attic chamber.[18]

The contractors were to dig a cellar five to six feet deep under the kitchen... "if practicable." To keep the floor above the seawater that periodically swept the island, it was to be at least two feet above the ground. For $130, the contractors would also furnish five cedar water cisterns, each with a capacity of 120 gallons. Such cisterns were standard equipment for lighthouse sites where there was no water source other than rain.[19]

The terms of the agreement concluded with the condition that payment would be made for the completed work "provided that no member of Congress shall have any concern or interest in said contract." This phrase suggests that already there had been cases of congressmen lining their pockets, and it became standard in later lighthouse contracts. The Boon Island contract called for completion of the work by the end of October, dangerously close to the season of fall storms. A notation on the contract for receipt of payment on November 15, 1811 indicates that the lighthouse was finished very nearly on schedule.[20]

It is difficult to imagine the building of the lighthouse at this desolate spot, where landing could be impossible in rough weather and storm-driven seas swept across the island during seasons of unusually high tides. There is no record that the contractors had their own vessel. They and their workmen and their equipment were probably deposited on the island by the revenue cutter out of Boston. No provision was made in the contract for boatways to haul boats and supplies onto the island, but presumably the contractors built a ramp or boatways of some sort to facilitate their work. They may also have constructed temporary huts to shelter the laborers and craftsmen during their months of work on the island, unless the contractors had a vessel on which they could sleep.

The stone used for the lighthouse and keeper's house was what was available on the island. The rough, rocky surface would probably have precluded the use of oxen for hauling stone or pulling hoisting lines to lift the stone onto the structures, so this work must have been powered by the men themselves.

On October 30, a terrific southeast gale lashed the coast, accompanied by "a higher tide than has been known for twenty years." During the storm, two vessels were driven ashore at Kittery Point and another wrecked and sunk on the East Sisters, off Gerrish Island. This must have been one of those storms during which the seas swept across Boon Island. We do not know whether the workmen were then putting the finishing touches on the lighthouse buildings, or if the first keeper was already in residence. Snow writes that the first, unnamed keeper of Boon Island light resigned within a few weeks of his appointment, on December 16, 1811.[21]

There was no description in the contract of the lamps that were to be placed in the lighthouse lantern, and no reference to oil to fuel them, so we know nothing about the lamps used by this first, unknown keeper of Boon Island. We do know that they were replaced soon thereafter by lamps with reflectors installed by Winslow Lewis.

Winslow Lewis and His Reflector Lamps

In July 1812, Winslow Lewis, of Boston, a former shipmaster, installed new and more efficient lighting equipment in the lanterns of Boon Island and Portsmouth Harbor lighthouses. It consisted of Argand oil lamps with glass chimneys and shiny metal reflectors, a type of improvement in lighthouse lights Joseph Whipple had heard of twenty years earlier.[22]

Winslow Lewis (1770-1850) dominated lighthouse equipment, supply, and construction in the United States for forty years. He was a man of considerable entrepreneurial energy, and was extremely shrewd if not actually unscrupulous. He turned to the development and promotion of lighthouse lighting equipment shortly after Jefferson's 1807 embargo stifled maritime commerce and put an end to his livelihood as a shipmaster.[23]

Lewis's patented lighting device combined elements that had long since been brought together to improve the lights in European lighthouses. Its main components were the Argand lamp, an invention of the early 1780s, and a shiny, curved metal reflector to deflect the light outward, used in British lighthouses as early as the 1770s. These two devices had been combined for the first time at the French Cordouan lighthouse in 1783, and the apparatus was soon adopted in Great Britain. Critics of Lewis, who had been a shipmaster in the Boston-Liverpool trade from 1796 through 1806, later claimed that he had pirated his device. Lewis himself asserted that he had not actually visited the English lighthouses where he might have seen this equipment until several months after he obtained his patent in 1810.[24]

The Argand lamp, invented by the Swiss Aimé Argand, was fitted with concentric brass tubes. A tubular wick passed through these tubes, increasing wick surfaces exposed to the air and creating a brighter flame than that produced by a solid, flat wick. With a tubular glass chimney added to keep the flame steady and create an updraft, a single Argand lamp could produce the equivalent of the light of eight candles. The European reflectors were formed into a parabolic shape mathematically determined to be best for reflecting the rays of the lamp into a horizontal beam and silvered to increase their reflective quality. Lewis added another element to his patented device: a glass lens about nine inches in diameter, intended to magnify the light. Because the lens Lewis produced was of crude, greenish bottle glass, it was later found to obscure rather than enhance the light.[25]

In the 1830s and 1840s, Lewis's accomplishment had its detractors among those who looked mainly to Europe for technological and scientific legitimacy. They assumed that he could not have devised his lighting equipment independently, even though the elements he combined in his patent were already in household use in various forms in the United States.[26]

Lewis's successful promotion of his apparatus resulted in the first adoption of standardized lighting equipment in the U.S. lighthouse system. The way he accomplished this provides a textbook example of effective marketing. First he manufactured prototypes and, to protect his invention from piracy, applied to the U.S. government for a patent. Next he enlisted the support of Boston Customs Collector Henry Dearborn, who arranged for Lewis to demonstrate the lamps at Boston Harbor Lighthouse on Brewster's Island before a committee of men from the influential Boston Marine Society.[27] In May 1810, three members of the society sailed out of Boston Harbor to compare Lewis's lamps with those already in use at the Boston Harbor lighthouse and at Baker's Island lighthouse. Lewis orchestrated his demonstration skillfully. He

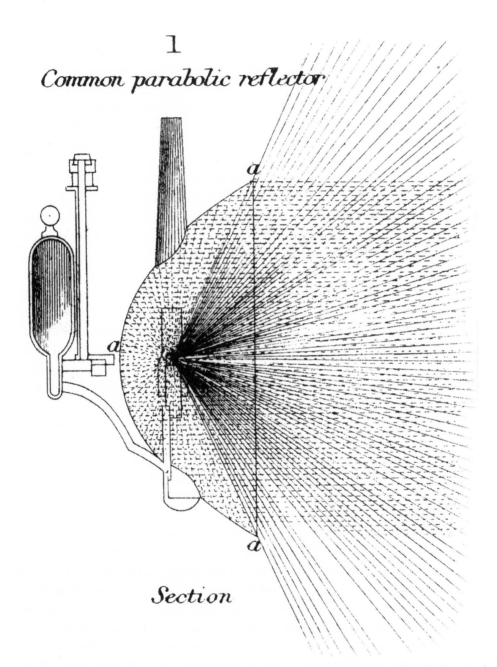

A reflector, of the type used in lighthouses in Europe and the British Isles. No image of Winslow Lewis's reflector lamp has been located, but it was probably similar in appearance. To his patented device Lewis added a glass lens nine inches in diameter. It was intended to intensify the light, but because the lens was of a crude, greenish glass it actually interfered with its dissemination.

arranged to have the existing lamps lit in the Boston lighthouse until 10 P.M.; then six of his reflector lamps were substituted, with dramatic effect. The impressed observers wrote a testimonial stating that "the difference in the brightness of these and the light at Baker's Island was as great as would appear between a well trimmed Argand lamp and a common candle." They also pointed out that these lamps would use no more than a third of the oil consumed by the existing lamps.[28]

Soon after Lewis's patent was approved in June 1810, Treasury Secretary Albert Gallatin gave collector Dearborn permission to have Lewis install the new apparatus in one of the twin lights at Cape Ann for a longer trial. In a letter to Gallatin in December, Dearborn declared the light produced by the new lamps "a large brilliant star" compared to the "small common star" produced by the old-style lamps in the other Cape Ann light.[29]

Lewis then traveled to Washington with models of his device to show Treasury Secretary Gallatin, wrote follow-up letters, and gathered support from Dearborn, the Boston Marine Society, and the lightkeepers at Boston Harbor and Cape Ann. He was able to produce a statement signed by more than sixty men urging the adoption of his equipment system-wide. Finally, he presented a detailed plan for doing the proposed work.[30]

Lewis's salesmanship was successful. With a sixty-thousand dollar appropriation in 1812, Congress authorized Gallatin to purchase rights to Lewis's patent and to contract with him to install the reflector lamps and lenses in the forty-nine existing lighthouses during the next two years. For this work, Lewis was to be paid a total of twenty-four thousand dollars in three installments. He was also to furnish tubular wicks at three dollars per gross and chimneys at thirty-three cents apiece, and to make any necessary repairs to the lighting apparatus for seven years for five hundred dollars per year. He guaranteed not only improved lights but also a fifty percent reduction in oil consumption, which he calculated would save thirty-two thousand dollars annually. Finally, he persuaded the government to buy a ninety-ton schooner, the *Federal Jack,* and refit her for his use. He would pay an annual fee of two thousand dollars, promising that this would cost twenty-six hundred dollars less than leasing a vessel privately. Before the War of 1812 interrupted his work, Lewis had fitted forty lighthouses with the new equipment.[31]

Lewis was free to decide the number of lamps and the size of the reflectors installed in each lighthouse. His decisions seem to have been based largely on the size of the existing lighthouse lanterns rather than the strength of the light needed at a particular location. He installed as many as fifteen sets of lamps, reflectors, and lenses in a single lighthouse lantern by fastening them to an iron framework, or chandelier. In some lighthouses he installed a clockwork device to rotate the framework and produce a distinguishing characteristic for the light. The first of these had been installed at Boston Harbor lighthouse by 1811. It was commemorated in a poem dramatizing the five minutes it took for a single, creaking revolution:

> First a speck it dimly glows,
> Soon, howe'er more brilliant grows
> Flames around then sinks in night,
> All its lustre ceasing.
> Thus, delusive hope, thy ray
> O'er life's billow shining
> Rises high in fancy's views
> Beams a while with vivid hue
> Fading then in gloom away
> Leaves the wretch repining.32

The *Federal Jack* arrived off Boon Island in July 1812. The vessel had been fitted out to sleep thirteen men and had a blacksmith shop and a carpentry shop, as well as stowage for the lighting equipment. She carried two boats for landing the equipment and the men to install it. At Boon Island, Lewis and his crew installed seven sets of lamps, reflectors, and lenses. In an 1828 inventory, lightkeeper Eliphalet Grover listed seven lamps and two spares, seven reflectors, and eight "lencers," indicating that the greenish glass lenses were on the lighthouse premises sixteen years later, though we do not know whether they were still in use.33

At Portsmouth Harbor, Lewis installed eleven sets of the new apparatus, giving this lighthouse far more power than the offshore one at Boon Island, where a stronger light would seem to have been called for. Portsmouth keeper David Duncan, whose many pleas for a raise were seldom answered, asked again for more pay, claiming that he needed to hire an assistant to help with the new, more complex, equipment.34

The declaration of war against Britain in June 1812 did not deter the intrepid Lewis. He proceeded south along the coast, putting in at Boston to pick up more of the equipment as it was produced in his shop, until his work was finally interrupted off the Charleston, South Carolina, lighthouse in March 1813, when the *Federal Jack* was captured by the British frigate *Aeolus*. The British took Lewis and his men prisoner, commandeered everything aboard, and burned the schooner. Lewis and all the crew of the *Federal Jack* except the master were paroled four days later. After the war, Lewis finished installing the new equipment at the remaining lighthouses; his work was completed by the fall of 1815.[35]

In 1817, Portsmouth customs collector Timothy Upham wrote a testy letter to Winslow Lewis about his reflectors and lamps: "Mr. Duncan informs me that his lamps are very much out of order. I have tried to get them repaired here but there is no one willing to undertake it. I am not instructed whose duty it is to keep these Lamps in order, whether yourself or mine. Will you have the goodness to inform me on this subject as it is necessary that something should be done immediately."[36] This would not be the last complaint about Lewis's equipment.

In 1816, the enterprising Lewis also obtained a seven-year contract to deliver to all lighthouses the sperm oil purchased by government bid, for a fee of twelve hundred dollars a year. For another five hundred dollars he contracted to repair and adjust the lamps and report on the state of the lighthouses. He was to be furnished half the oil formerly used annually at each lighthouse before the introduction of his lamps— even though he had earlier demonstrated that they would consume only a third as much as the old lamps. It has been calculated that over the period of the contract he profited by as much as $12,400 a year from the surplus. Not until his contract came up for renewal in 1822 was the discrepancy noted. His next contract, for five years, cut the oil allowance but upped his fee for delivery to twenty-two hundred dollars and for lamp repair to fifteen hundred dollars.[37]

The War of 1812

Within two weeks after the declaration of war on June 12, 1812, Portsmouth Collector of Customs Joseph Whipple was responding to requests to arm privately owned vessels. Privateers proved a boon to the local economy: the vessels and cargoes captured in 1813 and 1814 fetched three million dollars at auction, but it has been estimated that the total of losses to Portsmouth shipping during this time exceeded the gains. In addition, during the war, Portsmouth endured a fire that devastated a quarter of the town center. Among those buildings destroyed was the customs house, to which the seventy-six-year-old Whipple rushed to salvage as many records as possible. He reported great hardships in Portsmouth as a result of the fire. Supplies of firewood and building materials like lumber and the Thomaston, Maine, lime needed for mortar were desperately low. The blockade of the northeast coast by a squadron of British warships made supply hazardous.[38] British vessels of war in evidence off the Isles of Shoals were also seen as a threat to the seventy-four-gun *Washington*, under construction at the Portsmouth Navy Yard, which was located on an island about a mile up the Piscataqua from the lighthouse. If the British attempted to sneak upriver at night to destroy the ship, the lighthouse would make it easier for them.[39]

On March 22, 1813, Treasury Secretary Gallatin ordered all lighthouses extinguished for the duration, but after a period of compliance, there was evidently local pressure to re-light them. In spite of the requests of fishermen and coasters, in August 1814, Joseph Whipple wrote to Commissioner of Revenue S. H. Smith recommending "a continuation of withholding the lights." The *Portsmouth Oracle* noted on October 1, 1814: "The lights in all the lighthouses are ordered to be discontinued." Whipple, acting on the advice of Colonel Walbach at the fort, had the buoy removed from Stileman's Rock for the duration of the British threat to Portsmouth and the Navy Yard.[40]

During the period when the lights were extinguished, the keepers at New Castle and Boon Island had a respite from their usual duties (although there may have been a vacancy at Boon Island that would not be filled until the end of the war). The war forced lightkeeper David Duncan to look for a temporary place to live because Walbach requested his house for use as a barracks. Whipple gave his permission despite misgivings that "without a care commonly exercised by them," the soldiers would inflict a lot of damage. The fort's commandant also asked for Whipple's approval to strip the lighthouse to its timber framework. He argued that in case of attack, "which was hourly expected," the enemy would set fire to the lighthouse. The removal of shingles and boarding from the lighthouse would lessen the chance of fire spreading from the lighthouse to the wooden buildings at the fort. The construction workers at the fort removed these materials, and the boards were taken to Portsmouth for storage along with the lighthouse lantern, the lamps, and the vats of sperm oil.[41]

The Portsmouth Harbor light needed many repairs after ratification in February 1815 of the Treaty of Ghent ended the war. Even

The Light-House,

AT the entrance of Portsmouth harbor, is to be repaired as soon as may be.

Therefore, notice is hereby given, that proposals for performing the said repairs, and providing all the materials, will be received at this Office; twelve days from the date hereof, or until the 8th day of April next, on which day it is intended to enter into contract for the same, the undertaker to give bond for the fulfilment of the contract. The said contract to embrace the following objects :—

The said Light-House to be covered with good seasoned pine Stuff, free from defects, from the stone underpining 12 or 15 feet up, or as far as the sea breaks against it, with two inch seasoned plank, clear of knots; the rest of the covering to the lanthern, to be of the best seasoned merchantable pine boards, one inch thick, and laid on of equal thickness; which boarding is to be covered with the best pine shingles of 18 inches in length, and laid out 5 inches; all the wood work, without and within, to be repaired in the best manner, including the stairs; the railing to the stairs, and the flooring of the different stories, where floors have been heretofore laid; a well laid deck as a floor to the lanthern, convexing upward, and made perfectly tight around the eaves; all the outside wood work to be painted with three coats of white lead paint, and good linseed oil; the lanthern which was taken down, to be repaired and put up, or a new one constructed of a different size, as shall be agreed upon. All the workmanship to be performed in the best manner, and the materials of the best kind.

J. WHIPPLE.

Custom-House, Portsmouth, }
March 27, 1815.   }

Joseph Whipple's ad soliciting contractors to restore the Portsmouth Harbor lighthouse after the War of 1812. New-Hampshire Gazette, 28 March 1815.

before the lighthouse was restored, Whipple made arrangements for a temporary lantern for the lights. Provided by Benjamin Gilman, contractor for the structure in 1804, it consisted of a wooden box with two windows, one facing southeast and the other southwest, to be placed atop of the timber skeleton of the lighthouse. That April, Gilman contracted to reboard the lighthouse, applying an extra layer of one-and-one-half-inch-thick boards to the lower twelve feet of the structure. He also contracted to refurbish the structure with shingles and three coats of the best linseed-oil-based white lead paint and to rebuild, re-glaze and copper-sheathe the lantern. Gilman was also to repair and reshingle the roof of the keeper's house, and replace wall clapboards as needed. The composition roof of the oil vault was to be tarred again and graveled, and posts, railings, and planking of the causeway restored.[42]

Portsmouth residents witnessed a strange craft in September 1817, when the steamboat *Massachusetts,* built in Philadelphia for the Massachusetts Steamboat Company, docked at Portsmouth Pier. Its owners advertised daily excursions up and down the Piscataqua for "Parties of Pleasure" at fifty cents per person. This was the first-known steam-powered vessel to make its way into Portsmouth. The owners planned to stay for a week, "provided sufficient encouragement is offered." How much encouragement the people of Portsmouth provided is not known, but probably not much, given the depressed postwar state of the local economy.[43]

Some Portsmouth privateers, like the brothers Abraham and Thomas Shaw, flourished during the war, but many lost their shirts. Most merchants struggled to get back on their feet after the war ended. Piscataqua shipbuilders, who in 1811 produced fifteen vessels averaging nearly three hundred tons apiece, in the first few years after the war built fewer and smaller vessels. Between 1816 and 1820, duties collected in Portsmouth on foreign imports inched upward from $62,596 to reach an average of about $100,000.[44]

After Joseph Whipple's death in 1816, James Ladd served as acting customs collector until the appointment of Timothy Upham by the newly elected President James Monroe. The son of a Deerfield, New Hampshire, minister, Timothy Upham (1753-1855) moved to Portsmouth in 1807 to open a dry goods store, and during the war was a lieutenant colonel with the Twenty-first Maine Infantry Division. He served as Collector until 1829; during his dozen years in the post several important aids to navigation were established to assist vessels navigating the waters in and around Portsmouth Harbor.[45]

Stephen Pleasonton, Fifth Treasury Auditor and superintendent of lighthouses, 1820-1852, was responsible for greatly increasing the number of lighthouses and other aids to navigation in the United States, and was the target of intense criticism for his penny-pinching approach to his responsibilities. LC.

V The Fifth Treasury Auditor, White Island Lighthouse, and Other Eighteen-twenties Aids to Navigation

... the said Light to be fitted up with fifteen patent fourteen inch Lamps with reflectors... Exhibiting on one side a deep blue light, on one side a bright red light and, on the other, the natural color of the light.

—Articles of Agreement...between Timothy Upham...and Winslow Lewis, 30 September 1820. Lighthouse Contract Files.

IN THE 1820s, THE LIGHTHOUSE SYSTEM of the United States comprised some fifty-five lighthouses and 156 buoys.[1] The peacetime development of the nation's manufacturing and export resources, territorial expansion, westward migration, and commercial development around the Great Lakes and along the Mississippi River required tremendous expansion of the system, as well as the addition of new resources for long-established ports like Portsmouth. The man put in charge of overseeing this expansion was Stephen Pleasanton.

Stephen Pleasonton, Fifth Auditor of the U. S. Treasury

Beginning in 1820, Stephen Pleasonton presided for thirty-two tight-fisted years over the U.S. lighthouse establishment. The first to hold the post of Fifth Auditor of an enlarged Treasury Department, he was a career federal employee who had administered the Indian Affairs department before his appointment as Fifth Auditor; his responsibilities in this new job included lighthouses and other aids to navigation. Pleasonton had no experience at sea and no knowledge of lighthouse construction and lighting equipment. He seems rarely to have left Washington in the line of duty. For advice he turned to Winslow Lewis. Already the established authority on lighthouse lighting equipment, in 1818 Lewis began to be involved in lighthouse construction as a contractor, and eventually he became an inspector of work done by other lighthouse contractors. With his experience and extensive firsthand knowledge of the system, Lewis became an indispensable advisor to Pleasonton.[2]

During his years in office, Pleasonton oversaw the building of 276 lighthouses on the Atlantic and Gulf Coasts and on the Great Lakes; buoys multiplied twentyfold to more than three thousand, and more than forty lightships were built and anchored at locations too difficult for lighthouse construction.[3] The bottom line was evidently all-important to Pleasonton, often at the expense of the purposes for which these structures were built—the saving of vessels and their human and "merchantable" cargoes. He was prone to citing chapter and verse of the federal enactments that dealt with his domain. It was, however, the Congress that made appropriations for lighthouse and other aids to navigation. Members representing the interests of the seacoasts and of the regions with inland lakes and rivers had to divide the federal pie with those whose regions needed roads or canals; and representatives of all these constituencies had to compromise with colleagues who objected to any federal expenditures for improvements that benefited a particular region or segment of the population.

Stephen Pleasonton's received views on the functions of the federal government have not been discovered, though they may be inferred from records. In 1801, when he was a young clerk in the Secretary of State's office, he was described as a "Nothingarian." Perhaps the most meritorious accomplishment of his early career came during the War of 1812 when, in 1814, the British were about to take Washington. Secretary of State James Monroe sent word to his staff to save documents from destruction by the British, and it was Pleasonton who saw to the gathering of such documents as the Declaration of Independence, the Constitution, national treaties, and George Washington's letters, and had linen bags made to put them in. He had the bags full of these precious papers loaded into carts and personally escorted them to safekeeping thirty-five miles away to Leesburg, Virginia, from which he saw the glow of the burning Capitol that night. Later in life he was characterized as a person of rigid habits, honest but not especially bright. His wife was regarded as a beauty and an influential hostess.[4]

It is clear that Pleasonton saw his duty as guarding the federal purse rather than advocating for improved aids to navigation, and that he was defensive about criticism. He claimed with pride that because of his insistence upon accepting only the lowest bids from contractors, he spent less than Congress appropriated. Between 1820 and 1842, he boasted of accumulating a surplus of precisely $283,337.66, amounting to savings of more than seventeen percent of the cumulative allocations of $1,608,308.38 for his department.[5]

Beginning in the 1830s, most of the lighthouses built on his watch, including those serving vessels in the waters around Portsmouth, were sharply criticized for shoddy construction and the inadequacy of their lighting equipment. Pleasonton would also be taken to account for the poor quality of the sperm oil supplied for the lighthouse lamps and for the minimal supervision of lighthouse keepers.

Around Portsmouth, the major works during the first decade of Pleasonton's long tenure were White Island and Whale's Back lighthouses. In the early 1820s, two seawalls between islands at the Isles of Shoals and a stone beacon to mark Sunken Rocks in the Piscataqua River were also funded, with Pleasonton keeping an eye on the accounts. In the early 1830s, Boon Island lighthouse was rebuilt. Only the beacon on Sunken Rocks survives as local testimony to the Pleasonton-Lewis period of domination of the U. S. lighthouse system. These two men seem to have been cavalier about the quality of construction, equipment, and supplies they were responsible for, and little concerned about the living conditions and safety of the lightkeepers and their families. Pleasonton's achievements have few defenders, but it has been pointed out that his job included many other responsibilities besides aids to navigation. He kept the accounts of a number of other agencies of the federal government, including the diplomatic and consular services abroad and the State Department and Patent Office. George Putnam, commissioner of the U.S. Lighthouse Bureau from 1910 to 1936, credited Pleasonton for his execution of the federal response to requests from a large, rapidly developing area and from expanding commercial interests by putting in place many aids to navigation at bargain basement cost. A photograph of Pleasonton hung on the wall in Putnam's office.[6]

Both Pleasonton and Lewis were suspicious of the expertise represented by the few professional engineers in America during this period. Lewis may have imparted to Pleasonton an attitude shaped by his personal experience with the monumental, structurally complex, and innovative lighthouse designed by the architect and engineer Benjamin Latrobe (1764–1820) and his son Henry for the mouth of the Mississippi River.

Benjamin Latrobe, who immigrated to the United States in 1796, had strong credentials as an architect and engineer. Born in England and educated in Europe, where he had seen the monumental, architecturally detailed lighthouses of France, Latrobe had also worked with John Smeaton, the giant of English civil engineering who designed the Eddystone lighthouse.[7]

The lighthouse Latrobe and his son designed for Frank's Island at the mouth of the Mississippi was intended not just as an aid to navigation but also as a monument to the great territorial expansion represented by the Louisiana Purchase. Stylistically, the lighthouse tower and the encircling keeper's house, with a colonnaded piazza at its base, embodied Benjamin Latrobe's avant-garde, stripped-down Neo-classicism. Structurally, it involved an elaborate interlocking system of arches and vaults, inverted hemispheres and barrel vaults of masonry, and a spiral staircase integrated into the structure to contribute to its strength and stability. Henry was to have supervised the project, but died before a building contract was executed. Benjamin Latrobe had written very detailed specifications designed to "frighten the people who understand nothing but the common work," but still, he feared, "some Yankee will be the lowest" bidder. Notwithstanding his efforts, the contract was awarded in 1818 to a Yankee—Winslow Lewis. [8]

According to a detailed study of the design and building of this lighthouse by Michael Fazio, it was Lewis's first experience as a building contractor for a lighthouse. He accepted the contract only reluctantly, at the urging of the Treasury Department's commissioner of revenue, and there is no evidence that he took part in the actual building. Because the pragmatic Lewis doubted the feasibility of a project beyond the scope of his own experience, he insisted on the appointment of an outside, on-site inspector to make sure the specifications were followed, as well as a guarantee of payment if the foundation failed. The inspector, however, was not yet on the job during the building of the all-important substructure.[9]

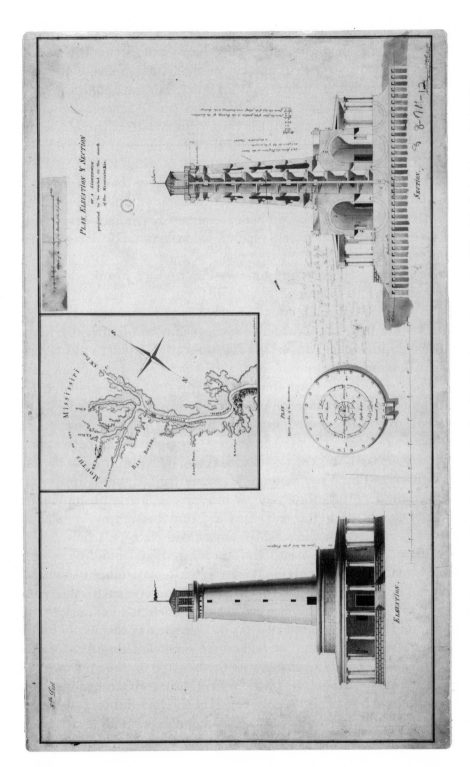

Plans by Benjamin Latrobe and his son for a lighthouse on Frank's Island near the mouth of the Mississippi River. NARG26.

To counteract the unstable alluvial soil of the Mississippi Delta site, the architects' plans had called for an extensive system of subterranean piles, and specified fill of bricks and oyster shells to stabilize the ground on which the tremendous structure would rest. But the builders cut corners, resulting in an unstable foundation for the lighthouse as it rose above ground. As construction of the tower proceeded, it began to settle alarmingly, and then to tilt. The lighthouse was nearly finished in 1819—at the then staggering cost of eighty-five thousand dollars—when it collapsed. It was in ruins by the time the last of a number of government-appointed inspectors made his report in 1820. Only this last inspector focused on the problems created by the improper building of the foundation, poor workmanship, and the use of bad mortar. He was incensed that the country had been "fleeced of its resources... by men who appear to be destitute of every moral and virtuous tie, that binds human society in union."[10]

His report was ignored, however, in favor of those who placed the blame not on contractor Winslow Lewis or the men he hired to do the construction but on the plans of the Latrobes.[11]

Regardless of the merits of the Latrobes' design, it was of a complexity and sophistication that required careful and knowledgeable construction and supervision for its successful realization. These skills were not readily available in the United States in 1818, especially at a remote site like Frank's Island, where the temptation to cut corners was perhaps irresistible. For decades to come, no American lighthouse would be designed by a professional, formally trained engineer.

Even in the 1820s, there was no community of civilian engineers in the United States with the expertise to build these very particular lighthouse structures, or the scientific knowledge to tackle the specialized problems of light sources and dissemination that they posed. Besides men trained in Europe and England, like Benjamin Latrobe, the only other potential source of engineering expertise at this time was the Army's engineering officers, who had trained at West Point. Their training was influenced heavily by French models emphasizing science and mathematics and embodying a somewhat grandiose vision of what a nation's public works should be.[12]

In the United States, those who built lighthouses and those—like Winslow Lewis—who inspected and approved their work were pragmatic, basing their work on craft traditions and experience of what had worked in the past and, for new problems, intuition about what might work. Those who made decisions in the government tended to be more comfortable with this outlook, perhaps because it almost always cost less than the solutions of a trained engineer.

In 1822, Stephen Pleasonton gave Winslow Lewis the contract to demolish the remains of the Latrobe lighthouse at Frank's Island and to build a new one using material salvaged from the ruins. Pleasonton must have been impressed that Lewis's replacement structure, a bare-bones tower in the form of a truncated cone, cost only $9,750.[13]

Some of the projects undertaken during the Pleasonton years to aid navigation around Portsmouth were ambitious in concept but unsophisticated in design and execution. They were almost doomed to fail, given the low level of funding provided and the bias against professional expertise. Also, although local superintendents of lighthouses, such as Portsmouth customs collector Timothy Upham, were in most cases conscientious men, they were ill equipped for their responsibilities, which included choosing sites, soliciting bids, and supervising the work of the low bidders.

In 1820, the Port of Portsmouth was in the midst of an upswing in commercial maritime activity. Duties on foreign goods imported were $62,596 in 1816. By 1818, they were $102,185; in 1820, $108,166; and in 1822, $156,609. The bulk of these imports was from the West Indies and South America—sugar, molasses, rum, coffee, and cocoa. From the British Isles and continental Europe came salt for the fisheries, English textiles, cutlery, china, and other manufactured goods. A fact that did not bode well for the future of the port, however, was that in none of the years from 1821 to 1830 was the value of exports greater than that of goods imported. There was little to take the place of the depleted forest resources that had been the mainstay of the eighteenth-century economy.[14]

By 1814 the total tonnage of Portland, Maine, vessels in either domestic or foreign commerce surpassed that of Portsmouth; the gap widened by 1820, when Portsmouth recorded 23,335 tons, to Portland's 33,335. Other Maine ports were growing rapidly, and vessels totaling 140,368 tons were owned in the state in 1820. The bulk of these vessels, along with many from the maritime provinces of Canada, passed along the southern Maine and New Hampshire coast, many putting in to Portsmouth during their voyages. The need for more navigational aids for these waters was increasing.[15]

A Lighthouse for White Island

Stephen Pleasonton's work as superintendent of U.S. lighthouses began with a flurry of activity. On May 15, 1820, Congress authorized expenditures for aids to navigation along the coasts of the eastern United States, from a fog bell at the lighthouse at West Quoddy Head in Maine to a light vessel at the mouth of the Mississippi. In some cases, the Treasury Department was given discretion as to whether a lighthouse or light vessel should be established at a particular site. In all, six lighthouses, two light vessels, four buoys, and one beacon were approved, as well as the bell for West Quoddy and a pier at the mouth of the Kennebunk River in Maine. At the top of the list was an appropriation of $5,000 for a lighthouse on one of the Isles of Shoals, "to be distinguishable from other lighthouses on the east and west of the same."[16]

The Isles of Shoals are a cluster of islands and ledges about nine miles offshore from Portsmouth—the islands originally dubbed Smyth's Iles by Captain John Smith. The small archipelago consists of nine islands and as many ledges, sprinkled along a north–south path six and a half miles long. The largest and highest, Hog Island (known since the mid-nineteenth century as Appledore) is about a mile long; the smallest, Malaga, has an area of two and a half acres. At the northern extremity of the group is the low-lying Duck Island, ringed with treacherous rocks and ledges. The southernmost is White Island, with a high, rocky knob on the northeastern end; joined to it on the northwest, at low tide, is Seavey's Island. The other islands are Star, Smuttynose, Cedar, and Lunging (or Londoner's). The invisible line that divides New Hampshire from Maine places Star, White, Seavey's, and Lunging Islands in New Hampshire; Appledore, Malaga, Duck, Smuttynose, and Cedar islands are in Maine.

The Shoals, as the islands are known locally, may have been occupied seasonally before Smith's 1614 report on the potential of New England fisheries. Estimates suggest there were in the neighborhood of one thousand year-round and seasonal inhabitants by the mid-seventeenth century. It was certainly not timber or fertile ground that attracted them. Christopher Levett, a visitor in 1623, wrote of the islands that he "neither could see one good timber tree, nor so much good ground to make a garden." He also noted, "The place is found to be a good fishing place for six ships, but more can not well be there, for want of convenient stage room... "[17]

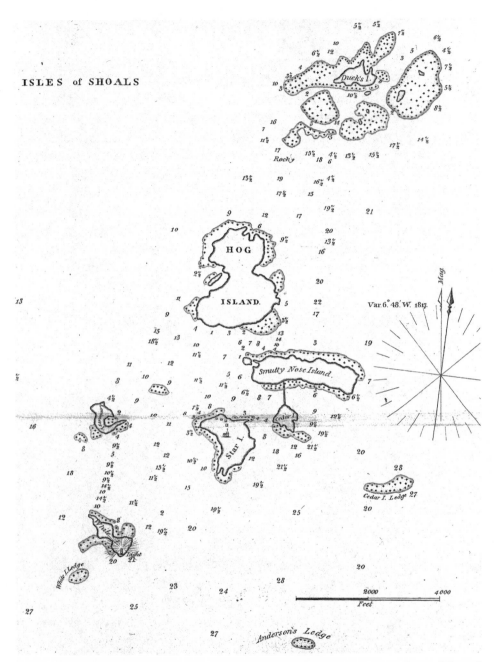

Map of the Isles of Shoals from the 1841 edition of Blunt's American Coast Pilot. *A version of this map appeared in the 1827 edition, also showing the chapel on Star Island, the 1821 White Island lighthouse and the Smuttynose-Cedar Island breakwater which was already in ruins by then.*

Plentiful fish in the surrounding waters and openness to the sun and air made the islands suitable for both fishing and for setting salted fish to dry, on raised wooden frames called flakes. Their offshore location meant less chance of disturbance from Indians. Later, in the eighteenth century, when the fishing grounds off Nova Scotia and Newfoundland proved richer, many Shoals fishermen moved to the mainland, where they could be better supplied for the long voyages to these grounds and where their families could live more comfortably than at the Shoals. By the start of the Revolution, only 175 year-round inhabitants remained. They were ordered ashore to prevent them from helping the British; many floated their houses to the mainland when they left. The islands were repopulated after the war, but in the 1820s there were barely one hundred people living at the Shoals, most in the village of Gosport on Star Island. There, on the island's highest point, is a small stone chapel, which Blunt's 1804 *Coast Pilot* noted as a landmark for mariners.[18]

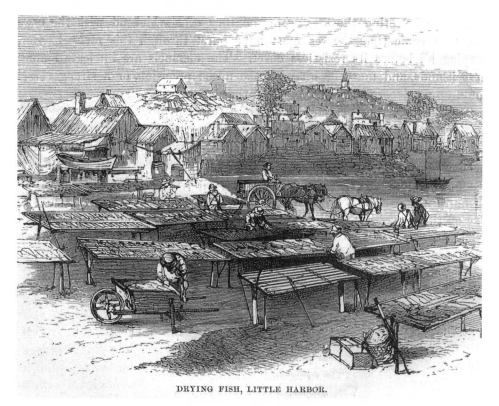

DRYING FISH, LITTLE HARBOR.

Isles of Shoals fishermen dried salted cod on lath platforms called "flakes," like those illus-trated in Samuel Adams Drake's Nooks and Corners of the New England Coast.

A lighthouse at the Shoals would warn of the dangers of these islands and ledges, where innumerable wrecks must have occurred, although few have been recorded prior to the early 1800s. A 1798 account reported rather imprecisely that in "a boisterous tempest" a schooner from Kennebeck, Maine, had struck and upset on either York Ledge or one of the Isles of Shoals. Three men were drowned attempting to get into the schooner's boat. Three others stayed on the wreck for eight hours, clinging to the quarterdeck, until they were driven ashore at Hampton Beach on the mainland. York Ledge and the Isles of Shoals are nine miles apart, but because of the blinding violence of the storm, the survivors could not tell exactly what ledges they had struck.[19]

The story of the Spanish ship *Conception* (some say the vessel was the *Sagunto*), which drove onto the west point of Smuttynose at night in a gale-driven snowstorm in January 1813, has been told many times. The bodies of fifteen of those aboard were found on the island—they died of exposure before they could reach help at the house of Samuel Haley. Ironically, it was the practice of the Haleys to keep a light lit in a window as a nighttime guide for vessels in the vicinity. In the first two decades of the nineteenth century, the federal government reimbursed Haley, his sons, and other men of the Shoals for their many rescues of people aboard vessels wrecked on the islands and ledges. They were often able to bring damaged vessels into a safe anchorage in a small harbor created by a breakwater Haley had built between Smuttynose and Malaga.[20]

In June 1820, Portsmouth collector Timothy Upham wrote to Stephen Pleasonton that he had sailed out to the islands with Captain John Porter, commandant major of the Navy Yard, and "several of our most experienced Ship Masters" to decide on a site for a lighthouse. The spot they chose was White Island, the most southerly of the islands. Upham wrote that it was in a direct line with Cape Ann, "the most prominent westward point of land on this Coast," and also in line with the Portsmouth Harbor light at New Castle. A light on White Island would not only mark the dangers of this cluster of islands and ledges, but also provide an important guide for coasters and oceangoing vessels heading into Portsmouth.[21]

The uninhabited island was owned by New Hampshire, and Upham, after a trip to the state capital in Concord, reported no difficulty persuading the legislature to cede this "certain rock or Island" to the United States. His letter to Pleasonton accounts for the uninhabited state of the island. He wrote that the surf "dashes around it in all directions," and noted that the "sea not infrequently breaks over the Rocks on which it is intended to erect the Light House."[22]

Upham recommended a stone tower forty-eight feet high, tapering from twenty-two feet in diameter at the base to ten and a half feet at the top. The site, the highest point on the southwestern end of the island, would give the lantern of the proposed lighthouse an elevation of sixty-seven feet above the sea. Upham must have been given considerable advice from the local shipmasters he consulted as to features to make the lighthouse on White Island a truly useful aid to navigation— and perhaps a status symbol of sorts for New Hampshire.[23]

He requested equipment evidently never used before in American lighthouses, but which his advisers may have been seen on European coasts. For the lantern, he proposed a revolving light exhibiting "two or more distinct colors," to distinguish it from the twin lights at Cape Ann and the fixed single lights at Boon Island and Portsmouth Harbor. Although not the first revolving light in the country, no lighthouses displaying other than a white light are known to have existed in the U.S. at the time. The model may have been engineer Robert Stevenson's Bell Rock lighthouse, first lighted twelve miles off the east coast of Scotland in February 1811—described by Sir Walter Scott as a "ruddy gem of changeful light" because of its revolving red and white lights.[24]

Upham also urged the installation of a fog bell in the light tower, which he airily suggested could "be tolled by the same machinery which turns the light." A cannon placed at the Boston Harbor lighthouse on Little Brewster Island in 1719 is considered to have been the first American fog signal; it was to be fired in response to guns sounded from vessels groping their way in fog or blinding storms. The first U.S. fog bell was probably the one installed in the summer of 1820 outside the West Quoddy lighthouse. But the bell at White Island appears to be the first to be machine-struck, and must have been the first—and last such—to be installed inside a U.S. lighthouse.[25]

Upham feared that the difficulty of landing building materials at the site would make construction costly, especially as stone would have to be brought from neighboring islands. He successfully negotiated with Pleasonton for a slightly larger house than the one originally proposed. Because the island was distant from the mainland, and difficult to land upon, the keeper would need "to employ two men to live with him on the island at least eight months in the year or he will not be able to leave it." Upham hastened to reassure Pleasonton that these men would be no added expense to the government, for they would be "employed by the keeper in fishing, or as mechanicks in some useful occupation." [26]

By mid-August a contract had been signed by Jonathan Folsom of Portsmouth, designated as "carpenter" on the contract, and William Palmer of Dover, "mason." Folsom (1785–1825), a native of Exeter, was a builder who had been especially active constructing brick houses and commercial buildings in Portsmouth both before and after the great fire of 1813. He is credited with the design of many of these buildings, including the customs house where Timothy Upham had his office, still standing at the corner of Penhallow and Daniel Streets, and the Samuel Larkin house on Middle Street. Folsom was also the contractor for the shiphouse built at the Navy Yard in 1813 for the seventy-four gun warship *Washington*. His last major project was the stone South Church (Unitarian) in Portsmouth, finished in 1826, the year after his death.[27]

Much less is known for certain about William Palmer—there was more than one William Palmer of Dover. In an 1821 testimonial as to the partners' competence, John Parrott of Portsmouth stated that the two men had "erected many buildings in this town, of late years." Palmer may also have worked with Folsom on such other construction projects as the building of a stone wharf at the Navy Yard in the teens. A "Capt." William Palmer is credited with building two three-story brick Federal-style houses in Dover around 1813. A William Palmer was also busy in Dover when that town was developing as a textile-manufacturing community in the 1820s, advertising that he could build "Russian stoves, on a new and improved plan, with or without fireplaces." [28] At the end of the 1820s, Palmer and Daniel Haselton, another mason, would undertake the difficult construction of Whale's Back Lighthouse at the mouth of the Piscataqua and in the middle of the 1830s they would build the stone customs house designed by architect Robert Mills, that still stands in Newburyport.[29]

The contract signed by Folsom and Palmer was more detailed in some of its specifications than the one signed by the contractors for the Boon Island lighthouse nine years earlier, perhaps because of improved knowledge of the requirements of windswept offshore construction sites and of the necessities of life for those maintaining island light houses.

It called for a tower rising forty feet (instead of the forty-eight feet originally proposed) to the platform for the lantern. The walls were to decrease in thickness from three feet at the base to one and a half feet at the top, rising above a two-foot-high stone floor. One important design difference from Boon Island was that the tower was to be circular, rather than octagonal, in cross-section, so that buffeting winds would flow around the curved walls rather than meeting head-on the sides of an octagon or other flat-sided form. The mortar was to be mixed with fresh water; some evidence must already have surfaced that using the much handier salt seawater resulted in defective mortar, although the debate about the effects of salt on mortar would continue for some years.[30]

The contract called for a wooden stairway winding upward inside the tower to an iron ladder to complete the final ascent to the lantern. At Boon Island, the platform on which the lantern rested was made of iron sleepers covered with sheet iron, tar paper, and sheet copper, and must have proved vulnerable to rust and corrosion. At White Island, soapstone slabs would create a platform twelve and a half feet in diameter. The dimensions of the octagonal lantern were based on the size of the eight iron sashes, each of which was to have fifteen lights of ten-by-twelve-inch panes of the "best double glass from the Boston manufactory" inserted in a framework of iron bars an inch and a half thick. Copper panels were to fill the lower tiers of the lantern windows.[31]

For access to the platform circling the lantern, one side of the octagonal lantern was to have a door with an iron sash of twelve squares, with copper used in the three lower openings in the grid and glass in the upper squares. Atop the copper roof of the lantern, there was to be a "transversing ventillator" with a copper vane three feet long. There were to be two copper lightning conductors on the roof. The contract specified black paint for the dome of the lantern and white lead paint for the iron lantern door and window sashes; the tower itself was to be "twice whitewashed." [32]

The contract was revised within ten days. The original agreement had called for the use of copper bolts to fasten the first tier of masonry to the site and to join the facing stones of the first ten feet of the tower to each other. Now, instead of using bolts, Folsom and Palmer were to begin the first masonry tier in a groove cut into the rock site "at least two inches" deep. At Boon Island, the groove for the first tiers was three feet deep. The two inches specified at White Island was likely an error in the handwritten copy filed in the National Archives; presumably two feet was intended. Eliminating the copper bolts saved sixty-two dollars on the $4,450 contract. It was probably argued that the cumulative weight of the stone of the lighthouse would make these fastenings unnecessary to stabilize it. Another change called for the use of slightly larger panes of glass in the lantern, twelve by twelve inches, making for a somewhat larger lantern. The width of the wooden stairway that was to wind around the inside wall of the tower to the fourth story was revised from three feet specified in the contract, to three and a half feet in an undated amendment to the contract, presumably to make carrying oil to the lamps less cumbersome.[33]

The most interesting revision specified four windows, rather than the one originally called for, at the third (top) story, immediately below the lantern. These windows, unlike the others, were to have "sills and facings of hammered stone and of sufficient size to reach through the walls." They were to be fitted with blinds, probably louvered, rather than with the glazed sash of fifteen lights specified for the other windows.[34] These alterations suggest an attempt to deal, belatedly, with the problems of where to hang the planned fog bell inside the light tower and how to make its sound heard outside the walls—issues no American lighthouse contractor had faced before. The bell would have had to be placed as high as possible in the light tower to allow the weighted chain of the clockwork bell-striking mechanism to descend as it unwound. The additional unglazed window openings would let the sound of the bell be heard in all directions outside the walls of the lighthouse tower. The plan calls to mind the belfries of churches; the concern to strengthen the openings may have reflected knowledge of the effects of bell vibrations on masonry.

The contract called for a one-story house of thirty-four by twenty-eight feet, with walls eighteen inches thick, a cellar six feet deep, a chimney "near the middle of the house," with four rooms on the first story, and two chambers in the attic. Two windows for each downstairs room, with fifteen panes of eight-by-ten-inch glass, were specified, and for each of the upstairs rooms, a single window with twelve panes; all were to be fitted with "good double shutters on the outside, with suitable fastenings." The contractors were to attempt to dig a well for a supply of fresh water and provide it with a windlass, chain, and an iron-hooped bucket. If no water was reached after digging and blasting to a depth of twenty feet, they were to build a cistern under the house to hold two thousand gallons of water collected by roof gutters.

There were to be closets with shelves in each room, and fireplaces in the two front rooms. The kitchen fireplace oven should be "not less than three and a half feet deep, with an iron door... to be fitted up with a crane, trammels and hooks."[35] A pump in the kitchen would bring up

water from the basement well or cistern, with a drain spout leading
through the outside wall to dispose of waste water from the kitchen sink.
At Boon Island, the attic chamber of the keeper's house did not have the
insulating benefit of plastered laths over the stone walls, but at White
Island rooms were to be lathed and plastered both upstairs and down.[36]

An amenity not mentioned in the Boon Island contract was "an Outhouse of stone, 5 feet by 4 feet (inside), the roof to be shingled and
painted." This "outhouse" was probably a privy, though it may have
been a storage building.[37]

The building of the lighthouse brought a temporary population explosion to the Shoals. Folsom and Palmer, evidently confident that they
would get the job, placed an ad in the *Portsmouth Oracle* on August 12,
1820, five days before the contract was signed. They were looking for

> **THIRTY ACTIVE MEN** for the purpose of doing the
> Carpenter-work, blacksmith-work, Gondolaing, and
> blowing, digging and hauling rocks.
> **Also Wanted**
> A quantity of dimension Pine ranging Timber, and Oak
> Boards and Planks, and a quantity of Thomastown lime,
> to be landed at Haley's dock, Isles of Shoals.38

Construction continued until near the end of November 1820. The
base of operations was probably Smuttynose Island, where Haley's
Cove had the only dock at the Shoals. No account has been found of the
builders' sojourn at the islands. Some may have boarded with the Haley
family on Smuttynose, or with people of the village of Gosport on Star
Island, but a small village of temporary huts or shelters may have been
built for the workers on White Island itself.

The "split, undressed stone" specified for the lighthouse and
dwelling was readily available on the various islands of the Shoals. The
advertisement in the *Oracle* makes clear that gondolas, or gundalows
would be required. These were sturdy, shallow-draft craft more usually
employed on the Piscataqua River and its tributaries, where they carried cargo off-loaded from larger vessels in Portsmouth. Because of
their shallow draft, gundalows could be poled close in to the shore to be
loaded with stone at the Isles of Shoals. Sails could be used in these
scow-like boats when the wind was favorable, but rowing and poling
were often necessary. Oxen were used at the Shoals two years later for
seawall construction, and may well have been used in the 1820 lighthouse construction project as well.[39]

HALEY DOCK AND HOMESTEAD.
(In the third House from the left the Wagner Murder was committed.)

Haley's dock on Smuttynose Island, where lighthouse building materials were landed, from Samuel Adams Drake's Nooks and Corners.

A subcontractor worked "furnishing" the buildings with the necessary woodwork for window frames, stairs, doors, and closets. The man who received nine hundred dollars for this work was subsequently identified as the one who built the lighthouse at Fort Constitution in 1803. Benjamin Clark Gilman, of Exeter, had been the contractor then, but the man who did the carpentry at White Island and evidently at the Portsmouth Harbor light was the joiner Nathaniel Marston.[40]

One wonders how carefully Upham and his advisers studied the site when they made their original proposal. There was not enough room for a house at the site chosen for the lighthouse, and it had to be built on a spot separated from the tower by a gully that was washed by storm seas. Toward the end of September, Upham signed another agreement, with Folsom alone, to construct for $260 "a Bridge and covered way over the Gully & Ledges which lay between the Light-House now building on White Island and the site selected for the Dwelling-House." This covered way, some 330 feet long and six feet wide, would rest on five rubblestone piers.

For the lamps, revolving mechanism, fog bell, and other equipment, Upham put out separate requests for bids. He received two. One, for $950, came from Benjamin Gilman; the other, for thirteen hundred dollars, from Winslow Lewis. Perhaps prodded by Stephen Pleasonton,

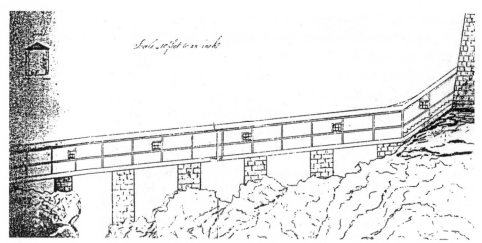

Plan for the original covered passageway from the keeper's house to the lighthouse.
NARG26.

Upham wrote that although Gilman's bid was lower, and he had a reputation for ingenuity, it would be preferable to have the more experienced Lewis undertake the work. And at the end of September, Winslow
Lewis signed an agreement with Upham for the lighting apparatus, fog
bell, and "every other Article usually furnished by Contractors, for fitting up the Light-Houses of the United States." The final agreement was
for two thousand dollars, plus forty-five cents a pound for a bell of at
least six hundred but no more than eight hundred pounds in weight. The
bell, "securely hung in such part of Said lighthouse, as may be required
by the Superintendent," should be audible at least four miles away in
"moderate weather." [41] On November 28, 1820, Winslow Lewis arrived at
White Island with this special equipment. Nathaniel Marston, whom
Upham had hired to stay at White Island until the equipment was
installed and a keeper appointed, was there when it arrived.[42]

The fog bell Lewis brought with him was cast by Joseph W. Revere,
son of Paul Revere, and was considerably larger than the 579-pound
bell Revere cast for West Quoddy lighthouse. It weighed 806 pounds, or
six pounds more than the maximum originally specified. Rather than
swallow a cost overrun of less than three dollars, Lewis brought with
him from Boston a certificate signed by N. Porter, perhaps the Noah
Porter who had been one of the mason contractors for the Boon Island
light, and was a member of the Boston Mechanics Association. Porter
affirmed that in his opinion "a Bell of less weight could not be heard

over three miles"—as if the six extra pounds made a significant differ-ence! Lewis's contract had specified ambitiously that the bell should be fitted "with such machinery as may be necessary to keep it tolling 12 hours without winding up." (Four or five hours was the maximum most later fog bells could operate without rewinding.) Marston signed a receipt for "A clock to set the hammer in motion, with an iron weight of five hundred pounds." The receipt listed no separate clockwork mecha-nism to rotate the framework for the lamps in the lantern, although the contract specified one "made on the plan of Willard's latest improve-ment in Light-House clocks."[43]

Other equipment delivered by Lewis included two spare lamps, one stove with funnel (stovepipe), wick and tube boxes, scissors, snippers, files, "wick formers," a solderring iron and solder, and tube cleaners.[44]

Lewis provided White Island with seven tin "oil butts," each of which could hold ninety gallons of sperm oil. He had been responsible for the government's adoption of these metal containers. They were a significant improvement over the wooden barrels used previously, from which a substantial amount of oil was lost due to the shrinkage of the wood staves. (Back in 1804 and 1806, Joseph Whipple reported losses of one or two gallons per seventy-eight-gallon cask during shipping, and nearly the same amount of leakage after delivery.) [45]

In the lighthouse lantern, Lewis placed fifteen lamps with fourteen-inch-diameter reflectors, fitted to a rotating triangular iron framework. Upham's request for a light of more than one color was more than ful-filled. The five lamps on one side of the framework exhibited a "deep blue light," on the second side a "bright red," and on the third side "the natural color of the light."[46] The receipt for supplies signed by Nathaniel Marston shows the ingenious but not very practical means Lewis devised to produce this patriotic color scheme. It lists ten "globe tubes" and a gallon each of red and blue "liquor" to pour into them. We do not know whether colored glass, in either sheet or chimney form, was unavailable or simply too expensive, nor do we know the exact charac-ter of the globe tubes or what was used as "antifreeze" to keep the dyed liquid from freezing and cracking the glass tubes.[47]

Before Lewis left Portsmouth, he examined the lighthouse, the keeper's house, and the covered way. He left letters with Timothy Upham stating that all had been built as agreed in the contracts, and "in a workmanlike manner." No one was required to pass on Lewis's own handiwork.[48]

On December 1, 1820, a "Notice to Mariners" in the *Portsmouth Oracle*: announced that the lighthouse would begin operations on the sixth, and described its features. The framework holding the lamps would make a complete revolution every three and a half minutes. This notice also made evident the disadvantages of the colored lights: The white, or natural, lights of the lantern were supposed to be seen for seven leagues, or about twenty-one miles; the red lights to be visible for eighteen or nineteen miles, and the blue ones for only fifteen or sixteen miles. These figures were doubtless provided by Winslow Lewis; according to later measurements, they were grossly inflated, but they do indicate the lower power of the colored lights.[49]

Uphams's notice also stated that the fog bell, "suspended in the tower," would be "kept tolling by the machinery at the rate of ten strokes a minute, by night and day, whenever from fog, or any other cause, the Light ...cannot be seen at least four miles; at which distance it is calculated the Bell may be heard in moderate weather."[50]

Compass bearings and distances from the lighthouse to a number of locations—Portsmouth, Boon Island, and Cape Ann lights; Rye and Star island meeting houses; and several nearby ledges and points—were published.[51]

Timothy Upham recommended an annual salary of four hundred dollars for the keeper of White Island lighthouse, midway between the four hundred and fifty dollars paid the Boon Island keeper and the three hundred fifty dollars earned at Portsmouth Harbor. He wrote to Stephen Pleasonton in early November that because the salary was rumored to be high, there had been many applicants for the job. His own first choice was Nathaniel Marston, but he was over-ruled in a letter from Fifth Auditor Pleasonton, who informed him that President Monroe "had been pleased to appoint Clement Jackson."[52]

Problems with the structure and equipment were soon evident. Upham reported in June 1821 that because the masonry work had been done so late in the season, the mortar had not had time to dry thoroughly before freezing weather set in and had thus been seriously affected. Much of the original mortar was removed and replaced, but problems persisted, with storm-driven water penetrating to the interior of the buildings. Drastic corrective measures were in order after a December 1823 gale. Although the contractors used Thomaston lime, considered a standard of excellence for "common lime," they were apparently unaware of "hydraulic" lime which contained elements that make it harden in damp or wet locations. Upham adopted a solution

NOTICE TO MARINERS.

Custom-House,
Portsmouth, N. H. Dec. 1, 1820.

☞ A LIGHT-HOUSE has been erected on *White-Island,* (the South-westernmost of the Isles of Shoals,) which will be lighted on the night of Wednesday the 6th of December inst. The lantern is at an elevation of 67 feet from high water mark, and contains 15 patent lamps with reflectors on a revolving triangle, which will make one complete revolution in three minutes and thirty seconds ; exhibiting on one side, a bright red light, on one side a blue, and on the other, the natural color of the light.

The color of each light may be distinctly seen about 50 seconds. At the distance of nine miles, the light will be wholly eclipsed about ten seconds between each color ; within that distance, it will not entirely disappear in clear weather ; but taking the medium, the greatest power of light will be to the least as 40 to 1. The bright, or natural light, will be first discovered in clear weather, at the distance of about 7 leagues, and on approaching, the red and blue in succession. The bright light may be seen two or three miles farther than the red, and the red about the same distance farther than the blue.

A Bell, of 800 lbs. weight is suspended in the tower of the Light-House, which will be kept tolling by machinery at the rate of ten strokes a minute, by night and day, whenever from fog, or any other cause, the Light or Light-House cannot be seen at least four miles ; at which distance it is calculated the Bell may be heard in moderate weather.

New-Hampshire Gazette, *5 December 1820 notice to mariners. Customs Collector Timothy Upham placed this notice in local newspapers announcing the forthcoming lighting of White Island lighthouse and describing its unusual features: red, white, and blue lights, and a fog bell suspended in the tower.*

he said was common for brick or stone buildings in cold, wet regions: The lighthouse was boarded and shingled, transforming it into an octagonal structure.[53]

There were difficulties with the sperm oil delivered late in 1821: Half of it congealed in cold weather and could be used only in summer. In addition, no boats or boatways had been provided for. In 1821 Upham successfully advocated construction of boatways with a capstan (a hand-powered winch) for hauling a boat up the ways, and asked the government to furnish two boats—one equipped with sails and large enough for trips to the mainland for provisions; the other a small, light boat to use as a tender. The gale of December 1823 heavily damaged both the boatways and the boathouse.[54]

Less than three years after its installation, in October 1823, Upham reported hat the fog bell had been discontinued, but did not specify when it ceased to be used. He explained that the bell was too small to be heard over the noise of the surf at the island, and that the machinery was not adequate to operate a heavier bell. He suggested that the machinery be sent to the Portland Collector and altered for use as a revolving mechanism for a lighthouse being built in his district. This strongly indicates that there had been two clockworks: one for the bell and the other for the lights, though only one was specified in the contract. Upham recommended selling the bell.[55]

The *American Coast Pilot* reported a fog bell "suspended in the tower of the lighthouse" at White Island as late as its 1827 edition. This is not surprising, as there was no established procedure for providing the publisher with up-to-date information about changes in aids to navigation. Before publication of the next, 1833, edition, Captain Thomas M. Shaw of the revenue cutter stationed in Portsmouth was consulted about local aids to navigation and their bearings, and reference to the fog bell at White Island was finally dropped—at least ten years after it had been discontinued.[56]

An intriguing question about the bell comes to the mind of anyone who has read Dorothy L. Sayers's mystery, *The Nine Tailors,* in which a man tied up in a belfry is killed by the vibrations of the church bells: What was it like to be inside the lighthouse when the sound of the fog bell reverberated against its stone walls?

The method of creating the colored lights at White Island was evidently altered at some time in the 1820s. The globe tubes filled with colored liquid were doubtless as vulnerable as clear-glass chimneys to the

White Island lighthouse as it appeared at the end of the 1850s, not long before the building of the second White Island lighthouse, and showing the covered walkway that replaced the original one in 1842. NARG26.

extremes of temperature—freezing weather and the heat of the lamps' flames. Even though there was a stove in the lantern to keep the oil from congealing (as well as to warm the lightkeeper), there may well have been times during the day when the fire was allowed to go out.

A December 1, 1829 letter from Portsmouth collector John P. Decatur recorded another "tremendous Gale" during which the "heave of the sea" tore many shingles off the lighthouse and damaged the east end of the house and the cistern under it. The same storm also broke glass in the lighthouse lantern. Decatur requested funds the following April for repairs, including six lights of common glass for the lantern and "three lights of coloured glass." This strongly suggests that the globe tubes filled with colored liquid had already been replaced with colored glass panels. It is not clear how long the blue sector of the light was maintained. Blunt's *Coast Pilot* as late as its 1837 edition described the colors of the light as "a bright red, and a bright and [a] dim natural colored light," the dim natural light perhaps being produced by blue-tinted glass. New apparatus placed in the lantern in 1840 included red glass only.[57]

Regardless of the deficiencies of the light at White Island, it helped eastbound vessels. It was much less useful for coasters proceeding southward along the Maine coast, many of which came to grief on the ledges around Duck Island, at the northern extremity of the Shoals. Within several hours on a single day in April 1827, two schooners from Saco, Maine, tangled with these ledges. The *Hiram* struck on the eastern ledges and managed to beat over them, but lost rudder, cable, and anchor and limped into Portsmouth Harbor with a split keel. The *Phaeton* was less fortunate. After striking the same eastern ledges, Captain Dunleavie ordered the boat lowered. The eleven people aboard—Captain Dunleavie himself, his crew of four, his wife, his sister, and his son, and two other male passengers—pulled for another ledge where "within five minutes they watched the schooner being dashed into 1,000 pieces." The crew and passengers clung to their ledge for close to twelve hours. After repeated attempts, islanders were finally able to rescue them from the violent seas. The cargo of flour, pork, and chain cables was lost.[58]

There were periodic pleas for a lighthouse on Duck Island, but one was never built. Swept by the ocean during storms and ringed with ledges, this site remained too problematic for building and maintaining a lighthouse.

Other 1820s Aids to Navigation in the Portsmouth Seacoast Area

Because of increasing maritime commerce, in 1821 President James Monroe appointed Portsmouth merchant William Rice to head up a three-man commission to propose solutions for problems to navigation in the Portsmouth area. Rice, a shipmaster in the 1790s, had experience of both European and West Indies ports. In the first decades of the nineteenth century he was part or sole owner of numerous vessels, including privateers in the War of 1812, and was an importer and merchant with a store on Portsmouth Pier. His fellow commissioners were John L. Thompson, listed in the 1821 Portsmouth directory both as a shipmaster and as a clerk of the United States Bank in Portsmouth; and Samuel Muir, another shipmaster who had been involved in both European and West Indies trade.[59]

They proposed three projects. One was for a stone beacon on Sunken Rocks in the Piscataqua River off Pierce's Island. The other two were designed to create a harbor of refuge at the Isles of Shoals for vessels larger than the small fishing boats that used Haley's Cove to shelter from storms. The first project was to repair a small existing seawall between Malaga and Smuttynose Islands. The second, far more ambitious project, was a new seawall between Smuttynose and Cedar Islands.

The first step toward a better anchorage at the Shoals, was the repair of the Smuttynose-Malaga island seawall. Captain Samuel Haley had built the seawall before the turn of the century to create Haley's Cove. Haley had reputedly financed his project with bars of pirate silver he had found on Smuttynose. (In 1800, he asked the federal government for compensation for building this seawall.) In this cove, according to Blunt's *Coast Pilot* of 1804, "15 or 20 small vessels may lie safe from all winds," and it was here that the contractors landed building materials for the White Island lighthouse. The repair work was relatively simple and was accomplished by Amos S. Parsons by November 1821 at a cost of $426.[60]

In 1793, Joseph Whipple had identified Sunken Rocks as a major hazard to navigation for vessels coming up to Portsmouth wharves. Whipple had then requested funds for a stone beacon for the site, but there was only enough money for a timber buoy to mark its downstream edge.

In June 1821, after the commission's recommendation was approved, the New Hampshire Legislature ceded the ledges to the United States—and included in the act the usual clause permitting the officers of the state access to the site to apprehend criminals there. In July, Timothy Upham published requests for bids. Jonathan Folsom, William Palmer, and Thomas Haven submitted one, but soon found that the place chosen by the commissioners, which was covered by seven feet of water at lowest tide, dropped off sharply on all sides, leaving an inadequate base on which to build the foundation of the beacon. The contractors refused to guarantee even for one year a structure built at this site. By the time the commissioners had decided that another spot on the ledge would serve the purpose, Palmer had dropped out of the partnership, and it was Folsom and Haven who signed the September 3, 1821, contract to build the beacon for fourteen hundred dollars. For guidance, the commissioners supplied the contractors with a wooden scale model to supplement the written contract.[61]

By the middle of November, the partners had already brought down-river sixty tons of split granite, hauled the stone onto the ledge, and

"View of Portsmouth from the Navy Yard," from Farmer's 1823 Gazeteer of the State of New-Hampshire *showing the Sunken Rocks beacon on the left side of the channel. Another navigational marker is in evidence on the right.* PA.

built the foundation nearly to the high-water level, where the beacon itself would be constructed. They wrote Upham on November 16 that they would have to stop work until the following June. Although the extreme low tides of this season would have been ideal for work on the project, they came before dawn and after dusk, when the men could not see to work. Storms also hampered the project, and finally autumn temperatures made the water too cold for the workmen. The contractors agreed to place a buoy on the ledge until they could finish the work.[62]

The stone beacon they laid above the foundation in June was forty by twenty-five feet at its base, tapering to thirty-two by seventeen feet at its top, sixteen feet above high tide. In plan the beacon was an attenuated diamond, with the long dimension running in the direction of the swift current of the river to reduce the impact of the powerful tidal current and to deflect the chunks of ice and debris it swept downstream.[63]

No mortar was specified in the contract. The split-granite pieces used to face the structure were to extend at least three feet into the pier, and each was to be bolted by at least two copper dowels one and a quarter inches in diameter. All the granite slabs on top were also to be copper-bolted. Steps built into the Pierce Island side of the beacon and an iron railing around the top were made so that workers could climb onto it for maintenance of the white oak post rising six feet above the masonry. On top of the post a spindle with a beacon and vane were placed and finished with two coats of white paint. For boats tying up for maintenance work, and perhaps also to furnish a place for vessels in distress to tie up, Folsom and Haven were to attach ten twelve-inch iron rings to the masonry, firmly attached by iron staples extending into the center of the masonry.[64]

No records for replacement or substantial alteration of the Sunken Rocks beacon have been found, and the granite structure still marking these rocks is evidently pretty much the one built by Folsom and Haven. It is virtually the only aid to navigation from this era surviving in the waters around Portsmouth.

POINT OF GRAVES.

Image from Drake's Nooks and Corners…, *showing Sunken Rocks beacon in the river beyond the Point of Graves burying ground.*

Jonathan Folsom and Thomas Haven also won the contract to build the extremely ambitious second step toward creating a harbor of refuge at the Isles of Shoals: the seawall between Smuttynose and Cedar Islands recommended by the three-man commission. This seawall would provide a sheltered harbor for larger vessels than could anchor at Haley's Cove. The commissioners reported that such a seawall was feasible, and noted that the Shoals were "very much in the track of vessels employed in the coasting trade of Massachusetts, New Hampshire, and Maine." Their statement also revealed that Portsmouth Harbor had its drawbacks for vessels caught in "boisterous" weather north of Cape Ann, for

> in the whole extent of Ipswich Bay, there is no harbor that can be made in heavy gales from the northeast, which are prevalent in the winter season, and occasion much damage and many losses both of lives and property. This is particularly the case with regard to vessels bound to Portsmouth and other ports on the northern shores of the bay, which, for want of such an anchorage as would be by this means obtained, are frequently driven off the coast, or on a lee shore.[65]

Collector Upham advertised the job early in June 1822, with the contract going to Folsom and Haven, both of Portsmouth. The role of Haven in both the Sunken Rocks beacon and in the Cedar-Smuttynose seawall is unclear. A merchant, he may simply have provided up-front funds for these projects—$11,500 in the case of the seawall—and perhaps the gundalows to be used for transporting stone. In early July 1822, the men advertised for "a number of labourers" to build the seawall.[66]

The project required moving thousands of tons of stone from the islands within a two-mile radius of the site to create a 784-foot seawall between Cedar and Smuttynose Islands. Oxen and gundalows were to haul the stones, some of which weighed as much as five tons. Because the work was offshore, it was expected that the gundalows could not be loaded as fully as they were for river transport. On average the water depth between the two islands was twenty-five to thirty-five feet. Work began on July 15; Upham wrote to Pleasonton on the sixteenth that from eighty to one hundred men, with teams, boats, and gundalows, were already at work. They continued until October 15 and resumed work on April 25, 1823.[67]

The first phase of the work involved "casting stones into the water, until they reached low water mark; from thence the wall was built by regular masonry." Upham reported in early August 1823 that the contractors' expenses had already exceeded the amount allowed. Instead of the expected twenty-eight thousand tons of stone, the wall had already "absorbed" forty thousand tons, with five to eight thousand more needed to finish it.[68]

The seawall was completed on October 18, 1823. It extended six feet above high-water level, its sides sloping upward from a base about ninety feet wide at a forty-five-degree angle. The top formed a causeway eleven feet wide. The *Portsmouth Journal* of November 1, 1823, reported as follows:

> The bay, which is now formed between Smutty-nose, Cedar, and Star Islands, will afford a safe harbour for vessels bound to this port, when a northerly wind and ebb tide prevent them from entering the river. The wall makes safe anchorage also for small craft whenever the wind is from South East to North, and protects the boats on Star Island beach in any easterly storm.

The seawall survived intact for little more than a year. Though all three commissioners were experienced shipmasters, in their optimistic proposal they underestimated the force of the sea on a wall at this exposed, offshore location. Early in 1824 Upham wrote to Pleasonton that in a late-December storm, "more violent and producing a heavier swell of the Seas (as the Inhabitants of the Islands inform me) than has been known for several years," about two hundred feet of the wall had been damaged. In fact, most of this section had been so much diminished in height that it did not become visible until half tide. Upham, relying on information from the islanders, reported that the tremendous undertow had dragged out the loosely piled rocks of the lower part of the wall from under the upper section. When he finally visited the scene in June, he found that 340 feet of the wall had been affected, with its height reduced by nine feet. It still formed a "tolerable breakwater," he wrote.[69]

No new attempt to grapple with the engineering problems of this offshore breakwater was attempted by the federal government until early in the twentieth century. The jumble of stone created a barrier that kept vessels from running between the islands, but in the violent gale of November 1888 the hulk of an entire vessel, the *Teal*, after being swept off Boon Island, was lifted up and over the ragged line of stones.[70]

Fire at Portsmouth Harbor Lighthouse

The preference for masonry rather than wood for lighthouse construction was forcefully validated at Portsmouth Harbor light early in
1826. On the stormy night of February 1, with the temperature said to be
fifteen degrees below zero and the wind blowing a gale from the northwest, the wooden lighthouse was nearly destroyed by a fire started by the
coal stove used to keep the oil from congealing in the lamps. In his report
to Pleasonton, Upham wrote that the hot fire in the stove had probably
melted the lead used to seal the seams of the lantern platform, causing
the wood planks and timbers below to smolder and finally catch fire.[71]

The salvation of the lighthouse was the garrison at Fort Constitution. The keeper discovered the fire when he went to tend the light
around nine P.M. When he opened the door to the tower, billows of smoke
greeted him. The fort commandant, Captain Whiting, turned the soldiers out of their beds. Sergeant Zachariah Chickering, battling the
choking smoke and ignoring the showers of burning coals and molten
lead that poured out of the seams of the lantern deck, rushed up to the
lantern where the fire was blazing. The other soldiers formed a bucket
brigade to the shore, skidding on the ice-coated rocks to scoop up seawater to douse the fire. Most of Chickering's clothes were burned from
his body. He finally succumbed to the smoke and had to be carried out
of the lighthouse. Several of the soldiers, who had no time to dress
warmly, suffered frostbite and some lost their hats to the high wind.[72]
Upham reported that because of the soldiers' swift action there was only
small damage to the lighthouse. In recognition of the heroism of the men
and their losses, Upham gave twenty dollars to CaptainWhiting, with
the recommendation that eight dollars be given to Sergeant Chickering
to replace his clothes, with "the remainder to be used to buy wine with
which the soldiers could drink the health of the President." Upham's
generosity was, of course, reimbursed by the government.[73]

The occasion provided Timothy Upham an opportunity to express
his loyalty to President John Quincy Adams, at whose pleasure he
served as Collector of Customs. There was little money to be gained in
superintending the two lighthouses under his jurisdiction; in 1824 he
received $24.46 for this task. (The figure was based on a commission of
two and a half percent on expenditures for lighthouses and other aids
to navigation in his charge.) But Upham's position in the customs
house was quite profitable; his earnings as collector for the same year

amounted to $2,335—more than four times the $547 Joseph Whipple had earned during the economically depressed early 1790s.[74]

In fact, the earnings of customs collectors provide a handy index of the relative prosperity of the ports they supervised. Portland collector Isaac Ilsley's 1823 earnings of $2,562 reflected the fortunes of that port. The rise of Portland and other Maine ports and the gradual decline of the Port of Portsmouth are shown by the collectors' pay four years later. In 1828, Upham made $2,186, whereas Ilsely earned $3,400. By 1832, the new Portsmouth collector, William Pickering, made only $1,016, and Portland Collector John Anderson's remuneration remained at $3,400. The growing prosperity of the port of Bath, Maine, was indicated by Collector William King's earnings of $1,987 for 1832, substantially more than Pickering's.[75]

During the 1820s, local efforts were made to bolster the sagging prosperity of the Port of Portsmouth. One serious difficulty for vessels entering the port after dark was the lack of a light at the mouth of the Piscataqua to mark the hazards there. By the end of the decade, a lighthouse had been built on the Whale's Back ledge—probably the most difficult site on which the U.S. government had yet attempted to place a manned lighthouse.

Portsmouth Light **Whale Back Light**

Etching from the margin of 1866 Portsmouth Harbor map showing the approach to Portsmouth Harbor bearing "N. ¼ E. distant ¾ Mile." Courtesy of Image Archives of the Historical Map & Chart Collection/Office of Coast Survey/National Ocean Service/NOAA.

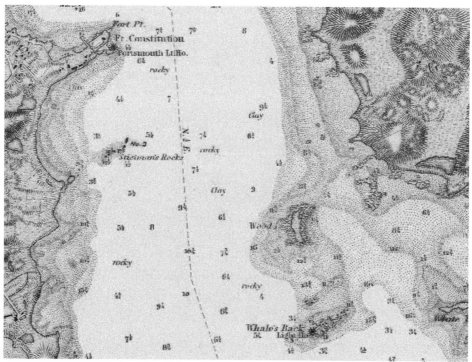

Detail from the same map shows Fort Constitution at the upper left and Whale's Back at lower right.

VI Whale's Back Lighthouse, a New Lighthouse for Boon Island, and the Inspection of 1837

*What sort of a Light House and Keepers House could
be erected, on an Island furnishing no materials, for
fifteen hundred dollars?*

—Timothy Upham to Stephen Pleasanton, 1827

The Port of Portsmouth in the 1820s

THE FUTURE OF THE PORT OF PORTSMOUTH began to brighten in the mid-1820s. Private shipyards in the Piscataqua region were meeting steadily growing demand. In the 1820s, nearly one hundred ships, brigs, schooners, and sloops ranging from thirty to four hundred tons burden were produced in local shipyards. In 1827, 191 vessels, including forty-two ships, twenty-five brigs, and 110 schooners, totaling 25,238 tons burden, belonged to the Port of Portsmouth. A news item in September of that year described the Portsmouth wharves as packed, and bristling with masts. The *Portsmouth Journal* counted twenty-one ships, nine brigs, fifty-one schooners, and six sloops, and added—to make the point that they were not idle because of lack of business—that "most... have arrived within a few days."[1]

A toll bridge built in 1822 to span the Piscataqua from Portsmouth to Kittery eased communication and commerce between the communities on both sides of the river. Another boost to the regional economy and its

131

maritime interests in the 1820s was the coming of the industrial revolution to the upriver towns on the tributaries to the Piscataqua. Towns like Dover, Great Falls (now Somersworth), Newmarket, and Exeter built water-powered textile mills. Southern cotton for the mills and the goods needed by the expanding populations of these developing manufacturing towns began coming into Portsmouth to be freighted upstream by gundalows and small, short-masted packet boats.[2] In the 1820s, the Portsmouth papers were also full of hopeful reports of a canal (proposed but never built) from the tidal head of the Cocheco River in Dover to Lake Winnepesaukee. Its proponents, aware of the benefits derived from the Middlesex Canal in Massachusetts and the even more ambitions Erie Canal in New York, wanted to link the Port of Portsmouth with the New Hampshire hinterland both to exploit potential export resources and to expand markets for goods entering the port. At the end of the decade, federal funds were appropriated to make a survey of the Cocheco from the falls at Dover to the Piscataqua, with an eye to removing obstructions in this tributary.

The owners of the wharf located off what is now Prescott Park placed the following advertisement in the *Portsmouth Journal* of February 4, 1826:

> **Notice**—a light will be kept on the eastern end of the store on Long Wharf, in Portsmouth Harbor, except on moonlight nights, for the benefit of vessels coming to the wharves in the south part of town; Boston & Portland papers will please to give this information.

It is not likely that many strangers to the port would have ventured this far up the Piscataqua River at night, as the river was difficult to navigate even during daylight hours.

A Lighthouse at the Entrance to Portsmouth Harbor

The ledges and rocky islets jumbled in the waters to the south of Gerrish Island, at the mouth of the river presented enormous difficulties for nighttime navigation. Many rudders had been lost and many holes smashed in hulls on the Whale's Back and other ledges at the mouth of the river. A wreck on Whale's Back in April 1821 occasioned a daring nighttime rescue by soldiers from Fort Constitution. The schooner *President,* of Warren, Maine, was being dashed to pieces on the ledge in a wild storm. Several times local men had taken out boats to try to save those aboard, only to be thrown back by pounding seas. Corporal George McAuley and five other men from the fort made a final rescue attempt, reported with gusto by the *Portsmouth Oracle:*

> In this situation, McAuley put the question to his boat's crew—
> 'shall we save them or perish in the attempt?' "Yes,' was the
> unanimous answer of these brave fellows; and they immediate-
> ly dashed among the breakers, and fortunately succeeded in
> saving seven fellow creatures from a watery grave. The officers
> of the Fort intend presenting McAuley a Medal as a reward for
> his meritorious conduct.[3]

In 1826 there were several wrecks at the river's mouth, including the total destruction on Whale's Back ledge of a ship from Liverpool and the loss of its valuable cargo. This series of wrecks precipitated a petition for a lighthouse to warn of the hazards at the mouth of the river. We do not know whether the petitioners consulted Collector of Customs Timothy Upham before sending their request directly to New Hampshire Congressman Ichabod Bartlett. Bartlett was a Portsmouth lawyer who sat on the Naval Affairs Committee that handled propos- als for aids to navigation. Bartlett in turn asked Upham for his sug- gestions and a cost estimate. Upham was evidently ill at the time and did not respond to Bartlett, who may have used the petitioners' unre- alistic cost estimate when he added the proposed lighthouse to a bill for aids to navigation.[4]

Congress authorized the project on March 3, 1827, and specified Whale's Back as the site. Just a day or two before, there had been yet another wreck there, of a wood-laden coaster during a snowstorm: "The cargo is totally lost, and the vessel has bilged."[5] The Whale's Back ledge lies on the Maine side of the Piscataqua River; when Upham received word of the legislation authorizing the lighthouse, he wrote to the Portland collector of customs requesting that the Maine Legisla- ture cede to the United States both Whale's Back ledge and Wood Island, which lies about four hundred yards upriver from Whale's Back. Because of their proximity to Portsmouth it was decided that Upham, rather than the Portland collector would have jurisdiction over the proposed lighthouse.[6]

A lighthouse was built and finally lit on Whale's Back by the end of 1830, but the process by which it was funded and a plan for it devel- oped exemplifies the shortcomings of the U.S. lighthouse system of this era. Upham was startled when he learned that Congress had authorized only $1,500 for the Whale's Back lighthouse. Records are incomplete, but this was perhaps the unrealistic sum estimated by the petitioners and submitted by Bartlett, although it may have been the result of a recommendation from Stephen Pleasonton. Upham wrote an edgy letter to Pleasonton, inquiring what kind of lighthouse could be built for such paltry amount.[7]

Soon after the passage of the bill, Pleasonton asked Upham to inspect the sites. Upham went to have a look with Representative Bartlett, U. S. Senator Levi Woodbury, and local shipmasters, pilots, and merchants. All agreed that a lighthouse was urgently needed at the river's mouth and that Whale's Back was the most logical site. (Whale's Back was one of the possible lighthouse sites that Joseph Whipple, back in 1795, had rejected as too difficult because it is submerged at half tide.)[8] They were also unanimous that the available funding would not begin to pay the cost of even a foundation for such a sea-battered site, let alone the lighthouse itself; there was no point in proceeding until there was an adequate appropriation. Upham described the difficulty of the site to Pleasonton and enclosed Woodbury's and Bartlett's letters supporting his opinion.[9]

Even before Upham reported on the site and the need for a greater appropriation, Pleasonton had sent him a description of a lighthouse and dwelling house "united." By "united" Pleasonton did not mean that the lighthouse structure would serve also as a place for the keeper to live, as was the case with the French Cordouan, the English Eddystone, and the Scottish Bell Rock lights—all offshore lights built on sea-washed ledges. He apparently had in mind a type of lighthouse that had been built elsewhere in 1827, consisting of a regular house with a lantern mounted on its roof. He may simply have had one of his clerks copy for Upham the description of such a lighthouse. If Pleasonton had an adequate chart of Portsmouth Harbor—and had looked at it—he would have seen that this kind of structure was out of the question for this site.[10]

Whale's Back ledge (later known as Whalesback and more recently as Whaleback) is bare for only a few hours either side of low tide, and is completely exposed to the full force of onshore gales. Around the British Isles, at such lighthouses as the 1759 Eddystone, designed by John Smeaton, and the 1811 Bell Rock, built by Robert Stevenson, there existed successful models for lighthouse construction on ledges similar to the Whale's Back. These, like the lighthouse built some thirty years later on

Minot's ledge off Boston Harbor, were constructed at great expense. Granite blocks, painstakingly cut with keys and dovetailed to lock them to each other in both vertical and horizontal planes, were cut, fitted, and assembled ashore and then dismantled and taken to their sites. There they were keyed and locked into their rocky positions, which had been carefully prepared to receive them.

In October 1827, the schooner *Fame,* of Dennis, Maine, bound for Salem, was totally wrecked on Whale's Back, and early in February 1828 the *Portsmouth Journal* reported yet another wreck there. The sloop *Aurora,* of Newburyport, "taking the wind ahead... bore up for this harbor...went on shore on Whales-Back at 12 at night, and bilged, and will probably be a total loss.—This is the second vessel that has been recently lost there for the want of a light-house. How many more wrecks must be made before Congress will make an appropriation for this object?[11]

An appropriation of eight thousand dollars in May 1828 made ninety-five hundred dollars available for the lighthouse. Pleasonton, apparently thinking that funding was now adequate, sent Upham a printed request for proposals for a lighthouse and keeper's house, for newspaper publication. It is probable that Winslow Lewis had prepared this. Pleasonton had asked him to provide standardized specifications for lighthouses of five different heights, from twenty-five to sixty-five feet high, with the idea that they could be pulled off the shelf for use at any location.[12] No copy of the specifications Pleasonton sent Upham has been found, but Upham thought them totally inadequate. He wrote Pleasonton that he was not going to publish the advertisement because the difficulties of the site made it necessary to "deviate from the usual form." Again he described the site:

> The Whale's Back as it is called, is the hump of a ledge of rocks... which is entirely covered at high water, and over which, when the wind is at any point between S. W. and N. E. the sea breaks with great violence. It is surrounded on all sides, except towards the main channel, by dangerous rocks, all covered at high, and many of them at low water... It is distant from Wood Island, which is the nearest place to it, 410 yards. From this view you will perceive the difficulty which will attend the erection of a Light house there, and the necessity of having a large and strong foundation. You will also observe, that it will be impossible to have a separate dwelling house for the Keeper, on the same rock, and the expediency of making

the lower part of the tower large enough to accommodate him,
at such times as he may be confined there, which in some seasons may be for weeks in succession, when it will be unsafe, if
not impossible, for him to leave.[13]

Furthermore, Upham wanted the light to have a "characteristic" different from other lighthouses in the area. He also suggested that it
become the principal harbor light, as the one at Fort Constitution was
too far upriver to serve this function adequately. Upham predicted that
once the Whale's Back light was built, a smaller one could be used at
the fort, perhaps incorporated into new walls then being proposed to
improve the fortifications. Finally, he questioned the adequacy of the
ninety-five hundred dollars available to build the structure. The stone
would have to be transported from a great distance on decked vessels,
and the delays that were inevitable at such a tide-covered, exposed site
would make the work costly for any contractor who undertook it.[14]

Pleasonton's failure to respond adequately to the Whale's Back
site's difficulties forced Upham to propose a two-part contract. The first
was to be for the lighthouse foundation pier on Whale's Back ledge and
a keeper's house, which he suggested be built on Wood Island, where
the contractors could work on it when the tide was too high at the lighthouse foundation site. The second part was for the lighthouse itself, to
be constructed on the foundation pier.[15]

He enclosed a general outline of the plan he had in mind. Some of the
features he proposed suggest that he had studied the illustration and
condensed description of Smeaton's Eddystone light in *Rees's Cylopaedia,*
available at the library of the Portsmouth Athenæum, of which Upham
was a proprietor. He doubtless also consulted local masons. Upham proposed a massive foundation pier, circular or octagonal in form, fifty feet
in diameter, to be built of split granite, doweled or dovetailed together
and laid in waterproof mortar, with a height of twenty feet to bring it a
few feet above high-tide level. Unlike Smeaton's Eddystone design, however, in which the entire base was a solid mass of interlocking, closely
fitted stones extending to the core of the structure, Upham proposed
walls of split-granite slabs six feet long and two feet square, with the
"interior filled with common stone of not less than one foot in diameter,
to be regularly laid in good mortar." The top of the foundation was to be
covered with split stones no smaller than those used for the walls. On
top of this would be built a forty-foot-high lighthouse tower twenty-six
feet in diameter at the base. This would be built like the one described

The Eddystone Lighthouse, from The Penny Magazine, *July 28, 1832. PA. The diagram shows a cross section of the lighthouse with its interlocking granite pieces is similar to the one illustrated earlier in Rees's* Cyclopedia *that may have influenced Timothy Upham's outline of plans for the Whale's Back lighthouse.*

in the printed advertisement Pleasonton had provided, but adapted to incorporate living quarters for the keeper. To create a distinguishing characteristic of two lights, he proposed building a second lantern into the walls of the tower, ten feet below the main lantern.[16]

A sure way to find out if an appropriation was adequate was to see if anyone would bid within the amount allowed, and requests for proposals advertised in the summer of 1828 produced no acceptable bids. In March 1829, $10,500 more was appropriated, making a total of twenty thousand dollars available—an amount Upham considered sufficient to build both the foundation pier and the lighthouse above it. The idea of a separate keeper's house on Wood Island was abandoned. The *Portsmouth Journal* credited Representative Ichabod Bartlett (1786–1853) with securing the needed appropriations. The paper praised him for championing causes dear to Portsmouth merchants: aids to navigation and lowering the protective tariffs on imports, which Portsmouth shipping interests believed crippled their businesses. In addition, he persistently,

Ichabod Bartlett (1786-1853) a New Hampshire member of the U. S. Congress, was instrumental in obtaining the first appropriation for the Whale's Back lighthouse. 1890 copy by Ulysses Dow Tenney of a portrait of Bartlett probably painted in the teens of the nineteenth century. Hood Museum of Art, Dartmouth College.

though unsuccessfully, advocated construction of a dry dock at the Portsmouth Navy Yard.[17]

One of collector Upham's last acts as superintendent of Ports-mouth district lighthouses was to advertise, late in March 1829, for three separate bids for the Whale's Back project: the foundation, the lighthouse itself, and the lighting apparatus. A model, scaled one-quarter inch to the foot supplemented the lengthy specifications.[18]

It is not known who provided the model and wrote the specifications. Stephen Pleasonton himself had no expertise in construction or engineering, and this project presented problems not dealt with in existing lighthouse specifications. It is possible that he asked Winslow Lewis to provide them based on Upham's rough outline. There were some changes in dimensions and more detail, but Upham's concept of a hollow foundation pier filled with "common stone" was unfortunately perpetuated in the final specifications.[19]

The specifications provided by Pleasonton called for a foundation pier two feet narrower and two feet higher than Upham's proposal. Upham's suggestion of dovetailing the stones was abandoned. All the stones of the pier were to be doweled together with white flint or beach stones not less than four inches in diameter. The uppermost tier of the foundation pier was to consist of granite capstone slabs twelve feet long, to be secured to the third tier from the top with iron clamps. Roman cement was to be used to bed the upper four tiers of stonework. As Upham had originally proposed, the hollow interior of this pier was to be filled with "common square stones, regularly laid" and topped off with split granite at least six inches thick, laid in Roman cement.

Upham, well aware of what had happened to the mortar at White Island lighthouse built nine years earlier, had requested Roman cement, sometimes called hydraulic or waterproof mortar. John Smeaton had described this hydraulic mortar in 1759. Made from relatively "poor" lime containing a high proportion of foreign matter, it was supposed to harden underwater and was thus considered well suited for masonry structures such as piers, docks, and seawalls, as well as for lighthouses that were submerged or exposed to moisture for any length of time.[20]

The specifications called for a light tower rising forty feet above the foundation pier, circular in cross section, graduating from twenty-six feet in diameter at the base to ten and a half feet at the top, with the walls diminishing in thickness from four feet at the base to eighteen inches at the top. Granite, the full depth of the walls at each point, "dressed or hammered so as to lay fair," was to be pointed with Roman cement. The lantern platform would rest on an arched form built at the top of the tower, with the platform itself consisting of either six-inch-thick granite or four-inch-thick soapstone slabs, the joints filled with lead. An opening, or scuttle, at one side of this platform would provide access to the lantern mounted on the platform. In the interior of the structure, a trapdoor in the floor of the first floor was to lead down to a shallow basement, four feet high, for storage of four forty-gallon water casks of white oak. Above this basement, the tower would consist of four eight-foot-high stories, with brick flooring laid over the planking on the first and fourth floors. Because the lighthouse was to serve as a dwelling for the keeper, the two lower stories, each divided into two rooms, were to be lathed and plastered. In one of these was to be a cooking stove, "of the size of James' patent #4."[21]

The specifications called for an octagonal iron lantern similar to the one at White Island, with double-thick, eight-by-ten-inch glass panes set into an iron framework, and an iron balustrade. The second light Upham requested would be displayed from a second iron lantern, actually three eighths of an octagonal lantern, of "sufficient size to admit six lamps and reflectors." This lantern, ten feet below the principal lantern, would rest on four iron bars, braced against the exterior wall of the light tower with additional iron bars. Access to this second lantern would be from the fourth floor, through an opening with a pointed arch cased with soapstone.[22]

This secondary lantern was an economy-minded attempt to create for Whale's Back lighthouse a double light characteristic to distinguish it from both the single fixed white light at Fort Constitution and the revolving red and white lights exhibited at White Island. A similar attempt to provide twin lights at low cost was part of 1827 alterations to an existing lighthouse at Scituate, Massachusetts. There, a second set of lamps was placed in a room below the main lantern, to shine through a range of four windows placed close together on the seaward side. Neither at Whale's Back nor at Scituate did the double light prove successful, however. An 1842 examination revealed that these two lights were so close together that within a few miles they merged and appeared as a single light.[23]

The diameter of the foundation pier would be over twenty feet more than the diameter of the lighthouse itself, creating a ten-foot-wide platform encircling the lighthouse. The specifications called for an iron ladder up the side of the foundation pier, and davits for hoisting onto the platform small boats and supplies—food, coal or wood for the stove, oil for the lamps, and water.

A clause in the specifications published in the *New-Hampshire Gazette* recognized the difficulty of the site and appeared to permit a degree of flexibility in fulfilling its terms: "If by reason of the exposed situation, the proposed plan should be found defective or insufficient for the purpose intended, the contractors are to make such additions or alterations, as may be required, on receiving therefor a reasonable compensation, not exceeding the actual expense."[24]

A Model of the Light-House, graduated on a scale of one fourth of an inch to the foot, may be seen at the Custom-House.

In the Proposals the sum required for building the foundation, and that for the Light House and fixtures must be stated separately. The Superintendant will reserve the right to make such alterations, as may in the progress of the work be found necessary, either for its security or convenience, which shall not on the whole, increase the expense to the contractor. And if by reason of the exposed situation, the proposed plan should be found defective or insufficient for the purpose intended, the contractors are to make such additions or alterations, as may be required, on receiving therefor a reasonable compensation, not exceeding the actual expense. The whole to be completed in a substantial and workmanlike manner on or before the fifteenth day of October next, to the satisfaction of the Superintendant.

Detail of specifications for Whale's Back lighthouse, providing for deviation from them if warranted by the difficulty of the site, published in the New-Hampshire Gazette, *7 April 1829.*

One impact of the acrimonious election campaign of 1828 which made Andrew Jackson president, was the wholesale replacement of federal officeholders after years of Republican presidencies. Timothy Upham was naturally a casualty. The pro-Adams *Portsmouth Journal* was indignant that he was not permitted to stay in office for the few remaining months of his appointment, and was "ordered to deliver the keys of his office to his successor, even before that successor had in all respects become qualified to receive them." The new collector was John P. Decatur, an ardent supporter of Jackson, who had been keeper of the stores at the Navy Yard. Isaac Hill, of Concord, engineered Decatur's appointment, against the wishes of Portsmouth Democrats. Decatur was named after Congress had recessed, and had not been confirmed by the Senate. Upham, who had campaigned actively for Adams, had been smeared by accusations that he had been involved in smuggling during the War of 1812. Politics cost him not only his job but also the usual commission accorded collectors on the cost of new aids to navigation—in his case on the cost of building Whale's Back lighthouse.[25]

In April 1829, before his removal from office, Upham received several proposals. One came from partners in Quincy, Massachusetts, whose combined bids for the foundation and lighthouse totaled $24,800; another from two Boston men, for $27,770; and a third from three local men—William Palmer (who had been one of the contractors for White Island lighthouse), Joshua Johnson, and Samuel Shackford, for $23,675—all above the twenty thousand dollars available. The Boston partners' bid for the foundation pier alone was more than $21,000. Everyone except Palmer dropped out of the running at this point, including his erstwhile partners Johnson and Shackford. By early May, Palmer had found another partner, Daniel Haselton, and on May 12 they signed a contract with the new collector of customs, John Decatur, to construct both the foundation pier and the lighthouse for $19,400.[26]

Daniel Haselton (1795-1852) was born in Suncook, a small town south of Concord, the state capital. Daniel spelled his last name differently than his father, James Hazeltine, a master bricklayer who had worked on many buildings in Portsmouth in the early nineteenth century. When he was old enough, Daniel began to work with him; another son, Ira, became a metalworker. Daniel married a Portsmouth woman in 1821. The couple's only child was born the next year in Concord, where Haselton was evidently then working. By the mid-1820s, he was back in Portsmouth, involved in constructing the brick Baptist church that once stood the

Daniel Haselton, one of the two contractors for building the Whale's Back lighthouse. Photo courtesy of Rachael Wolford.

corner of Middle and State Streets. After working with Palmer on the
Whale's Back lighthouse and the Newburyport Customs House in the
mid-thirties, Haselton moved south to New York City. There he worked
on a Dutch Reformed church and was also contractor for the lighthouse
at Robbin's Reef in New York Harbor, another tide-covered site. He later
worked in Panama; he died in Florida.[27]

Palmer and Haselton were apparently skilled masons, but the
Whale's Back ledge site presented problems that few, if any, American
builders had encountered—although Palmer, as one of the contractors
for White Island lighthouse, must have become aware of the problems
that had arisen with the mortar used there. Like many of the structures
built during the Pleasonton era, the lighthouse Palmer and Haselton
built on this ledge was seriously flawed. The prime culprit was the meager appropriation: It did not permit use of the construction techniques
the site cried out for, such as were used at the Eddystone, but which
were more labor-intensive and thus much more costly. Furthermore, neither Upham, whose suggestions formed the basis for the detailed specifications issued by Pleasonton's office, nor Pleasonton himself, who had
the authority and the responsibility to see that they were adequate, had
the expertise to design a lighthouse, especially for a site as difficult as
Whale's Back. Later critics blamed collector Decatur and the contractors
for "fraudulent" construction; Decatur in turn blamed his predecessor
Timothy Upham for the plans. The published specifications themselves
were bound to create problems, regardless of who was Portsmouth customs collector. It is not clear who prepared them, though it is tempting
to attribute them to Winslow Lewis, on whom Pleasonton depended
heavily for technical advice.

Regardless of the contentious political situation, collector Decatur
seems to have been conscientious in fulfilling his responsibilities as collector of customs and superintendent of lighthouses for the Portsmouth
district. In May 1829, he announced the placement of several new or
replacement buoys to aid navigation in local waters. These were minor
in size and cost, but important to mariners.[28]

The contract terms for the lighthouse, however, which he had inherited, must have been a major concern for Decatur. He was uneasy about
the responsibility of overseeing the work, and early in June wrote to
Pleasonton: "It will be of very great importance to have some competent
person to superintend the building of the Light House, and particularly, the laying of the foundation. If such a suggestion meets with your

approbation, I shall be pleased to receive your instructions to that effect, stipulating the compensation to be allowed." The assignment went to a "Mr. Blasdel," probably Abner Blaisdell, a Portsmouth mason.[29]

Contractors Haselton and Palmer used nearby Wood Island for their base of operations, probably bringing the needed granite down-river from quarries near Durham. Before the first tier of the foundation was laid, a man identified only as "Mr. Rogers" visited the Whale's Back site with collector Decatur to confer with him and the contractors. (Whether Mr. Blasdel was involved in the conference is not recorded.) Rogers was concerned that the individual granite slabs of the first tier of the structure were not even to be fastened to the ledge. He also predicted that the stone dowels specified for the upper tiers of masonry would rotate with the force of the seas and contribute to the destruction of the foundation. He advised copper-bolting the first tier to the ledge and substituting copper bolts wedged with granite wherever the specifications called for round flint beach-stone dowels. The partners had been worried too, and Decatur arranged with them to do the copper bolting. The terms of the verbal agreement made that day on Whale's Back ledge were so ambiguous that the contractors later had to petition Congress to recover their extra expenses.[30]

Decatur made another change to the foundation pier design. He had the contractors build an inner wall to broaden the surface of the granite foundation walls on which the lighthouse itself was to rest. Otherwise, all but the outer nine inches of the lighthouse walls would bear on the common stones packed into the center of the circular foundation, rather than on the more solidly built outer foundation walls.[31]

The entire lighthouse was to have been finished by October 15, but in mid-September the contractors wrote to Decatur asking for an extension until the following summer. They wrote that during June, work on the lower tiers of the foundation had been possible for only three or four hours per day because eight or nine feet of water covered the ledge at high tide, and because of the "Powerful Sea Continually breaking over the Ledge." By mid-September they had built the foundation to fourteen feet and promised to finish it before stopping work until spring of 1830.[32]

Before the contractors wrapped up work for the season, a violent storm struck on October 31. This was the same storm that broke onto White Island lighthouse, tearing off shingles and smashing glass in the lighthouse lantern. The next edition of the weekly *New-Hampshire Gazette* reported much damage to shipping all along the coast, but boasted that with one exception there had been none in Portsmouth Harbor, either to the vessels at the wharves or to those taking shelter in the lower harbor. The exception was a small vessel loaded with stone, perhaps Haselton and Palmer's, that parted her cable and went ashore at New Castle, apparently with little damage.[33]

Meanwhile, a political storm was brewing for collector Decatur. Portsmouth Democrats had been angered by Isaac Hill's support for Decatur over their candidate, Abner Greenleaf. In an obvious attempt to discredit Decatur, Thomas B. Laighton, secretary of the Portsmouth Democratic Committee, and Ezra Young, a Portsmouth tanner and cordwainer, wrote to Treasury Secretary Samuel Ingham late in October asking a question to which they probably already knew the answer: Had the Treasury Department authorized any deviations from the lighthouse contract? Decatur soon heard from Ingham. From Decatur's reply, it is apparent that he had not cleared the changes with Washington. He claimed, probably correctly, that the structure would not stand if the specifications had been followed exactly, and took the opportunity to blame the problems on "the plan of Mr. Upham."[34]

The disgruntled Portsmouth Democrats mounted a concerted campaign to persuade President Jackson to rescind Decatur's nomination or, failing that, to have his nomination rejected in the Senate. In January 1830, at a meeting of Portsmouth Democrats, one thousand of them voted to sever all connections with Decatur, leading to a brawl with fifty of Decatur's loyal customs house workers. By the end of March, the Senate had rejected Decatur's nomination, and in April William Pickering was appointed to replace him.[35]

Work on the lighthouse resumed in the spring of 1830. By early June it became evident that without another departure from the specifications, the lamps in the secondary lantern could not be lit because the design did not account for the slope of the tapered lighthouse walls. Lime mortar for bedding the stones of the lighthouse, paint for the cranes and boat davits, and guard rails for the iron ladder had been omitted from the specifications and had to be added. (The ironwork for the lanterns, cranes, davits, railings, and ladder, and the copper stove pipe may well have been supplied by Daniel Haselton's brother Ira, though there is no record of this.) By mid-August, the lighthouse was complete except for the lighting apparatus.[36]

The specifications called for ten patent lamps and reflectors for the upper lantern, with provision for two more to be added later, and six for the lower lantern; eight ninety-gallon tin oil butts; and "all the neces-sary apparatus in the same form and manner and of the same mate-rials as the Light Houses in the United States have been fitted up by said Winslow Lewis, with the addition of Black's patent heater for conducting the heat of the lamps to the oil." Not surprisingly, the eight-hundred-dollar contract for the lighting and other apparatus went to Winslow Lewis; it was signed in June. Typically, Lewis had refused to accept an addition to the contract, requested by Pleason-ton, that each reflector have seven ounces of pure silver on it, as had been specified in the request for bids but for some reason had been omitted from the actual contract.[37]

Samuel Hascall was appointed keeper at an annual salary of five hundred dollars. Pickering announced the September 16, 1830, lighting of Whale's Back light in the Portsmouth papers. The notice reported the sixty-eight-foot height of the lighthouse, described its two fixed white lights, one ten feet below the other; and gave its position and bearings from the other lights and buoys in the vicinity.[38]

In spite of the political turmoil surrounding his appointment, William Pickering, the new collector, appears not to have been swept up by accusations by fellow Democrats that Decatur had been wrong to order changes in the specifications. One of Pickering's earliest let-ters to Pleasonton urged that Palmer and Haselton be paid for the extra expenses involved using copper bolts and broadening the walls of the foundation pier, as well as for those alterations to the lighthouse tower made under his own supervision, writing, "The alterations were absolutely necessary and the charges I believe to be fair, as they have received the sanction of Mr. Blasdell who was appointed to inspect the erection of the building."[3]

After he was replaced, Decatur had successfully persuaded Pleason-ton to reimburse him $100 for the copper bolting of the foundation, reminding him of the clause in the contract permitting him to make alterations because of the difficulty of the site:

> It is the opinion of every person capable of judging and who witnessed the tremendous gales of November and March last, (when the sea broke from fifty to sixty feet above the top of the foundation) —that the whole superstructure would have gave away, had it not been for the copper bolts and particularly those used in fastening the large bottom stones to the ledge.[40]

Whale's Back lighthouse, photo taken at some time after the installation of a Fresnel lens in the lantern in late 1850s. NARG26.

Why Decatur asked to be reimbursed one hundred dollars but did not advocate reimbursing the contractors for their extra expenses is not clear. Pleasonton refused to pay Palmer and Haselton for copper-bolting the foundation. He argued that Decatur had written him that the partners had agreed to do the work at their own expense. No copy of such a letter from Decatur has been located.

The contractors petitioned Congress in 1832. Their submissions to the Committee on Claims included Samuel Gerrish's bill of $288.47 for the copper bolts and testimony by two of the workers present on Whale's Back ledge when it was decided to add the copper bolts. Samuel Pray and John Meserve testified that Decatur had told the partners, "Government would do what was right." Portsmouth stonecutter Samuel Treat testified as to the labor needed to drill the bolt holes, making allowances for the fact that it was expensive "tide work." The committee recommended paying the partners $778 for their extra labor and materials; they were finally paid, but not until 1841.[41]

The conditions at Whale's Back ledge are in many ways similar to those at the infamous Minot's ledge off Boston Harbor, although Whale's Back is not so far offshore. A short-lived, and fatal, iron-pile lighthouse was built on Minot's ledge it 1850, and the stone lighthouse that replaced it in 1860 is often cited as the earliest successful American example of a masonry lighthouse built on a site bare only at low tide and exposed to the unobstructed, pounding force of the sea during storms. Whale's Back lighthouse preceded it by thirty years. Though seriously flawed, and despite many emergency repairs and periodic dire predictions that it would topple in the next big storm, Whale's Back light was manned for forty-two years, until a replacement was built next to it in 1872.

Collector William Pickering (1778–1850), a Harvard-educated native of the Piscataqua region town of Greenland, was a lawyer who served as state treasurer from 1816 to 1829. He was less tolerant of his predecessor's handling of repairs to the boatways at White Island than of the situation at Whale's Back, though his criticism was really directed at the Treasury's policy of always accepting low bids for projects. Pickering reported that the ways at White Island had been carried away in a storm because the repairs had been done improperly "by the most unsuitable person," who happened to be the low bidder. The keeper then had to moor his boat off the island—with the result that in a March storm the boat parted its mooring and had been "entirely stove to pieces" on another island. He asked Captain Thomas Shaw of the revenue cutter *Portsmouth* to look at the boatways at Boon Island, which had escaped damage in the gales of the past season. Shaw recommended building similar boat ways at White Island. Actually, the Boon Island boat ways, which had been rebuilt in 1829, were destroyed in 1835 and periodically thereafter, as were the White Island boatways.[42]

A New Lighthouse for Boon Island

In 1831, the cutters of the U.S. Revenue Marine were given the duty of cruising offshore in winter to help vessels in distress. They were also authorized to visit island lighthouses within their cruising grounds to check on conditions and offer help if needed. Even before the 1830s, collectors of customs used the cutters to supply these lighthouses with materials and workmen for building and repair projects and necessities not provided by the oil contractors. The oil contractors arrived once a year with fresh supplies of oil, lamp chimneys, cotton wicking, and other specialized lighthouse equipment.[43]

In the late 1820s, at Boon Island, the words "Came heare the Cutter" appear periodically in a log kept by lightkeeper Eliphalet Grover. The Portland-based revenue cutter *Detector* delivered coal, paint and lime for whitewashing, sails and boats to replace storm-damaged ones, window glass, and lumber, nails, and hardware necessary for making repairs.[44]

The revenue cutter *Portsmouth*, formerly *Hiram,* was assigned to the Portsmouth collector's district in the summer of 1829 and occasionally stopped at Boon Island, perhaps in response to a signal from Grover. The *Portsmouth* was described as "a sharply built vessel of 60 tons burden with a narrow deck and a ten foot draft," not at all suited to winter cruising in rough weather. Her captain, Thomas Shaw (1774-1838) was a highly competent master, having racked up an impressive record of success in command of privateers during the War of 1812 and after the war was master of the ship *Izette*. In January 1831, customs collector Pickering reported to the treasury secretary that the revenue cutter *Portsmouth* had arrived in Portsmouth Harbor so burdened with ice on her rigging that she would not have survived high seas offshore. The cutter's principal mission, to assist vessels in distress off shore, was hampered because

in freezing, stormy winter weather she often had to put into port at night. Shaw's request for a vessel more suitable for winter offhsore cruising was fulfilled two years later. He was given command of a new revenue cutter, *Madison,* one of a class of more substantial schooners built in the early 1830s.[45]

Thomas Shaw (1774-1838), master of the revenue cutters Portsmouth *and* Madison *in the late 1820s and early 1830s. Shaw had been a successful privateer. The portrait is an early 1820s copy by Samuel F. B. Morse from a late 1790s miniature by an unknown English artist.* PrC.

The Revenue Cutter Hamilton. *Painting by Robert Salmon. The location is unknown, as is the occasion. Of the early 1830s class of revenue cutters that included the Portsmouth-based* Madison *and the Portland-based* Morris, *she was assigned to Boston and made an occasional appearance in Portsmouth Harbor.* PEM.

The lighthouse built on Boon Island in 1811 withstood the elements for barely twenty years. Considering the imperfect American expertise in building offshore lighthouses, the penurious allocations of that time, and the violence of storm and tide visited almost annually on the island, it is remarkable that it stood so long. Grover's log noted the deteriorating condition of the iron sash of the lighthouse lantern on January 25, 1828: "Part of the Sash of the lanton Rusted of and came Down." Panes of glass in the lantern had to be replaced frequently.

At the end of October 1829, the tower took a terrible beating in the worst storm Grover had endured in more than thirteen years as light-keeper. The entire island was under water for four hours, forcing Grover and his family to take refuge in the light tower. Small stones in the foundations of both the lighthouse and the dwelling were washed out. According to Grover's log, Captain Thomas Shaw arrived in the revenue cutter *Portsmouth* eight months later. Shaw must have carried news of the state of the lighthouse to the Portland collector, who at that time was responsible for the Boon Island light. In August, *Detector* delivered new iron sash for the lantern, along with Portland blacksmith Jonathan Knight and his helper. In September, the cutter brought a new roof for the lantern, but it must have been obvious that these were stopgap measures. There seems to be no factual basis for the tale that the entire top of the tower was swept away in a storm; if Grover's log is to be credited, he kept the light shining except for the eleven days when the lantern roof and sash were being replaced.[46]

The building of a replacement for this failing lighthouse illustrates an almost total avoidance of responsibility by the Portland customs collector. A contract was signed on March 31,1831, between collector John Chandler and "Seward Merrill of Gorham, Maine, Esq." for building a new light tower about fifteen feet taller than the old one. The specifications were probably the standard ones for a fifty-foot-high lighthouse that Winslow Lewis had prepared for Fifth Auditor Pleasonton. For twenty-nine hundred dollars, Merrill was to build an undressed stone lighthouse, circular in form, tapering from a diameter of twenty feet at the base to ten at the top, with the thickness of the walls graduated from four feet to two. Hammer-dressed stone was specified for the sills and lintels of the door and the three windows of the tower. "Roman Cement" was specified for pointing the joints on the outside of the tower, but waterproof mortar was not required for laying the stone, using simply "the best of lime mortar." The contract did require that sand used "will never to have been wet with salt water," and that fresh water should be used for mixing the mortar. Soapstone slabs four inches thick, with seams "leaded" with the molten metal, were to be used for the lantern platform, instead of the iron sleepers, covered with sheet iron and sheet copper used for the old tower platform.[47]

For the octagonal lantern, the contract specified iron posts two inches square, inserted and anchored into the stonework to a depth of four feet. The lantern would have eleven-by-twelve-inch double-thick panes from the Boston Glass Manufactory, twenty-four lights per sash. On the outside of the lantern, an iron balustrade four rather than two feet high, as previously, would provide more security for whoever washed the windows and did the annual painting of the ironwork.[48]

The contract called for a circular staircase "connected with a sufficient center post" and "guarded by a good strong railing." No paint colors had been specified for the wood and metalwork of the earlier lighthouse, and no whitewash for the stone of the tower. At this new lighthouse, as at White Island, the domed copper roof of the lantern would be painted black and the window frames and woodwork white. Finally, to enhance the usefulness of the lighthouse as a daymark, the outside as well as the inside walls were to receive two coats of whitewash.[49]

The lantern would accommodate five more lamps and reflectors than the old one. Merrill was to provide for the lantern twelve patent lamps with fourteen-inch reflectors, "to have six ounces of pure silver in each," with "all the necessary apparatus (tin butts for keeping oil, excepted) in the manner, as to form, as the Light Houses of the United States have been fitted up by Winslow Lewis." Presumably Merrill would buy these items from Lewis. If they were usable, Merrill could take the glass, railing, ventilator, and vane from the old lighthouse, but they would have to be removed immediately before installation on the new one, so that the light would be interrupted as briefly as possible.[50]

On May 6, 1831, Eliphalet Grover wrote in his log, "Came heare the Contractor to Build the New Light house but could not land for the Want of Boat." The one provided Grover by the government had been unusable since being battered in a storm the previous July, and was not replaced until the next month. The next day Grover noted the arrival of the Portland cutter with building materials. It is not clear how frequently, if ever, contractor Merrill was on the job site during construction. Grover did not record any visits by him until the work was done, but it was his habit to omit references to specific people. A crew of masons must have arrived at the same time as the materials. On that day Grover wrote in his log, "Commenced superintending."[51]

Eliphalet Grover was a sea-wise, independent, and resourceful man, and a careful craftsman with a knowledge of carpentry, but his understanding of masonry was evidently sketchy and it seems odd that he was given this responsibility. Recalling the building process in 1843, he remembered placing a French five-franc piece under the first stone laid on May 31 at the new site, just south of the existing lighthouse, for good luck. He also remembered being unhappy with the first batch of mortar the masons mixed to bed the stones of the tower, and asking them to put more lime in it. He also worried about the cement used for pointing the stone joints once the tower was finished. He recalled that the workmen told him that the proper mix was half sand and half lime, but he was uncertain whether these were the correct proportions.[52]

Seward Merrill provided a new lantern and lighting apparatus at the additional cost of $375.56. The equipment was delivered on July 11, and on the twenty-first, Grover lit the lamps in the new lighthouse. The next day Merrill made an appearance and signed a receipt for the old lantern and apparatus, which he took away with him.[53]

Two weeks later, Eliphalet Grover sent a letter to Stephen Pleasonton, through the Portland Collector of Customs, requesting that Boon Island light be placed under the jurisdiction of the Portsmouth collector. As Portsmouth was only fourteen miles away and Portland forty-five,

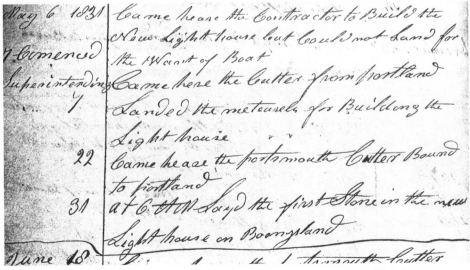

Eliphalet Grover's log entries regarding the building of a new Boon Island lighthouse. OYHS.

Grover wrote, it would make more sense for the Portsmouth collector and revenue cutter to serve his lighthouse. He pointed out that it had been "Nine years this Veary Day Seance there has Been a Superintendent Heare to see me on this island." He added a complaint about the stubby glass "tube glasses," or chimneys, that were supposed to be used in the summer for the lamps. He urged the use of "But one kind of tube glass and them nine inches in length for the short ones that is used in Summer Spiles all the Reflectors by burning of [sic] all the Silver of [sic] of the top of the Reflectors." [54]

The Portland collector concurred in the request to have Boon Island transferred to Portsmouth's jurisdiction, and by October 1, 1831, Boon Island light had been assigned to the supervision of William Pickering, collector for Portsmouth. Grover recorded much more frequent visits by the collector than was the case when the lighthouse was within Portland's jurisdiction. Pickering visited the lighthouse on July 9, 1832, and either he or his deputy, William Walker, made at least annual inspections. The cutters were an uncertain source of assistance, however, because during wartime they could be assigned duty with the Navy. In 1838, during the Seminole War, the Portsmouth cutter *Madison,* which replaced the *Portsmouth* in the early 1830s, was reassigned, and it then made more sense for the Portland Collector to have jurisdiction over Boon Island.[55]

Criticisms of the U. S. Lighthouse System

Criticism of the management of U. S. lighthouses began in the early 1830s and reached a crescendo by mid-century. In 1833, Secretary of the Treasury W. J. Duane, under whom Pleasonton worked, wrote,

> I am inclined to think the light-house system, as it is called, requires a thorough reform, both as to the style of lighting and the care provided by the keepers. I mean to omit no effort to place such an important and humane establishment upon a basis worthy of the country.

Duane had little time to pursue this goal because President Jackson soon replaced him with Levi Woodbury of Portsmouth, who became treasury secretary the next year. Edmund and George W. Blunt, publishers of the *American Coast Pilot* and successors to their father Edmund's publishing business, which by then was located in New York, corresponded at length with Duane and then with Woodbury.[56]

They wrote that there was currently no distinction, in terms of the brightness of their lights, among coast lighthouses, harbor entrance lights, and port and river lights. For lights "where the coast suddenly changes in direction, and has any dangerous shoal in its vicinity," they recommended the most powerful lights, like those installed by the French and English. They were highly critical of the practice of altering the characteristic of a lighthouse with little or no prior public notice. To avoid the danger of mistaking one light for another, they urged a year's notice before changes to an existing light were made. When new lighthouses were to be built, they advised at least six months' notice, including information on their bearings and distances from other lights. The Blunts also complained of the difficulty of getting from Stephen Pleasonton's federal lighthouse administration the information necessary to keep their *Coast Pilot* up to date. Not unreasonably, they felt that masters of vessels, particularly those returning to U.S. ports after an absence of months or—as was sometimes the case—years, needed to know what shoals or harbors the various lights indicated.[57]

The Blunts' complaints, though they reached Pleasonton, seem not to have affected the way local superintendents oversaw their lighthouses. Three years later, in September, 1836, only two days' notice was given in the Portsmouth newspapers before Winslow Lewis took down the old lantern at White Island in order to put up a new, larger one. The appropriation for the new lantern had been made back in July, and Daniel Drown, who succeeded William Pickering as collector in 1834, advertised for bids on July 11. On August 18, he signed a fifteen-hundred dollar contract with Lewis. The job required removing several feet of the top part of the tower itself to permit taking out the old iron posts anchoring the lantern in the masonry walls of the structure and inserting new ones. No newspaper announcement of the impending suspension of the light has been found in Portsmouth newspapers.[58]

Drown announced the completion of the new lantern at White Island and its re-lighting on October 22, 1836, after a suspension of six weeks. A typical week during this period saw the arrival of the ship *Margaret-Scott* from Turks Island in the West Indies and the brig *Aquila*, from St. Ubes, Portugal, both laden with cargoes of salt for preserving fish; the brig *Hopkins* from Philadelphia with coal; the schooner *Convoy* from New York with corn and flour; the Freeman brothers' schooner *Tabitha* on her regular weekly run from Wellfleet, Massachusetts with oysters; and packets—seven schooners and a sloop—on regular trips from

Boston, Salem, Philadelphia, and ports down east. Innumerable other vessels passed coastwise without putting in to Portsmouth. As the Blunts wrote of the White Island lighthouse in 1837,

> This is a very important light for vessels bound to Portsmouth from Europe and the West Indies; they often run for and make this light...Previous to the erection of this light, many deplorable shipwrecks took place on the rocks and shoals surrounding this dangerous group [of islands].[59]

Although Collector Drown had known of the imminent work at White Island since July, and perhaps earlier, he was evidently more concerned with people carving initials on the shingles of the lighthouse at Fort Constitution than with timely advanced notice that White Island light was to be extinguished. Early in August 1836 he announced a reward for information leading to the conviction of "persons who may deface the lighthouse at Newcastle, by cutting letters or figures thereon."[60]

Edmund and George Blunt continued their campaign for improvements to the lighthouse system, writing long letters to Levi Woodbury at the Treasury Department and rallying the support of shipmasters to their position that European lights were better organized and administered. Perhaps to impress Woodbury that problems existed in his own home port, they wrote in 1837 that the keeper of White Island light was frequently absent without authorization, leaving the care of the light "under charge of a female." The Blunts did not name the keeper, but he was Joseph L. Locke, who had held the post since 1830. According to the Blunts, the Portsmouth collector had tried, unsuccessfully, to have him replaced. The Blunts also criticized the quality of oil provided for the lamps; they charged that a vessel had to be sent the previous winter to Boon and White Island lights with charcoal for the stoves that kept the sperm oil from congealing in the lighthouse lanterns.[61]

The Blunts also argued that Stephen Pleasonton accepted without question Winslow Lewis's assessment as to the distance from which the various lights could be seen. Pleasonton claimed that Portsmouth Harbor Light could be seen for twenty-four miles, White Island twenty-seven miles, and Boon Island twenty-five miles. The Blunts showed that even if the lights themselves were of the greatest possible brilliance, visibility at these distances would have been physically impossible because Lewis failed to take into account the curvature of the earth and the height above sea level of the lighthouse lanterns. In the

1840s, after Lewis had made improvements to the lanterns and apparatus of Portsmouth area lights, a report showed that Portsmouth Harbor light was visible for 13.36 miles and the White and Boon island
lights only 12.69 miles each—only half the distances reported by Lewis.
Whale's Back light, which was supposed to be the principal light for
vessels entering Portsmouth Harbor, had a range of only eleven miles,
more than two miles less than the light upriver at Fort Constitution.[62]

In 1837, in the face of mounting complaints, Congress attached to
appropriations for new aids to navigation the condition that each site
was to be examined by a board of naval commissioners. Twenty-two
officers were dispatched in revenue cutters. Captain Joseph Smith
was assigned to investigate proposed sites in northern New England
aboard the Portland revenue cutter *Morris*. Locally, Smith recommended against building a projected lighthouse at the Nubble, a tiny
island a stone's throw offshore from Cape Neddick in York, Maine.
Nationally, the board recommended against building some thirty
other proposed lighthouses.[63]

In their March 1838 report, the board expressed many reservations
about how decisions were made to build new lighthouses. Two months
later, Congress went a step further and passed a bill appointing a naval
commission to examine existing lighthouses and recommend modifications to the system of lighthouse construction and management. President Van Buren ordered the lighthouse system divided into eight
districts, with a naval officer assigned to survey each one. In the meantime, Congress voted to halt any construction until the results of the
survey were reported, a politically judicious move, given the financial
woes brought on by the Panic of 1837. The freeze affected many projects
for which money had already been appropriated. Among them were a
lighthouse for York Harbor, a monument to mark York Ledge, and a seawall or pier on the ocean side of Whale's Back lighthouse.[64]

The naval officers assigned to the survey were given little time to
complete their work: They were to report their findings in mid-Novem-
ber. On August 4, 1838, Lieutenant Thomas Manning was assigned to
survey the first district, which extended from Eastport, Maine, to
Ipswich, Massachusetts. He then had to make arrangements for transportation to the many Maine, New Hampshire and Massa-chusetts
lighthouses in his district.[65]

Doubtless in preparation for Manning's visit, there was considerable activity at Boon Island that summer. Early in August, workmen

arrived to point the masonry of the lighthouse and other buildings and
to whitewash them. Portland Collector of Customs John Anderson paid
a visit. (In 1838, Boon Island had been placed back under the jurisdiction of the Portland collector, perhaps because the Portsmouth revenue
cutter *Madison,* commanded by Captain William Howard, had been
sent to Florida for duty with the Navy.) In mid-August, Portsmouth Collector of Customs Daniel Drown announced in the Portsmouth papers
that a new lantern and set of lamps and reflectors would be installed
in the Portsmouth Harbor lighthouse at Fort Constitution. Winslow
Lewis and his crew did the work. The *Journal* complimented Lewis for
the brief period—three days—the light was suspended while this
improvement was being made. During this time, however, a lantern was
placed in one of the windows of the tower as a substitute, an indication
that some attention had been paid to the problem of providing a substitute light during repairs or installation of new equipment.[66]

It is unclear how many other improvements, cosmetic or otherwise,
were undertaken in preparation for Manning's inspection. He reported
that the Portsmouth Harbor, Boon Island, and White Island lighthouses were "in fine order. But Whale's Back light, he wrote,

> appears to be exceedingly unsafe for the keeper in a gale of
> wind; the force of the sea is so great that it shakes it to its foun-
> dation; it being built of stone, I think that it cannot stand long.
> I think that to build a sea-wall for its protection would cost, at
> least, $100,000... if a house were built upon an iron frame, on
> the hump which is about 15 or 20 feet from the present light...
> it would be perfectly secure. [67]

This suggestion foreshadowed by a decade the short-lived iron-pile
lighthouse constructed on Minot's Ledge off Boston Harbor.

Manning recommended against the proposed York Harbor lighthouse. Of the shipmasters he consulted in this harbor, only three
thought a lighthouse necessary, and he noted that while he was at York,
only two vessels entered, and they were of small tonnage. One of the
complaints he heard was that there was a confusing plethora of lights
visible along the coast of the first district. Off Portsmouth, he said, ten
were in sight at the same time: the twin lights at Cape Ann, Ipswich,
and Newburyport, the double light at Whale's Back, and the single ones
at Fort Constitution, at Squam Harbor (in Massachusetts), at White
Island, and Boon Island. Manning rejected as "impracticable" the stone
monument proposed for York Ledge. Instead he recommended an iron

"trivet," or tripod, for which holes could be drilled during the three hours per tide when the ledge was exposed.[68]

Manning made a number of general recommendations. He wrote that eight out of nine lighthouse keepers interviewed complained of the quality of the sperm oil the contractor delivered for winter use, and suggested that the government take over the responsibility of supplying oil and monitoring its quality.[69] The difference between "winter" and "summer" sperm oil was illustrated by an 1841 article about C. H. and A. H. Ladd's Portsmouth sperm oil factory:

> In winter, when the mercury is 10 or 12 degrees below the freezing point, the crude oil is sufficiently hard to be transferred to sacks, where it undergoes pressing, and about one-third part is separated in a limpid state—this is Winter oil. When the temperature is about 50 deg., the oil is again submitted to the press—and another run is made. After the summer oil expressed, the residuum is manufactured into candles.[70]

The oil supplied to lighthouses came from the New Bedford whale oil entrepreneurs who had a lock on the oil contracts to supply U.S. lighthouses. Their winter oil was pressed at a relatively high temperature—only one degree below freezing—which meant that it was apt to congeal in the winter.[71]

Lieutenant Manning thought the government should perform its own inspections of lighthouse lighting equipment and also recommended clearer distinctions among the many lights visible at any one time along the coast. His final complaint did not relate specifically to the lighthouse establishment, but to an important component in the array of navigational aids available to mariners. In the first district, he wrote, a "navigator on the coast is destitute of a correct chart; there is but one and that is unfinished... the only one available was made before the Revolution." He himself had to borrow and copy a chart for the coast between Portsmouth and Salem.[72]

In some of the other lighthouse districts, the 1838 naval surveyors were more detailed in their criticisms than Manning, but much of what they reported could have been written about the lighthouses on the New Hampshire and Maine coasts. In the second district, Lieutenant Edward Carpenter reported that the heavy iron bars of many lighthouse lanterns obscured a large proportion of light; that some lanterns had too many lamps, including some aimed toward the shore, where they served no useful purpose and wasted oil; that many lightkeepers found ways to supplement their salaries away from their lighthouses and were casual about how their lighthouses were maintained; and that the contractors who constructed lighthouses were "equally lacking" in "skill or fidelity."[73]

The most critical of the investigators was Lieutenant George M. Bache, who inspected the lighthouses between Newport, Rhode Island, and New York. He stressed that lighthouse appropriations were "not founded on an estimate made after having the proper site selected, and the plan of building calculated for it drawn up; but the building is made according to the appropriation and site... Unsuitable buildings have been erected in order to bring cost within the sum to be expended." Bache observed that lighthouses built before 1800 were often better than those constructed more recently. He attributed the problem to the lack of engineering expertise of the customs collectors, who had the responsibility for arranging for specifications, bids, and contractors. Bache thought that Fifth Auditor Pleasonton's staff should include inspectors and specialists with expertise in engineering and optics.[74]

The First Fresnel Lenses for the United States

At the time Congress authorized the naval survey, it also appropriated fifteen thousand dollars to purchase one French lighthouse lantern and two Fresnel lenses for trial use in U.S. lighthouses. In France, optically sophisticated lenses were officially approved to replace reflector lamps in 1825, after a successful trial in 1822 at the Cordouan light off the mouth of the Gironde River, the "flagship" of French lighthouses. By 1834, Fresnel lenses had been installed in twenty-nine of France's seventy-four existing lighthouses; by 1845, they were in 109 of the 151 lighthouses that had been built by then.[75]

The lenses were the invention of the brilliant physicist Augustin Fresnel (1788–1827). An engineer for the Bureau of Roads and Bridges that administered the French lighthouses, Fresnel was honored by the French Academy of Sciences for his studies of the diffraction of light and was appointed secretary of the French Lighthouse Commission. Fresnel's earliest design for lighthouse lighting equipment involved a series of separate prisms of ground and highly polished glass positioned around a horizontal axis to concentrate the light of a single lamp placed behind them. He later distributed more prisms above and below the central band of prisms. These prismatic lenses were designed and carefully positioned to capture, bend, and reflect the lamp's light, most of which had been wasted with the old reflectors.[76]

In addition to providing a more brilliant and directed light, this efficient lens had the potential for substantial economies in oil, as only a single (though larger) light source was required instead of the multiple lamps and reflectors used in each lighthouse lantern in the United States. Alan and Thomas Stevenson, engineers for the Scottish lighthouse system, incorporated Fresnel lenses into the reflector system that continued in use in the British Isles. Some of the Stevensons' improvements were incorporated into the French apparatus.

Augustin Fresnel (1788-1827), the French physicist whose development of lighthouse lenses brought dramatic improvement to the quality of the lights in Europe and eventually in the United States. © Smithsonian Institution.

By the 1840s, Fresnel-type lenses were being adopted by the Scottish lighthouse establishment, as well as by the Dutch, Swedish, Norwegian, Prussian, and Russian lighthouse systems. The United States did not participate in this exchange of technological improvements.[77]

It was Captain M. C. Perry, of the Navy, now remembered for opening Japan to trade, who was sent to Europe to place orders for the French lenses and lantern that Congress authorized. He was also ordered to study the lighthouse apparatus used in England and France. Perry's report added ammunition to the arguments for an overhaul of the U.S. lighthouse system. He favored the Fresnel lenses over the English parabolic reflectors, but found even the latter to be much superior to those used in the United States. The U. S. parabolic reflectors, provided by Winslow Lewis, were, he wrote, imperfectly formed and made of shoddy materials. Perry was especially impressed by the administration of the French lighthouses and the inclusion of engineers and optics specialists in their administration. He felt that customs collectors, especially in the major ports of the United States, had little time for inspections. He considered the shortcomings of the U. S. lighthouse system to be a manifestation of a national attitude to human life that bordered on callousness:

> It is a peculiarity of the people of this country, that a proper
> regard to the preservation of human life enters too little into
> the concerns of the every-day transactions of the community.
> We are constantly hearing the most melancholy disasters on
> board of steamers and in vessels approaching the coast, by
> which numerous lives are sacrificed, not so much to the
> inscrutable chances of ill-fortune proceeding from inevitable
> causes, as from the unpardonable negligence of those whose
> duty it should be to guard against these catastrophes. And so
> in regard to the care of lights which are established to guide
> the anxious seaman along the dangerous coast or into the dis-
> tant port. How responsible is the trust of those who undertake
> the charge, and yet how little is the trust regarded![78]

From an early-twenty-first-century perspective, it may seem puzzling that these reports, so critical of so many aspects of the American lighthouse system, did not bring about immediate and fundamental reform. But during the twenty years that the Democratic Party dominated national government, from 1829 until 1849 (with a four-year hiatus from 1841 to 1845, during the politically complicated Whig presidencies of Harrison and Tyler), there was a powerful bias against federal expenditures for public works such as canals, lighthouses, and river and harbor improvements. Most Democrats of the period felt such projects benefited primarily the mercantile interests that promoted them. Fifth Auditor Stephen Pleasonton, with a rigid, bare-bones outlook on federal expenditures for aids to navigation, had enough political support to carry him through the 1840s. For the Democrats of the New Hampshire seacoast, it must have been awkward to subscribe to the party line, as improvements to navigation helped not only merchants and shipowners but also the many working-class people whose livelihoods depended on a healthy maritime economy; in addition, adequate aids to navigation could save the lives of the many Portsmouth men who made their living at sea.

Lieutenant Manning, when he visited White Island light in the late summer of 1838, found it in good shape. His examination must have been cursory, because later that year, on October 29, Customs collector Daniel Drown announced that from and after that date the light would be suspended during repairs to the cranky revolving mechanism, but that a fixed red light would be shown to the southwest. These repairs were of short-lived effectiveness. Repairs were necessary again by the end of November, with a stationary red light again being shown.[79]

A New Lighthouse for the Whale's Back Is Proposed—and Rejected

One impossible-to-ignore situation was Whale's Back lighthouse. Even before the naval survey report was contemplated, Congress appropriated three thousand dollars for the "erection of a pier on the east side of Whale's Back light house, to secure it from the force of the waves," and added another seventeen thousand dollar appropriation for this purpose in July 1838. This total of twenty thousand dollars was put into the surplus fund, perhaps because the amount was inadequate for such a project. Lieutenant. Manning's estimate for a seawall sufficient to protect the lighthouse was $100,000.[80]

Writing five years later about the state of this lighthouse, Stephen Pleasonton claimed that his concern about its security led him to consult two men with impressive design and engineering credentials, architect-engineer Alexander Parris and Colonel Sylvanus Thayer of the Army Engineer Corps. Parris himself, however, stated that it was not Pleasonton but rather Portsmouth collector Daniel Drown who requested their opinion, though payment for their services must have been cleared with Pleasonton. Thayer and Parris reported that "no breakwater could secure the present building," and that the solution was a new lighthouse built on the principles of the Eddystone light.[81]

Sylvanus Thayer (1785–1872) was a career officer in the Army's Engineer Corps, and a specialist in harbor defenses. He was superintendent of West Point from 1817 to 1833 and may be best known for the reforms that dramatically improved its organization and academic standards. West Point, considered the first institution in the United States to provide formal training in engineering, began producing engineer officers who were involved in major civil engineering undertakings as well as strictly military projects. Later in the nineteenth century, many of them would be involved in lighthouse design.[82]

Alexander Parris (1780–1852), was a housewright early in his long career. While still in his twenties he established himself as an architect and later was involved in engineering projects. He worked in the Boston area as both architect and engineer, as well as in Maine and

New Hampshire. He was the architect of Boston's Quincy Market. In Portsmouth, Parris is remembered as the 1805 architect of St. John's Church. And from 1847 until his death in 1852 he was engineer at the Portsmouth Navy Yard. There he designed several buildings and oversaw extensive leveling operations and work on a seawall.[83]

Parris is known to have owned a book on lighthouse design by John Smeaton, designer of the Eddystone light. Working with the Boston engineering firm of Brown and Hastings, Parris prepared plans for a

Alexander Parris's plans for a proposed new lighthouse for Whale's Back Ledge. NARG26.

new Whale's Back lighthouse to submit to Pleasonton. The drawings for this never built lighthouse are preserved in the National Archives and bear a November 1838 date. The shaft of the tower is swept up sharply from the base in a curve like that of Smeaton's Eddystone light. Smeaton compared this form, and its strength, to a branch growing from the trunk of a tree. The force of the waves would be sent up the sweeping curve of the tower, and its horizontal impact on the structure thus diminished. A cross-section drawing shows that the interior blocks

Parris's cross-section view of the proposed lighthouse. NARG26.

of stone are all dovetailed to interlock and create a rigid mass, depending little upon mortar to hold them in place. Probably following instructions to perpetuate the existing light characteristic at Whale's Back light, Parris incorporated a lower, secondary lantern, later discredited as an effective distinction from lighthouses displaying single lights.[84]

The price tag for the proposed lighthouse was estimated at seventy thousand dollars. Congress refused to fund the project, and even Stephen Pleasonton was worried. He wrote, "I am in daily expectation of information that the present building has been demolished by the force of the seas."[85]

New Hampshire's U. S. Senator Franklin Pierce opposed the seawall expenditure to protect the lighthouse; it is not known if he had an opportunity to respond to the proposal for a new Whale's Back lighthouse. Pierce, like other Democrats—particularly those who lived inland—was a foe of expenditures for river and harbor improvements and aids to navigation on the grounds that they were not the federal government's responsibility. His position on funding the breakwater became a campaign issue twelve years later when he ran for the presidency.[86]

Although Alexander Parris's design for Whale's Back was never realized, he designed other Maine lighthouses that were actually built, four of them in Maine: Saddleback in 1839, Matinicus Rock in 1846,

New Hampshire's Franklin Pierce, whose opposition while a U. S. Senator to federal expenditures for river and harbor improvements and for a breakwater to protect the Whale's Back lighthouse did not prevent his election to the U. S. presidency in 1852. Appleton's Cyclopaedia of American Biography.

and Mount Desert Rock and Libby Island in 1848, according to Edward Zimmer's study of Parris. He also designed a lighthouse for Execution Rocks in Long Island Sound in 1847, built the following year.[87] Because none of these was on a site underwater at half-tide, their price tags were evidently more palatable. In 1840 and 1841, he was involved with engineer Gridley Bryant in the design of an important iron navigational aid—the monument marking York Ledge (see chapter 7). Parris's designs marked the first involvement by a professional engineer in the design of navigational aids for the United States since the Latrobes' work in the early nineteenth century.

A violent two-day southeast gale in January 1839 again dramatized the dangers of lighthouse keeping and the deficiencies of the lighthouses around Portsmouth. At White Island, waves crashed through the gully between the house and the light, sweeping away eighty feet of the covered passageway connecting them. Boon Island lightkeeper Eliphalet Grover wrote a hair-raising report of the impact of the storm there. On the first night, at high tide, the sea came up around the buildings; the next day at high tide the seas broke onto them; Grover and his family retreated to the light tower for safety, while the seas tore off the porch and front door of the house and gushed into the first floor. The wooden walkways between the buildings were swept away along with half the shingles on the old stone monument where wood was stored. Seas also came into the lower part of the light tower, strewing seaweed and shells. Later in the day, the wind shifted and lessened, and at low tide, according to a newspaper account presumably based on an account by Grover, "… some of the family ventured out and beheld an astonishing spectacle. Fragments of wood were scattered over the Island, and large rocks which had laid quiet for more than 20 years, were torn from their places." [88]

And at Whale's Back, the "sea broke up over the building very much the same as it is represented in the *Penny Magazine*, lashing the famous Eddystone light house." When the sea struck the foundation there were "shocks as that of sudden and heavy blows and a passing off with a shaking and quivering motion." The *New-Hampshire Gazette* wrote of the indefinite plans for Whale's Back, adding, somewhat optimistically, as it turned out, "Something, However, will probably be done this year for the security of the light house and the keeper and his family." [89]

The Eddystone light in a storm, illustration in The Penny Magazine *of July 1832.*

VII Eighteen-Forties Improvements at White Island, Buoys and Beacons, and the Investigation of 1842

*Those practically acquainted with its defects...
who... know by sad experience the difficulties and
dangers of navigation... seem to be of the opinion
that our light-house establishment is susceptible of
some improvement.*

—Report of I. W. P. Lewis, Civil Engineer, February 1843

WHEN THOMAS LAIGHTON, THE NEWLY APPOINTED keeper of
White Island lighthouse, arrived at his post in the fall of 1839, he discovered there were problems with the lighting apparatus, even though
the lantern had been replaced by Winslow Lewis as recently as 1836 and
repairs made to the revolving apparatus twice in 1838. Laighton wrote a
detailed report soon after his arrival and copied it into his journal:

> The internal apparatus and machinery of the Lighthouse require
> some attention. The reflectors are so much worn and otherwise
> injured that I should think quite one half of the light from the
> lamps is absorbed, besides they are unfitted to the revolving
> apparatus and cause such a dispersion of the rays of light as to
> lose a great portion of the effect they were intended to produce.
> The lamps also are much worn, bruised and otherwise injured, so
> much so that the regulating screws appended to them fail to pro-
> duce the intended effect. The machinery for turning the appara-
> tus connected with the lamps is cumbrous and constantly liable
> to disorder; indeed, the utmost care and attention are required to

keep it in motion at all, and except a new one is substituted, or
this is most thoroughly repaired, it will ere long become exceedingly difficult to continue the rotary motion of the lamps. [1]

About a year later, in December 1840, Winslow Lewis contracted to
provide, "as early in the approaching Spring, as the weather will permit," another even larger lantern for White Island and to fit it up with
new equipment, for the sum of thirty-six hundred dollars. Once again
the top of the old stone tower was removed. It was rebuilt in brick, this
time straight up rather than tapered. The contract specified a new
lantern at least ten feet in diameter and nine feet high (not counting its
domed, copper-sheathed roof), with a new soapstone deck at least fourteen feet in diameter. The new brickwork was sheathed with boards
and shingled and painted to match the lower part of the tower.[2]

The arrangements for construction answered earlier criticism of
the problems that arose for mariners when a light ceased operation
during repairs. During previous lantern installation, the light had
been doused for weeks; this time Lewis agreed to "keep a temporary
light of the same character" during installation of the new equipment.
An 1850 report by Jonathan Howland, the sperm oil contractor, contains a clue as to how this was accomplished. Howland referred to "a
second tower of wood" outside the stone lighthouse; it is likely that
the old lantern, lamps, and revolving mechanism were moved to this
structure while Lewis made the alterations, and such a structure may
have been in place when earlier repairs were made to the lighthouse
equipment in 1838.[3]

The new lantern took advantage of superior French technology in
glass manufacture, and was glazed with the "best French plate glass."
There were eight lights on each side. At twenty-four-by-twenty-one-
and-a-half inches, the panes were almost twice the dimensions of those
in the replaced lantern. Lewis provided fifteen of the "new, improved
lamps," and replaced the fourteen-inch reflectors with new twenty-one-
inch ones, each coated with fifteen ounces of pure silver, "said reflectors
to be formed upon a die." To rotate the lights, he also installed a new
clockwork, "agreeably to Willard's latest improvement." Lewis placed a
red, twenty-one-and-one-half inch square stained-glass panel in front of
the reflectors on one side of the lamp chandelier.[4]

The alterations and improvements made by Lewis were evidently
not the result of Thomas Laighton's report. They were made instead

to accommodate the projected installation of one of the two Fresnel lenses ordered by Congress in 1838 for trial in U.S. lighthouses. The lantern had to be enlarged to house the French lens, and both Pleasonton and Lewis would doubtless have wanted the best possible glass in the lantern and the highest-quality reflector lamps installed before French technicians arrived with Fresnel's magnificent optical apparatus. One of the imported lenses, of the largest and most powerful type (known as a "first order" lens) was slated for the Navesink Highlands on Sandy Hook in New Jersey, for the benefit of shipping in New York Harbor; the one destined for White Island was a revolving lens of the second order, nine feet high. The Isles of Shoals site had been chosen because it was "in the track of a great commerce, and in a region subject to that weather and fogs which will bring the power of the light to the severest test." The project was abandoned, however, after it was decided that the tower was not high enough above sea level to test the potential range of the Fresnel lens. The two lenses were installed in the twin towers at Navesink in 1841.[5]

At Navesink, modifications to the lanterns of the lighthouse, the cost of the Fresnel lenses, and their installation by a French technician imported for the purpose ran to about twenty-three thousand dollars. Congress had virtually imposed the installation of this equipment upon Stephen Pleasonton, who praised "the beauty and excellence" of their light in an 1841 report. "They appear to be the perfection of apparatus." But then the defensive fifth auditor went on to write that the Fresnel lens was "unfit for use in the United States, upon a large scale." He thought that the single, Carcel-type lamp was "very apt to get out of order and the light extinguished, if the keeper be not an intelligent mechanic and capable at all times of making the necessary repairs." [6]

Because of Pleasonton's negative opinion of the abilities of the lighthouse keepers in the system he superintended, along with his dogged loyalty to the reflector lamps introduced by Winslow Lewis in 1811, no other Fresnel lenses were installed in the United States until 1850. In that year, Congress ordered one placed at Sankaty Head on Nantucket Island and another at Brandywine Shoal in Delaware Bay. Adoption of the Fresnel lens throughout the U. S. lighthouse system had to await the end of Pleasonton's tenure as superintendent.[7]

On White Island, Thomas Laighton was concerned not just about the light but also about the covered walkway leading from the keeper's house to the lighthouse. Soon after his arrival, late in 1839, storms swept away most of the walk, and he recommended an improved design. He suggested a structure "more elevated so that the sea can discharge itself beneath it," which should be "securely clamp'd and knee'd off at the posts and braced with iron." Laighton also thought that a wall of masonry twelve to fifteen feet high on the east side of the walkway would "effectually prevent a recurrence of mischief which has two or three times happened" to the walkway. He wrote that even if a storm destroyed it, this wall would provide at least some protection for the keeper as he made his way to and from the tower. Emergency repairs were made in 1839 and 1840, but an early October 1841 gale again tore it away, along with some of the wood sheathing on the lighthouse.[8]

An entirely new, and successful, walkway structure was built in 1842. The builder, according to a subsequent account, was George W. Pendexter of Portsmouth. Collector of Customs John Sherburne, appointed after the Whigs captured the White House, gave Pendexter a free hand to build a structure that would endure, permitting him all the timber and iron he required. A total of two thousand dollars was made available by Congress for the purpose. The covered way built by Pendexter is visible in many images of White Island. His structure lasted for nearly forty years without any need for major repairs, surviving unscathed even the devastating April 1851 storm that swept across the low-lying midsection of Appledore Island and wreaked havoc all along the New England coast.[9]

The structure, most of which still stands, was ingenious, and a good example of pragmatic local inventiveness applied to an engineering problem. Unlike Jonathan Folsom's 1820 walkway, which was square in section, Pendexter's was triangular, providing a more stable form with less surface area vulnerable to the forces of wind and waves sweeping through the gully. Instead of building the covered passageway atop a series of vertical rubblestone piers, as Folsom had done, Pendexter devised a complex web of timber braces bolted at angles to the structure. These braces, which gave the walkway the distinctive appearance of a multi-legged creature, posed less resistance to the sea. It is entirely likely that Laighton's conception of a more elevated structure, "knee'd off and brac'd," influenced Pendexter's design. In August 1842, when Joseph Cheever succeeded Laighton as keeper; he signed a contract with collector Sherburne for eighty dollars to furnish supplies and to paint the lighthouse and the "new walk recently erected." [10]

The Port of Portsmouth in the 1840s

The revenue cutter *Madison,* based in Portsmouth since 1833, in September 1837 was being prepared for duty with the Navy along the east coast of Florida, and arrived in Key West in March 1838 under the command of Captain William A. Howard of Portsmouth. The *Madison* was returned to Portsmouth in October of that year to serve again as a revenue cutter. However, she was reassigned to Wilmington, Delaware in July 1840 and then transferred again to the Navy for temporary service in Florida.[11] The Portland-based *Morris* and one of the two Boston cutters were instructed to come into Portsmouth "occasionally." The *Portsmouth Journal* published an editorial plea for the permanent assignment of a cutter to Portsmouth:

> If the rapidly increasing tonnage of this port is not sufficient call for her services, the innumerable number of vessels from East and West that harbor here and that too in the worst weather should not be neglected.—Everyone who knows the difficult and dangerous navigation of the coast, are aware that this is the only safe and accessible harbour between Cape Ann and Cape Elizabeth that vessels can and dare run into in boisterous weather; or when storms are threatened... The interest of the revenue, the mariner, the owner and underwriter are all benefitted by it and call for it.[12]

In fact, there was good reason for the Treasury Department to reassign the *Madison*. Revenue generated at the port had sagged markedly in the 1830s. In the 1820s, the average value of goods imported yearly had been $306,000; in the 1830s it sank to $128,000 and in the 1840s to only $54,000.[13]

The number of vessels registered in Portsmouth had increased—but by only five vessels between 1834 and 1839, to 201 vessels, with an aggregate tonnage burden of 26,356. More than half of Portsmouth's vessels were involved in freighting to foreign ports from other U.S. ports. These averaged about 160 tons; those in the coasting trade averaged only sixty tons. The Portsmouth Directory, which published these customs house statistics, was at pains to note that of the vessels engaged in freighting to foreign ports, "Many... return home in the summer or fall, laden with foreign merchandise," and that the numerous vessels engaged in fishing in the summer were active in the coasting trade in the fall and spring.[14]

The next decade saw a development that further cut the number of vessels headed for Portsmouth Harbor. In June 1840, the "Marine Notes" of the *Portsmouth Journal* reported the arrival of the bark *Eliza* from Bristol, England. She was one of a number of vessels coming into Portsmouth with railroad iron for the Eastern Railroad line. By late 1840, the rails extended from Boston through Salem and Newburyport and into Portsmouth; by the end of the next year, they had been laid all the way to Deer Street near the Piscataqua. Late in 1842, the line was opened from Portland to the Portsmouth Bridge, with passengers and freight making the trip across the river in coaches and wagons. The same year, the trains of the Boston and Maine Railroad began arriving in Dover and other inland Piscataqua region towns.[15]

Reporting that the railroad would soon take the place of the steamer *Portsmouth,* which had provided regular passenger and freight service between Boston and Portsmouth, the *Portsmouth Journal* announced its sale in May 1840.[16]

To make matters worse, the harbor itself was getting some bad press. In 1841, the owner of the steamer *M. Y. Beach* stopped putting into Portsmouth regularly on her Portland-to-Boston run and publicized the reason in the Boston papers. It was not the imminent competition from the railroad, but rather "the dangerous rocks surrounding Portsmouth harbor." The *Journal* heaped scorn on the *Beach*. When the fifty-gun frigate *Congress* was launched at the Portsmouth Navy Yard in August, the steamers *Portland* and *Huntress* were on hand to escort the new vessel to her moorings. And then, "huffing and blowing as if out of breath with trepidation at the narrow escape from the dangerous rocks," came the steamer *M. Y. Beach* with spectators.[17]

The Narrows were indeed a cause for trepidation, however. They were a constriction in the river opposite Seavey's Island, where beyond the ledges off Goat Island the river took a right-angle turn north beyond Henderson's (or "Pull-and-Be-Damned") Point, which projected from Seavey's Island southward into the river. The rate of the powerful and treacherous current here was shown as seven knots in a chart published in Blunt's 1833 *Coast Pilot*. Local mariners, although scornful of those who found navigation past the narrows difficult, planned their passages carefully with a sharp eye to the stage of the tide and the direction of the wind.

The most persuasive of the arguments put forward in favor of reinstating a Portsmouth-based cutter was that the numbers of vessels passing Portsmouth from the eastward and southward were increasing steadily. Tonnage in Maine ports was doubling and sometimes tripling every decade, and Portsmouth was well situated to be an emergency shelter for coasters in distress. The *Portsmouth Herald* of November 15, 1845, noted forty-five coasters entering the lower harbor between Fort Constitution and Whale's Back lights to shelter on a single day.[18]

When seeking refuge during easterlies blowing from both northerly and southerly quarters, however, coasting vessels often found it impossible to make it into the principal anchorage, or, when the wind was easterly, into the lower harbor. In easterly gales they often parted their anchor cables and had to put to sea, sometimes with disastrous results. A case in point was the schooner *Maine,* of Bath. Bound from Wiscasset, Maine, to Boston in October 1841 with a cargo of wood, potatoes, and hay and seven passengers, she anchored about half a mile outside Whale's Back light, in heavy seas. The vessel's situation seemed so precarious that New Castle men went out in boats to offer assistance, but the master of the *Maine* refused their help. The anchor cable parted, and twelve hours later the schooner was driven onto Cohasset rocks off the entrance to Boston Harbor, and finally onto the beach. The *Maine* was a total loss, and five passengers, one seaman, and the captain's daughter perished. In this same storm another schooner, with no one aboard at the time, dragged her anchors and ended up on Squam Beach.[19]

A letter to the *Portsmouth Journal,* signed "W," pointed out that if the masters of these vessels had known of Little Harbor as a safe anchorage, lives and property would have been saved. In storms, a broken bar that partially blocked the harbor entrance kicked up a formidable line of breakers; without knowledge of the channel, most masters would hesitate to enter. The writer urged publishers of charts and sailing guides to provide this information. "W" did not mention, however, that there was barely three feet of water across the bar at low tide, nor that the harbor itself was so shoal in places that all but the smallest vessels would have to "ground out" at low tide.[20]

Another refuge from storms was Pepperrell's Cove, on the north side of the lower harbor, nearly opposite Fort Constitution. Here vessels could anchor relatively well sheltered from easterlies, but there were shoals and ledges at its entrance that only the knowledgeable could negotiate. By the early 1840s, a buoy had been placed to mark Logy Ledge near the cove's entrance, but unsophisticated methods of anchoring it made it susceptible to being pulled out of position.

In November 1840, the sloop *Rhoda and Betsey* from Portland, along with other coasting vessels accompanied by the revenue cutter *Morris,* entered the lower harbor of Portsmouth during an easterly gale, and took refuge in Pepperrell's Cove. When the gale shifted to the southeast, many of the vessels dragged their anchors and were in danger of being blown onshore. Their masters flew signals requesting the assistance of the *Morris.* Using its boats, the cutter, commanded by Captain Green Walden, helped a total of four vessels to get under way and anchor again in safer waters. Aboard the *Rhoda and Betsey* were the iron components of a new type of navigational marker destined not for Portsmouth Harbor, but instead for York Ledge.[21]

York Ledge Monument

York Ledge is nearly three miles offshore from York, and the site is especially dangerous because the irregular rock formations, about an acre in area, are covered at most tides. They are in an exposed position where storm seas create turbulent breakers. Vessels running afoul of these ledges were far from help. In the mid-nineteenth century, when most year-round residents still chose to build their houses in locations sheltered from coastal weather conditions, they were not always observed from the sparsely-settled shoreline. One of many wrecks on the ledge was reported by a York correspondent to the *Portsmouth Journal* in late December 1836. After spotting a wrecked schooner, he wrote,

> some of our citizens immediately went out in a schooner to see if any assistance could be rendered, and returned Monday evening with three dead bodies, reporting the vessel as the schooner *Leander*, of Cambridge. The next day some of our citizens went out to the wreck again to see if there were any more bodies on board, (for she was under water) and (Tuesday) in the afternoon, the three strangers were decently interred.

The *Journal* editorialized:

> It is surprising that so dangerous a place as York-Ledge has no buoy to indicate the dangerous rocks which are hid at high water, and always fearful to mariners. A Spar-Buoy might have been the means of preventing the disastrous accident." [22]

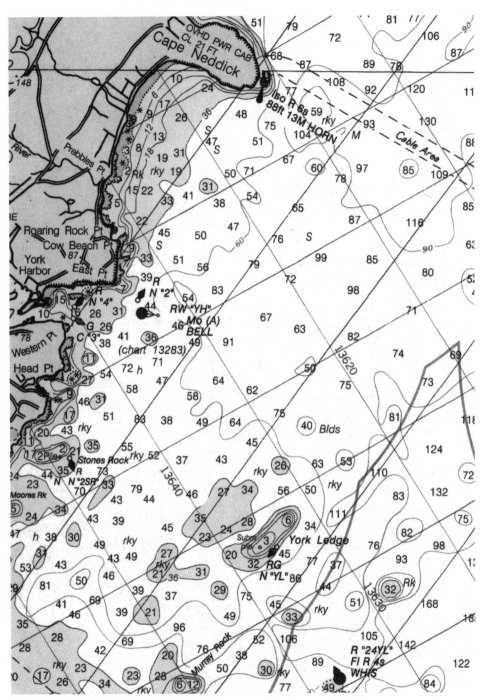

York Ledge. From Ocean Service chart #13286.

Lieutenant Manning, in his report on the First Lighthouse District, had recommended an "iron trivet" for the York Ledge site, rather than a spar buoy or the stone monument proposed earlier. Cast iron had already been successfully used for a multi-legged navigational marker designed by a member of the respected Stevenson family of civil engineers for a similar location on Carr's Ledge off the Scottish coast.[23]

The pieces of cast iron carried into Portsmouth Harbor by the *Rhoda and Betsey* in November 1840 were for a monument, thirty feet high, for York Ledge; there were six legs and a hollow circular cage to mark the top of the monument. Its designer was Alexander Parris, who wrote a fascinating account of the construction of the monument, published in the *Portsmouth Journal*. It is the only detailed account known of the construction of a nineteenth-century navigational aid in the waters around Portsmouth.[24]

Parris's engineering partner and the superintendent of construction for this project was Gridley Bryant (1789–1867), an inventive and ingenious builder. While contractor for the 1823 U.S. Branch Bank in Boston, he devised a portable derrick, of a type later widely used. Soon thereafter, he was construction engineer for a three-mile-long, horse-powered railway to carry granite for the Bunker Hill monument from a quarry in Quincy to the Neponset River. The railroad switches and turntables and the eight-wheeled car he developed for this project were incorporated into later steam railroad equipment.[25]

Parris cited the Stevensons' Scottish work as the prototype for his design. His plans were exhibited at Quincy Hall in Boston, strongly suggesting the novelty of the design in this country. It may have been the first of its kind in the United States, although single-shaft iron spindles had already been used to mark hazardous ledges.[26]

In February 1840, Bryant established a shore base of operations with a temporary house at Godfrey's Cove, about a mile and a half south of York Harbor and the nearest mainland point to York Ledge, three miles distant. The contractor for the iron work was a Mr. Emerson—probably Stephen Emerson, a Portland blacksmith. Bryant designed and had built three sturdy, shallow-draft boats, and set up shop facilities for repairing tools and making a drilling machine. This machine was to be fastened to the rock, to drill holes in which to insert the legs of the structure. The eight-man work party included foreman Joseph W. Coburn, of York, and blacksmith Elisha Turner of Windham, Maine.[27]

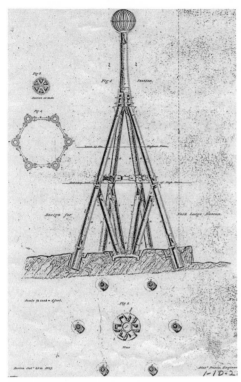

York Ledge monument design by Alexander Parris. NARG26.

It was possible to land on the ledge only at low tide when no high seas were running; the best seasons for work were spring and fall, when exceptionally low tides exposed the ledge for the greatest length of time. These were also stormy seasons, however, when high seas were likely, and water temperatures would make prolonged work impossible for the men.

The work of preparing the site began on May 19, 1840, with the installation of the drilling machine. This was probably similar to a giant auger or drill with cross bars attached to it; the workmen could turn it by walking around and around it, pushing on the bars. Rough seas made it impossible to land again until the very end of the month. The men could work for only an hour and a half when a landing was possible; when low tides and daylight coincided, they could sometimes make two trips a day to the site. Once the drilling rig was in position, the men would cling to it when waves broke over the ledge, and by the end of September had managed about sixty landings. (Parris did not record what the men wore to insulate themselves against the frigid water.) In October only three landings were possible, in November none, although several attempts were made. Bryant finally disbanded the team on November 23.[28]

Work resumed in February 1841. The men could land only twice that month, once in March, and twice again in April. It was not until the end of May that the center plate of the beacon and the first of its six hollow legs could be put in place, with the men "working to the middle in water." The rest of the beacon was installed in June and early July. Parris wrote that when the men worked at the site, they clung to the structure when "waves would lift them entirely off the rock, while the body… would rest in a horizontal posture until the force of the wave was spent and relieved the feet from this elevated position."[29]

Once the tubular legs and its braces were installed, they were filled with hydraulic cement, and the finished beacon was painted black. Atop this structure was placed a hollow ball of wrought iron with vertical ribs painted alternately black and red. The monument was finished on July 20, 1841 after placement of a label on the hollow ball—"York Ledge, 1840"—probably of cast iron manufactured at the same time as the components of the structure.[30]

Captain Green Walden of the revenue cutter *Morris* provided a description of the hazard marked by the monument, giving distances to lighthouses and harbors in the vicinity. Parris sent his account of the building of the monument to Portland collector John Anderson, suggesting that there were many other sites like York Ledge where monuments like the one just finished would be of great benefit to mariners. An observer the following year predicted—incorrectly as it turned out—that the York Ledge beacon "will undoubtedly stand for centuries, an honorable testimonial of the skill and energy of its constructor." [31]

The Investigation of 1842

After the election of a Whig president in 1840, another attempt was made to reform the U.S. lighthouse system. A survey of the lighthouses in Maine, New Hampshire, and Massachusetts was conducted in 1842. The man chosen for the job by Treasury Secretary Walter Forward was Isaiah William Penn Lewis, a nephew of Winslow Lewis. The younger Lewis had spent time as a shipmaster in the Caribbean trade and had then studied engineering. After working with his uncle on lighthouse construction and fitting-out contracts, he then set out to compete with him. According to an apologist for Winslow Lewis, his nephew attempted to get into the lighthouse contracting business by bidding below cost, with the expectation that the inevitable overruns would be reimbursed. When Stephen Pleasonton refused to go along, I. W. P. Lewis became a determined and vituperative critic of the U. S. lighthouse establishment.[32]

While Lewis was preparing to conduct his survey, Pleasonton hustled to arm himself with reports from the various local superintendents, writing in March 1842: "As we have been charged with erecting bad buildings every-where, and very probably the charge will be repeated, it is highly important that we should obtain correct information upon the subject."[33]

Pleasonton dispatched Nathan Cummings, the Portland Collector of Customs, to Boon Island and Whale's Back lights, both under Portland's jurisdiction at the time, to make a firsthand reconnaissance. He brought with him Portland mason Nahum Libby. Cummings's report to Pleasonton must have been discouraging. He wrote that the mortar of the walls on the seaward side of Boon Island lighthouse "is washed out in places, and what remains has lost its adhesiveness... the exterior wood work of nearly all the buildings is quite bare of paint." He minimized the precarious condition of Whale's Back, though, admitting "it has been represented to be insecure." He noted that only two or three small stones were missing from the foundation, recommending their replacement and the addition of twelve more iron straps at the top of the foundation pier. He also reported that the ladder up the side of the foundation, the ventilator, the stove, and the water casks "want repairs, and the lantern, oil butts, floors, windows and boat need painting." The lighthouse needed pointing and whitewashing but the lantern, lamps, and reflectors were in 'tolerable order." At both lighthouses, Cummings left supplies for essentially cosmetic painting and whitewashing.[34]

Late in May 1842, Treasury Secretary Forward detached the revenue cutter *Rush* from New York Harbor duty for six months' use by I. W. P. Lewis. Assisting Lewis were trained engineers Julius W. Adams and Charles O. Boutelle. Adams's job was to take measurements at each of the lighthouses to determine the heights of the sites. Boutelle, using quality chronometers and astronomical instruments—many supplied by the Blunts—concentrated on establishing accurate bearings for the lighthouses and the distances from which they could be seen.[35]

Lewis submitted his report to Congress in January 1843; not surprisingly, it was damning. He could not resist commenting on the competence of those in control of the lighthouse system. In an apparent reference to the landlubberly Pleasonton, he wrote: "It is very well for those who are totally ignorant of navigation in its simplest form... those whose limit of experience is not beyond the scope of a steamboat cruise in smooth water, to declaim about he superior character, economy and efficiency of our light-house establishment... " [36]

He wrote of the superior systems in place in France and Great Britain, which "have called upon their most eminent scientific men to improve the construction and illumination." In a pointed condemnation of his uncle's work, Lewis went on to say, "the establishment of this country has languished under the rule of ignorant and avaricious contractors, unrestrained by law." He added to his report the signatures of some seventy masters, a dozen interested parties, and twenty-six insurance company officers from New York and Boston.[37]

Lewis's report reinforced many of the complaints made by the naval commissioners in their 1837 lighthouse survey: the irrational concentrations of lights along certain stretches of coast, leaving vast areas unmarked or unlit; the lack of distinguishing characteristics among coast lights visible simultaneously; the unsuitability of the keepers at many lighthouses; and the shoddy construction of many of the towers. In general, he found inherent defects in the design and construction of many lighthouses, especially those built under Pleasonton. He charged that a few standard designs of varying heights had been prepared in advance and were used wherever a new lighthouse of a particular height was needed, regardless of the special conditions and requirements of each site. Sites for lighthouses built on rock were not properly leveled; the use of common lime and sand resulted in mortar that would not set; and rounded, irregular beach stones were routinely used in place of cut stone.[38]

A widespread problem he observed came from the use of soapstone slabs to form the platforms for the lighthouse lanterns. The wedge-shaped slabs, each about four inches thick, were laid down with vertical joints, as many as fifty for a platform, permitting water to pass through the joints and into the interior space between the platform and the brick arch that formed the top of many light towers. In addition, these slabs were not anchored by anything but their own weight; Lewis wrote that in gale winds they were lifted at their outer edges, with the result that more water was forced inside the lighthouses. This water caused mortar to dissolve, and wood lintels and stairs to rot; in freezing weather, a staircase could become "a perfect glacier." [39]

But Lewis focused especially on the lighting apparatus at each of the lighthouses he visited—all, of course, installed by his uncle Winslow—and on the lanterns, many also installed by his uncle or built to specifications he had furnished to Pleasonton. Thick iron bars obscured a large proportion of the light. He also charged that Stephen Pleasonton had permitted Winslow Lewis to copy improvements made to the design of lamp reflectors submitted to the Fifth Auditor by the Boston firm of H. N. Hooper in 1839. According to his nephew, Winslow Lewis used the

27th CONGRESS,   **Doc. No. 183.**   HO. OF REPS.
3d Session.   Treas. Dept.

EXAMINATION—LIGHT-HOUSE ESTABLISHMENT.

LETTER

FROM

THE SECRETARY OF THE TREASURY,

TRANSMITTING

A report from I. W. P. Lewis, civil engineer, upon the condition of the light-houses, beacons, buoys, and navigation, upon the coasts of Maine, New Hampshire, and Massachusetts.

FEBRUARY 25, 1843.
Read, and laid upon the table.

TREASURY DEPARTMENT, *February 24, 1843.*

SIR : I have the honor to transmit, herewith, in compliance with the resolution of the House of Representatives of the 23d of December last, the report of I. W. P. Lewis, civil engineer, on the examination of the light-house establishment of the United States so far as it has progressed, and which comprehends the description of seventy establishments in the States of Maine, New Hampshire, and Massachusetts, being one-third of all the lights on the seaboard, and also the correspondence relative to this examination.

The light-house establishment having become a prominent branch of expenditure committed to the supervision of this Department, my attention was arrested by an examination of the annual cost of maintenance, and the very large increase of expenditure devoted to this object for several years past. Believing that there must be some defect in the system of building, and that the large sums annually required for repairs pointed to such a cause, it was deemed proper to institute a special survey and examination, for the future guidance of this Department.

The points on which the Department required information are expressed in the letter of instructions to Mr. Lewis, to which the attention of the House is respectfully requested.

Impressed with the value of our light-house establishment, in its intimate connexion with the safety and security of commerce, and of the revenues dependent thereon, and believing that a greater degree of system in its details, and economy in its administration, are demanded by the public interests, I have to submit to the consideration of Congress the following suggestions, with the fullest confidence in their importance and necessity.

1st. That no appropriation shall be made hereafter, for the erection of a

Title page of I. W. P. Lewis's 223-page report of 1843.

Hooper design to manufacture and install these improved reflectors himself. The "new, improved" apparatus installed in 1840 by his uncle at White Island may have been of this pirated design.[40]

I. W. P. Lewis went into lengthy detail about the mechanism for adjusting the flow of oil to the lamps according to the temperature and the level of oil in the lamp reservoirs. The set-screws adjusting the angle at which oil flowed to the lamps also controlled the angle of the lamps in relation to their reflectors. When the oil flow was eased by adjusting the set screws, the relationship of reflector to flame was often skewed out of the intended focal plane, and the light from Winslow Lewis's lamps was reflected at widely varied angles. The reflectors themselves, the younger Lewis charged, were made of thin, pliable, and easily distorted copper, so they rarely functioned to concentrate the light from the lamps effectively. The silver plating was so thin that it was easily worn off by polishing with the abrasive cleaning compound issued to the keepers, resulting in "a surface like that of tin-ware— barely reflective." Lewis also contended that the inadequate system of ventilation in the lanterns caused condensation on the glass, and in freezing weather layers of obscuring frost up to a half-inch thick.[41]

A number of these criticisms echoed those written by Thomas Laighton in his 1839 report. Even though the apparatus Laighton complained of was replaced by Winslow Lewis in 1841, the following year I. W. P. Lewis found much to criticize at White Island, where Joseph Cheever was then keeper. He wrote that ten of the fifteen reflectors were skewed out of the perpendicular, with the relationship of the burners of the lamps to the apex of the reflectors varying from two to three inches. The reflectors were supposed to have been shaped on a die to guarantee a uniform parabolic form, but Lewis noted "four different curves." [42]

The red-glass screens that produced the red sectors were set in thick wood frames, each divided longitudinally by a wooden bar three-quarters of an inch wide, "which exactly covers the axis of its respective reflector, cutting off the most intense portion of the light." As a counterbalance to the weight of the red-glass panels, a twenty-four-pound lead shot was hung from the lantern—"a rude contrivance considering the great cost of the lantern and apparatus." As to the lights of the red sector, he wrote that the lamps should be much more powerful to compensate for the absorption of nearly fifty percent of the light by the red glass. Because the red lights could be seen only half as far off as the white, shipmasters crossing the Atlantic could mistake their landfall, assuming at a distance that White Island light was the revolving white light in Boston Harbor.[43]

Lewis next attacked the recently installed "machine of rotation," the clockwork that revolved the lights. He deemed the "train of light brass wheel-work, set in motion by the descent of a weight hung with a cord and two pulleys... too light for the purpose." The works "are stopped by the slightest obstruction," and "require to be carefully covered from the effects of dust and moisture." The clockwork was still causing problems more than three years later, when Thomas Laighton was again keeper at the island. He wrote in his journal on January 5, 1846, that the machinery stopped between two and three A.M., and it failed again on the eighth. On February 15, the resourceful Laighton himself "cast lead weights for clock," presumably to add weight to keep the pulleys from twisting and jamming the cords.[44]

Lewis reported horrendous conditions at Boon Island. The replacement light tower, built only eleven years earlier, had been constructed on an inadequately leveled rock surface, and with bad lime mortar. A lot of water had flowed through the seams of the soapstone slabs of the lantern platform. "The tower leaks in all directions. The staircase is rotten and unsafe, window frames and casings are rotten and leaky, walls inside are covered with ice in winter and green mould in summer; the whole structure is in bad condition." He found all but one of the twelve reflectors out of plumb and the relationship of the lamps' burners to the reflectors widely varied. More significantly, he considered Boon Island such an important light that it should have twenty-four lamps, double the existing number. Also, the reflectors were only fourteen inches in diameter, in comparison to twenty-one inches at White Island.[45]

In the summary remarks of the report, Lewis made a striking observation—remarkable for this era in the United States—about the relationship between adequate housing for lightkeepers and the amount of attention they gave to keeping the lighthouses in good order and seeing to their maintenance: "Many keepers are compelled to endure extreme suffering, from the wretched condition of the dwellings, to the want of a good boat... and from the absence of any means of obtaining pure water on the premises." At Boon Island, he reported the keeper's house "in quite as bad condition as the tower," and noted that the northeast corner wall had been battered down three times "by the force of the sea heaving large boulders against it." Finally, Lewis noted, "the keeper absents himself frequently, leaving a hired man in his place."[46]

Turning to Whale's Back lighthouse, Lewis repeated Lieutenant Manning's 1837 criticisms of the site preparation and construction, and noted open joints, one to six inches wide, between the stones of the foundation pier. "Storms shake the structure from base to dome; and it will probably soon be demolished in some severe storm... the keeper asserted that the vibration was so great as to move the chairs and tables about the floor." Lewis compared the aggregate cost of building and continually repairing Whale's Back lighthouse unfavorably with that of Saddleback, off the Maine coast, where a lighthouse designed by Alexander Parris had been built under Gridley Bryant's supervision a few years earlier for fifteen thousand dollars. The "only one erected in New England by an architect and engineer," Saddleback lighthouse had been built with interlocking blocks of hammered granite on a leveled base sunk below the surface of the ledge. Lewis noted that the design of Whale's Back, however, required yearly emergency repairs; during his inspection workmen were trying to secure the foundation pier with iron straps. And as at the other lighthouses, he found that many of the lamps and reflectors were improperly aligned. Finally, he reported that the lower partial lantern with its five lamps and reflectors was essentially worthless as a means of providing a distinguishing light characteristic. At a distance of five miles, its light merged with that of the upper lantern to give the appearance of a single light.[47]

At Fort Constitution, Lewis discovered that the keeper was living in New Castle village rather than in the keeper's house. The wooden lighthouse tower was "in excellent condition and in good order," but there were problems with the new lantern, lamps, and reflectors Winslow Lewis had installed in the summer of 1838. Twelve of the thirteen reflectors were out of plumb, and many of the lamps were misaligned with them. Four of the lamps and reflectors faced land, serving no navigational purpose and wasting sperm oil. The small panes of the lantern were of impure glass, and the one-inch-thick iron sash bars and three-inch-thick bars at the angles of the octagonal lantern further impeded the light. At a more important lighthouse, these would have been deficiencies of great significance. But Lewis observed that since the building of Whale's Back light at the entrance to the harbor, Fort Constitution light could be relegated to minor status, its height reduced from eighty to thirty feet and all but one of the lamps eliminated—at a substantial savings in fuel. As it was, this light had one more lamp than the important sea light at Boon Island, and its lantern was twenty-three feet higher above sea level.[48]

Portsmouth Collectors Timothy Upham in 1828 and Daniel Drown in 1838 had both recommended that with the building of Whale's Back the status of this light could be lowered, as I. W. P. Lewis recommended in his report. Why didn't the economy-minded Pleasonton take their advice, instead of ordering, as he did in 1838, the installation a new lantern and lighting apparatus? It is tempting to think that he was helping Winslow Lewis unload a stockpile of lighthouse equipment before it was declared obsolete, but he may have been too preoccupied with other matters to pay attention to these recommendations.[49]

I. W. P. Lewis reported navigational buoys and beacons "in abundance" in "snug" harbors like Portsmouth, although he had nothing to say about the ineffectiveness of the Logy Ledge buoy marking the entrance to Pepperrell Cove. Offshore, where there were no pilots to guide shipmasters, most rocks and ledges remained unmarked. He noted that there was not a single buoy in Penobscot Bay, where there was by that time extensive maritime activity.[50]

Isaiah W. P. Lewis was not the period's only strenuous critic of the U.S. lighthouse system. The Blunts, publishers of the *American Coast Pilot* since before the end of the eighteenth century, shared many of his views about its inadequacies, and had provided Lewis with measurement instruments for his survey. They frequently noted that France and Britain had committed the best available scientific and engineering talent to the improvement of lighthouses and other aids to navigation. In his report, Lewis took pains to single out for praise York Ledge beacon and its designer, Alexander Parris, the "first professional man employed on works of this description." [51]

Reaction to the Report of 1842

I. W. P. Lewis included signed and witnessed statements testifying to deficiencies from virtually all of the keepers of the lights he surveyed, (For an unknown reason there were no statements from keepers under the supervision of Portsmouth Collector of Customs John N. Sherburne, who was appointed in 1841 and resigned after only a year in the post.) In an 1843 rebuttal of Lewis's charges, however, Stephen Pleasonton accused Lewis of "drawing up false certifications as to the condition of the lights, which he induced the keepers to sign without reading." Pleasonton claimed these statements were contrary to what the customs collectors told him and instructed the collectors from

Maine to Louisiana to solicit the opinions of hundreds of captains and pilots as to the adequacy of American lighthouses. He claimed that nine tenths of them had a positive opinion. In Portsmouth, 129 masters of ships and "others interested in navigation" signed a statement that "as far as our observation extends," the U.S. lights "are equal to the lights on other coasts." [52]

However, the observation of most of the signatories did not extend beyond the coast of the U. S. and virtually none of them could have seen the lights with Fresnel lenses on the French coast or the superior reflector lights used in the British Isles. Most of those who signed were masters of Maine or Massachusetts vessels in the coasting and West Indies trades. Only ten of the signers who gave Portsmouth, New Castle, or Kittery as their home port were currently masters or owners of any vessels at all. Many of the testimonials Pleasonton obtained from other ports were likewise from masters of coasting vessels who lacked first-hand observation of European lights as a basis for comparison with those of the United States.[53]

Winslow Lewis did not take his nephew's criticisms lying down. In 1843 he published, probably at his own expense, a heated defense of his work over the previous thirty-six years, against what he called his nephew's charges of "fraud, ignorance and incompetence." He blasted him for "arrogance [and] exaggerated statements" and impugned his motives. The vehemence of I. W. P. Lewis's attacks on both Pleasonton and Winslow Lewis, who together had nearly sixty years of experience in the lighthouse system, may have worked against the Congressional acceptance of his recommendations. Another reason was surely that the Democrats—lukewarm, at best, about spending money for projects in aid of navigation—had gained control of the House of Representatives in 1842.[54]

To drum up support for the adoption of the Fresnel lens in American lighthouses, I. W. P. Lewis obtained lenses of various magnitudes from the French manufacturer Henri Lepaute and lectured on their merits in major ports from Boston to Washington. Pleasonton accused both Lewis and Lepaute of attempting to enrich themselves by creating demand for the lenses.[55]

Stephen Pleasonton's troubles continued to build, but, amazingly, he held on to his job as federal lighthouse superintendent until the early 1850s. Congress, however, made no appropriations for building new lighthouses or lightships between 1842 and 1847.[56]

28th CONGRESS,
1st Session.

Doc. No. 62.

Ho. OF REPS.
Treas. Dept.

LIGHT-HOUSES.

LETTER

FROM

THE SECRETARY OF THE TREASURY,

TRANSMITTING

Fifth Auditor's report relative to light-houses and lights.

JANUARY 19, 1844.
Read, and referred to the Committee on Commerce.

TREASURY DEPARTMENT,
January 18, 1844.

SIR: I have the honor to transmit, herewith, a report from the Fifth Auditor, who has charge of the light-house establishment, accompanied by information respecting the efficiency of the lights, and a list of the lights in the United States, in Great Britain, and in France.

I am, very respectfully, sir, your obedient servant,

J. C. SPENCER,
Secretary of the Treasury.

Hon. J. W. JONES,
Speaker of the House of Representatives.

TREASURY DEPARTMENT,
Fifth Auditor's Office, January 3, 1844.

SIR: The light-house establishment within the States of Maine, New Hampshire, and Massachusetts, and its management, having been grossly misrepresented by a man employed by your immediate predecessor to inspect the same, and these calumnies having been communicated to the House of Representatives of the United States, on the 24th of February, 1843, in a document printed and numbered 183, I took occasion in April last to instruct the several superintendents, not only in these States, but in all the States bordering upon the Atlantic, to open books at their respective custom-houses, and to ask the masters of ships and other vessels, as they visited the custom-houses to make entry, to enter in those books their several opinions as to the quality of all the lights from Maine to Louisiana, and to forward these books to me prior to the meeting of Congress at its present session. Having received these books and opinions, (with the exception of

Blair & Rives, print.

Title page of Stephen Pleasonton's 1844 defense.

President Polk's secretary of the treasury, Robert Walker, was concerned about the poor quality of U.S. aids to navigation revealed by I. W. P. Lewis's report. In June 1845 he dispatched two naval lieutenants who had worked on the 1838 lighthouse survey, Richard Bache and Thornton A. Jenkins, to study European lighthouses. Their report confirmed the superiority of most foreign lighthouses, especially the French ones with Fresnel lenses. They considered it "a libel on our country" to suggest, as Pleasonton had, that "persons cannot be procured capable of managing these lights." In England and Scotland, a few Fresnel lenses had been installed, but reflectors were still being used at most lighthouses. Bache and Jenkins found them more precisely shaped and their fittings made of more substantial materials than in the U.S. They, too, deemed an engineer in the lighthouse administration "absolutely indispensable to a properly organized light-house establishment." As to the European lighthouse structures, they wrote that they stood "not only as beacons to guide the mariner, but as monuments of the ability and faithfulness of the engineers and constructors." Walker was impressed by their report, and suggested to Congress that a single individual could no longer provide the range of practical and theoretical knowledge needed for a system that had grown so large. He proposed management by a board, in which he tactfully included Fifth Auditor Pleasonton, along with the superintendent of the coast survey, two naval officers, and two army engineers. Pleasonton was resistant. He cranked out statistics comparing building and maintenance costs between the American and European lighthouses, and once again solicited testimonials to bolster his position.[57]

In March 1847, when Congress approved the first lighthouse construction appropriation in five years, the repeated pleas that trained engineers be involved in lighthouse design finally had an impact. Responsibility for overseeing the design and construction of the six authorized lighthouses was given not to Pleasonton but to the Army Corps of Topographical Engineers.[58]

This corps was distinct from the Army Corps of Engineers from 1831 until 1863, at which time the two services were merged. While the Corps of Engineers concentrated on military projects, the topographical engineers were involved in virtually all engineering projects the government considered essential to the nation's development and prosperity. Like the officers of the Corps of Army Engineers, the "Topogs," as they were called, were trained at West Point. In wartime

29th CONGRESS,
1st Session.

[SENATE.]

[488]

REPORT

OF

THE SECRETARY OF THE TREASURY,

ON

Improvements in the Light-house system and collateral aids to navigation.

AUGUST 5, 1846.

Read, and ordered to be printed.

TREASURY DEPARTMENT,
August 5, 1846.

SIR: I have the honor to submit to the Senate of the United States a report in relation to improvements in the light-house system of the United States, and in collateral aids to navigation.

The improvement of our system of light-houses has attracted at different times the attention of Congress and of the Executive. Impressed with the necessity for obtaining full information in regard to the improvements alleged to have been made in Europe, emanating principally from France, I applied in June last to the Navy Department for the detail of two officers, who might, under instructions from this department, visit the countries into which the improved system had been introduced, make themselves practically acquainted with the different parts, and establish the necessary comparison with our own. Lieutenants Thornton A. Jenkins and Richard Bache were detailed for this service, and visited some of the principal lights on the shores of the Baltic and North seas, the coast of England, Ireland, and Scotland, and the establishments for the construction of the new lighting apparatus in France; collecting, with care, zeal, and intelligence, the full and varied information upon this important subject, and others connected with it, which is so ably presented in their report to this department.

The subjects are systematically treated in their report, and it will be necessary merely to refer here to suggestions for the improvement of our system, which meet my hearty concurrence.

In countries where the system of lighting is good, a general plan for the classification of lights, selection of sites, construction of the light-houses and apparatus, and inspection, has been adopted, or improvements have been slowly introduced, under the directions of existing authorities. The most perfect system in Europe is the result of the former plan; and it must be obvious, that, for a growing country like ours, no other can secure, on the greater part of the coast, a due attention to the wants of commerce and navigation.

Ritchie & Heiss, printers.

Two-hundred seventy-eight page 1846 report on lighthouses in the British Isles and continental Europe by Lieutenants Richard Bache and Thornton Jenkins, with twenty-seven plates.

their duties included surveying sites for fortifications and mapping war zones. In peacetime, they mapped western territories and boundaries, incidentally recording flora and fauna, and identifying the groups of native Americans who inhabited these areas. They were also involved in harbor, river, canal, and railroad surveys; bridge engineering; and supervision of the construction of federal buildings such as post offices and customs houses.[59]

In 1847, Whale's Back lighthouse was the subject of yet another review, this time by the Corps of Topographical Engineers under its chief, Colonel J. J. Abert. His report recommended that Wood Island or the nearby White Island (one of the small ledgy islets off Cutts Island, rather than the one at the Isles of Shoals) might be a preferable site. If neither the stone tower design of Alexander Parris nor the iron pile structure suggested by Lieutenant Manning back in 1838 was built, the existing structure could be made secure by encasing the entire foundation in "heavy masonry of the best kind," using large, hammered stones laid in cement.[60]

No funding was forthcoming for these solutions. This was the era of Manifest Destiny – the belief articulated in 1845 by John O'Sullivan that "Providence destined the United States of America to possess the entire continent." The issues and events surrounding the subsequent territorial expansion to the Pacific evidently overshadowed the interests of Atlantic maritime commerce in the second half of the 1840s.[61]

Opposing Portsmouth newspapers weighed the cost of the Mexican War against federal expenditures for harbor and river improvements and the aids to navigation favored by the Whigs: The Democrats' *Gazette*, arguing that "Providence favors our arms," stated that

> All wars are very expensive – but at the same time, we might be paying the cost of half a dozen wars at a time, and the aggregate expenses would be but a drop in the bucket compared with the millions on millions which the federal party are disposed to waste in constructing harbors on the lakes, where Providence never designed they should be built...

The Whig's *Journal* retorted:

> If the same principle were to be fully carried out, we should never have had the lighthouse on Whale's Back. Providence placed a very dangerous rock there, on which about one ship a

year used to be lost, and sometimes goods and lives—but the "federalists" wasted money enough to build a lighthouse there several years ago, and since that time not a vessel nor a life has been lost at this place. For this dreadful waste they were smartly reproved by a penny-wise and pound-foolish editor of Concord, who... denounced the policy of·multiplying lights in general and of building this light house in particular. Providence placed no light there, yet any one who would tell our fishermen, coasters and seamen that "Providence never designed" that a light should be sustained there would run some risk of being called a madman.[62]

In February 1849, the *Journal* reported that nothing was to be done at Whale's Back until the experimental iron-pile lighthouse being completed at Minot's Ledge had been tested. This structure was designed by Captain William H. Swift of the Topographical Engineers. In 1840, Swift had seen the new iron screw-pile lighthouse designed by the Irish engineer Alexander Mitchell for use on sandy or muddy shoals off the British Isles. Mitchell's design incorporated an idea as old as the 1776 Small's Rock lighthouse off the west coast of Wales, where the lantern was elevated above the sea-washed rock on wooden piles, through

which storm seas could pass with little resistance. On this principle, Mitchell designed lighthouses raised on iron piles tipped with huge auger-like points, which were literally screwed deep into the shoals, and stabilized by pad-like flanges. Further stability was provided by cross-braces between the multiple iron piles.[63]

At Black Rock, Connecticut, Swift successfully adapted Mitchell's iron pile principle for a small, unlighted beacon on a rocky site, the piles being inserted deep into pre-drilled holes instead of being screwed into the softer mud or sand of Mitchell's lighthouse sites. In 1847, Swift was given the

Sketch of the iron lighthouse on Minot's Ledge off Boston. NARG26.

job of designing a much more ambitious iron pile structure for a light at the infamous Minot's Ledge off Boston, where conditions were perhaps worse than at Whale's Back. Those concerned with the condition of Whale's Back light—especially the lightkeepers—must have been very interested in the progress and success of the Minot's Ledge structure.[64]

VIII *Some Early Lighthouse Keepers I: Fort Constitution and Boon Island*

... he described the loneliness as something absolutely fearful, and declared it had pursued him all through his life.

—Celia Thaxter, *Among the Isles of Shoals*, 1873

THE SAVING OF VALUABLE CARGOES AND VESSELS, rather than lives, was perhaps the overriding motivation for the men "Concerned in trade" who first petitioned for a Portsmouth lighthouse in 1765. After the establishment of federal control over the lighthouse system, the amount of duties levied on foreign imports influenced considerably decisions about building lighthouses. But both the dangers of the seafaring life itself and the dedication required of lighthouse keepers who kept the lanterns lit for sailors throughout the night, often in situations of hardship and isolation, early generated a romantic view of these aids to navigation and their guardians. "Friendly edifices" like the lighthouse at Fort Constitution were seen as symbols of human kindness, hope, and even eternity. Governor John Wentworth spoke in 1771 of "Animating Glows of Humanity." The anonymous author of a poem, "The Light-House," published in the *New-Hampshire Gazette* in 1814, looked out to sea at dusk toward a "dim distant isle" to see a sudden blaze of light when the lamps of the lighthouse were lit, "lovely as hope," "a star on eternity's ocean."[1]

Interest in visiting lighthouses by those who did not make their living at sea was evident in the area as early as the 1830s and 1840s. In August 1838, a "dim distant isle" with a lighthouse was the destination for an afternoon excursion on the steamer *Portsmouth*; weather permitting, the curious could take a trip to Boon Island for twenty-five cents.[2]

The *Portsmouth Journal* reprinted an account of an 1843 summer visit to the lighthouse at Fort Constitution:

> ... we found Mr. Edward Yeaton, the keeper, and proceeded to ascend to the bright midnight guardian. I could not help noticing the perfect order which prevails in every part of this building, the kindness and polite attention of the keeper. Witnessing all these I could not refrain from publicly noticing them, that those who love a ramble or a sail, or are at all interested in the protection of our seacoast by these cheerful friends of the sailor, may not pass without visiting this building, from whose summit a most beautiful land and sea prospect is presented.[3]

A literary urbanite with a taste for dramatic displays of nature wrote a piece for a Boston newspaper in 1847 about a winter visit to the Isles of Shoals and White Island lighthouse. He wrote that the lightkeeper (Thomas B. Laighton) has

> a copious library of books and miscellaneous publications, and his lady informs me, that here the summer herbage is ever the haunt of humming-birds... Messrs. Editors, I could wish you were here at evening, when "the lighthouse looks lovely as hope," to see our beautiful twilights, and the splendid hues which often the occident presents, or at sunrise, when the saffron mantle of Aurora gilds the horizon. I often lean against the bluffs in sunny hours, to see the swelling flood rush in to the chasms beneath me, and make its foamy and precipitous retreat, like "the tone of an echo from the bosom of a ruined sepulchre."

The writer had been at White Island during the December 1846 storm in which the steamer *Atlantic* was wrecked on the Connecticut coast with the loss of more than half the eighty-three people aboard:

> While viewing the foaming billows which encompassed me, I little dreamt of the fate of that noble steamer. This sublime

spectacle was the first clashing of the elements I ever witnessed in so isolated a position. I was as one in the midst of the ocean, at White Island.[4]

Vignettes like these suggest tidy, dependably maintained lighthouses and cheerful lightkeepers enviably situated in picturesque surroundings where they could admire the awesome power of nature in storms and, of an evening, contentedly read books in their snug houses. The reality was often quite different. In the 1830s and 1840s, proponents of reform of the U.S. lighthouse system stressed the need for a better means of choosing and supervising lightkeepers. In his 1843 report, I. W. P. Lewis wrote of the politics involved in appointments and of the many keepers who often left their posts, supplementing their incomes in a variety of ways and leaving the lights in the care of their wives and children or a hired hand. He was also highly critical of the horrible living conditions endured by many lighthouse families. Lieutenants Jenkins and Bache in 1846 contrasted the U.S. system of patronage appointments and sketchy instructions with the training provided European lightkeepers, the detailed printed instructions with which they were furnished, and the standards of behavior they were expected to meet. Europeans could expect to keep their jobs until old age if they kept their lighthouses carefully. Thought was given to their material needs: Bache and Jenkins reported that the keepers of offshore Scottish lights were even provided with plots of land on the mainland sufficient to sustain a cow, a new uniform every three years, and life insurance.[5]

Who were the human beings providing the "animating glows" at the lighthouses around Portsmouth through the mid-nineteenth century? Aside from their names (and sometimes even these are unknown), we know little if anything about most of them and the reasons that led them, perhaps drove them, to take on lighthouse responsibilities. Their lives are shadowy and those of their wives and children yet more so. Occasional references in government records, brief newspaper items, listings in sources like town directories and tax rolls provide most of what can be learned about many of these early lighthouse keepers. Few appear in the published histories of the towns they came from. Rare journals, usually spare documents of routine activity, offer a few more clues about them and their work and the conditions they endured.

Early Fort Constitution Lighthouse Keepers

Before the Revolutionary War, the titular keeper of the light at the fort at New Castle was Captain John Cochran, the commandant of the small garrison stationed there. The fish-oil lamps were actually tended by one of a succession of soldiers of the garrison. There is a record of the names of the men garrisoned at the fort, but no indication as to which were assigned lighthouse duty. Memorials from Cochran to the provincial legislature document that, contrary to Governor Wentworth's expectations, whoever did the job expected supplemental pay. Soldiers were not going to do the extra work of keeping the lamps burning simply for the honor of providing an important service (see chapter 2).

When the lighthouse was reactivated after the war in 1784, it was Sergeant Elias Tarlton, a native of New Castle stationed at the fort, who tended the light under Lieutenant Mesech Bell. Bell was a New Castle resident and the caretaker-commandant of the inactive fort and its small complement of soldiers; like Cochran, he was designated keeper of the light. Captain Titus Salter, a shipmaster who had a role in the Revolutionary War defenses of the port, took over after Bell's death in 1786. His supervision of the lighthouse and of Elias Tarlton, who continued to tend the lighthouse under his command, may have been perfunctory; he lived, not in New Castle but in Portsmouth, well out of sight of the lighthouse. During the hard economic times after the war, however, when his pay was cut back, Salter petitioned the General Court for relief, pleading that he was owed the considerable amount he himself had paid the fort's soldiers out of his own pocket; moreover, he claimed that he had "by his Exertions" cut the cost of maintaining the lighthouse by one third.[6]

After the federal government assumed administration of lighthouses—and President Washington in 1793 ordered the keeper to live on the premises and to make sure the lighthouses lamps were kept lit throughout the night—Salter decided he no longer wanted the job. Sergeant Tarlton likewise refused the keepership under Washington's conditions.

A critic in the early 1850s, Lieutenant W. B. Franklin, of the Topographical Engineers, suggested that many lightkeepers were marginal members of society, unable to cope with life's setbacks and economic uncertainties, and that they lacked the qualities needed to compete in the world. In general, he wrote, they were men "who are fit for no business, and who apply for these positions because even with the small salaries now given, they get more money in a year than they could get in the same time by doing anything else." [7]

David Duncan, keeper of Fort Constitution light from 1793 to 1820, may well have been one of these marginal people, although it is impossible to know if he was unsuited for better-paying work because he had the misfortune to be injured in the Revolutionary War or because of some character defect. He was described on the one hand as a conscientious keeper of the light and on the other as "easy and weakminded" (see Chapter 3). In the early years of his employment as keeper, when the maritime commerce of the Port of Portsmouth was far from vibrant, he was paid the same wage as Sergeant Tarlton. For Tarlton, this had been over and above his soldier's pay; Duncan, however, occasionally had to rely on the charity of the town of New Castle for survival.[8] Duncan contended with low pay, poor housing, and the disrespectful, pilfering soldiers at the fort—as well as with the low-life members of his own family described earlier. But he and the men who followed him at Fort Constitution did not have to endure the conditions confronted by the keepers of the off-shore lights.

Life Offshore

Particularly intriguing are the men who remained with their families for years, even decades, offshore at the lonely and often downright dangerous lighthouses on Boon Island, White Island, and Whale's Back. At Boon Island, keeper Eliphalet Grover must have hoped for a more secure and well-built lighthouse when he placed a good-luck coin under the first stone of the light tower that in 1831 replaced the disintegrating 1811 structure where he had tended the light for sixteen years. No one knows what went through his mind when he and his family endured the inevitable, frightening storms that periodically inundated the low-lying island and drove them out of their house and up the steps of the lighthouse. And what were the feelings of Samuel Hascall and his family at the precarious Whale's Back light in the terrible storm of February 1838? And how did this family occupy itself cooped up in this dim, cramped tower?

It is doubtful that many of the early keepers of these offshore lights were motivated by the challenge of providing a valuable service under difficult circumstances; many may simply have been desperate for a

livelihood during hard times. Others, especially during the first half
of the nineteenth century when there was little supervision, may have
seen a lighthouse job as a sinecure that would let them pay someone
else to do the work while they themselves spent much of their time on
more profitable activities ashore. Some may have been loners, perhaps even social misfits, who welcomed a guaranteed income, no matter how minimal, in a self-contained world where they could control
everything but the weather.

In the intense politicking for federal appointments in the decades
after Andrew Jackson's election, especially when the economy was not
good and jobs were scarce, appointments increasingly became a way to
repay a political debt or help a friend in need. In 1843 the *Portsmouth
Journal* pleaded for the appointment of seafaring men who understood
by experience the importance of lighthouses, noting that "instead of
mariners, men from behind the mountains have been appointed—men
unused to the roar of the ocean—and men whose knees have trembled,
like Belshazzar's when stepping in to the boat that was to convey them
to the place of their appointment." [9]

Most keepers who adjusted well to life at offshore lighthouses do
seem to have been mariners, sometimes islanders, accustomed to isolation from mainland life. They possessed the sea wisdom and boat-han-
dling ability crucial to their survival. A visitor to White Island, standing
in the lantern at the top of the lighthouse, sensed the attraction a lighthouse post could have for former seamen:

"There is a superb view from the top, and one gets there a sense of
airiness and freedom such as must stir in sailors' breasts...as they
stand high up on the foot-ropes of the yards." [10] Conceivably they took
satisfaction in surviving the challenges of these offshore posts, much as
a shipmaster might pride himself on bringing his vessel safely through
a gale, and their experience at sea gave them a powerful understanding of the importance of maintaining a reliable light.

It surely was different for the women who went to live at offshore
lights with their husbands. Life at sea was unlikely to have been part
of their experience. Those who went to Whale's Back were close enough
to the mainland to catch glimpses of human activity ashore; in mild
weather friends and family could row out for a visit, and they themselves could get to the mainland fairly easily. But when the weather
closed in, they had to endure an extremely confining situation, and it
could not have helped to read in the newspapers, after every major

storm, that the structure could be toppled by the next heavy gale. At White Island there were families at the other islands at the Shoals to call on in an emergency or to visit when the seas were reasonable, but storms could cut off lighthouse families from contact with the other islands for days, and from the mainland for weeks. Those who went to Boon Island, however, were abruptly separated from family, friends, and neighbors whom they might not see for months on end.

In late spring, summer, and early fall, local fishermen were frequently in the vicinity of Boon Island and the Isles of Shoals. They could bring news from ashore and provide male companionship for the keepers. But their wives, especially if they had no daughters or household help, had to do without the sharing of chores and visiting within the circle of women family members and neighbors that would have been part of their lives on the mainland. They were often left behind at the lighthouse, perhaps with small children and a hired hand, while their husbands went ashore for provisions, to take care of lighthouse or other business, and, doubtless, to enjoy a bit of sociability.

It is difficult to imagine how these women coped with the ordinary aspects of daily life that were their traditional responsibilities: doing laundry with a water supply dependent on the rain water gathered in the cisterns, cooking meals with scanty provisions when it was too stormy for a boat to get ashore—to say nothing of the more unusual but inevitable occurrence of pregnancies, sickness and even death.

If there were children, offshore lighthouse parents needed the inner resources to help them cope with a life circumscribed not only physically but also socially. They had to teach them about the dangers of their water-surrounded world and to provide whatever schooling they were to get unless the children could stay with family or friends on the mainland when schools were in session.

Early Boon Island Lighthouse Keepers

It was understandably hard to find a keeper for Boon Island light after it was built in 1811. Its keepers, their families, and their helpers were for a good part of the year often virtual prisoners on this distant ledge. The storms that were a normal occurrence in the months from October through March delayed their comings and goings and frequently made travel dangerous. The history of Boon Island is full of accounts of terrifying storm damage to the house, the light tower, the boatways, and the small open sailboat used to get to the mainland. There were no island neighbors nearby, as there were at the Isles of Shoals, to keep an eye on the lighthouse keeper at Boon Island. Only if the light did not shine out as usual at dusk would an observer in York, seven miles away, have an inkling of trouble.

No official record of the first Boon Island keeper has been located. Lighthouse historian Edward Rowe Snow wrote that the experience of a single storm on the island caused this unknown man to resign after only a few weeks on December 16, 1811. He was followed by David Oliver, one of the men who worked on the construction of the lighthouse. Oliver "soon became weary of the loneliness and also resigned, to be replaced by a man named Thomas Hanna" in March 1812. Hannah came from Portland, where the customs collector there had nominated him for the job. He had a wife and two sons, twelve and fourteen, who presumably accompanied him to the island. By the end of a year Hannah found the $300 annual pay inadequate because of the expense of provisioning this remote location and obtaining adequate firewood for heat and for melting ice to produce a water supply. He asked for an increase of $150; only $100 was forthcoming, but Hannah stuck it out until May 1816, when he resigned.[11]

The writer Celia Thaxter, who spent six childhood years at White Island when her father was lightkeeper there, wrote of Boon Island that it was "the forlornest place that can be imagined. The Isles of Shoals, barren as they are, seem like Gardens of Eden in comparison." She told a story of a chance encounter with a man who told her he had been born on Boon Island and lived there until his mid-teens:

> . . . he described the loneliness as something absolutely fearful, and declared it had pursued him all through his life...While living on the island he discovered some human remains which had lain there thirty years. A carpenter and his assistants, having finished some building, were capsized in getting off, and all were drowned, except the master. One body floated to Plum Island at the mouth of the Merrimack; the others the master secured, made a box for them,—all alone the while,— and buried them in a cleft and covered them with stones. These stones the sea washed away, and, thirty years after they were buried, the boy found the bones, which were removed to York and there buried again. He spoke with bitterness of his life in

that terrible solitude. It was on board a steamer bound to Bangor, that the man told his story. Boone Island Light was shining in the distance... All his relatives were dead, he said, and he had no human tie in the wide world except his wife. He ended by anathemizing all islands, and, vanishing into the darkness, was not to be found again; nor did his name or any trace of him transpire, though he was sought for in the morning all about the vessel.[12]

Eliphalet Grover of Boon Island

The man Thaxter told of may have been Samuel Grover, the son of Eliphalet Grover, who was appointed keeper at Boon Island in 1816 and remained at this post until he was replaced, against his wishes, on May 10, 1839. Eliphalet Grover knew to the day how long he had been keeper at Boon Island: twenty-two years, ten months and twenty days. He was born in 1778, probably in York, Maine. For three years, from 1803 to 1805, his name appeared on the tax rolls of Portsmouth, where he was listed as a ship's mate; he may have sailed with Captain Edmund Grover, of the brig *Planter,* on voyages to Grenada. He was married near the turn of the century, and his first child, Jeremiah, was baptized at St. John's Church in Portsmouth in 1802. Eliphalet was later known as Captain Grover, and he may have become a shipmaster in the years before the Embargo. In 1810, he paid $415 for a house on a half-acre of land in York; he was designated simply "mariner" on the deed of sale. Perhaps hard times led him to take the job at Boon Island after Thomas Hanna resigned in May 1816.[13]

A genealogy based on Grover's will notes that he had three children: Jeremiah, born in 1802; Eliphalet, born in 1814; and Samuel, whose birth date is not given, but who was born around 1820. There may have been another son old enough to help his father and Jeremiah with a rescue attempt in April 1817, when young Eliphalet was only three:

> On Sunday morning of last week, Capt. Grover, keeper of Boon
> Island light, was awaked at 2 o'clock by his dog, and the cries
> of persons in distress. On repairing, as soon as possible to the
> southern part of the island he perceived a small two masted
> vessel which had been just shoved off, by oars. He soon after
> saw her near the south east part of the island, the wind being

> brisk at south west; and about half an hour after on the north
> west ledge, about gun- shot distance, apparently at anchor, and
> the people crying for help. Capt. Grover, with his two sons,
> immediately went in a boat, to their aid, but before they could
> reach the spot, the vessel had disappeared. The last words
> heard were, "Come out quick with your boat." Nothing could be
> discovered of the vessel at day light, and Capt. Grover is of the
> opinion that she went to the bottom.[14]

There may well have been other children who did not survive their
father.

A "Logg" kept by Eliphalet Grover from 1828 to 1839 is preserved at
the Old York Historical Society. In it Grover recorded details of his work
as lighthouse keeper, entering a few scanty references to his family on
the back and front inside pages of the log, set apart from his entries
about lighthouse matters. Jeremiah does not appear among these family notations. He must have gone to the mainland to make his own life
by the time Grover began his log. Grover's notes show that in 1829 his
son Eliphalet, then about fifteen, went ashore to York to board with
Mrs. Emerson; Grover paid E. A. Emerson $1.25 a week for his board,
sometimes in codfish. He paid for one month's board at a time, and
although his log records very few trips ashore, he must have gone regularly to settle his account with the Emersons. From another source we
know that at some point Samuel also went ashore for schooling.[15]

Eliphalet Grover made only a single reference to his wife in this log,
noting neither her name nor that of the child referred to:

> May 18, 1832: wife and Child went on Shoare and My uncle
> Andrew Grover came to See me.

In a late-1839 letter protesting his replacement as lightkeeper,
Grover wrote, "My wife has been stupified for seven years." She was evidently the victim of a stroke. A notation of June 12, 1838, presumably
refers to his wife: "came heare the Cutter and took me to Cearer hir in
to York." Another entry, "Widow Susanna Goodwin to Board with Mr.
Morgan Trafton May 3 1834 at 2/6 per Week" could refer to the aged
mother Grover was still supporting in 1841, or perhaps to a widowed
daughter in need of assistance. Uncle Andrew came to the island again
in August 1834, and on June 19, 1835, "Uncle Andrew went from me."
Samuel's name and the names of other children do not appear among
these references to personal matters.[16]

The National Archives contain evidence of another member of the Boon Island household who was there almost as long as Grover. This was a woman, Mary Ann Lowdar, whose name in York vital records is spelled variously Lowder and Lowden, and who is recorded in a prenuptial record as "Miss" but in the record of her 1846 marriage to Benjamin Avery as Mrs. Mary Ann Lowder. She died in 1863 at an unspecified age. She went to live with the Boon Island family around 1818, when she was about twenty-six, and was still there in 1838. Why she was there is a mystery. She might have been a widowed sister of Eliphalet Grover or of his wife. It is a possibility that she was a destitute woman who went to live with the family, providing household help in exchange for housing, food, and clothing. She may even have been "farmed out" by a town in the area to the person who offered the lowest bid for taking her in—a common practice at the time, though no substantiation has been located in town records. The Boon Island household also included hired hands referred to at various times but never named in Grover's log.[17]

Several objects made by Grover survive to provide a tantalizing glimpse of the man and how he passed the stormy months when he and his family were isolated on Boon Island. One is a small, carefully made hinged pine box with a brass handle. It is painstakingly veneered with maple, cherry, and mahogany cut-outs of soldiers and geometric shapes, with painted details. The box is lined with pieces of an 1832 newspaper—a hint, at least, that he maintained an interest in events on the mainland. Another object is a violin made in 1821 and embellished with a carved woman's head resembling an archaic Greek sculpture. A smaller version of this violin was made by his son Samuel in 1834. Grover also made an instrument described during the period as a "bass viol," although in size it resembles a cello. This he presented to the York Congregational Church in 1834 for use with the choir.[18]

The construction of musical instruments like these required careful and precise workmanship. Whether Grover taught himself to make them while at Boon Island, perhaps using another instrument for a model, or had worked with a craftsman at some point before becoming a lighthouse keeper is one of several mysteries about this man. Presumably he made the instruments for the family to play. Did the Grovers, of an evening, accompany themselves on them as they sang hymns? Perhaps they performed or improvised other, livelier kinds of music.

Violin made by Eliphalet Grover in 1821 at Boon Island, and a smaller one made by his son Samuel in 1834. OYHS.

The bitter recollection of his childhood on Boon Island by the man Celia Thaxter encountered on the steamer makes it difficult to imagine pleasant times of any sort at Boon Island, and colors one's reading of Grover's log. This manuscript, covering eleven years and several months, is a rare document of lighthouse life in the area over an extended period during the first half of the nineteenth century. A valuable record of the conditions faced by offshore lightkeepers and their families, it also reflects the minimal supervision and support provided by the administrators of the U.S. lighthouse system at this time.

Grover's appointment came during James Madison's presidency, in 1816. The lighthouses in the District of Maine were superintended by the Boston Collector of Customs, Henry A. S. Dearborn, until Maine became a state in 1820. At that time, Portland customs collector Isaac Ilsley, who previously had a role in nominating lighthouse keepers for the District of Maine, became superintendent of Maine lighthouses.[19] In the years before the Boon Island lighthouse came under the Portland collector's purview, there must have been little contact between the Boston-based lighthouse superintendent and the keepers of lighthouses in the District of Maine. For information about Maine lighthouses, Collector Dearborn may well have depended upon Winslow Lewis, whose contract for supplying lighting equipment and sperm oil extended through 1827. But even this contact could be uncertain. Lewis's delivery of items for Boon Island was delayed on at least one occasion by lack of transportation. On November 14, 1817, he wrote to Jeremiah Bradbury, Collector of Customs for York:

> I have had some articles packed up for Boon island Light house for 2 months & never have been able to find a Vessel for York to deliver them & I must request the Favour of you to ask the Captain of any Vesell that may be coming here from your Place to Call att my store No. 4 Central Wharf. When the articles arrive att York while not the Keeper be off I will thank you to send some craft over to island with them & I will pay the Expense. [20]

Unfortunately, we have no detailed record of Eliphalet Grover's first dozen years at Boon Island. An 1818 letter to the Boston collector reveals his anxiety about being replaced by competitors for the post, including one who alleged that Grover was dead![21] The log at the Old York Historical Society begins with a January 1, 1828, inventory of the lighting apparatus and supplies on hand. The entries are not daily; the majority deal with matters Grover was evidently expected to keep track of. Surprisingly, for a former mariner, Grover does not mention the weather except when there is a storm. There is, however, a distinctly seasonal rhythm to the activities recorded, in ways comparable to those in a farmer's diary. Like these rural journals, the entries do not record thoughts or feelings, although Grover's voice and accent can almost be heard through his odd spellings and turns of phrase.

Every year, on either December 31 or January 1, he inventoried what was on hand: winter and summer sperm oil, and how much had been consumed over the past year; tube glasses (lamp chimneys); and deerskins for polishing the lamp reflectors. In the spring he writes: "Took down my heaters"(the devices used to keep the sperm oil from congealing in cold weather), and "Clenzed out my lamps." In the warmer months, Grover noted maintenance work on the buildings, the boat, and the boatways, jobs for which he received extra pay: "Employd painting the Lanton outside," "Employd Scrapeing and painting my Boat," " Employd trying to Secuare the Slip," "putting in new window frames and Windows in the house," "Employd White washing the Buildings on BoonIsland," and "Employd hooping and painting my Warter Sisterns." [22]

Every July or August the oil contractor arrived, and Grover recorded the amounts of winter and summer sperm oil and other supplies delivered, in addition to the quantity of unusable oil taken away by the contractor. In the back of his log he listed the men who succeeded Winslow Lewis as oil contractors: Charles W. Morgan, Samuel Rodman Jr., William R. Rodman, and Edward Merrill (all New Bedford men). In 1834 he noted that Jonathan Howland Jr., had taken on the contract. Grover occasionally wrote that the contractor left him the oil sediment, or "settlings," remaining in the oil butts. These he used to grease the boatways. Late-fall entries indicate the onset of cold weather: "put up my Oil Heaters," "made a fier in the Lanton for the first time," and "Begun to Burn Winter Oil."

In most of these years he refers to substituting long lamp chimneys or "tube glasses" for short ones. The use of short chimneys in the warmer months was evidently an economy measure. In an 1831 letter to a lighthouse official, Grover complained that the short chimneys exposed the reflectors to the direct flame of the lamps, which "Spiles all the Reflectors" by melting the silver plating off them.[23] The entry "1 tube Glass Broken" appears an average of thirteen times per year over the eleven complete years covered by the log. In 1829, however, only two glass

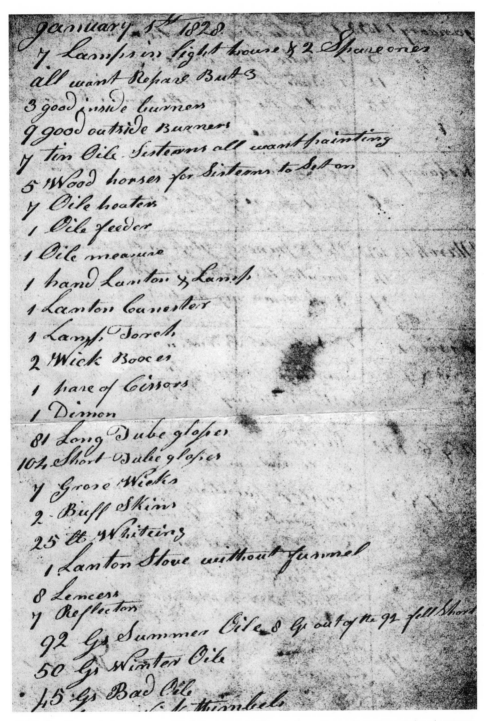

January 5th 1828.
7 Lamps in light house & 2 Spare ones
all want Repare But 3
3 good inside burners
9 good outside Burners
7 tin Oile Sisterns all want painting
5 Wood horses for Sisterns to Set on
7 Oile heaters
1 Oile feeder
1 Oile measure
1 hand Lanton & Lamp
1 Lanton Canester
1 Lamp Torch
2 Wick Boxes
1 pare of Cissors
1 Dimon
81 Long Tube glasses
104 Short Tube glasses
7 Grose Wicks
2 Buff Skins
25 lb Whiteing
1 Lanton Stove without funnel
8 Lencers
7 Reflectors
92 Gs Summer Oile & 8 Gs out of the 92 fell Short
50 Gs Winter Oile
45 Gs Bad Oile
4 thimbels

Eliphalet Grover's inventory of lighthouse supplies and equipment at Boon Island. OYHS.

chimneys were broken during the year; more than twenty were broken in 1831 and 1834, with breakage occurring in every month save October and December in 1834. This breakage was probably related more to the uneven quality of the glass chimneys provided than to seasonal temperature fluctuations. In his January 1, 1838 inventory Grover counted "225 Tube glasses Not good" and "91 Tube glasses good."

Every so often the log is punctuated by the words, "Came heare the Cutter." The revenue cutters from both Portsmouth and Portland made only rare visits to the island, usually with building materials and official messages from the collector's office, especially before 1831. In that year, revenue cutters were first assigned to cruise offshore in the winter months to assist vessels in distress; they were also authorized to stop at lighthouses to check on conditions and, as needed, to provide supplies and material. The Portland cutter *Detector* stopped at the island only once in 1828, for example, to drop off paint, whiting, a paintbrush, and panes of glass in early September.

The pattern of routine entries is also broken by notations of damaging, life-threatening storms and dangerous landings at the island. Grover's log shows that he spent a lot of time repairing storm damage to the long wooden boatways. The boatways (or "slip," as Grover usually wrote) consisted of parallel timbers spaced by iron ties or braces so that a boat could be slid along them into the water. The ways extended about one hundred feet from the boathouse at the north end of the island to a point where a boat could be launched or hauled out at low tide by means of a hand-operated capstan. The boatways were crucial to the survival of the Boon Island keeper and his family. No boat could be safely moored off the island during storm seasons, and hauling the boat onto the island was the only way to ensure that it would be available to go ashore for provisions, to catch the fish with which Grover supplemented both his salary and his larder, or to seek help in case of serious illness or accident. Storms frequently snapped the iron braces securing the timbers, sections of the ways were carried away, and occasionally storms "rackd" both the ways and the boathouse itself. In a storm on September 19, 1828, Grover wrote:

> Sea Started my Slip Caried away 2 Braces Stove in all the underpining of the monement of the Southern Side Beet of 10 Corses of the Shingels and Some of the Boards up Set my Warter Sisterns Stove all my platforms to pieces and hove Down my Wall.

On February 27, 1829:

> Lost the lower part of the Slip

On March 6, 1829:

> The Sea Rackd my Slip all to pieces the Lower part gone and
> midle part the Bolts Broaken of and the upper part Rotten and
> tumbled Down So that it all wants to bee made New

During this period, nearly half a year, Grover recorded no visits by
a revenue cutter, and his terse entry for March 30 was "Went to Portland." Presumably he waited for favorable weather and set out in his
boat to report to the collector of customs the state of things at Boon
Island, especially the condition of the boatways. He negotiated to do the
necessary work himself, and between May 19 and July 15 he made
repairs to the slip, the buildings, and the "platforms." He may have
meant either structures made of laths for the drying of salted fish, or,
more likely, boardwalks laid down to make it easier to walk over the
jumble of rocks and ledges on the island. On September 12, 1829, he
received two hundred dollars toward payment for repairing the boatways, noting on the front page of the log that he was still due $275.

No sooner was the boat slip repaired than a late October storm
struck the island. Grover's record of this event runs on almost breath-
lessly and is one of the few occasions when the word *I* appears in his log:

> October 31 at 9 PM all my famely was forst to go to the Light-
> house and Stay until 5 Next morning at our return to the
> house found all our Warter gone and all the platforms gone and
> all my Turneps and Cabbage Washt away and my Walls all
> Down I have Been heare 13 years 4 months and 28 Days and
> Neve See Such a time before the Sea Washd the Small Rocks
> from under the Light house and Dwelling house the island Was
> all under Water for 4 hours.

During the winters of 1829 and 1830, the iron framework of the
lighthouse lantern began to disintegrate. Grover recorded replacing
many panes of glass in the lantern. He also noted that a March storm
"Rackd the upper part of the Slip and tore up all the platforms." The
Portsmouth revenue cutter finally stopped at the island on June 16,
and word of the situation evidently reached the Portland collector. Early
August saw considerable activity at Boon Island, with both the
Portsmouth and Portland revenue cutters arriving on the fifth, the latter

with new iron sash for the lantern and a blacksmith and his helper to install them. Grover carefully wrote in his log, perhaps as insurance against any suggestion of dereliction of duty, that he had been ordered not to light his lamps for eleven nights during the installation of the new sash. He did not mention the presence of the blacksmith and his helper—perhaps a clue to his personality. In September, the cutter arrived again with a new top for the lantern "and took a way the Old Sashes and Black Smiths Tules" (and presumably the blacksmith and his helper as well). 24

Grover noted the date, May 7, 1831, when he began superintending the building of the new lighthouse (see Chapter 6). Except for the entry of July 22: "Went of the Crew that Built the New Light house," there is no reference to the builders—how many there were, or their living arrangements during their more than two months' stay on the island. Soon after the new lighthouse was finished, Grover sent a letter to Stephen Pleasonton, via the Portland collector, complaining that no district lighthouse superintendent had visited him in nine years, even though this was supposed to be one of the collector's duties. Grover successfully advocated that Boon Island lighthouse be placed under the jurisdiction of the Portsmouth collector, William Pickering.25 On October 1, 1831, he wrote, "BoonIsland Set of to the Superintender of Portsmouth NH William Pickren Esqr Colector."

Even with the assignment of Boon Island to the Portsmouth collector, much more frequent visits by the Portsmouth revenue cutter *Madison* and twice-yearly visits by Collector Pickering or his deputy William Walker, there are times when Grover's log hints at desperation. Storms in January, February, and March 1835 again carried away sections of the boatways, and in March Grover wrote that the slip needed to be entirely rebuilt. The Portsmouth cutter had stopped in February, and its master, Captain Thomas Shaw, had seen the damage done by that date. The captain "Lost his hat and like to lost him Self a landing." Nevertheless, on April 9, "Went past the Cutter." It was not until April 22 that Grover made arrangements with Daniel Drown, the new Portsmouth collector, for the repair of the slip. In early May Grover made two trips ashore to get the necessary iron and timbers, landing them at the island with great difficulty.

On May 20, the cutter came "with new Orders to Keep me at home." Had Grover in his concern for the condition of the boatways exceeded his authority by fetching the materials himself instead of waiting for them to be delivered? It appears from the entries in the back of his log that he occasionally spent time ashore—making repairs to his house in York, shingling a roof, buying eight acres of farmland, building a fence, arranging to rent his house, and selling his hay crop. In 1829, the only entry for the month of August was "Nothing metearel," perhaps a clue that he was ashore during that month. In October of that year he sold the farmland he had bought three years earlier, presumably going to the mainland to close the deal. We do not know how many of his absences came during time off he was entitled to or if he simply took off, leaving the light to be cared for by members of his family or a hired hand.[26]

The log entries are almost devoid of subject pronouns and few people are named. It is thus impossible to say how many of the lighthouse chores were done by Grover himself and how many by family or hired men. On September 25, 1834, he wrote, "Mr. Wm. Tetherly Died on Boon I. at 3 am aged 78." Tetherly was from York; it is possible that he was a hired hand, although he may have been a fisherman driven by a storm to take refuge on the island. There are only a few specific references to others involved in lighthouse work: August 1833: "from the 4 until the 10 my Self and one hand employed White-washing the Buildings on Boonisland;" December, 1834: "He made the first fier in the lanton." In September 1838, Grover wrote, "Both my men" had wrecked the lighthouse boat attempting to land at the island in heavy weather.

There are two references to rescues. One was in 1829:

> September 3 to 4 Strong gales from NW took up 2 Boats with
> 2 men in each Boat most Dead.

One of the survivors, Daniel Nason Jr., of Kennebunk, Maine, later described the help Grover and his family provided:

> I was driven on there at Boon Island in a Boat, Daniel Merrill being with me. We had been exposed to the cold and seas and were entirely exhausted. Mr. Grover and his family rendered every assistance in their power, got us out of the Boat, saved our Boat and entertained us three days. He supplied me with clothes and when we left refused to receive any pay, though I had means to pay him and urged his receiving pay. At the same time two other old men got on shore there and were treated as kindly as we were. I do not think these last named men would have lived two hours longer had they not received the aid of Mr. Grover, and declined receiving any pay from them.

Nason, when he got back home, published a card of thanks to Grover in the *Kennebunk Gazette.* [27] On another occasion Grover helped salvage a vessel and its cargo and may have helped guide the vessel under tow to safety on the mainland, as is not entirely clear in his log entry:

> August 14, 1835: Schoonar Growler of Newbury got on the NW Leag and Beet over and fild nearly full of Warter and I got most of his mackrel on the Island and the rest on Board a mackrel vessel and then I got 2 Vessels to take hir in to and Wen with hir to Cape Nedek [Neddick].

Another wreck occurred at Boon Island early in November 1836. The little steamer *Tom-Thumb* arrived with a large iron storage tank, probably manufactured in Portland, to replace the wooden water cisterns, which were susceptible to being upset when storms inundated the island. Loading at the foundry was delayed, and the *Tom-Thumb* did not arrive with her two-ton cargo until half tide. It would have been impossible to bring the tank ashore until the tide had risen further, so the vessel anchored off the island to await daylight. A Portsmouth paper reported the sequel:

> In the rising wind and increasingly rough seas, she parted her chain cable, and valiantly steamed towards home for five hours making in that time only 9 or 10 miles, when finding that she made water fast, by which her fuel had become wet, rendering it impossible to keep up steam, she again bore away before the wind to Boon Island, and at about 2 o'clock went **pell mell** upon the rocks Her crew were providentially saved, but it is feared the vessel will be lost. Her boilers and a part of her machinery have been saved. No insurance.

Eliphalet Grover noted the wreck in his log, but did not mention taking part in the rescue of the crew.[28] Within less than two years, there were problems with the iron water cistern delivered at such risk by the *Tom-Thumb.* Grover wrote on July 25, 1838:

> Hove all the warter a way out of the Tank it Stunk So that we could Du nothing with it for the Want of Beeing paid over in Side with Bees Wax.

It is possible to detect a proprietary attitude on Grover's part about the government's property on Boon Island: He refers in the log to "my light," "my platforms," and "my boat." But after an official came to inspect the premises on October 19, 1831, he wrote—as if he had just been reminded whose property it was—"Came heare the Cutter from Portsmouth to Examon the State of the things belonging to the United States." The government provided a two-masted spritsail-rigged open boat, similar to those used by local fishermen through the nineteenth and early twentieth centuries, to be used for going ashore to get provisions and to take care of official business. We do not know for sure, but it is likely that for fishing Grover used a similar boat of his own. Boats had to be laboriously hauled up the long boatways into the boathouse by means of a capstan, which was turned by hand. Grover described his return to the island on October 8, 1832. Here there is the rare use of the first person pronoun as well as evidence of a fatalistic attitude about the dangers of his job:

> At 7 PM Came from York in my Boat With a full Load of provision in hir and got Within one mile of the island When She Sprung a Leak and When I got on the island the Warter was over the thorts and She filled and turnd Over and I Lost all my things my main mast and Main Sail Both Oars spreats and thort and my Compass and Stove the Boat Veary much Before I Could git hir up out of the Sea I was Veary near Drounding my Self But it Was not So to bee.

The lighthouse boat was smashed beyond repair in mid-September 1838. On the sixth, Grover had sent the two helpers he had at the time to get coal from York for the stove in the lighthouse lantern, but, he wrote, "the Wind and Sea was So Ruf that they Could not Return until the 15 and Landing stove my boat all to pieces and Lost 46 Bushels of Coal and Came near to Lusein Both my men in the Boat."

Grover wrote "my boat," but it must have been the government's. By the end of the month, a replacement arrived from Collector Anderson in Portland. (Boon Island had been returned to the Portland collector's jurisdiction.) Grover recorded—perhaps in anger, perhaps with scorn—that the boat was delivered "Without Cable or Anchor or mast holes or Steps."

Except for the fish he and other household members caught in the vicinity of Boon Island, the family depended for food on what they brought from York or Portsmouth. They could expect to be cut off from the mainland from early fall through March, and tried to stock up in September with enough staples—flour, sugar, lard, salted meats, hard tack, and dried beans and perhaps apples—to see them through the winter. Their diet must have been dreary. Milk was out of the question during these months, though they may have used heavily salted butter and cheese. Keeping hens would have been an uncertain proposition during the stormiest months in fall, winter, and early spring, but were likely kept during the rest of the year; they doubtless did without fresh poultry during the bad seasons. The family could have used a solution of lime water or a coating of grease to seal the pores of eggs to preserve them for months. Their vegetables would have been cabbages, carrots, turnips and potatoes, all of which could be stored for a long time.

In January 1832, the family must have been running short of food, when Grover wrote in the back of his log that he owed Captain Thomas Shaw of the revenue cutter *Madison* for 206 pounds of ship's bread; on the other hand, when Shaw left a bushel barrel each of salted beef and pork on February 5, 1835, Grover carefully noted that he had not asked for these provisions.

> April 10, 1838: Examend Before John Anderson Esqr for mis-Conduct and Destroying a Buye Belonging to the United States.

The episode of the buoy marked the beginning of an attempt to discredit Eliphalet Grover as a suitable lighthouse keeper, perhaps to justify his replacement with a supporter of the party in power in Washington. The hearing was precipitated by a February 1838 letter to Secretary of the Treasury Levi Woodbury from Joshua Herrick, deputy collector for Kennebunk. Herrick wrote that he would not have made the report against Grover "were complaints of him less general, or his general deportment and character less reprehensible":

> Some time since a valuable ceder buoy placed at the Fishing Rocks at the entrance of this harbor broke from its moorings and drifted on to Boon Island, and having been directed by the superintendent of Lights at Portland to replace the buoy, I made exertions to find it—Capt. Stephen Ward of the Packet Schooner *Grape* of this place being on the Island notified Grover that the buoy he had ashore belonged to the United States and must not be destroyed, and as is the usual fate of those that visit the Island he was at once assailed with a volley of vulgarity and abusive oaths seldom equaled any where else. He gave Capt. Ward however to understand that the buoy would or should be cut up and if I wanted the irons I might have them for $10—about the value of new ones. [29]

The "irons" were evidently pieces fastened to the base of the cedar timber to weight it so that it would float more or less upright when tethered by a chain to an anchor or rock. Herrick wrote that because there was no cedar available along the seacoast, the buoy timber had been brought from the interior at great expense; he was anxious to retrieve it. An emissary, Captain William M. Emery, went to Boon Island with an offer to pay Grover for his salvage of the buoy. Grover refused, according to Herrick,

> and the same abusive language applied to him as to Capt. Ward, repeated with addition not only of myself but of the Collector—the President of the U. States—the Secretary of the Treasury—the Superintendent of Lights etc.—and challenged the whole to get it from him and swore that it would be cut up, and that anything else he could get hold of belonging to the United States should share the same fate.

Herrick stated that he sent Captain Emery and Daniel Murphy back to the island with an offer to exchange the buoy for three sticks of pine equivalent to the large cedar timber, but they found that the buoy had already been cut up. They retrieved the irons after paying seven dollars and fifty cents for them, and left the island with Grover telling them that if Herrick did not send him two dollars and fifty cents more he "would raise h-ll with me." Herrick concluded by saying that Grover in his long years at Boon Island "is said to have found ways and means to make himself rich, had grown insolent, and become exceedingly abusive."

The April 1838 hearing in Kennebunk, presided over by Portland Collector of Customs John Anderson, who was also a justice of the peace, involved an incident that occurred in August 1836, twenty months earlier. The testimony at the hearing and in depositions offered conflicting testimony as to the facts and as to Grover's character and personality.

Grover had the services of a lawyer, and several witnesses testified on his behalf. Grover's son Samuel, who was about fifteen at the time of the events, said that he had been mackerel fishing with Joel Newell, of York, when they spotted the top of a large floating timber about three miles away and went to salvage it. Without realizing it was a buoy, they towed it to the boat slip at Boon Island, a job that took them several hours. They then tried to haul it out. It was so heavy that everyone on the island—the family and two men living with them— turned out to help. Even using the boatways capstan, it took them hours to get it only partly up out of the water. Joel Newell testified that "Mr. Grover, the old man, said he could not think what the damd thing could be." Still not realizing it was a buoy, young Grover and Newell sawed off the part that had been hauled out of the water. When they pulled out the rest of the timber, they discovered the irons at the end of the timber and realized it was a buoy.[30]

George Davis, of Kennebunkport, testified that he had been the first to report the whereabouts of the buoy to the collector in Kennebunk, and said that it had already been cut up. He had been a passenger aboard a schooner bound to Boston; the vessel being becalmed, he had gone ashore on Boon Island and seen the buoy in pieces, with the irons cut off. According to Davis, Grover asked him to report to the collector of Kennebunk that he had the buoy irons, which the collector could have if he would pay Grover the cost of salvage.

Another witness, Daniel Murphy, agreed that Grover swore a lot, but no more than most seamen. He testified that the lighthouse and dwelling were in good order and that he thought Grover a good man for the lighthouse job. Murphy also revealed one source of Grover's frustration with the government, saying that most of Grover's oaths had to do with the delayed delivery of a new water tank for the island, the one subsequentyly delivered by the ill-fated *Tom-Thumb*.

Captain Ward, in an earlier deposition, had repeated Herrick's charges and added that though at the time he did not think Grover was drunk, "from what I have since heard of him suppose it might have been the case." At the hearing, Captain Ward admitted that the buoy was already cut up when he saw it on Boon Island, and that Grover had told him the buoy was so heavy it couldn't be gotten entirely out of the water without cutting it. Grover's attorney also elicited the information that Ward had gone ashore on Boon Island to get some oil for his vessel's lamp and that Grover had helpfully provided about a quart at no charge. Ward also admitted that his brother-in-law was a candidate for the keepership of Boon Island!

Solomon Brooks, of York, served as a character witness, stating that though Grover's expressions were "ungentlemanly," he was an "honest and upright man." Daniel Nason recounted the kindness with which he had been treated when cast away on Boon Island in 1829, and staid that Grover, who was generous in every other way, had been unable to provide the rum one of the survivors asked for because he did not keep any on the island.[31]

Collector Anderson, in his August 1838 report to Secretary Woodbury, indicated that no case for dismissal had been made against Grover. Grover himself wrote to Woodbury that he had been proven "as Innocent of the charges against me as the Angels in heaven." [32]

There the matter seemed to rest. Grover appeared to be more than usually industrious in the months following the hearing. Entries in his log record that he painted the lighthouse lantern, made two trips to York for iron and timber for repairs, painted his boat, made new door and window frames for the house, and worked on the boatways. He white-washed the rooms of the house, painted the floors, and cleaned out the oil cisterns. In August he went to York to get supplies in preparation for the arrival of a crew of masons, who arrived on the eighth to repoint the masonry of the lighthouse and dwelling and apply a coat of whitewash to them. He was sent beeswax for coating the inside of the water tank. Much of this activity must have been related to the impending survey of lighthouses by naval inspector Lieutenant Thomas Manning. (See Chapter 6.) Manning's arrival is not noted by Grover in his log, whether because Grover was ashore getting his winter supplies or because he often omitted names of people from his log entries.

In January 1839 another severe storm raked the island and drove everyone into the lighthouse:

> January 25th. Saturday Strong gales from the South- East Sea making very fast. Sunday morning left the House and went into the Light-House Sea carried away all my Plat Forms and Riped the Shingles of the Monument and Porch of the House unhung the Porch Doors and came in to the Dwelling House the Sea washed away the Rocks before the Door So as to make a fair Breach on the House Sea went into the Light House door broke the latch and like to have destroyed my Oil. I have been here 23 Winters and never See Such a time before Damage Done cannot be repaired Short of one hundred dollars.—at 3 P. M. tide Down So we could Venture out.

This is the only entry in the log written in a hand other than Eliphalet Grover's. The wording is very much like his, and the use of *I,* which typically cropped up only at times of stress, suggests that he was dictating to someone, perhaps his son Samuel. We learn later that he had injured his hand trying to batten things down as the storm mounted.

The next entry, three days later, is in Grover's own hand:

> January 28 But the Rocks has almost Shet us up in the house they are pild up Round the Doar So the Sea has washt the Luse Rocks away So as to make a fair Breach agains the frunt of the house and if there isn't a wall made in frunt of the house it will not Bee Safe to Stay heare. 29 & 30 Employd

> Clearing a passage from the Doar to the Lighthouse and
> monement. The Sea Stove my Warter Sistern at the corner of
> the house.[33]

The next days were spent trying to launch his boat so he could go
ashore. Much of the following spring he worked on repairing the storm
damage to the buildings. During this time, the bones of two men were
discovered and taken to York for burial:

> April 11, 1839: took Down my heaters and Employd Secuare-
> ing my Slip and taking up the bones of 2 people that were
> Drowned heare when the first monument was erected heare to
> send on shoare to put in the graveyard in York.

Next, an undated entry:

> Boght 1 Keg of White Lead and 2 Bundles of Shingles
> And 2 lb. of Nails for the Repair of the Buildings.
> April 19: I Tube glass Broaken

Then, probably the last entry written at Boon Island:

> April 26: painted and Whitewashed the New Shingles that I
> put on where the Sea washt them of.

On May 10, 1839, Grover wrote on the back page of his log:

> Turned of [sic] of Boon island after Serving as Lighthouse
> Keeper 22 years 10 months and 20 days without Cause.

Given the widespread application of the spoils system of rewarding
political partisans with federal appointments after Andrew Jackson's
inauguration in 1829, it seems in retrospect remarkable that Grover
held on to his job as long as he did.

Back in his house in York, Grover began a campaign for reinstate-
ment as lightkeeper. His letters, many evidently penned for him by his
son Samuel, added considerable bulk to the many linear feet of material in the National Archives labeled "Correspondence Concerning Keepers and Assistants," much of which is the legacy of the patronage
system. In a late-May letter to Levi Woodbury, Grover wrote of his
being replaced:

> I should much rather you would have come or Sent and Shot
> me on the Island.

He pleaded poverty, his wife's incapacity, and his own injured
right hand, begging that either he or his son Samuel be given another

lighthouse job as soon as a vacancy occurred. The letter was signed "Eliphalet Grover Broken Keeper without cause."

The sixty-year-old keeper had bipartisan support. In July, Portland Collector Anderson (a Democrat) forwarded to Woodbury his own favorable comment and two petitions signed by five York men (at least some of whom were also Democrats). One petition was for the appointment of Eliphalet Grover, the other for the appointment of his son Samuel to the first available Maine lighthouse vacancy. Samuel seems to have been suggested not only because he had learned from his father how to tend a lighthouse and was "industrious, sober, discreet and honest," but also because his mainland schooling had given him a polish his rough-edged father lacked: "His studious habits, industry and amiable conduct while on shore in getting an education, has recommended him to the best Society, in which he is greatly respected."

Grover wrote many letters to Woodbury, without success. Many bear the pencilled notation "usual reply. W." or "file." After Woodbury permitted Grover's replacement on Boon Island, Joseph P. Junkins, to trade jobs with Mark Dennett, collector for York, Grover wrote that this maneuver had left "the State of Maine, New-Hampshire and Massachusetts all in an uproar and the Parts of the People in each state are crying out Grover you must go back to Boon Island."

After the 1840 election returned a Whig to the White House, he resumed his campaign, with a January 1841 letter to Stephen Pleasonton. He tried flattery: "I now address you as 5th Auditor but I am in hopes the next time I write to you it will be to the Secretary of the Treasury." He wrote that Junkins "did not know a Light-House from a Meeting House." Further, of the six men in York now contending for the Boon Island job, none needed it. In March he wrote in his own hand to the new secretary of the treasury, Thomas Ewing, that he had been turned off Boon Island by Woodbury to make room for a radical, "loco" Democratic farmer. (Grover did not name him, but this must have been Mark Dennett.)

Because of the six hundred dollar annual salary many were "mad" for the job at Boon Island, Grover wrote, even though it was the most dangerous lighthouse on our northern coast. "George Molton has Been to Washington to try to git the Birth and I now inform you that he has a good farm and Owns a grist mill and part of 2 or 3 Coasten Vessels and such a man ort not to have the Birth it ort in my Opinion to Bee given to poor Seafaring men and I am one if there is one in the States."

He also wrote to the collector for Portland at the time, Nathan Cummins. He provided testimonials from Winslow Lewis, who had visited

Boon Island many times, to deliver oil and to inspect or install equipment, and two revenue cutter officers who were familiar with the Boon Island light when Grover was keeper. In September 1841, Eliphalet Grover was finally given a lighthouse appointment, not to Boon Island, but at another dangerous lighthouse—Whale's Back, oversight of which had just been transferred from the Portsmouth to the Portland collector. Grover remained there until August 1843, when Whale's Back was returned to the domain of the Portsmouth collector.[34] He presumably spent the remaining dozen years of his life in York, where he died in 1855. He is buried in the graveyard there beside his wife Susanna, who outlived him by three years.

Other Early Boon Island Lightkeepers

There was considerable turnover at Boon Island after Eliphalet Grover was displaced as keeper in 1839. Seven different men were appointed keeper over the next decade. Although a few of the keepers resigned, the frequent changes were mostly the result of the intense political rivalries of this period, not only between the Whigs and Democrats but between factions within the two parties as well. These brought changes in collectors of customs, each of whom tried to exercise the power of patronage and some being overruled in Washington. In addition, Boon Island was caught in a tug-of-war between Maine and New Hampshire. During the presidency of John Tyler, New Hampshire Whigs in 1843 engineered the return of both Boon Island and Whale's Back lighthouses to the Portsmouth collector's supervision.

Mark Dennett

One of the lightkeepers who followed Eliphalet Grover at Boon Island was Mark Dennett, a fifty-four-year-old Kittery farmer, schoolteacher, and politician. He began his Boon Island keepership at the beginning of July 1840. He took with him his fourteen-year old son, Charles, to help and his twenty-three year old daughter, Betsey, to keep house, leaving his wife and other children at home in Kittery.

We know a great deal about Mark Dennett because as soon as he was settled at the island, he began to write his autobiography, "Sketches of Life," beginning with his earliest memory of himself in 1789, when he

was three and still wearing dresses. The first twelve of the closely written pages take his life up to the time he went to Boon Island. He had been
brought up on a farm in Kittery, which he took over at the age of seventeen on the death of his father. Educated in local schools, he was taught
Latin and Greek by ministers and was qualified to teach school himself
at eighteen. Probably raised a Congregationalist, he became a Free-Will
Baptist in 1808. A Jeffersonian Republican turned Jacksonian Decomoc-
rat, he had held numerous political offices in the town of Kittery, was representative to the Massachusetts General Court before Maine became a
state, and was a state senator in the 1820s after statehood.[35]   .

*Mark Dennett, keeper of Boon Island light in the early 1850s. Photo taken when Dennett
was an old man.* Collection Armistead Dennett.

First married in 1808, Dennett remarried in 1820 after the death of his first wife. By the time he went to Boon Island, he had ten living children, many of whom, except Alexander, the eldest, were probably still at home on the Kittery farm. It may well be that he took the keepership because he was not reappointed customs collector for York, even though this was not a lucrative position. The six-hundred-dollar annual salary at Boon Island may have been an attraction for a man with such a large family.

Another manuscript by Mark Dennett survives, "Daily Journal kept by Mark Dennett, Keeper of the Light House at Boon Island."[36] Except for better spelling and punctuation, it reads very much like Eliphalet Grover's "Logg." Soon after he arrived at the island, Dennett recorded the oil contractor's annual visit with winter and summer oil for the lamps, seventy-five tube glasses, wicks, scissors, a buff skin, an oil carrier, and a small lamp for the house, plus twelve pounds of whiting. On July 25, 1840, he wrote that the thimble to lamp No. 6 was out of order. An average of five tube glasses broke each month. Winter storms did major damage to the boatways. In late1840 and early 1841 he recorded the breakage of iron braces holding the timbers of the boatways in place, and attempts to repair them; by April more bolts and braces had been wrenched away by storm seas.

Dennett earned extra money fishing; in October 1840, he noted the sale of 145 pounds of codfish to T. Pettegrow. He also received extra pay for a number of maintenance chores: whitewashing the razee of the old lighthouse, the boathouse, the "back-side" of the dwelling house, and the inside of the house; painting the kitchen floor; taking ashore for repairs a broken iron brace from the boatways after the slip had been "rent to pieces by the sea"; shingling the old monument "where stript by the sea in the late Storm"; and puttying the seams of the boat and painting it "within and without."

Nearly twenty years after he left Boon Island, in July 1841, Dennett resumed writing his life's story, beginning with two paragraphs about his year as keeper at Boon Island. While they do not explain the politics involved in his taking the lightkeeper's job, the second paragraph explains why he left and is a reminder of the prevalence of tuberculosis during this period.

> I resigned my employment as Keeper of Boon Island Light and left that Island on the first of July 1841 having spent an interesting year principally on that lonely Rock. During the summer season we had considerable communication with the Main

Land by Visitors and Fishermem; but in the Winter None but once when my son Sylvester with Mr. Trafton came off and stopped while Betsey and Charles and myself made a visit home about two weeks. Betsey was attacked with bleeding at the lungs in June when I immediately brought her home and she lingered and declined until November and deceased on the 18th November 1841.[37]

Dennett's daughter Betsey wrote a letter from Boon Island in May 1841 to her younger half sister Alice; it has been preserved by the Dennett family. Her letter, begun on May 13, says as little about life on Boon Island as her father's journal and biographical sketch, but it reveals the solitude of her situation. It had been seven months since Betsey had seen Alice: "I expect I shall stay here untill the last of June and perhaps untill September." She wrote that she had "no news to write and only write for the mere pleasure of writing to you, since I have not the privilege of an association in any other form." Betsey referred neither to her health nor to the condition of the keeper's house and lighthouse, which I. W. P. Lewis found to be terrible on his inspection two years later. Instead, much of her letter is about the religious tracts on sanctification and eternal life, which evidently sustained her in her illness and isolation. Nine days later Betsey wrote a postscript to her letter that suggests that her father, who had a farm, a wife, and many other children to be concerned with on the mainland, must have been away from his Boon Island post considerably more often than his much later reminiscence indicates:

> Alice—Pa came out yesterday but forgot to take your letter which disappointed me some, as I thought it likely I might receive one from you, and I forgot to send mine in, as it was most night when they came and did not stop. Alexander [her older brother] never got out of the boat so it was all hurry—I am agoing to try to send mine in next week by some of the fishing Boats—George N. Holman [perhaps a hired hand] is here with us. Yours.
> Adieu. B.[38]

Captain John S. Thompson, of York, took Mark Dennett's place. Like most Boon Island keepers before him, he fished the near waters and set up wooden racks or "flakes" for drying salted fish. On October 3 and 4, 1841, Boon Island endured a violent gale, and an account of it he gave in a letter to his son Charles was published subsequently in the *Portsmouth Journal:*

My Dear Son:—You have undoubtedly felt anxious to hear
from me, since the late dreadful storm of the 4th inst. It has
been very destructive—more so than was ever known by those
long acquainted with this Island. In short, the whole face of the
Island is so changed, that an old acquaintance would scarcely
believe himself on Boon Island.

The storm commenced the night of the 3rd and continued
with unabated fury 30 hours, wind veering and hauling from
the NE to ESE. The tides being very full, the whole island was
under water about three hours each high water—and the sea
making an uninterrupted breach over the whole island, overturning huge rocks which had probably rested in quiet for centuries, to find a new resting place. Among others, a huge rock,
which has been located (since time began) about half way
between the high part of the island and low water mark, now
rests on the highest part of the island; the weight of this rock
I will not attempt to conjecture; it is of the following dimensions, viz: 23 feet long, 16 feet wide, mean thickness 6 feet. It
will remain a monument of the restless power which placed it
where it now is, to astonish all beholders who may be told how
it came there. Damages sustained as follows: NE corner of the
dwelling-house knocked away from foundation to the eaves; a
thick stone wall between the house and old Light-House, driv-
en away; the plat- form in front of all the buildings, gone to sea;
underpinning of the front porch washed out, floor ripped up;
cellar doors driven in; two water cisterns of 400 gallons each,
driven from their stations; Light-House door driven open; 4 of
7 butts of oil upset, and 168 gallons of oil lost; shingles rent
from the buildings; Boat- house driven from its station; fish-
flakes gone to sea. In short, the whole island washed as clean
as the earth was by the flood. The Boat-Slip we had just
repaired; it stands firm, with but little injury.[39]

It was this storm that persuaded keeper Joseph Currier to resign
from his position at Whale's Back light. Thompson was not deterred by
the storm—but evidently made more trips ashore than he should have.
When I.W. P. Lewis made his inspection in 1842, he reported not only
on the bad conditions at the island, but also that "the keeper absents
himself frequently, leaving a hired man in his place." Thompson
protested when word reached him in the summer of 1843 that he was
to be replaced. The reason for his replacement, however, was evidently
not being delinquent as keeper, but rather the return of both Boon

Island and Whale's Back lights to the Portsmouth collector's supervision. Portsmouth collector George Dennett appointed John Kennard of South Berwick, a tailor who had been keeper at Whale's Back in 1840, to the Boon Island keepership. John Thompson tried to salvage his job with a letter to President John Tyler:

> I have been a seaman from a boy—being now 60 years old, am poor, have a family support, with a little or no means. I voted for your Excellency for Vice President and intended to exert my feeble influence to promote another election for you for President— why I am removed, I am at a loss to determine.[40]

The next month, the *Portsmouth Journal* reported that Thompson had been reinstated, although government records show that his appointment was not effective until June 1844. Thompson lost his job again in 1846 in the wake of the election of James K. Polk. His replacement, recommended by Portsmouth Collector Augustus Jenkins, was Nathaniel Baker, another seafaring man from York. Baker became a local hero by rescuing the crew of the schooner *Caroline* when she was wrecked on ledges off the island. After the Whigs gained the presidency in 1848, there was partisan agitation in York to have John Thompson reinstated. When Thompson was reappointed, collector Jenkins, himself displaced, went to bat for Baker with a letter to Washington.[41] Another man wrote a letter in support of Baker:

> Captain Baker is a man of strict integrity of character and has always to my knowledge kept a good light... will state also that this Island is situated nine miles from land in the wake of all the Eastern bound vessels engaged in coasting to the West— and it is very necessary that there should not only be a good keeper on the Island but a good pilot. I believe all parties are satisfied with Capt. Baker, and would not desire a change on any account. Capt. Baker is the third keeper I have been here with and I can truly say that he is far the best man that has kept the light.[42]

The writer was Benjamin O. Fletcher, who had been the hired helper not only of Baker but also of Thompson and Kennard before him. Fletcher is one of a handful of hired lighthouse helpers who can be identified from among the many who must have given the appointed lightkeepers of this period considerable freedom to come and go. These men, about whom even less can be learned than of the lightkeepers

themselves, were not subject to the patronage system and thus provided continuity as one keeper after another was appointed.[43] Their pay
must have been abysmal, since it came from the keeper's own salary,
and may have consisted of little more than room and board. Fletcher
stayed on at Boon Island as helper when John Thompson returned in
1849, and figured in a local newspaper account of the fatal attraction
the lighthouse lamps held for birds:

> The Boon Island Bird Trap
> We have heard many strange stories about the great number
> of birds, which, being bewildered by the bright glare of the
> Lamp on Boon Island, fly against the iron railing which sur-
> rounds the light with such force as to kill themselves. We had
> heard that some mornings several bushels of dead birds have
> been gathered up around the light, which had fallen victim to
> the brilliancy of the previous night.
>
> A few days since we inquired of Capt. Thompson, the keep-
> er, whether there is any truth in the stories. He says that such
> devastation was not of daily occurrence, but that frequently a
> large number of dead birds was found around the light-house.
> One morning, about three months since, there was a rather
> larger number than common. His assistant, Mr. Fletcher, gath-
> ered in one heap three hundred and sixteen birds, which had
> fallen the previous night. There were in this heap at least
> twenty varieties of land and sea birds – some of beautiful
> plumage, such as he had never seen before. Walking around
> the light, Capt. Thompson saw many more, which would have
> added largely to the heap.[44]

Thompson, perhaps seeking to demonstrate his reliability and constant presence on Boon Island, in November 1849 wrote to Lory Odell,
the Portsmouth collector at the time, of the number of vessels that
passed Boon Island:

> In looking over my daily journal, I find that the following num-
> ber of vessels have passed this island between the rising and
> setting sun of each day, from Oct. 20th to Nov. 20th, 1849.

Steamers,	9	Brigs,	89
Ships,	5	Schooners,	935
Barques,	6	Sloops,	6
			1050

> Fishing Vessels not included. Many more probably passed
> which were not seen, during those foggy and smoky days, and

no doubt quite as many passed during those long nights. This goes to show the importance of a Light of the first magnitude on this Island, situated as it is, 10 miles from the main land, directly in the track of the great coasting trade from Halifax, along the coasts of Maine, New-Hampshire, to New York, &c. and surrounded as it is with many dangers. I doubt if there is any Light on the United States Atlantic coast more needed than Boon Island Light.[45]

Thompson may not have mended his ways, though. A letter published in the *New-Hampshire Gazette* (a Democratic newspaper) reported that the Whig appointee was frequently absent from his Boon Island post:

Mr. Editor:—In making our usual excursions we notice that the Keeper of Boon Island Light absents himself from duty on long visits on shore, having left the island on the 23rd day of March, and did not return until the 11th day of April, leaving one person only on the island for that length of time, and that one known to be visiting vessels a mile and a half from the island, leaving the public property in charge of nobody. It is said that keepers are instructed not to leave their stations without the consent of their superintendents at any time, and not to be absent over twenty-four hours at a time. Whether the Boon Island gentlemen had such consent we are not informed. These things would not be published had not the above named keeper been re-appointed by the present administration in spite of former delinquencies charged upon him.

A FISHERMAN [46]

Thompson nevertheless hung onto his job until another change in administration in 1853, when he retired from lighthouse keeping at the age of seventy.

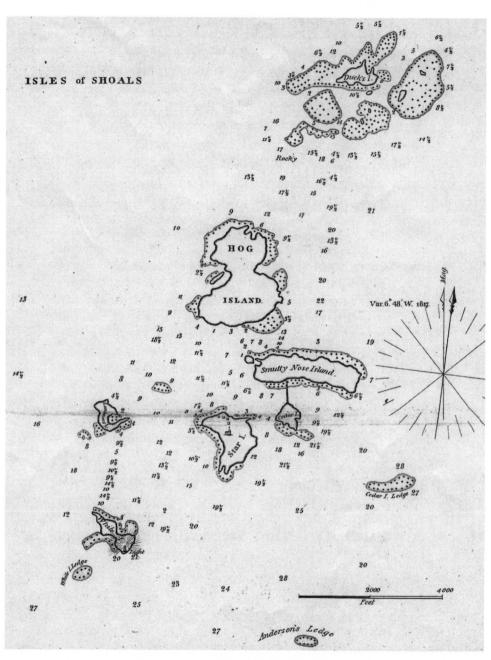

A chart of the Isles of Shoals, where Thomas B. Laighton bought Smuttynorse, Cedar, Malaga and Hog (later Appledore) islands, from the 1841 edition of the American Coast Pilot. *The White Island lighthouse where he became keeper in 1839 is indicated, as are the many hazards to navigation at the Shoals. The Cedar-Smuttynose breakwater, though largely destroyed soon after construction, made passage between the islands impossible.*

IX *Some Early Lighthouse Keepers II: White Island and Whale's Back*

Some one began to light the lamps in the tower. Rich red and golden, they swung round in mid-air; everything was strange and fascinating and new. We entered the quaint little old stone cottage that was for six years our home.

—Celia Thaxter, *Among the Isles of Shoals*, 1873

White Island

Clement Jackson

Clement Jackson was the first keeper at White Island when it was officially lit in January 1821. Little is known of him beyond what can be gleaned from Portsmouth tax lists and directories and a little correspondence with lighthouse administrators. He was in his mid-fifties when he took the White Island job. He was doubtless named for, and probably related to, the Portsmouth doctor of the same name who died in the late 1780s.

Portsmouth's first directory, published the year of Clement Jackson's appointment to White Island, shows him living on Jackson Lane. If he had a wife and children, it is not recorded. A merchant until 1803, he paid a comparatively large property tax from the late 1790s until the fire of 1802 destroyed a shop he rented in the business district of Portsmouth; he went into bankruptcy the next year. He evidently never recovered his former prosperity. He worked as a joiner from 1810 through 1813, but his means of livelihood thereafter is unknown.[1]

President Monroe's choice of Jackson for the White Island post ignored Customs Collector Timothy Upham's recommendation of master carpenter Nathaniel Marston ("a man of steady habits and of strict integrity") who had only recently finished work on the White Island buildings. Upham's response hints that he did not feel Jackson was cut out for the job: "Mr. Jackson is quite a respectable man, I should think much above the standing of those usually employed in such situations; and if he can content himself to remain on the Island (which he assures me he will do) I have no doubt he will make an excellent Keeper."[2] In spite of Upham's reservations, Jackson stuck it out for three years.

It must have been a difficult adjustment for the middle-aged Jackson, to move to this isolated situation and contend with all the problems there were in the years just after the lighthouse was built. (See Chapter 5.) Out of his four hundred dollar yearly pay, Jackson had to hire a man to help him tend the lighthouse. When he went ashore with his reports, which he was expected to do quarterly, he needed to hire an additional helper because the White Island lighthouse equipment, with its clockworks machinery for revolving the lights and tolling the fog bell, was too demanding for one man to handle; Jackson or his helper had to stay in the lighthouse all night to tend the equipment.

In 1822 Jackson spent more than his salary to hire helpers. The hoped-for income from fishing did not materialize for him and his assistant, perhaps because of the constant problems with the boatways and the difficulty of keeping a boat at the island. It also could be that Jackson simply lacked the necessary resourcefulness and sea wisdom; there is no evidence that he had any experience at sea before he went to White Island. Collector Upham, requesting a raise for Jackson, wrote that he had been a "steady, correct and temperate man, which in a situation so far removed from observation is of the first importance," but that he lacked "any emoluments or advantages of any kind from which he can increase his income." At the end of 1823, Jackson himself wrote to Treasury Secretary William Crawford, without success. With no prospect of more pay, Clement Jackson resigned in November 1824. He did not resettle in Portsmouth, and we do not know how he fared in the years before he died in Rochester, New Hampshire, in 1844.[3]

Benjamin Haley

Clement Jackson's replacement was Benjamin Haley, described by Upham in his recommendation as a native of the Shoals, "accustomed to the climate and the dreary solitude of the place." For the previous four years, Haley had been a shipmaster, living in Portsmouth; he was expected to bring his small family to live with him at the island. Whether Haley actually moved his family is unclear; he retained his house in Portsmouth. By at least March 1828, he had hired William Godfrey to help with lighthouse duties. Haley's tenure was cut short when he died in Portsmouth in June 1829 at the age of only thirty-three. After Haley's death, Godfrey stayed on until a replacement was appointed in July.[4]

Joseph L. Locke

Customs Collector John P. Decatur, whose presidential appointment, made during a recess of the U.S. Congress, was ardently opposed by Portsmouth Democrats, had his appointment rescinded by the U. S. Senate in 1830. Decatur had accused Godfrey of stealing iron rails (perhaps used for hauling building materials onto the island) and sperm oil for resale in Seabrook, New Hampshire. He successfully recommended Joseph L. Locke of Rye, New Hampshire, for the keepership.[5]

Joseph Locke, who carried the title of major, became a thorn in the flesh of Decatur's Portsmouth opponents and the customs collectors who succeeded him. Not long after his appointment, the following letter appeared in the March 2, 1830 *New-Hampshire Gazette:*

In spite of this and other complaints, Locke kept his job at White Island for ten years. He took his wife, Sarah, to White Island; their six children, ranging in age from about twelve (Thaddeus) to the infant Andrew Jackson Locke, must have gone with them. As at Boon Island, the White Island boatways caused almost continual problems, a situation that often left the keeper and his family dependent

New-Hampshire Gazette, 2 March 1830.

MR. BECK—Why is it, that Joseph L. Locke, Keeper of the Light at the Isle of Shoals, is spending his time in this town and vicinity, month after month, when the approach of our seafaring friends to our harbor at this season of the year is so hazardous? Has not enough already been done to break the ranks of the Democratic party, which has so long labored for the ascendency, but *this man must abandon his duty to the government,* for which he is receiving *ample compensation* and obtrude himself upon the independent electors of this town and State in electioneering against the Democratic party?

Who will refund the property which may be lost by his neglect of duty, to say nothing of the sacrifice of valuable lives?

Is it not time that the President should be informed of this State of things?

ONE WHO KNOWS.

upon neighboring islanders for help. The boatways had been entirely rebuilt in the summer of 1829, but William Pickering, who replaced Decatur as collector, reported that they were carried away by a storm in March 1830. Locke had to tie up his boat off the island, and in another storm the boat parted from its mooring and was smashed to pieces on another island of the Shoals group.[6]

Three more children were born to the Lockes during his tenure as White Island keeper. It is likely that his wife went ashore to give birth, and it is possible that she did not return to the island at all after 1832. At the end of this year, Locke wrote to collector Pickering that his wife had become so ill that he had taken her (and presumably the children) home to Rye, where he could care for her and where a physician could visit her regularly. This he did not report until more than two weeks after the fact. He asked, and was given, permission to leave Shoals native Asa Caswell in charge of the lighthouse until spring, assisted by "Mr. Dunkin" (perhaps the Samuel Duncan who had helped his father tend the lights for so many years at Fort Constitution). In April, however, Locke asked for an extension and produced a physician's statement that it would be bad for his wife's health for her to go back to White Island, the place "where her disease was contracted." Mrs. Locke recovered from her unspecified ailment, and in fact outlived her husband by more than twenty years.[7]

In 1837, Edmund and George Blunt, publishers of the *American Coast Pilot,* wrote a long letter to Secretary of the Treasury Levi Woodbury, filled with complaints about the U.S. lighthouse system. They reported that the White Island keeper was often away from the island without authorization, leaving a woman to take care of the light. (Whether or not this was Mrs. Locke has not been established.) The Blunts wrote that the Portsmouth collector (Daniel Drown at that time) had not been able to dislodge Locke from the keepership.[8]

Locke used his political connections to keep his job at White Island until the fall of 1839. The solution to the problem was evidently to appoint him to the position of keeper at Whale's Back lighthouse, a job with an equal annual salary of six hundred dollars. Though one local newspaper described this as a "promotion," the precarious condition of this lighthouse and the fact that Locke's comings and goings could more easily be observed at this location, raise the possibility that this appointment was actually a maneuver to get rid of him. Locke obliged his political enemies by his continued cavalier attitude about the requirements of the job.[9]

Thomas B. Laighton

In the fall of 1839, Thomas B. Laighton, of Portsmouth, was appointed keeper of White Island lighthouse, replacing Joseph Locke. More has been written about Laighton and his family than about any other lightkeeper in this area, thanks to Laighton's local prominence as a political figure, the successful summer hotel he established at Appledore Island in the late 1840s, the writings of his daughter, Celia Laighton Thaxter, and the numerous books and articles on her life and works.

Thomas Laighton (1805-1866) was born to a family of grocers and seafaring men in the coasting trade. A childhood illness or accident left him with a limp and forced him to use a cane to get around. He had a high school education and was an avid reader. Before his appointment to White Island, he was active in civic affairs as a selectman, school committee member, tax assessor, and proponent of an insane asylum in New Hampshire. He was a charter investor in the short-lived Portsmouth Whaling Company formed in 1832 and a clerk at the customs house and post office. He had been a co-editor of the *New-Hampshire Gazette*. A passionate adherent of the radical "loco-foco" wing of the Democratic Party and a member of the Portsmouth Democratic Committee, he was one of the 1834 founders of the politically oriented Portsmouth Working Man's Reading Club and a member of its book selection committee. Laighton was one of the handful of local lightkeepers entitled to be addressed as "the Honorable," as he had served in the New Hampshire Senate. An intense and forceful speaker, he was considered an obnoxious, "low-down" political operative by those who disagreed with his strongly held political views. During construction of Whale's Back lighthouse, Laighton was one of the two local Democrats who tried to discredit Collector of Customs John P. Decatur.(See Chapter 6.)[10]

Friends as well as political foes were startled when Laighton took his wife Eliza and their two children, four-year old Celia and Oscar, who was only a few months old, to White Island in late September 1839. (Another son, Cedric, was born in 1840.) Ben Whaling, a Portsmouth man, went with the Laightons as lighthouse helper. Many have speculated about Laighton's move to White Island, and away from what appeared to be a promising political career. His decision may have been a pragmatic one based on the need to find a way to make a living during a time when the economic future of Portsmouth was not promising.

With the proceeds of the sale of land to the new railroad line that was to terminate at the Portsmouth waterfront, he and his brother Joseph had bought four of the islands in the Isles of Shoals group: the largest one, Hog (later renamed Appledore) Island, along with Smuyttnose, Cedar, and tiny Malaga Islands. The men had plans to revive the once thriving Shoals fishery and develop a wholesale fish business. Joseph Laighton, a grocer with whom Thomas was joint owner of a wharf and cooperage in Portsmouth, would tend to affairs on the mainland.

By the early 1830s, the salary for the White Island keeper had risen to $600 per year, and Laighton may have taken the job in order to have a steady income while he got this enterprise under way. It is entirely likely that through his political connections he was able to engineer his appointment in place of Joseph Locke.[11] Others have theorized that Laighton took the White Island keeper's job to tide him over until his expected appointment as Portsmouth postmaster to succeed Abner Greenleaf. This argument is given credence by a January 1840 *Portsmouth Journal* report of a petition by four hundred local Democrats on behalf of Laighton's appointment to this position. In spite of this substantial support, the job went to Samuel Cushman. Laighton's political career seemed far from over, however. In the fall of 1840, he won election as a state representative. There is considerable evidence that Laighton was, like Joseph Locke, one of the many lightkeepers who had no qualms about leaving his lighthouse in the care of a paid helper. A political enemy, signing himself "X. Y. Z.," commented in the *Portsmouth Journal* (a Whig paper) on a speech in which Laighton attacked bank cashiers, "because they do not labor or produce":

> Thinks I to myself, how much has Mr. Laighton produced or labored either in his grocery store or his Light-House? Which works hardest.—Mr. M. of the Commercial, or Mr. L. of White Island?—Most of the Cashiers of Banks are confined to their counters year after year, but Mr. Laighton can spend weeks away from his post electioneering, and 'tis nobody's business![12]

Laighton was keeper at White Island for a total of six years. After the Whigs won the White House he was replaced in 1841 by Joseph Cheever, a Portsmouth clothier, but managed to get himself re-appointed in September of 1843 and remained keeper until September 1847.

On a visit to the Isles of Shoals in August 1843, Richard Henry Dana (author of *Two Years Before the Mast*) visited with Laighton, who was then living on Smuttynose, in the course of a sail around the islands with Cheever, who was still keeper of White Island light. Dana had been told that Laighton, who was Cheever's brother-in-law, had the reputation for

clout in the Democratic party in New Hampshire next only to Levi Woodbury's, but noted, "There is something very unprepossessing about him."
"He was seated on the pier, dressed in the roughest manner, with a
coarse, dirty handerkerchief about his neck, chewing tobacco and whit-
tling a stick with a jack-knife." They discussed politics and the pros and
cons of different forms of government for a while, and Dana wrote of their
talk in his journal, "I found that he had read a good deal, and was a saga-
cious man, but had strong prejudices and a dislike of established laws
and orders, and of any persons who had positions better than his own."[13]

After their sail, Dana spent the night at White Island lighthouse with
Cheever and his wife,"a very pretty young woman, under thirty," their
three small children, and a hired helper. Cheever had already learned
that he was to be replaced as keeper, and Dana wrote of the difficulty this
placed him in, having "given up a good trade" to take the lighthouse job
and with a family to support. Cheever seemed unaware that Laighton
was to replace him. Dana also described Cheever's problems with the
new, government-issued lighthouse boat. Instead of hauling it up the
boatways one evening when heavy weather was predicted, he unwisely
anchored it off the island. The boat swamped during the ensuing storm.
Dana tried unsuccessfully to help him and was unable to enlist the aid of
Shoalsmen, who refused to assist because the boat was government property. They might help, they said, if Cheever flew a signal. Otherwise, they
could not claim salvage money from the government.[14]

The *Portsmouth Journal* wrote of Cheever after he left White Island:

> Mr. C., nothing daunted… opened up a clothing warehouse in
> Market Street, hung out his sign—and as evidence that he well
> understood the lighting business, has placed in his window a
> lighthouse, which may be seen in the evening outshining all
> the brilliance of the street.[15]

During the interval between April 1841 and his reappointment in
September 1843, during which Laighton established his family on Smuttynose Island, Laighton may have realized that the idea of reviving the
Shoals fisheries was not going to be a financial success and that a career
as a politician and federal officeholder was an uncertain proposition. He
apparently enjoyed life at the Shoals away from the frustrations of the
mainland, and began to develop another way to make a living at the
islands. He and his wife refurbished the two-story Mid-Ocean House of
Entertainment on Smuttynose, a boarding house formerly operated by
the Haley family. Laighton ordered plaster busts of Beethoven and

Shakespeare to impart an aura of culture to the premises. During the summer months, he and his wife catered to both day-trippers from the Portsmouth area and overnight guests from Boston and Salem. These visitors could enjoy fishing expeditions, explore the islands and learn their history, and partake of rum and Eliza Laighton's hearty home cooking.[16]

Thomas Laighton left White Island for good in September 1847, leaving the lighthouse in the care of "Mr. Becker" until a replacement could be appointed. Laighton moved his family to Hog, soon to be renamed Appledore, Island where he was completing the summer hotel that opened in mid-June of 1848. Boarders in search of health had been attracted to the Mid-Ocean House on Smuttynose, and the Laightons expected the salubrious sea air and substantial meals to attract invalids to the new hotel. During his lighthouse years, an array of political and literary visitors had made the pilgrimage to the Isles of Shoals. Among them were Richard Henry Dana, poet John Greenleaf Whittier's sister, and Judge Charles Woodbury (the son of Levi Woodbury). Later, their recommendations and those of their well-to-do friends made this pioneering island resort hotel a success.

Another early visitor was Bostonian Levi Thaxter, a Harvard graduate with intense interests in poetry and nature, who boarded with the family in 1846. He began tutoring the Laighton children the next year, after the move to Appledore, and was briefly a partner in Laighton's hotel enterprise. In 1851, at the age of twenty-six, he married the sixteen-year-old Celia Laighton; Karl, their first child, was born on Star Island in the summer of 1852.[17]

A laconic but thorough journal survives for some of Laighton's years as lightkeeper. In it he recorded daily weather conditions, the visits of the supply schooner, inspections by the collector of customs, and routine maintenance of the lighthouse and dwelling, as well as his own business activities and the comings and goings of family and friends.

In spite of his business and political interests and his occasional delegation of lighthouse chores to his hired helper, this journal shows him to have been conscientious about his responsibilities and resourceful about solving, or suggesting remedies for, problems he encountered. After the first three months at White Island in the fall and early winter of 1839, he wrote a long report on the state of White Island lighthouse and copied it into his journal. He noted defects in the lighting apparatus, and had suggestions for an improved covered walkway (see chapter 7). He observed that the heavy, government-issued boat was suitable for going to the mainland, but recommended a "boat built of the lightest materials… to afford prompt and effectual assistance in case of accident as the boat belonging to the station could not be launched in season to afford any aid in case any were required." Only "trifling repairs" would put the house in order, but the boatways needed work, and boulders should be removed from the cove adjoining the slip where the supplies for the lighthouse were landed.[18]

The Laightons were probably more prosperous than most other lighthouse families. In addition to lighthouse helper Ben Whaling, Nancy Newton, an Isles of Shoals woman, helped with housework, and a succession of other island women came over to White Island to do the laundry. In the 1840s Laighton bought an iron cook stove for the kitchen where his wife had previously used the fireplace for cooking.[19]

Laighton had a sizable library and often read aloud to the family in the evening; he was also the children's teacher, though Levi Thaxter tutored them in the late 1840s. (It is believed that Eliza Laighton was not literate.) He raised canaries; his wife kept houseplants in the windows and cooked the substantial meals for which she became renowned during the hotel years. Laighton guarded his family against smallpox by vaccinating them himself. There were hens, which laid more than enough eggs to supply the household; the surplus was sold on the mainland. A cow eked out a precarious existence on rocky White Island and nearby Seavey's Island, which was connected to it by a bar at low tide; for winter feed, hay was harvested on one of the larger islands owned by Laighton or brought from the mainland. The life of one Laighton cow ended tragically when she caught and wrenched off a hoof in a rocky crevice and had to be killed.[20]

For the family table at White Island and summer guests at the Mid-Ocean House, Laighton kept a large vegetable garden on Smuttynose to supplement the small patches of cucumbers and squash grown on White and Seavey Islands. For meat and wool, he kept as many as fifty sheep on Appledore. One spring's shearing yielded 193 pounds of wool. Oscar Laighton remembered his mother spinning wool and knitting stockings for the family. Fish was an important part of their diet; Laighton himself often went fishing and occasionally set out a lobster pot. Sea fowl were bought from the islanders.[21]

Letters, newspapers, and grocery staples came as often as weather permitted; Laighton arranged for Captain William Goodwin's pilot boat to make several trips a week from Portsmouth to the islands, although occasionally there were stretches of a week or two when no boat could make a landing at White Island. Once a year Eliza Laighton, sometimes with her daughter, Celia, went ashore on a shopping expedition in Portsmouth to buy yard goods with which to make the family's clothing.[22]

There is much evidence that Thomas Laighton was irascible and stubborn. Eighteen hundred and forty-three was evidently the last year he set foot on the mainland. An item in the *Portsmouth Journal* in 1851, a few years after he left White Island to open his hotel on Appledore—which is in Maine, unlike White Island—noted that he had not left the Isles of Shoals for nine years. The article referred to him as a disgusted politician:

> He forcibly reminded us of the enraged and angry Achilles in
> his tent. He has not only left the Invincibles, but has forsaken
> his native State. And lives in his moroseness and anger, upon
> this ledge of the ocean.[23]

Biographers of Celia Laighton Thaxter suggest that the cheerful outlook and warm personality of Laighton's wife bound them into a close-knit, affectionate family. And for her three children the islands had a life-long attraction. Until Cedric Laighton's death in 1899, he and his brother Oscar ran the Appledore hotel and another hotel on Star Island purchased in 1877. Oscar struggled to carry on the declining hotel operation until 1914. He spent his last twenty summers at the islands until his death in 1939 at the age of 99. Celia Laighton Thaxter returned almost every year after her marriage, often to help with the hotel operation and eventually to care for her aging, ill parents. Thomas Laighton died in 1866 and his wife Eliza in 1877; both are buried on Appledore Island.[24]

It was Celia Thaxter (1835-1894) who gave the Isles of Shoals and lighthouse life enduring dramatic and picturesque luster. The first of her three children was born at the Shoals, but much of her early married life she lived in Newtonville, Massachusetts, where she started writing poetry that drew upon her experiences at the lighthouse and her observations of her island world. Her first published poem, "Land-Locked," was written at the Thaxter's house near the Charles River, and appeared in the *Atlantic Monthly* in 1861. It is infused with a longing for her childhood island home:

Celia Thaxter as a young woman. Courtesy Isles of Shoals Collection, UNH Department of Media Services.

A View of New Castle with the Fort and Light House on the Entrance of Piscataqua River.

View of New Castle and the Fort and Light House on the Entrance of the Piscataqua River," probably based on a view produced by Samuel Holland's survey team. Circa early 1770s. LC.

A View of Piscataqua Lighthouse from Kitterie Point. ƒ Chas Randle

"A View of Piscataqua Lighthouse from Kitterie Point." Chas. Randle was the artist and probably based his view on one provided by Samuel Holland's team. A handwritten note above the view is dated 1779, and contains information about the harbor, its tides and hazards. BM.

Thomas P. Moses 1872 painting, "Entrance to Portsmouth Harbor in the Glory of Her Commerce" is the artist's recollection of how the harbor and its lighthouse looked before the lighthouse was shortened in 1851. PrC.

In "Entrance to Portsmouth, NH Harbour," Moses painted the lighthouse as it looked in 1855, four years after its height was reduced. Whale's Back lighthouse is visible in the distance in both paintings. SB

Girl and Buoy on the New Hampshire Coast.

"Girl and Buoy," postcard showing a young woman in a bathing costume waving from atop a whistling buoy of the type that briefly marked Kitt's Rocks off the entrance to Portsmouth harbor in 1882 and was soon removed because of complaints about its unpleasant sound. Around 1911, local maritime interests successfully lobbied to have another whistling buoy set out to mark Kitt's Rocks. It is not certain that this is the one depicted in the postcard, which may have been a generic one available in many coastal resort areas and customized with the name of the town or harbor. PrC.

Below: Celia Laighton Thaxter, "White Island Lighthouse," 1883 watercolor. Courtesy Celia Thaxter Hubbard.

*Above: Childe Hassam
painting with White Island
lighthouse in the distance.
Courtesy Smith College
Museum of Art.*

*Left: White Island
Lighthouse, watercolor by
Childe Hassam. Courtesy
Jonathan Hubbard.*

"Off Portsmouth Harbor, N.H.," by Julian O. Davidson, 1878. Engraving. PrC

White Island in the distance, with a huge moon outshining the lighthouse. 1874 painting by John Christopher Miles (Collection of Douglas and Karin Nelson)

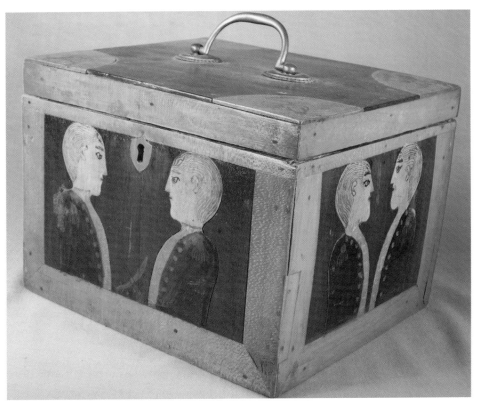

Box made by Eliphalet Grover at Boon Island. OYHS

Boon Island in a storm, 1872 painting by Clement Drew (1806–1889). PEM

The Nubble Lighthouse painted by Russell Cheney around 1940. Reproduced by permission of the Master of Eliot House, Harvard University

The Nubble Lighthouse, by George Morris. Collection of Robert Chase.

Land-Locked

Black lie the hills; swiftly doth daylight flee;
     And, catching gleams of sunset's dying smile,
     Through the dusk land for many a changing mile
The river runneth swiftly to the sea.

O happy river, could I follow thee!
     O yearning heart, that never can be still!
     O wistful eyes, that watch the steadfast hill,
Longing for level line of solemn sea.

Have patience; here are flowers and songs of birds,
     Beauty and fragrance, wealth of sound and sight,
     All summer's glory from morn till night,
And life too full of joy for uttered words.

Neither am I ungrateful; but I dream
     Deliciously how twilight falls to-night
     Over the glimmering water; how the light
Dies blissfully away, until I seem

To feel the wind, sea-scented, on my cheek,
     To catch the sound of dusky flapping sail
     And dip of oars, and voices on the gale
Afar off, calling low—my name they speak!

O Earth! thy summer song of joy may soar
     Ringing to heaven in triumph. I but crave
     The sad, caressing murmur of the wave
That breaks in tender music on the shore.[25]

Nine years later she began publishing a series of prose pieces in *the Atlantic Monthly*, collected in 1873 as *Among the Isles of Shoals*. She continued to publish poetry and wrote for children. Her final book, *An Island Garden*, was published in 1893, the year before her death. She learned to paint china, which provided her with needed income, as did the handwritten copies of her most popular poems that she illustrated with watercolor vignettes. She also painted watercolors of island subjects.[26]

A vivid, attractive, and sympathetic person, Celia Thaxter became something of a magnet, drawing many artists, musicians, and writers for summer visits to the hotel on Appledore, to the parlor of her nearby cottage, and to the lush, colorful flower garden she tended. Perhaps the most illustrious artist to spend time on Appledore was Childe Hassam.[27]

Thaxter was only four years old when she, her parents, and baby brother Oscar arrived at the lighthouse in the fall of 1839. Writing more than thirty years later, she described her first impressions of White Island:

> It was at sunset in autumn that we were set ashore on that loneliest, lovely rock, where the lighthouse looked down on on us like some tall, black-capped giant, and filled me with awe and wonder. At its base a few goats were grouped on the rock, standing out dark against the red sky as I looked up at them. The stars were beginning to twinkle; the wind blew cold, charged with the sea's sweetness; the sound of many waters half bewildered me... everything was strange and fascinating and new... How curious [the cottage] seemed, with its low, whitewashed ceiling and deep window-seats, showing the great thickness of the walls made to withstand the breakers, with whose force we soon grew acquainted![28]

Thaxter's retrospective account of her childhood years at White Island is intense and idyllic. She wrote of the winter months when the family was cut off for weeks from the outside world—of cozy evenings when her father read aloud to the children in the warm kitchen, of playing on stormy days in the covered way leading to the lighthouse, of pressing warmed pennies against the ice-frosted windows of the house to create little peepholes to see the "bright, windy weather, watching the vessels scudding over the intensely dark blue seas, all 'feather-white.'" She wrote of violent winter storms smashing windows of the house and sweeping away the henhouse and chickens. She wrote as well of island legends, of the lives of the islanders, and of tragic wrecks and drownings.

Thaxter recalled the excitement of exploring the island with her brothers in the warmer months. They discovered tiny creatures—limpets, sea spiders, minnows—and summer wildflowers, seaweeds and kelps. She gathered the corpses of the many birds that were blinded by the lighthouse light and were dashed to death against the lantern. She enumerated the varieties: sparrows, swallows, thrushes, robins, red-winged blackbirds, warblers, fly-catchers, yellow-birds, nuthatches, cat-birds, purple finches, scarlet tanagers, golden orioles. She told, too, of eagles, gulls and game birds that also died against the glass of the lantern. The keeper of another lighthouse told her of picking up 375 dead birds in one morning.[29]

From Celia Thaxter we learn what does not appear in official light-house reports: mutton and beef were hung in the lower story of the lighthouse; sometimes it took a whole day for the lighthouse sailboat to beat back to White Island against the wind with provisions purchased in Portsmouth; she occasionally was given the job of lighting the lamps in the lighthouse.[30]

Every summer, the lighthouse supply contractor arrived at the island with a year's worth of sperm oil and other necessities. His ves-sel, the *Gazelle*, was an eighty-foot-long schooner of 40 tons burden and carried about twenty thousand gallons of oil. There were ten men aboard to unload the supplies and make minor repairs to the lighthouse equipment. Thaxter recalled the "black, lumbering oil-schooner" and "the ill-perfumed whale oil... stowed in the round, dimly-lighted rooms of the tower. Very awe-struck, we children always crept into corners, and whispered and watched the intruders till they embarked in their ancient, clumsy vessel, and, hoisting their dark, weather-stained sails, bore slowly away again."[31]

The storm that swept away the covered walkway was recorded without emotion by her father. Celia Thaxter, writing many years later, re-created the drama and excitement of this storm, which must have been terrifying for a child:

> One night when, from the southeast, the very soul of chaos seemed to have been let loose upon the world, the whole pon-derous "walk"... was carried thundering down the gorge and dragged out into the raging sea. It was a distressing situation for us,—cut off from the precious light that must be kept alive; for the breakers were tearing through the gorge so that no liv-ing thing could climb across. But the tide could not resist the mighty impulse that drew it down: it was forced to obey the still voice that bade it ebb; all swollen and raging and towering as it was, slowly and surely, at the appointed time, it sank away from our rock, so that, between the billow that still strove to clutch at the white, silent, golden-crowned tower, one could creep across, and scale the height and wind up the machinery that kept the great clustered light revolving till the gray day-light broke to extinguish it.[32]

The same late-December storm that wrecked the covered walkway inspired a poem, *The Wreck of the Pocahontas*, about a vessel caught in its power and firing a cannon as a signal of distress:

...

When morning dawned, above the din
Of gale and breaker boomed a gun!
Another! We who sat within
Answered with cries each one.

Into each other's eyes with fear,
We looked through helpless tears, as still,
One after one, near and more near,
The signals pealed, until

The thick storm seemed to break apart
To show us, staggering to her grave,
The fated brig. We had no heart
To look, for naught could save.

One glimpse of black hull heaving slow,
Then closed the mists o'er canvas torn
And tangled ropes swept to and fro
From mast that raked forlorn... [33]

The Laightons read of the fate of the vessel when it was calm enough for the pilot boat to make its way to White Island with newspapers. An article in the *Portsmouth Journal* told that the brig *Pocahontas* was from Newburyport, and had left Cadiz in late October on her homeward voyage with a crew of Spaniards recruited by her master, James C. Cook, of Newburyport. She almost made it home, but was finally driven aground on the south breakers only 150 yards off Plum Island, near the narrow entrance to the Merrimack River and Newburyport Harbor. By daybreak, she had been dismasted. Crowds gathered to watch helplessly as one by one the three visible survivors disappeared into the wild seas. Papers washed ashore with the wreckage revealed the names of the captain and his chief mate, Albert Cook. There was no record of the names of the nine crewmen. Seven of their bodies were washed ashore within a few days, and their coffins were carried to a Newburyport church for memorial services. The local Ladies Seamen's Society later planted an elm at the burial place and erected a marble slab to commemorate the foreign crewmen, "By strangers honored, and by strangers mourned."[34]

Celia Thaxter described with a loving eye and keen ear the quality of the island light, the colors and moods of the sky, clouds and sea, the shapes and motions of the sails of passing vessels, and the "rote" of the sea breaking on different shores of the islands and their ledges in all kinds of weather. When asked to explain the meaning of the word "rote," she wrote that the island fishermen's ears were so sensitively attuned to these sounds that they could tell where they were even in thick fog, or at night:

> No matter how dark it is, they can judge with curious accuracy the distance between them and the sound, whether the breaking waves are gentle or furious, whether they break on long sand beaches or the shore or the ragged rock of the Islands and each island, each small isolated rock has its own peculiar rote, different from the rest. [35]

Few people who have lived at lighthouses wrote with such intensely observed detail about island life as Celia Thaxter. But others who stayed for years—even decades—at these offshore posts, like Eliphalet Grover and later William C. Williams of Boon Island, may have responded to and loved the beauty and excitement of island life and lighthouse keeping as strongly as Thaxter expressed in her writing. And like Thomas Laighton, they doubtless took pride in maintaining the lights and in creating a self-sufficient world under sometimes desperately difficult circumstances.

L. H. D. Shepard

The White Island keeper from 1849 to 1853 was L. H. D. Shepard, a former writing master. He does not seem to have been at all well suited to island lighthousekeeping, and must have been one of those lightkeepers for whom the isolation and occasional danger of lighthouse duty were deadening and degrading. In 1851, close to two years after his appointment, he wrote to Portsmouth Collector of Customs Lory Odell: "Would you send me a float as soon as possible. I have never yet been able to leave the island since I left Portsmouth on account of not having a float."[36]

Presumably, Shepard was requesting a floating platform of some sort to which a boat could be tied instead of being hauled up and down the island's boatways. Did he ask for a float because he had been unable to launch the heavy government boat used by his predecessors? No previous keeper had the convenience of a float, and at any rate it would have been impossible at an offshore location like White Island. In the same letter, Shepard revealed that there were no basic hand tools on the lighthouse premises. His letter—written in a hand that suggests he might not have been particularly successful as a writing master—he asked for "a little box of tools such as a plane, hammer and such things as you think I need here. Things are out of order and I can't fix them... I never have been able to put the sash in that was made for me it was perhaps 1 1/2" to wide and I have no plane to fix it."

We do not know whether earlier keepers had brought their own kit of tools with them or whether government-issued tools had been wafted away by his predecessors. There is no indication in lighthouse documents that a set of basic tools was provided at this time for each lighthouse. Odell sent him a hammer, a plane, pliers, two sizes of nails, plus turpentine, oil, and white lead for painting chores.

In 1852, Nathaniel Hawthorne was a visitor at the Shoals where he had arranged to meet his Bowdoin College classmate Franklin Pierce, whose presidential campaign biography he was writing. During his stay, Hawthorne visited White Island. His unflattering comments about Shepard, published in *American Notebooks,* were doubtless influenced by the Laightons' opinion, perhaps embroidered, of the hapless Shepard:

> The keeper of the light-house was formerly a writing-master. He has a sneaking kind of look, and does not bear a very high character among his neighbors. Since he kept the light, he has lost two wives,—the first a young creature whom he used to leave alone upon this desolate rock, and the gloom and terror of the situation were probably the cause of her death. The second wife, experiencing the same kind of treatment ran away from him, and returned to her friends. He pretends to be religious, but drinks.

Shepard had evidently found someone to keep house for him; Hawthorne heard a woman's voice inside the house. Shepard had no hens, pig, or cow, but did tend a garden, in soil Hawthorne described as "marine mud." He had a crop of insect-ridden onions, marrow squash that had been damaged by a recent storm, and cabbages and turnips.[37]

Shepard was obviously not knowledgeable about the sea, but by the time of Hawthorne's visit had found a way to launch a rowboat. Hawthorne wrote that on one occasion Shepard unwisely set out alone against a head wind and tide and had to be rescued to prevent his drifting out to sea. He was replaced the next year.[38]

Whale's Back

Keepers of lighthouses on rocky reefs around the British Isles had long experienced the restrictive confinement of living in a light tower, but the Whale's Back lighthouse is the first known American light where the keepers actually lived in the tower itself rather than in a nearby house, although some lighthouse lanterns were built as extensions above the roof of a regular home. The interior of the Whale's Back tower was only about eighteen feet in diameter at the lower stories; each of the two lower floors was divided into two rooms for living quarters. The stairway would have used up a good portion of the space on each story. There was one window in each of the four stories, leaving one of the two rooms of each of the two "living" stories without a window. Some of the windows on the open ocean side of the tower were within a few years smashed by seas. In 1837, this side of the tower—and presumably the windows there—was sheathed with planks, further darkening the interior.[39]

The ability to get along with people and to tolerate these close, dim quarters must have been crucial. The only places to breathe fresh air or escape an uncongenial coworker or family member were the narrow catwalk around the lantern at the top of the light tower and the platform formed by the top of the foundation pier, and the latter retreat was not possible in storms when the seas swept across it.

Samuel Hascall

The first keeper at Whale's Back light was Samuel Hascall, who inaugurated the lights in September 1830 and continued on the job until the fall of 1839. Hascall, about whose background nothing could be discovered, was paid five hundred dollars a year when he began at Whale's Back. At Boon Island, pay for Eliphalet Grover, who had been keeper since 1816, had gradually increased from four hundred fifty dollars in 1820 to six hundred in 1831, and White Island pay was raised to the same amount.[40]

News of these raises prompted a letter from Hascall to President Jackson asking for equal pay. Portsmouth Customs Collector Pickering agreed that he should be paid as much. It was true that Whale's Back, being nearer the mainland, was an easier place from which to get supplies, he wrote, but getting on and off could be extremely difficult when the weather was bad. (The lighthouse boat had to be lowered into the water by davits mounted on the foundation pier, and sometimes was wrenched off by storm seas.) He also wrote that the keeper at Whale's Back was separated from his family for half the year, and it was expensive to hire an assistant because of the "supposed danger of the employment." Stretching things a bit, he added that unlike the Whale's Back keeper, those at Boon Island and White Island were provided with "convenient and comfortable dwelling houses." Hascall was awarded a raise of fifty dollars in 1832, and by 1838 was being paid as much as the other offshore keepers.[41]

Hascall must have succeeded in hiring an assistant to help him and, if he had a family, he probably sent them ashore to live during the stormiest part of the year. But family members apparently came to visit during these times. A newspaper account of a late-January 1839 storm during which waves topped the lighthouse "very much the same as it is represented in the *Penny Magazine*, lashing the famous Eddystone light house," refers to both an assistant and family. In the lantern, it was impossible for a person to be heard over the rattling and shaking commotion of the lighting apparatus, and the whole structure shuddered each time a sea struck it. The newspaper predicted that something would be done soon for the "security of the light house and the keeper and his family—Conscious of the weakness of the masonry which protects them, their feelings can be more easily imagined than described, while the angry sea is dashing over their lodgings."[42]

Joseph Locke and Successors

After Hascall left the job later in 1839, a steady succession of keepers followed him—partly because of the precarious state of the lighthouse, partly due to the political rivalries of this period. The first was Joseph Locke, who had been frequently absent when he was keeper at White Island light for the previous ten years, but he overestimated his political clout. He did not appear at the lighthouse until a week after October 1, 1839, the effective date of his appointment, to the frustration of Samuel Hascall, who was ready and eager to leave the post he had held since the lighthouse was first lit in September 1830. Collector Drown arranged for Zachariah Chickering to fill in as temporary keeper until Locke got there; Chickering arrived on the same day as Locke.

Locke did not stay long, however. Drown, on a visit to the lighthouse on October 28, found that Locke had hired someone to keep the lighthouse for him, and that he had only spent two days at the lighthouse since his appointment. Drown fired Locke, and early in January the *Portsmouth Journal* reported "for the benefit of the numerous applicants for the office," that Zachariah Chickering was to be given the job. Locke then placed an ad in the *Journal*.

> For the information of the numerous Applicants for the office of Keeper of Whales Back Light, the undersigned would give notice, that up to the 8th inst. no new appointment had been made to said office, as fully appears by letters from Washington. This information is given in consequence of having seen in the papers of Portsmouth, a semi-official notice that Mr. Z. Chickering has received an appointment from Daniel P. Drown, Esq. which I consider as no great consequence, as the same individual received one from the same source on the 8th of October last before I had or possibly could commence the duties of said Light in person.

Rye, Jan 16, 1840 JOSEPH L. LOCKE[43]

"Letters from Washington" notwithstanding, Locke was out of a lighthouse job. After the intercession of President Van Buren and an investigation, Collector Drown's action was upheld. By May 12, 1840 Locke had managed to obtain another, though less lucrative, federal appointment as Rye postmaster.[44]

Joseph L. Locke's brief tenure as Whale's Back keeper evidently included a late December gale. Even Locke's "stout heart quailed" reported one newspaper, "when he heard the waves dashing furiously around his isolated tenement, the mad ocean forbidding his departure and threatening every moment to engulph the whole concern. This Light house, however, is never without its tenant, or without numerous applicants when a vacancy is expected."[45]

Locke was followed by John Kennard early in 1840 and Joseph Currier in 1841. Currier resigned after a wild October storm that year, during which he expected the lighthouse to be carried away. He reported that the structure seemed to "rock like a cradle." Eliphalet Grover, who took his place, was on duty at this lighthouse when I. W. P. Lewis inspected it in 1842. Grover told him that during storms the whole lighthouse quaked, and the vibrations sent chairs and tables moving across the floor. Two other men held the job between 1843 and June 1849, when Jedediah Rand, of Rye, was appointed keeper.[46]

In all the critiques of the lighthouse establishment under Fifth Auditor Stephen Pleasonton, virtually nothing had been said about safety and the ongoing practice of permitting keepers to have family members live with them at dangerous lighthouse posts. In the fall of 1849, the *Portsmouth Journal* reported the dramatic rescue of Whale's Back's keeper Rand and his teenaged daughter. Rand was aware of the dangers and difficulties of the lighthouse for family living, but in spite of this "kept one of his children with him, making a change every few weeks, each desirous for an opportunity to visit the romantic resort." His daughter Eliza Jane took her turn, and on the twenty-fifth of September Rand prepared to go ashore with her to New Castle to get supplies. Eliza Jane was seated in the small boat that had been lowered on davits from the foundation pier, but before her father could get in, the boat was upset by a sea, and Eliza Jane was pitched into the water. Rand leapt into the water and pulled her to the overturned boat. Another sea immediately flipped the boat over again, throwing them both off. Rand again rescued her and got her into the boat. Again it was overturned and Rand grabbed his daughter and clung to both her and the boat while the seas broke over them. The *Journal* reported that Eliza Jane felt she was doomed, crying, "Father, do I not love you… I want to go to heaven." Fortunately Captain Richard Seawards, of Kittery, was heading out of the harbor at the time in the schooner *Clarissa Ferron*. Seawards dispatched a boat, and the unconscious Eliza Jane and her father were hauled aboard and taken to New Castle. On the way ashore, Rand held his apparently lifeless daughter across his knees, with her face down. She suddenly vomited and revived. Wrote the *Journal*: "And notwithstanding the perils she had undergone, her attachment to her father led her to choose to return with him to his post of duty that afternoon rather than remain with strangers separated from him."[47]

The *Journal* proposed a breakwater at the lighthouse to make departures and landings less hazardous, but did not question Rand's right to endanger his children, or a government that permitted him to do so.[48]

X   *The Light-House Board, Two New Lighthouses, and Other Developments*

Our light-house establishment seems to be the sole exception to our practice of building for the future as well as for the present. In it there seems to be ever a lurking apprehension that our naval and commercial existence is but temporary.

—Senate Executive Document 28, 1852.

MAJOR IMPROVEMENTS to lighthouses around Portsmouth had been on hold through the 1840s. Except for the York Ledge monument of 1841, nothing was done to add navigational markers to help strangers avoid the hazards along the coastal approaches to the Port of Portsmouth or to find a safe anchorage in the harbor itself. At the beginning of the 1850s, appropriations were made for several buoys and beacons in the area. By 1851, plans were under way to reduce the height of the lighthouse at Fort Constitution to a more appropriate elevation—a change that had been advocated since 1829 when the Whale's Back light was built at the entrance to the Piscataqua River. A decision about a replacement for the precarious Whale's Back lighthouse awaited study of the iron pile lighthouse on Minot's Ledge, finished late in 1848, to see if a similar structure was feasible for the ledge at the mouth of the Piscataqua.[1]

As the 1850s began, Portsmouth had a minimal role in the nation's expandinginternational trade. Direct foreign imports were mainly railroad iron from England, salt from Cadiz, plaster from Canada, and

sugar and molasses from the West Indies. Pennsylvania coal and
Maine wood products and lime were carried into the port regularly.
The major export was Piscataqua-built vessels, including the magnificent clippers chronicled by Ray Brighton. The shipping notes published by Portsmouth newspapers showed that the most important
vessels built in the Piscataqua rarely ever returned home and, as
Brighton has shown, Portsmouth-built clippers never did. These vessels, many owned by out-of-town interests, were reported all over the
world—in the Orient, Europe, and Mediterranean African ports—and
were much involved in transporting passengers and cargo around the
Horn to San Francisco during the Gold Rush. But when they came
back to the East Coast, they went into Boston, New York, and ports to
the south rather than Portsmouth.[2]

Coastwise traffic was significant, though. John S. Thompson, during
his last stint as keeper of Boon Island light, kept track of passing vessels, not counting local fishermen, during daylight hours. Even in the
three stormy months of October, November and December 1852, when
traffic was much less than in late spring and summer, Thompson
recorded 2,865 passersby: 2,488 schooners, 217 brigs, sixty-three barks,
thirty-eight steamers, thirty-one sloops, twenty-two ships, and six U.S.
revenue cutters. Thus an average of more than thirty vessels, representing substantial investments in transport vessels and cargo and
hundreds of lives, plied the waters off Portsmouth daily, and Thompson
guessed that as many more passed during the night. The offshore lights
at Boon and White Islands were important to these vessels; Portsmouth
harbor, with Whale's Back light marking its entrance, continued to be
a crucial storm refuge for them, except during easterly storms.[3]

The existence of the Portsmouth Navy Yard undoubtedly added
weight to pleas for improved aids to navigation in and around the
Port of Portsmouth. Eighteen-fifties launchings included the rebuilt
frigate *Santee* and the sloop *Mohican,* both steam-powered. The long-
sought floating dry-dock was finally completed in 1853, enabling a
succession of naval vessels, among them the *U.S.S. Constitution,* to be
docked and hauled out for repairs or rebuilding. By the end of the
decade, however, activity at the yard was at a virtual standstill,
though the number of civilian employees had grown from sixty-nine
to 348 by the end of the decade.[4]

Elsewhere in the United States, there was tremendous need for
more aids to navigation, especially along the coasts of recently acquired

territories. The Pacific and Texas coastlines had no lighthouses at all, and many more were needed for the Gulf of Mexico, the southern Atlantic Coast, and the Great Lakes. And the problems reported in the 1830s and 1840s with existing lighthouse construction and equipment and with oversight of the people who maintained them had not been resolved.

In March 1851, Congress authorized yet another study of the U.S. lighthouse system, this time with important results. Only three months earlier, Fifth Treasury Auditor Stephen Pleasonton submitted a report to the Secretary of Treasury in which he defended the system he had superintended since 1820; he persisted in maintaining that the United States lighthouses were equal in quality to Europe's and much less expensive to operate. This document included reports on lighthouses along the Atlantic Coast submitted by oil contractors Jonathan Howland Sr. and Jr. Their notes are mostly a record of annual oil consumption and the physical condition of the buildings and equipment at each lighthouse, with occasional comments on the keepers.[5]

The Howlands' report was hardly a validation of Pleasonton's claims. Their notes do not analyze the range or brilliance of the lights, but the overall impression is of shabbiness and decay, of lighthouses with crumbling mortar, of leaky lanterns with cracked glass, and of stop gap measures to jury-rig repairs to antiquated or faulty lighting equipment. The lighthouses around Portsmouth received their annual supplies from the contractors in August 1850. At Boon Island, the Howlands found the tower and its domed roof very leaky.

> A new tower and all new lighting apparatus, and a new dwelling house, are much needed. This is a very important light, and a very dangerous rock lies to the north and east of it some three miles... the lamps and reflectors are poor; they have been on seventeen years.[6]

At Fort Constitution light, seven panes of glass in the lantern were broken, buildings needed painting, and the wooden causeway to the lighthouse was in disrepair. Since their last visit to Whale's Back, they found that the falling plaster in the livingquarters had been patched and a few minor repairs had been made. At both Whale's Back and White Island, the keepers refused to accept any of the lamp chimneys the Howlands brought with them because of their poor quality, and at White Island two of the large panes of French plate glass in the lantern were cracked, and replacements were not obtainable.[7]

31st Congress, 2d Session.	[HO. OF REPS.]	Ex. Doc. No. 14.

LIGHT-HOUSES.

LETTER

FROM

THE SECRETARY OF THE TREASURY,

TRANSMITTING

The report of the general superintendent of the light-house establishment

---

DECEMBER 20, 1850.

Referred to the Committee of Ways and Means.

TREASURY DEPARTMENT,
December 19, 1850.

SIR: I have the honor herewith to transmit a report from S. Pleasonton, esq., the general superintendent of the light-house establishment, dated the 14th inst., showing the mode of supply, inspection, general condition, and extent of the establishment, &c.

I am, very respectfully, your obedient servant,

THO. CORWIN,
Secretary of the Treasury.

Hon. HOWELL COBB,
Speaker of the House of Representatives.

TREASURY DEPARTMENT,
Fifth Auditor's Office, December 14, 1850.

SIR: In the management of the light-house establishment, besides an examination of the lights annually (in June or July) by the several collectors, who are charged with the superintendence of them, and a report of their condition made to this office, the captains of the vessels which are employed to convey and deliver the oil, tube-glasses, buff-skins, &c., to the light-houses on the Atlantic coast annually, are required not only to report the repairs deemed necessary at each light-house, but also the repairs they may cause to be made to the apparatus by means of lamp-makers whom they carry with them. These captains are furnished with the necessary quantity of oil, with lamps and reflectors, and parts of lamps, with tube-glasses, wicks, buff-skins, oil butts, &c., to maintain efficient lights in the several houses during the ensuing year. They are required to obtain the receipts of the respective keepers for the oil and all other things delivered, and to transmit them to this office with their reports.

Title page of Stephen Pleasonton's 1850 report containing the oil contractors' description of each lighthouse on the Atlantic Coast from Georgia to Maine.

The Report of the Light-House Board

The 1851 act of Congress authorizing a new study of the U.S. light-house system directed Treasury Secretary Thomas Corwin to convene a board to report on the existing system and recommend legislation to improve it. The board consisted of two high-ranking officers of the Navy, two Army engineers, a civil officer of "high scientific attainments," and a junior naval officer to serve as secretary.[8]

The result was a thick report of 760 pages, replete with diagrams and tables, a study of the Fresnel lens commissioned by the Franklin Institute of Philadelphia, and large chunks of earlier reports on U.S. and European lighthouse systems. There were illustrations of European lightships, buoys and lighting apparatus. Members of the Board had visited and reported on selected sea and harbor lights all along the Atlantic Coast from Portland Head south to North Carolina. Among them were White Island and Fort Constitution lights. These lights were examined on July 7, 1851.

At the Isles of Shoals, the reflectors and lamps at White Island light were found defective. The reflectors varied from nineteen to twenty-one inches in diameter, and only two of the fifteen were of the parabolic shape calculated to direct the light outward from the lamps. This report reveals that the large panes of colored glass used to create the red sector of the light's "characteristic" had been replaced by red-glass chimneys provided by the customs collector. These chimneys were difficult to find, and were of varied shapes, depending on what was available. The board's inspection declared the painting of the stairs in the lighthouse and the floors of the house a "waste of paint." Some of the oil for the lamps was kept in the first story of the lighthouse, some in the cellar of the house. The inspectors also criticized the suitability of lightkeepers and the training they had received. L. H. D. Shepard, White Island's keeper, was a schoolteacher who had been given only a few days' training before taking over, the report said. He did not know how to use the ventilators in the lantern to achieve the best possible light; he didn't have a timepiece; his daybook entries were sketchy ("Could not furnish the quantity of oil consumed last year from it".)[9]

The inspectors arrived at Fort Constitution lighthouse at five-thirty on the same day. Lightkeeper William Vennard, a farmer, had been given no training for the job and relied on the sketchy printed instruction sheet issued by Fifth Auditor Pleasonton in the mid-1830s. Even this late in the day the lantern had not been cleaned, the "dome of the lantern black inside—all dirty—everything very dirty. Oil spilled on the floor and steps." Vennard did not have proper scissors for trimming the wicks of the lamps. The reflectors instead of being paraboloid in form were spherical and were old and "much worn." The oil for the lamps was, "as usual" kept on the lower floor of the lighthouse.[10]

A few months after the visit of the board's inspectors, the lighthouse at Fort Constitution was cut down in height from eighty-one to sixty-one feet, and a new lantern was installed. This alteration very belatedly followed the 1829 recommendations of collector Timothy Upham and earlier government-sponsored surveys. The work was done by George Pendexter, who had built the covered walkway at White Island a decade earlier. Contemporary accounts note that he planned the job so skillfully that only two days elapsed between taking down the old lantern and installing and lighting the lamps in the new one, and that a temporary light was exhibited from a window on the south side of the lighthouse during the alterations.[11]

The Light-House Board's report, presented to Congress early in 1852, contained a list of thirty-eight lighthouses that should be taller so that their lights could be seen from greater distances. Boon Island light was one of them. If the lighting apparatus was good (which it was not, the report noted), this light could be seen from only thirteen miles away. It recommended a taller lighthouse with the most powerful, "first-order" Fresnel lens.[12]

A letter from M. D. Ricker of Portsmouth, master of the ship *John Haven,* was published in the report. Ricker made an average of seven passages a year between New York and Liverpool, and admired the clarity and reliability of Irish and English lights, complaining only that the Kinsale Light off Cape Clear was so high that its light was sometimes shrouded by low-lying fog. Of the lights in the United States, he thought the best were the Fresnel lens lights at Navesink Highlands and the twin lights at Thacher's Island (Cape Ann), and Boston Harbor light. The latter had been fitted up with English reflectors of superior quality in 1839. Ricker mentioned none of the aids to navigation around Portsmouth, and in fact probably only rarely entered his own home port.[13]

The board's report contained little new information, but the cumulative effect was impressive and compelling. Virtually every aspect of the lighthouse establishment was found wanting. The report challenged the government to meet European standards and to match those for other undertakings of the federal government of the United States. Our maturity and competence as a nation became an issue:

> ... it seems to us that the nation owes so much of its prosperity and power, and so much of the renown it has acquired, to our marine, military and commercial, that its safety, whilst afloat, should be carefully provided for... Very large sums of money are yearly expended by the government in erecting not only solid but richly decorated structures for the storage of the cargoes of our merchant ships, and for the collection of revenues arising from them;... in the case of public buildings at the seat of government; in the fortresses of the country; in its arsenals, and in its great naval establishments.... [W]e may reasonably hope that liberality may be extended hereafter to the lighthouse system... since the nation has attained to a character for permanency... and because, in so doing, we will be countenanced by the practice of the wisest and most successful of the maritime powers of the world.[14]

Fifth Auditor Stephen Pleasonton again defended the existing U.S. lighthouse system and marshaled testimonials and statistics to show its quality and relative economy. A Whig in the White House, and the most favorable political climate in years for federal expenditures to improve navigation along the seacoasts and for inland public works, brought dramatic change to the administration of the lighthouses of the United States. Disregarding Pleasonton's protestations, Congress paid attention to the Light-House Board's report—and acted. In August 1852, Congress passed legislation creating a permanent U.S. Light-House Board, and added a second civilian with scientific expertise to the board that produced the report.[15]

The board was to equip all new lighthouses with Fresnel lenses; existing lighthouses were to be refitted with them as soon as possible. The quality of oil and apparatus would no longer depend on the "faithfulness" of the low bidder for contracts as it had in the past; the board would control the quality of the oil used in the lamps of the lighthouses. In place of men like Jonathan Howland Sr. and Jr., whose schooner worked under contract with the government for oil delivery and maintenance of the lighting apparatus, the board would have its own fleet of vessels for carrying building materials and fuel, and for transporting Navy inspectors and Army engineers to the lighthouses. Study and recommendations by naval officers and hydrographers would become the basis for the placement of buoys and beacons, rather than the advice of local pilots who were suspected of having a stake in perpetuating difficult access to harbors.

When it came to the patronage issue, however, the legislation creating the board was not so successful. In their 1852 report, the Light-House Board stated that "the frequent changes in the persons employed [as keepers], not resulting from neglect of duty, or want of qualification on the part of the incumbent, are necessarily very injurious to the efficiency of the light-house service," and recommended public service examinations for candidates for keeperships. The board, evidently recognizing a political hot potato, did not directly recommend the elimination of the patronage system, and it continued until almost the end of the nineteenth century.

Customs collectors were still designated superintendents of lighthouses in their collection districts, but their role was diminished in several important ways. They would still nominate lightkeepers and disburse payments to them; they would also report problems in their districts to the Light-House Board. But they were no longer in charge of lighthouse site selection, construction and maintenance, and would not have direct supervision of lighthouse personnel. These functions would go to the military officers assigned to each district by the Light-House Board.[16]

Perhaps as important, men of scientific, engineering, and naval expertise would be in charge of the lighthouses of the United States. The two civilians on the board represented the leadership of the emerging scientific establishment in the county.

Alexander Dallas Bache (1806-1867), a great-grandson of Benajmin Franklin, was an 1825 graduate of West Point and taught science at the University of Pennsylvania. He became superintendent of the U.S. Coast Survey in 1843, perpetuating the European scientific standards brought to the Coast Survey by his Swiss predecessor, Ferdinand Hassler. Bache had a reputation for organizational ability and for providing excellent training in the precise measuring techniques required for the survey. He could also furnish the board with the latest survey information about hazards to navigation before new charts were completed, and could deploy coastal survey teams to work on areas of particular interest to the board.[17]

Joseph Henry (1797-1878) was added to the permanent board in 1852, and remained on it until his death. He was a former Princeton physics

Joseph Henry (1797-1878), one of the two civilian members of the Light-House Board and long-time chair of its experiments committee. He was chairman of the board in the 1870s. LC.

professor who had done important research on electromagnetism independent of but paralleling Faraday's work in England. He became the first secretary of the Smithsonian Institution in 1846. Throughout his years on the Light-House Board, Henry was a member of the Committee on Experiments which investigated and tested fuels for lighthouse lamps and explored in depth the baffling problems of fog signals and the projection of sound. He was board chairman for almost seven years during the 1870s.

Well before the federal government was involved in funding scientific undertakings, both Bache and Henry had found ways to bring junior officers of the Army's Topographical Engineers (highly trained in science and engineering and considered by some to be the cream of the West Point crop), into exploring, mapping and recording expeditions in the vast new western territories acquired by the United States in the 1840s.[18]

The Navy officers on the board, Commodores William B. Shubrick (1790-1874) and Samuel F. Du Pont (1803-1865), were to oversee selection of sites for lighthouses, placement of buoys and beacons, and the maintenance of the lighthouses by the lightkeepers. Shubrick was the first chairman of the board and served as such for nineteen years. Both men had been involved in reform of the Navy. In 1849 Shubrick headed a commission, of which Du Pont was a member, to improve the education of Navy officers at Annapolis; Du Pont in the late 1830s and early 1840s had been an advocate of reform of naval administration. The "Navy connection" also eased access to Navy Yards for the construction of such equipment as cables and anchors needed for mooring buoys.[19]

Admiral William B. Shubrick (1790-1874) was the first chairman of the Light-House Board and served in that capacity for nineteen years. Harper's New Monthly Magazine.

The Army Engineers on the board, with responsibility for lighthouse design and construction, were Brigadier General Joseph G. Totten and Lieutenant Col. James Kearney. Totten (1788-1864), of the Corps of Engineers, was chief engineer for the U.S. Army and a specialist in harbor fortifications. He had studied the composition of mortars, translating French works on the subject and writing a paper about common and hydraulic mortars for the Franklin Institute. Kearney, an Irish immigrant, by 1813 had become an officer in the versatile Topographical Engineers, and since 1845 had been in charge of the survey of the Great Lakes, which provided charts for navigators on these commercially important inland seas where more lighthouses were needed.[20]

John O. Sands, in his study of the Light-House Board, considers almost unparalleled the accomplishments of this essentially voluntary board in its substantial overhaul and reform of an important agency of the federal government. The members of the Board met quarterly, and also sat on committees on finance, engineering, lighthouses, lighting, and experiments. None of them were paid for their Board service, and all were involved in other work.[21]

Acting as full-time executive secretaries to the board were an officer of the Navy and one from either the Corps of Engineers or the Topographical Engineers of the Army. The first of the Navy officers to serve the board as executive secretary was Thornton A. Jenkins (1811-1893), who was already extremely knowledgeable about both American and European lighthouses. He entered the Navy in 1828, and from 1824 to 1842 was assistant to Ferdinand Hassler on the coast survey. In 1837, he was one the Navy officers assigned to investigate U.S. lighthouses, and in 1845 was sent to Europe with Lieutenant Richard Bache to study lighthouses there. (See Chapters 6 and 8.) In 1850, he began two years as secretary to the temporary Light-House Board while it was conducting its survey and preparing its massive report. The first Army officer assigned to the board as the other executive secretary was Edmund Hardcastle, an officer in the Topographical Engineers, a veteran of the Mexican War, who had been involved in determining the boundaries of Texas.[22]

Each of the twelve lighthouse districts was to have a Navy officer in charge of inspection of lighthouses and their keepers and the placement of buoys and beacons, as well as an Army engineering officer to design and oversee construction and repair of lighthouses. In reality, however, these officers were often spread thin. Frequently a single military officer combined the duties of both engineer and inspector in a district, or would be assigned responsibility for two adjacent districts. In addition, these officers often had other, concurrent assignments; the Army engineer officers' responsibilities could include superintending work on coastal fortifications and construction of federal buildings within their districts. These officers might also be designated District Engineers for the Army's Engineer Corps, and studied harbor and river conditions to report their findings to their superiors in the corps, who passed on to Congress their recommendations regarding proposed projects. And at times of war, both Navy and Army officers could be reassigned as needed.

By the end of the 1850s, the Light-House Board had installed Fresnel lenses in all the lighthouses in the Portsmouth area. Salaried assistant keepers were provided for Boon and White Islands and at Whale's Back by 1853. Only at the Fort Constitution light was it left to the discretion of the keeper to either hire an assistant or keep his salary to himself and use family members to help with lighthouse duties. As did the lighthouse built in the late 1870s at the Nubble on Cape Neddick, this lighthouse remained a one-keeper, "family light" until the middle of the 20th century. Incredibly, Whale's Back lighthouse, so often pointed to as being on the point of falling down, was not rebuilt until 1872.

The Whale's Back situation was, however, the focus of an intense political debate in the local newspapers in the late summer of 1852. The *New-Hampshire Gazette* supported Franklin Pierce, a New Hampshire native and a Democrat. The *Portsmouth Journal* favored Winfield Scott. The *Journal* criticized Pierce for not voting in favor of a breakwater to protect Whale's Back light when he was in Congress in the late 1830s. Pierce was also chastised for voting against funding for the York Ledge monument and the dredging of the channel of the Cocheco River, which had its tidal head at the cotton textile manufacturing town of Dover. The breakwater may not have been the solution to Whale's Back problem, and in fact an iron pile lighthouse had been recommended for the site since the late 1830s, but the *Journal* maintained that Pierce's general opposition to lighthouse, harbor and river improvements was still alive in 1852. Pierce was held to consider that such "internal" improvements were not the function of the federal government. Pierce of course won the election of 1852. But by the time he took office the Congress had already approved the new Light-House Board, and major improvements were already in the pipeline.[23]

A violent April 1851 gale toppled the experimental iron Minot's Ledge lighthouse and swept the two lightkeepers on duty there into the sea—and also blew away plans for a similar structure for Whale's Back Ledge. If the Minot's lighthouse had proved successful (or if the gale had not occurred when it did), a similar structure would undoubtedly have risen on Whale's Back—perhaps with the same result.[24]

Interestingly, the Light-House Board's 1852 report, published less than a year after this disaster, made no reference to this engineering failure, although it had much to criticize about the light vessel that marked the ledge after the lighthouse was wrecked. The fate of Minot's Ledge light must have been an embarrassment to those who had promoted professionally trained engineers like Captain William Swift of the Topographical Engineers, whose design it was. It was General Totten, of the Light-House Board who designed the successful and enduring masonry Minot's Ledge lighthouse begun in 1855 and finished in 1860, considered one of the most outstanding engineering achievements of the Light-House Board during the more than fifty years of its existence.[25]

Artist's conceptual drawing of the destruction of the Minot's ledge iron lighthouse in 1851. Century Magazine.

William B. Franklin and a New Lighthouse for Boon Island

Another testament to the board's determination to build light-houses comparable in monumentality and solidity to the great British and French stone towers was the structure that replaced the 1831 lighthouse at Boon Island in 1854. Late in 1852, the man responsible for designing and overseeing its construction arrived in Portland, Maine. He was Lieutenant William Buel Franklin, assigned by the Light-House Board to the First Lighthouse District, which encompassed Maine and New Hampshire.

Franklin (1823-1903) was an officer in the Army's Topographical Engineers, a branch of the Army with an identity distinct from that of the Corps of Engineers until 1863 and which specialized not only in surveying but also in civil engineering projects. He graduated at the top of his class at West Point in 1843. His assignments before his arrival in Portland were varied. He worked as a topographer for western survey-

ing expeditions for two years, was a reconnaissance officer for General Zachary Taylor during the Mexican War, taught at West Point for several years, and worked on harbor and river surveys and improvements in New York and North Carolina.[26]

Franklin's new assignment presented entirely new challenges. A large percentage of the forty-odd existing lighthouses in Maine and New Hampshire, like the one at

William Buel Franklin (1823-1903), as a lieutenant in the Army's Topographical Engineer Corps, was the first Army engineer assigned to the first lighthouse district after the creation of the Light-House Board. He designed many lighthouses and keepers' houses and was for a time in charge of installing buoys and beacons and lighthouse inspections. This studio photograph was taken in the early 1860s, when he held the rank of brigadier general. York County (Pennsylvania) Heritage Trust photo.

Boon Island, needed to be replaced. New lighthouses had to be built, too, at many as yet unlit sites, especially the increasingly busy north-eastern coast of Maine. Fresnel lenses had to be imported from France and installed in all the lighthouses. Until mid-1856, when the first naval officer was assigned to the First District as inspector, Franklin was also lighthouse inspector, charged with establishing and maintaining standards for the lightkeepers and also with maintaining existing buoys and beacons and placing many new ones at previously unmarked locations. He was also superintending engineer for building the Portland Customs House and Marine Hospital. In July 1856 after a Navy officer became inspector, the Second Lighthouse District, which included the Massachusetts coast, was added to Franklin's lighthouse engineering responsibilities. His last assignment to lighthouse work was as engineer secretary of the Light-House Board in Washington at the end of the 1850s, until the Civil War.[27]

Franklin was evidently a man of extraordinary ability and energy. During his years with the Light-House Board he was responsible for the design and building of an estimated twenty-two lighthouses in Maine, at White Island in New Hampshire, and the replacement twin lighthouses at Thachers Island on Cape Ann in Massachusetts, and perhaps two or three other Massachusetts lighthouses. Some of these, like the Cape Ann lighthouses, were finished after he left the Light-House Board. Almost all of them still exist and are well-known landmarks. They include the red and white striped West Quoddy Head light, and the lighthouses on Petit Manan, Matinicus Rock, and Seguin Islands. Franklin also designed many lightkeepers houses, although most of these have been replaced, demolished, or substantially altered. Franklin was described by a historian at the Maine Historic Preservation Commission as "probably... the most prolific of the lighthouse engineers who served in Maine."[28]

Even before the creation of the Light-House Board, a replacement for Boon Island lighthouse and the lightkeeper's house was in the works. In 1850, a survey of the buildings and the topography of the island was produced at the request of Portsmouth collector Augustus Jenkins by civil engineers Brown & Hastings under the supervision of Gridley Bryant. Their rendering shows flags flying, a massive eagle atop the light tower, and a jaunty little two-masted boat perched on the boatways. It imparts a rather festive look to the establishment. The drawing also shows the position of the various structures. The roofed-over remnants, or razees, of the stone monument built in 1804 and of the 1811 light tower were still standing, and used for storage.

Boon Island keeper John Thompson wrote of the devastating effects of the two-day gale "of Minot's ledge notoriety" on April 16 and 17, 1851, "the most dreadful tempest I ever witnessed, on land or at sea." Its effects, recorded by Thompson in his journal, and published in a local newspaper, must have made Franklin keenly aware of the difficulties of

1850 survey of Boon Island by Brown and Hastings under the supervision of Gridley Bryant. NARG26.

the site. The intense northeast storm, making "a fair breach over the island," wrenched the boat skids from the slip and smashed the boat, tore the wall leading to the old lighthouse from its foundation, ripped shingles from the razee of the monument, swept away the plank platforms between the buildings, and finally peeled off the board sheathing intended to keep the mortar from washing out on the east side of the keeper's stone house. Huge rocks were heaved around, and on the morning of the eighteenth Thompson "found every thing in ruins, and the whole island a perfect chaos."[29]

Expenditure of only twenty-five thousand dollars for the new lighthouse and keeper's house was approved in late summer 1852, with the expectation that much of the stone of the existing tower could be recycled—a penny-pinching arrangement that suggests that before the Light-House Board began its work in October 1852, Fifth Auditor Stephen Pleasonton had been involved in figuring out how much money this construction should cost.[30]

In December 1852, Franklin was ordered to draw up plans for a new Boon Island lighthouse and keeper's house as soon as possible; by late February 1853, he had sent the plans to the Light-House Board's Committee on Engineering. He also gave his opinion that the stone in the old lighthouse could not be reused because it was not suitable and because to do so would mean temporarily suspending a very important light. Later in the year, the amount available for building was nearly doubled by an additional appropriation of $19,973. Franklin was instructed to arrange for all building materials except for the lantern and illuminating apparatus; it would be cheaper to order them from a French manufacturer—and in fact there was no American manufacturer of Fresnel-type lenses.[31]

Franklin designed a lighthouse 136 feet high to the top of the lantern dome. It was, and still is, the tallest in New England, although others built on higher ground give their lanterns greater elevation. By fall 1853, Franklin must have had a better understanding of the difficulty of landing materials at Boon Island. His original specifications called for huge blocks of cut granite for the lower tiers of the structure. His revision of the plans to reduce the height (and therefore the weight) of the granite blocks to two feet for the upper tiers and to one foot for the first foundation tier was approved by the board.[32]

In charge of supplying the materials for the light tower was J. B. Leonard, acting as government agent and clerk of the works. Construction began in June 1854. The eighteen hundred tons of granite needed were quarried and cut to specifications in Biddeford, Maine, and loaded in installments on a sloop for shipment to the island. In early September, a reporter from the *Eastern Argus,* a Portland newspaper, made the trip out to the island with Leonard in the sloop *Northern Light* carrying the granite prepared for the last five courses of the tower. He wrote that it had already risen 110 feet. The next phase of construction was to line the entire interior of the light tower with brick, and would require seventy-thousand.[33]

The *Argus* reporter wrote that because of a summer drought and the number of workmen on the island, water had to be imported from the mainland. When rain finally came, the men dipped water into storage containers from the rock crevices in which it had accumulated. He also reported that the keeper, George Bowden, came from York, where his family had a farm. Bowden was experienced as a master mariner and, like lighthouse keepers Thomas Laighton and Mark Dennett, had been a Democratic state legislator. He seems to have done some politicking at Boon Island. The observer from the *Argus* noted that the men working on the lighthouse were calling for a Democratic caucus in the town of York.[34]

A photograph taken after the lighthouse was finished shows that the razees of the old stone monument and first lighthouse were removed when the new lighthouse and dwelling were built. The large frame structure to the south of the tower evidently was built to accommodate the workers and their equipment. What appear to be tracks led from it toward the water and extended to the base of the tower, and were doubtless used for moving granite-laden cars. A steam "donkey" engine may well have been used for hauling and hoisting the blocks of granite onto the structure.

Unlike the previous lighthouse, which used stone available on the island, where much mortar compensated for the irregularities of the crudely fitted stone, the Biddeford granite used for the tower was hewn and closely fitted with tight joints for the vertical surfaces, or "builds," as well as the horizontal "beds." Unfortunately, Franklin's plans for the lighthouse have not been found, but presumably the granite blocks were dovetailed to lock together. From the base, where the diameter is twenty-five feet, the tower tapers inward for the first ten or so feet and then rises nearly vertically to a cavetto cornice forming a lip about ten feet below the top of the stone tower. Above this the stonework flares outward again to accommodate a catwalk with an iron railing. The last few feet of stonework were built straight up to the lantern platform. On the inside of the tower at its base, a series of four arched niches were built into the brick interior walls for storage of oil containers. A spiral stair of 167 steps of patterned, cast-iron open work wound nearly to the top of the lighthouse, with the final ascent to the lantern by means of an iron ladder.

The iron lantern and the fixed, second-order Fresnel lens manufactured in France arrived and were installed late in December 1854. First-order lenses were the largest, with second through sixth orders of descending importance. According to a contemporarydescription, the light produced by a second-order lens with its single lamp was equivalent to light from 450 Argand lamps. Until 1993, a Fresnel lens was in place in the lantern at Boon Island. It bore the imprint of one of the principal manufacturers of Fresnel lenses at this time: "Sautter. Paris. Constructeurs," and was probably the lens installed in 1854.

The jewel-like, beehive-shaped lens had an interior diameter of nearly four and a half feet and was about nine feet high. The highly polished glass components were precisely positioned within a brass framework. A continuous refracting lens belted the apparatus at the level of the light source inside the lens. Above and below this belt, ranges of refracting and reflecting prisms were set at angles mathematically determined to collect and bend the light above and below the focal plane and to direct it outward. The original light source was a single lamp of the type perfected by Fresnel for use with lenses of varied sizes; the lamp for a second-order lens was fitted with three concentric, tubular wicks. Because of its efficient capture and transmission of light and spectacular economies in oil, in that only a single lamp was needed, this equipment, though costly to install, was a dramatic improvement over the old multiple lamps and reflectors.[35]

For access to the exterior of the lantern for cleaning the glass and painting the metal frame of the lantern, a second catwalk was built about a third of the way up the side of the lantern, reached by a ladder from the lower catwalk. The French-manufactured lantern was capped with a copper domed roof with a finial containing the ventilator for the lamp. The light in the lantern was first lit on January 1, 1855.[36]

Unlike the many keepers' houses Franklin designed for "dry" sites, which were wood-frame, board-and-batten cottages with label moldings

The new Boon Island lighthouse, ca. 1854. NARG26.

around door and window tops and painted in then fashionable "earth" tones, the Boon Island dwelling was designed without regard for currently popular architectural style but instead with the storm-beaten site in mind.[37] The Boon Island house was of the same closely fitted Biddeford granite as the lighthouse. Like it, the house was brick-lined, with an "air streak" between the outer and inner walls to foil the effects of dampness that penetrated to the interior of unlined masonry structures.

The house, partitioned down the middle to create separate quarters for the keeper and his assistants, was of one and a half stories. On the east side was an ell, also divided, to create one kitchen for the keeper and another for his assistants. Below the kitchens, space was excavated for water cisterns, one for each half of the house. Water collected from the roof gutters was stored in the cisterns and brought up into the kitchen sinks by hand pumps. The bleak, windowless front façade of the house faced westward toward the mainland and had a separate entrance for each half.

Drawings made later in the century indicate that there were two windows on each side of the house and two more on the sides of the kitchen ell and at the rear, east elevation of the kitchen. Each kitchen ell had another door to the outside. In the ell, a chimney with two flues was shared by the kitchens; each house had a chimney for a parlor stove. Light for the upstairs bedrooms came from windows at each gable end and skylights on the roof. The house was placed only a few feet north of the light tower and was connected to it by a roofed stone passageway leading from a door on the south side of the house.

From the Isles of Shoals, Celia Thaxter kept an eye on Boon Island lighthouse. She wrote:

> ... its slender column against the sky... is easily mistaken for the smokestack of a steamer by unaccustomed eyes, and sometimes the watcher most familiar with its appearance can hardly distinguish it from the distant white sails that steal by it... Sometimes it looms colossal in the mirage of summer; in winter it lies blurred and ghostly at the edge of chilly sea and pallid sky. In the sad, strange light of winter sunsets, its faithful star blazes suddenly from the darkening east, and sends a friendly ray across to its neighbor at the Shoals.

Thaxter visited Boon Island and found morning glories at the base of the tower, planted by some "tender thought," their beauty intensified by the bleak granite setting.[38]

Fresnel Lenses for Fort Constitution, Whale's Back, and White Island Lighthouses

All the new lighthouses Lieutenant. Franklin had built were fitted with Fresnel lenses. Another of the Light-House Board's missions was to refit with Fresnel lenses lighthouses not being replaced by new structures; by the time Franklin left the first district he had arranged for the refitting of virtually all of them. Late in 1854, a three-foot-high, stationary Fresnel lens of the fourth order showing a white light was installed at the lighthouse at Fort Constitution. A local newspaper commented on the economy of oil possible with this new apparatus. With the old reflector lamps, the article said, "over 600 gallons of oil was consumed yearly, or about two gallons per night,—The present light consumes about one quart per night, or 90 gallons per year. It was expected that the savings would take care of the cost of the new equipment and later save enough to pay a keeper's salary." [39]

A new lantern and new lighting apparatus to create a new, distinctive light characteristic for Whale's Back was installed in 1855, eliminating the ineffective double-lantern arrangement. The equipment was displayed in January at the customs house prior to its June installation, following the newly required six months' public notice to mariners when the light characteristic of a particular lighthouse was to be altered. The *Chronicle* took the occasion to urge mildly that "some substantial repairs and improvements ought to be made on the Lighthouse itself, to render it more comfortable as a residence." [40]

The Whale's Back lighting apparatus was furnished by another French manufacturer of Fresnel lenses, L. Lepaute, at a cost of nearly sixty-four hundred dollars. To create the new characteristic—a fixed white light of the fourth order varied by flashes—required in addition to the lens itself two panels holding bulls-eye-like, annular lenses known as flash panels. Clockwork machinery rotated these panels around the fixed lens to create an intense flash every ninety seconds. This feature distinguished the Whale's Back light from the fixed white light at Fort Constitution and the red and white revolving light at White Island. Similar fixed lights varied by flashes, of various magnitudes, were installed the same year at four other Maine lighthouses. [41]

At White Island, however, new reflector lamps rather than a lens light were installed in 1854. It may be that manufacture and shipment of a revolving second-order Fresnel lens from France was delayed and the quality of the light was temporarily upgraded in this way. A second-order Fresnel lens, perpetuating the existing red and white characteristic, was not installed at White Island until the second half of 1858. The lens in the lighthouse lantern in 1909 was manufactured by L. Sautter, and was probably the one originally installed. Twenty bullseye flash panels were integrated into the lens; red glass panels were affixed to alternate segments of the lens. The entire lens rotated on a "chariot" of wheels set in a groove with ball bearings. It made a complete revolution every five minutes, and at fifteen-second intervals showed alternate red and white flashes lasting fifteen seconds.[42]

Buoys, Beacons, and Bells

Until a naval officer was assigned to the First Lighthouse District, Lieutenant Franklin also had to supervise the maintenance and installation of buoys, beacons, and fog bells. Even before the creation of the Light-House Board, Congress had moved to establish uniform standards for the shapes and colors of buoys marking hazards and navigable channels along the American coasts. An illustration in Blunt's *American Coast Pilot* of 1850 shows the ingenious but ineffective distinctions then

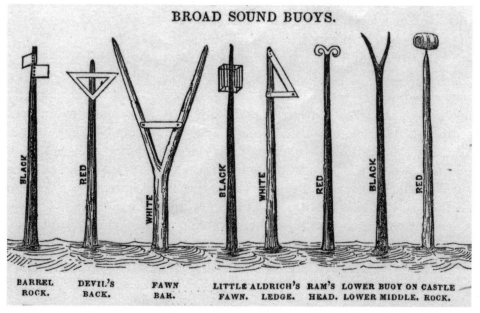

Buoys for the approaches to Boston Harbor illustrated in the 1850 edition of Blunt's American Coast Pilot.

being used for buoys in the channel approaches to Boston Harbor.

Portsmouth Harbor already had a semblance of a system, with not very visible white buoys marking hazards that entering vessels should keep to starboard and black for those to be kept to port. A September 28, 1850 Act of Congress required the use of red buoys to mark the right side of channels and black for the left side. This reform was probably the result of the 1846 report by Lieutenants Jenkins and Bache on European aids to navigation. They wrote of the uniform shapes and colors of buoys and the numbering system used in Liverpool Harbor and illustrated their report with a sheet of drawings of the various types of iron buoys used there.

The 1850 legislation mandated a similar system for the United States: even and odd numbers were to distinguish the right (starboard) and left (port) channel markers. Black-and-white vertically striped buoys were for the centers of narrow channels, red and black horizontal stripes indicated hazards in the middle of a channel where vessels could pass safely on either side. Cylindrical "can" shapes with white numbers were prescribed for black entrance markers on the port side, and conical "nun" shapes with black numbers for the red starboard buoys.[43]

Later in the 1850s the Light-House Board began using nun and can buoys formed of iron boiler plate, replicating the hollow shapes formerly made of wooden staves sheathed with iron or copper or of iron-sheathed solid wooden forms. More often the buoys were much less costly metal-tipped wooden spars. The buoys were anchored by stone weights, mushroom anchors, or specially designed "sinkers."

Beacons—unlit navigational markers of stone, wood or iron—were reserved for ledges, including those exposed at low tide. Buoys, where tides ran swiftly, as they did in the Piscataqua River, were liable to be pulled sideways by the river's tidal force and were difficult to see. Offshore, they could be wrenched from their positions. But battering seas could also dislodge beacons, and because they were rigid, they were also susceptible to damage by vessels running into them.

In October 1850, twenty-five hundred dollars was appropriated for marking the entrance to Little Harbor, a potential harbor of refuge for vessels unable to make Portsmouth Harbor itself in northeasterly gales. Since at least 1841, local interests had advocated providing information about this harbor in published sailing directions.[44] Off Jerry's Point, a red-painted iron beacon was placed at the end of a shoal point now covered by the stone breakwater built in the 1880s. A black spar buoy was placed nearly opposite, off Frost Point ledges. A photograph of about 1894 shows an iron beacon with a six-legged base supporting a spindle with a distinctive perch, the letters *L.H.* and a vane on top. It may be the one manufactured by Portland blacksmith Stephen Emerson and installed in the fall of 1851. A preliminary chart of Portsmouth Harbor published by the U. S. Coast Survey in 1854 shows the positions of the Little Harbor beacon and buoy. But not until 1857 did Blunt's *Coast Pilot* mention these markers, and even then provided no directions for finding a good anchorage once inside Little Harbor. This may well have been because there was a bar with less than three feet of water at the entrance to the harbor and within it many shoal areas where the water was not deep enough for any but the lightest draft vessels. Little Harbor was useful mainly to small local fishing boats whose masters were familiar with the harbor.[45]

An appropriation was also made in 1850 for a buoy on the ledge three miles east of Boon Island. The small appropriation of one hundred and fifty dollars suggests that it was for a wooden spar buoy. The *Journal* in July 1851 carried an announcement that "a buoy painted in red and black stripes has been placed in fifteen feet of water on the northwest side of Boon Island Rock, bearing E. from Boon Island, distance one league."[46]

The 1851 Little Harbor beacon, showing the much later Jerry's Point breakwater partially completed. A post light was installed in 1903 on the built-up section to the right. NARG26.

Alexander Parris's touted iron York Ledge monument had proven vulnerable. The March 1851 storm that toppled the Minot's Ledge light-house carried a good part of it away; repairs amounting to six thousand dollars were accomplished in June of that year.[47]

Other early 1850s appropriations called for iron beacons on Logy's Ledge at the entrance to Pepperrell's Cove, a shoal anchorage opening to the northeast of Portsmouth Harbor, to replace the buoy that formerly marked this hazard; and another beacon for Willey's Ledge, off Badger's Island. These unlit markers had not been put in place by the time Lieutenant Franklin began his first district duties. One of his early tasks was to see to their installation. These were placed in 1853, along with a spar buoy with perpendicular stripes for Half-Way, or Gangway Rock.[48]

A working drawing for the Willey's Ledge beacon shows that its shaft was of wrought iron, six and a half inches in diameter. It was inserted to a depth of two and a half feet into a hole drilled in the ledge. A layer of zinc and a protective sleeve of cast iron protected the first eleven feet of the beacon, which rose forty-one feet above the ledge. It was painted red, and had ornamental distinguishing features near the top that must have added considerably to its cost: a ten-foot-high copper cylinder surmounted by large and small disks, and a three-and-a-half-foot vane with a gilt ball on top. The Logy's Ledge beacon was also a red-painted iron spindle top-ped by a copper cylinder. By late 1856, this beacon had been damaged, probably by a boat striking it. It was repaired, but in 1862 it was destroyed and a stone monument was recommended to replace it.

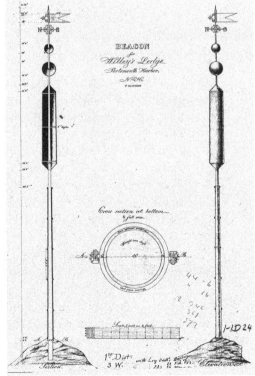

Drawing of the Willey's Ledge beacon put in place in 1853. NARG26.

Another Light-House Board innovation was the establishment of buoy and lighthouse supply depots at strategic locations along the coasts to supplement the principal depot on Staten Island. In the First District, the main depot was on a Casco Bay island off Portland. A smaller one was at the Portsmouth Navy Yard, authorized in October 1852.[49]

With its many bays and inlets, the coastline of Maine, which with New Hampshire comprised the First Lighthouse District, is estimated at twenty-five hundred miles in length, not counting the navigable rivers extending far inland. Especially in the down east portion of Lieutenant Franklin's district there were many hazards and harbor approaches lacking buoyage and lighthouses. Franklin's annual report covering his work in 1855 hints at the logistical problems he had to contend with in his extensive district. *Wave,* a sixty-five-foot-long schooner of seventy-seven tons and a draft of six feet built in Northport, New York, in 1853 and in service in the First Lighthouse District until 1861, carried Franklin along the coast to make lighthouse inspections and to see to works in progress.[50] This vessel also served as a buoy-tender, except for Portsmouth Harbor and Kennebec River projects, for which local vessels were hired for the purpose. The transport of building materials and supplies for the lighthouses had to be done by chartered vessels. Franklin urged the purchase of a small steamer and suggested a propeller-driven, schooner-rigged vessel of about 250 tons burden:

> One such steamer could perform all of the service, which now requires two and sometimes three schooners; and in addition, the time and transportation of workmen would be saved, which in themselves are large items. She could also deliver the annual supplies from Portland or Portsmouth... The supply-vessel is always in a hurry, and in several cases has left supplies which are not fitted for the light... But the great number of outside buoys in the district which require attention, is the principal reason why a steamer would be particularly useful. There are many more buoys on ledges exposed to the full force of the sea, along the coast of Maine and New Hampshire, than along any coast of the same length in the United States, and I have sometimes had a vessel waiting more than a month to replace one buoy. Two weeks is not an uncommon time to take up in changing one. A steamer could place ten such buoys before a schooner could place one, under the most favorable circumstances.[51]

In spite of Franklin's recommendation, no steamer was provided for this lighthouse district until after Civil War.

An offshore ledge that caused many wrecks, and proved hard to mark, was Boon Island Ledge. The buoy placed there in 1851 was torn from its site. The nun buoy replacement of April 1853 also proved inadequate; by the end of 1855, Franklin suggested that a bell buoy would be preferable, especially when there was fog. Offshore floating bells to warn of hazards during thick weather were only just being developed. In Connecticut local ingenuity in the mid-1840s took a long boat from a whaler, decked it over and fitted it with a mast holding aloft not only seven cowbells but also a lantern to mark a sandbar hazard at the mouth of Bridgewater Harbor. It lasted barely two years before it parted its mooring in a gale and smashed onshore.[52]

As early as 1853 the Light-House Board ordered the manufacture of four iron bell buoys, sometimes described as bell-boats, for locations off New York and North Carolina and in Mobile Bay. These were probably modeled after one used in Liverpool Harbor and reported on by Lieutenants Jenkins and Bache. This bell boat, or bell-beacon, was described and illustrated in their 1846 report:

> the bell (2 3/4 cwt.) is on a mast, stepped in a boat-shaped hull, decked over, drawing three feet water, and heavily ballasted. From the peculiar construction of this vessel, the motion of the little sea where she is moored is quite sufficient to put the four hammers in play upon the bell, the sounds of which may be heard distinctly from four to six miles—sufficiently far to apprize the navigator of approaching dangers. There is a duplicate bell beacon, which is kept ready for instant service.

Franklin had one of these buoys placed off Portland Harbor in 1855.[53]

Tne iron bell boat for Boon Island Ledge, like most of the others, cost a hefty five thousand dollars and was set out to mark the ledge by summer of 1858, but by August of that year it went adrift. The Portsmouth collector arranged for the Boon Island lighthouse keepers to retrieve it in the island's boat, but this small craft was inadequate for the task of towing the heavy, cumbersome bell boat, and the men had to abandon the job. Captain C. H. Thurlow, of the Schooner *Coral,* came across the drifting buoy and successfully towed it into Portsmouth Harbor, and then tried to extract eight hundred dollars from the Light-House Board for salvage. He was finally awarded one hundred dollars.

The buoy may have been re-anchored within the month, but needed repairs again the next year. It was restored again to its Boon Island Ledge location in June 1859, but the annual report for that year reported that it had sunk. These early bell-boats appear to have been inadequate and very susceptible to parting their moorings or being sunk by vessels hitting them. No reference has been found to any after the Civil War. In 1868 a spar buoy was installed to mark the Boon Island Ledge. It was not until the 1870s that a more satisfactory floating bell buoy was developed.[54]

A tally of vessels passing Boon Island during 1859, kept by keeper Joseph H. Hart, provides an interesting contrast with a three-month count by keeper John S. Thompson only seven years earlier. For the same three months, Hart's total was nearly the same as Thompson's. But the types of craft were changing, with many fewer square-riggers and more fore-and-aft-rigged vessels and steamers in evidence. Instead

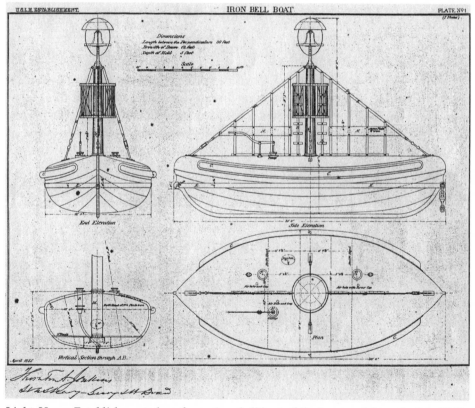

Light-House Establishment plans for an iron bell boat of the type used from the late 1840s through the 1850s. Lieutenant Franklin had one of these placed on Boon Island Ledge around 1858. NARG26.

of the twenty-two ships, 217 brigs and sixty-three barks of 1852, there were only three ships, twenty-seven brigs, and three barks passing in October, November, and December of 1859. The number of passing steamers had risen from thirty-eight to eighty-nine, sloops from thirty-one to 122, and schooners from 2,488 to 2,629.[55]

Higher Standards for Lighthouse Keepers

Lieutenant Franklin, during the several years when he combined the work of engineer and inspector for the district, also had the job of supervising the lighthouse keepers. During his first year he inspected every lighthouse, observing and reporting on the keepers as well as the physical condition of the lighthouses and lighting apparatus. He found that most of the keepers were newly appointed. Some, he said, had scarcely seen a lighthouse before, and none had been given any instruction as to how to do their work. A few had a difficult time getting the lamps lit at all; others did not even use the lamp chimneys that were intended to provide an updraft for the lamps' flames.[56]

In his 1855 report, Franklin wrote that regular inspections were paying off. The lighthouses were cleaner and the lights better tended. This was due partly to more experience with the job, but also, he wrote, because the keepers expected their performance to be inspected regularly. He also commented on the generally low quality of the keepers, many of whom he thought could not make a go of it in other work. He observed that the average pay in the district was three hundred fifty dollars per year, hardly enough to support a man with a family. One hundred dollars more, he thought, would attract more suitable lightkeepers.[57]

Franklin's view was echoed by the Light-House Board's Chairman, who pointed out that an enactment passed as early as 1828 had authorized salaries for the entire system to average four hundred dollars per keeper. Even in 1855 the average pay was lower than this, though some keepers like those at such offshore lights as Boon Island, White Island and Whale's Back lighthouses earned considerably more; masters of light vessels also received a pay differential. Keepers of the few Fresnel lens lights installed before the creation of the Light-House Board were paid more, because of the supposed difficulty of maintaining them. With Fresnel lenses slated for all lighthouses, the extra pay at these lights could no longer be justified.[58]

The Nantucket Shoals Lightship

In 1855, a lightship for Nantucket Shoals was built in Ship House Number Four at the Portsmouth Navy Yard. Although manned lightships, or light boats as they were early called, played no part in marking dangers around Portsmouth, they were crucial aids to navigation in locations where technology had not yet permitted lighthouses to be built. Lightboats had been used in England as early as 1732, when one was placed at the mouth of the Thames. The earliest in the United States was stationed at the mouth of Chesapeake Bay in 1820, and the first offshore lightship was placed at Sandy Hook in 1823 By the end of Stephen Pleasonton's years as fifth auditor, there were forty-two. The number peaked in 1858, with forty-eight, and then declined as lighthouses replaced them. Minot's Ledge was marked with a lightship between the time the iron frame lighthouse was destroyed in 1851 and the stone replacement was completed in 1860.[59]

Not surprisingly, U.S. lightships under Pleasonton's supervision came in for harsh judgement in the Light-House Board report of 1852: "This branch of the lighting service of this country is probably the most defective." The report cited antiquated lighting apparatus: un-reflected flames from multiple wicks protruding from openings in a covered bowl. The boats were moored to a single anchor with such a long scope of cable that a vessel described a huge circle around it, "destroying, in some degree, her usefulness as a range," and increasing the chance of the cable's fouling the anchor. The government maintained only a single relief lightship to replace any of the many vessels periodically blown off station or towed ashore for repairs, often leaving many stations unlighted for weeks. Absenteeism by masters, mates, and crew was widespread. In one case a lightship had been left with only a young teenageer aboard. There had been no attempt to find a hull design to minimize the rolling and tossing of the tethered ships, resulting in strain not only on the moorings and lighting equipment but on the crews as well.[60]

In its 1852 report, the board illustrated as a possible model the light vessels provided under the jurisdiction of Trinity House, which administered English aids to navigation. The report included the design of the *Prince,* Liverpool's northwest lightboat. The English boats were fitted with Argand lamps and reflectors, and were so successfully moored that they were rarely off station, the report claimed. No boat was removed from position until a replacement was provided. And, as with the rest of the Trinity House establishment, the duties of the masters and crews responsible for maintaining the lights were spelled out in great detail.[61]

The dreaded Nantucket Shoals, a group of four sandy shelves located about forty-one miles from the mainland and between twelve and twenty-four miles from Nantucket Island, lay in the path of many vessels bound into New York from Europe. The tide rips that swirled over the shoals when combined with an easterly storm created massive, turbulent breakers considered a threat to even the largest of vessels. These shoals had been a candidate for markers of some sort for a long time. In 1842, I. W. P. Lewis wrote that the "feasibility of erecting screw-pile beacons on these shoals will hardly be questioned," and in 1849 Congress had appropriated funds for a screw pile lighthouse for the Nantucket Shoals of the type developed in the 1830s by the Irish engineer Alexander Mitchell for use on sandy shoals. It was never built. The fate of the iron pile lighthouse on Minot's Ledge may have caused second thoughts about iron-pile structures at such exposed locations. Finally, in 1854, a lightship was placed on the shoals nineteen miles off Nantucket, but it broke adrift the next year and ended up in Montauk, Long Island. She was later used at a location closer to the mainland.[62]

The keel for her replacement was laid at the Portsmouth Navy Yard a month or two after the launch of the hull of the rebuilt frigate *Santee* in February 1855. As can be seen from the round-bottomed half-hull model of the lighthship at the Navy Yard, no evident attempt was made to solve the problem of rolling. The drawing of the English *Prince* shows a stabilizing flared keel, but the hull design previously used in the U. S. was perpetuated in the new lightboat, and in fact there were those who thought the English hull model unsatisfactory.[63]

Portsmouth Navy Yard logs show that work began slowly late in April 1855 with at first only ten or so carpenters, sawyers, joiners, and

Hull model for the Nantucket lightship built at the Portsmouth Navy Yard in 1855. PNS.

laborers at work on her. The lightship was constructed of the white oak and live oak regularly used at his time. On the thirtieth, a gundalow arrived from Durham with white oak timbers for the boat; teams of oxen, dubbers wielding adzes joined the work crew. On May 25, the schooner *Canton* brought timbers from Bangor. Thereafter, the pace quickened, with as many as thirty-nine men working on her each day. Mast-makers were added to the workforce before the launching of the hull on September 11, 1855, and afterwards were joined by riggers, sailmakers, joiners, machinists, coopers, ordnance men, a mason, and painters.[64]

Research compiled by Willard Flint shows that the 275-ton vessel had a bowsprit, a length of 103 feet between perpendiculars, a beam of twenty-four feet, and a draft of twelve and a half feet. She had two seventy-two-foot-high masts for the lighting apparatus, each topped with an oval daymark constructed of iron gridwork. Aft of each of these masts were subsidiary "spencer" masts for carrying the sails that were the vessel's only means of propulsion. Her hull was painted white. For fog signals, a bell, to be hand-struck, and a horn of some sort were provided. Guns were also furnished for use as fog signals.[65]

On January 23, 1856, one day before she left Portsmouth Harbor, the lightboat's lights were tested. The lighting apparatus was probably shipped in from the main Light-House Board depot on Staten Island. The

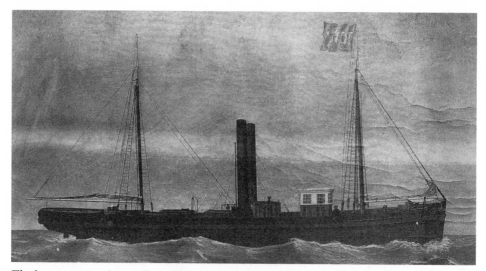

The large ocean-going tugboat R. B. Forbes, *was similar to the* Enoch Train *which towed the Nantucket lightship from the Portsmouth Navy Yard, where she was built, to Staten Island prior being stationed on the Nantucket South Shoals. From* Tugboats on the Piscataqua, *published by the* Portsmouth Marine Society.

lights, following the English example, were eight Argand lamps with reflectors in each of the glazed housings that circled the two masts and could be hoisted up them after lighting—Fresnel lenses were thought too heavy, although they were in use on French lightships. As it was, the lighting apparatus for each of the masts weighed a ton. On January 24, 1856, the lightship left Portsmouth under tow of the ocean-going steam tug *Enoch Train,* of Boston and arrived in that city the next day. By the end of the month, the vessel, with its master, mate, crew, and cook, was on station on the South Nantucket Shoal, twenty-four miles from the nearest land, at one of the most exposed and dangerous of all lightship stations in the world. The difficulty of the post was reflected by the one thousand dollar annual pay of the master.[66]

During her long years at Nantucket Shoals, the Portsmouth-built lightship parted her anchor twelve times and was sometimes off station for as long as twenty days. She was rebuilt in 1860. In 1887 she picked up the crew of the foundering British steamer *Caledonia* and the lightship's crew shared their accommodations with the steamer's survivors for twelve days before they were carried ashore by a tender.[67]

According to an account of the lightship written in 1891, her last year on the Nantucket Shoals, she had two hulls, "the space between

Taking in the light on the Nantucket South Shoals lightship. This involved lowering the glass enclosure for the reflector lamps into a shed-like structure on the deck, where the equipment was cleaned and the lamps filled. Illustration for an 1891 article in the Century *Magazine.*

The Nantucket lightship tossing in a rough sea. Century Magazine.

them being filled… with salt—'to keep her sweet.'" The lantern housings were raised only twenty-five feet high on their masts to keep the light-ships's center of gravity as low as possible. Engines were not provided to lightships until 1891. The minimal suit of sails the Nantucket vessel carried for emergency use in case her cables parted did not permit her to beat to windward. It consisted of trysails on the sail masts and a forestaysail and jib that could be raised on the fore lantern-mast. Twice a year, each crew member was given a two-month leave ashore; thus, each man was a prisoner on this tossing craft for a total of eight months per year. Many took part in the maritime equivalent of a cottage industry, making the nested baskets that are now prized collector's items.[68]

The lightship built at the Portsmouth Navy Yard was not retired from service until seventy-four years after her launching. Assigned the number one in 1867, when the board began numbering lightships, she remained at the distant, battering Nantucket Shoals location until November 1892. After being fitted with a steam whistle, she remained in service off the North and South Carolina coasts until finally being retired in 1930.[69]

The last years of the Nantucket Shoals lightship were spent closer to Portsmouth. She was acquired by the Sea Scouts in 1930 and towed up the Merrimack River to Haverhill, Massachusetts. She next was used by the Groveland Sea Scouts, farther downriver. In the great flood of 1936, she was swept downstream and went aground on the north bank of the river, where as recently as 1986 the remains of her hull still rested.[70]

A New Lighthouse for White Island

The last major lighthouse project of the 1850s around Portsmouth was the construction of a new light tower for White Island, to replace the old rubble stone structure that had stood since its completion late in 1820. A photograph in the National Archives, probably taken just before the new construction began, captured the establishment much as it must have looked when the writer Celia Thaxter lived there. (See Chapter 5.) It shows the broad-based old tower, with white-painted shingles over the boarding concealing its round, rubblestone form and the upper portion rebuilt of brick in 1841. The braced covered way leads across the gully on its multiple "legs" to the little one-and-a-half-story whitewashed stone cottage. The huge second-order Fresnel lens installed in 1859 is partly visible in the lantern, replacing the reflector lights of Thaxter's childhood. Strategically positioned at the edge of the tide-washed gully is the outhouse. Dories and rowboats are pulled up above the high-tide mark near the boathouse and boat ways. Several figures can be seen. On the catwalk around the lantern is someone posing with a spyglass, perhaps keeper Richard Haley, an Isles of Shoals native who replaced L. H. D. Shepard in 1853. At the base of the tower are a young man and a girl, and in the foreground in front of the boathouse is a boy. They are perhaps Haley's son Otis, who became assistant keeper in August of 1859; his daughter Elizabeth; and one of his other two sons.[71]

Although Lieutenant Franklin was serving as Engineer Secretary to the Light-House Board at the time of construction, he may have been its principal designer; there is correspondence about plans dating to 1854. Since 1857, William A. Goodwin, of Portland, had been clerk of works for the First District, and after Franklin went to Washington as engineer secretary, Goodwin corresponded with him about district projects.[72]

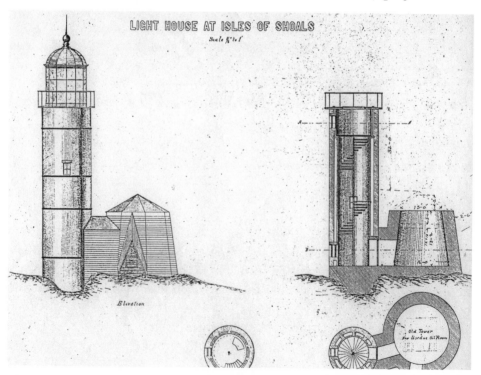

Plan for the new White Island lighthouse, showing its relationship to the original structure, which was cut down and roofed over for an oil storage shed. NARG26.

The replacement lighthouse was built in 1859, and still stands. The tower is of brick and is cylindrical in form, like a number of other lighthouses designed by Franklin. It rises, like the first White Island lighthouse, forty feet to the lantern platform. The confidence and efficiency of the design is displayed by the smaller diameter of the new tower—approximately fourteen feet, compared to the twenty-two-foot-diameter of the base of its predecessor. Four narrow string courses divide the cylindrical tower horizontally into five unequal tiers. As at Boon Island, arched niches for storing oil were built into the brickwork inside the tower at entry level. In the interior, the brickwork near the top of the tower is corbeled inward to receive the iron plates that form the floor of the twelve-sided cast-iron lantern and its roof of iron plates. The lantern, with its domed copper roof and surmounting cast iron ventilator ball, adds another eighteen feet to the lighthouse. Patterned, openwork cast-iron stairs wind around an iron center post, with their wedge-shaped treads anchored in the brickwork of the tower walls.

The National Archives contains an "after" photo, taken in 1860, showing the new lighthouse. The old stone tower was cut down and roofed over for an oil storage house and was connected to the new structure by a short covered passageway way. Celia Thaxter considered the

The new White Island lighthouse as it looked after completion in 1859. The photograph shows the old lighthouse of Celia Thaxter's childhood cut down and roofed over for use as an oil storage structure. NARG26.

old, broad-based, shingle-clad rubblestone lighthouse "by far the most picturesque," compared to the businesslike, cylindrical form of the new one.[73] It is unclear whether the cracks in the brick tower that now threaten its structural integrity are the result of flawed design or poor construction methods or are the result of insufficient attention to the masonry over the years.

The Civil War Years

The U.S. Census of 1860, showing Portsmouth's population stuck at something under ten thousand, was an occasion for soul-searching. Native talent, energy, and capital were looking, and going, elsewhere, according to a newspaper concerned that local capital was not investing more in manufacturing. The paper listed the amounts annually spent on such goods such as carriages, umbrellas, leather goods, farm tools, and paper made elsewhere that Portsmouth could have been producing.[74] The total tonnage and numbers of merchant vessels built in private Piscataqua yards peaked in 1855 with twelve vessels built, amounting to over 11,700 tons. In 1860 only seven vessels totaling thirty-six hundred tons were built; in 1861 only three vessels adding up to about two thousand tons, left the ways of local builders. Figures prepared by the customs office showed a diminished fleet of merchant vessels hailing from Portsmouth. Of the thirty largest Portsmouth-built vessels, the ships, five actually hailed from New Orleans, and another twelve were partly owned by Boston and New York interests. One bark and two brigs were registered in Portsmouth.[75]

Interestingly, while Portsmouth shipbuilders built impressive transport vessels for service in worldwide commerce in the 1850s, there had been little attempt to meet the demand for schooners for the coasting trade. Those that thronged the waters off Portsmouth were built mostly elsewhere; only six of the sixty-four schooners hailing from the Port of Portsmouth were built in Portsmouth, Kittery, York, or Hampton. Twenty were built in Essex, Massachusetts. Only a "half dozen" fishing vessels worked out of Portsmouth, a tiny fraction of those based in Gloucester. Before the outbreak of the Civil War, in April 1861, the *Portsmouth Journal* reported that there were less than one hundred civilians working at the Portsmouth Navy Yard, and that there was little prospect of new work.[76]

Lieutenant Charles Turnbull of the Army's Engineer Corps was assigned to the First and Second Lighthouse Districts in January 1860 and was given additional duty as first district inspector in May 1861. He had barely time to prepare plans for the replacement of the York Ledge beacon, which had again proven vulnerable, when he was assigned war duty. By the end of June 1861, almost every single Army and Navy officer assigned to lighthouse districts had been withdrawn for war assignments. Admiral Shubrick, the Board's chairman, and General Totten of the Army Corps of Engineers, both veterans of the War of 1812 and the Mexican War, were seventy-seven years old when war came. Shubrick was placed on the Navy's retired list late in 1861, but served as Light-House Board Chairman through 1870. Totten was given administrative work for the Army in Washington, and also continued his service on the board, until he died in 1864.[77]

The Civil War brought tremendous activity to the Navy Yard, and by 1862 more than two thousand men had jobs there. During the war years, more than a dozen steam sloops (including the famed *Kearsarge*), two ironclads, three sloops of war, two tugs, and a steam frigate were built and launched. The warship originally named *Alabama,* begun nearly fifty years earlier in 1817 and nearly finished a few years later but never launched, was renamed the *New Hampshire* and went down the ways in 1864 to serve as a training vessel. Many other naval vessels were rebuilt and refitted at the yard.[78]

The daily exodus of workers from the yard created a spectator sport, "at once picturesque and exciting," according to the *Portsmouth Chronicle.* At the end of the workday, the men who lived in Portsmouth competed to see who could most quickly get across the Piscataqua River, which separates the Navy Yard and Portsmouth. Hundreds of rowboats, from tiny punts to whaleboats manned by twelve oarsmen, thronged the river, jostling for position in favorable eddies in the swift-flowing waters, and gave the scene the festive air of a regatta. Intense competition developed among whaleboats like the *Zouave,* manned by the caulkers, the *Shakespeare,* rowed by riggers, and the *Nameless,* propelled by carpenters, and each was cheered by partisans along the Portsmouth shore.[79]

Although the Civil War was a boon to the economy of Portsmouth, it created major problems for the Light-House Board. After Lieutenant Turnbull's departure for war duty, the civilian William A. Gooodwin was appointed acting engineer for the First District in September 1861, and Charles Edwards, a Portland civil engineer, was hired to take care of repair work. Even Goodwin was pulled away because of the war. In 1862 and 1863, the Light-House Board sent him south on assignments along the South Atlantic coast and in the Gulf of Mexico, with Edwards moving up during his absence to become acting engineer.[80] Major new construction projects were put on hold for the duration.

Work was confined to emergency repairs, such as those needed after a powerful gale inthe fall of 1861 assaulted the vulnerable Whale's Back lighthouse, washing away the boats and davits and revealing serious leaks in the masonry of the light tower. At Fort Constitution, the walkway from the keeper's house to the lighthouse had been carried away, and the house damaged. Repairs were made, but the walk was removed when major work was begun in November 1862 at Fort Constitution to transform it into a fort of three tiers of granite casemates. It was never realized beyond the first tier. By mid-1863 the walkway to the lighthouse was back in place.[81]

Plentiful jobs at the Navy Yard created a shortage of men willing to take on lighthouse jobs. Portsmouth Customs Collector Joseph B. Upham was appointed by President Lincoln in April 1861. By the middle of the war years, he may have regretted exercising his patronage prerogative by replacing many keepers soon after he took office. On May 21, 1861, he wrote to Secretary of Treasury Salmon P. Chase, using what must have been a standard phrase, that "in my opinion the public good requires the removal of the present keepers" of Boon Island and New Castle.[82]

For Boon Island, he chose George B. Wallace of Concord, a man not personally known to him but "a highly reputable mechanic" strongly recommended by E. H. Rollins, congressman from the second New Hampshire district, and by "the leading men of Concord."[83] There is no evidence that Wallace had any experience with the sea, and one wonders how he coped with the rough conditions there and the difficulty of getting off the island in the open sailboat provided by the government. Wallace's tenure at Boon Island was short, however; on October 11, 1861, the *Portsmouth Chronicle* reported his death at the island.

For Fort Constitution,Upham's recommendation of Elias Tarlton, a master mariner from New Castle who understood firsthand the importance of a reliable light, was more suitable. In June, Upham replaced the keeper and assistant at White Island, Richard and Otis Haley, with Alfred J. Leavitt and Jonathan Godfrey of Hampton. In November, Upham also replaced the Whale's Back keeper and assistant with Joel Reynolds and Edward Parks.[84]

Early in 1863, Reynolds and his assistant were virtually helpless witnesses to the loss of at least three people right at their watery doorstep in a severe February storm. In the dim early-morning light on February 14, they discovered the partial remains of a wrecked schooner on the rocks off Whale's Back. They next saw three men clinging to a piece of drifting wreckage, about twenty feet from the lighthouse. They continually threw the men a line, but the men were too weak to grasp it. The seas were so violent that the keepers could not lower their boat, and one by one the men from the schooner disappeared into the turbulent water. The vessel was later identified as the *Rouser*, of St. John, New Brunswick, bound to Boston with a load of shingles, old iron, and pickled fish, some of which was salvaged. Two bodies and assorted luggage were later picked up, and held by the customs office for identification.[85]

Pay for lighthouse keepers was not competitive with that offered at the navy yard. This situation, and the number of men gone to war, made it more difficult to find lighthouse keepers as the war dragged on. The situation at Whale's Back was especially difficult because of the deteriorating condition of the light tower. In 1863, keeper Joel Reynolds resigned because of his wife's illness, and his assistant, Edward Parks, resigned to enlist in the Navy. Nathaniel Campbell, appointed keeper by Upham in June, resigned after a month for "more profitable and agreeable employment." Ambrose Card, who had replaced Parks as assistant, was made keeper in August, but resigned just a month later.[86]

Whether Card resigned to take a job at the Navy Yard or because a fog bell was installed at the Whale's Back light in August 1863, requiring extra work, or because he was uneasy about the condition of the lighthouse is not known. The fog bell was the first lighthouse bell installed around Portsmouth since the failed White Island lighthouse bell was hung there late in 1820. The Whale's Back bell had been authorized in 1859, and was operated by hand-wound clockwork machinery. The steel bell was placed in a twenty-five-foot-high, white-washed frame structure located on the foundation pier at the south side of the lighthouse. "During the prevalence of fogs, snow storms and thick weather," the machinery was to be activated to strike the bell at fifteen-second intervals. Its range was estimated at from a quarter of a mile to four miles, depending on wind direction and the amount of noise made by the wind and sea during storms.[87]

In July 1864, collector Upham reported to the Secretary of the Treasury the difficulty of finding suitable lightkeepers at the existing pay rates. Gilbert Amee, a seaman who had reluctantly agreed to become Card's assistant "only on the condition that he shall feel at liberty to leave in April next, if he should find it in his interest so to do," became keeper in September 1864. Substantial raises were authorized for Whale's Back. Amee's pay was raised from six hundred to seven hundred dollars per year, and his assistant's from two hundred-fifty to four hundred dollars. Amee's assistant was his wife, who was on the payroll until her death in December 1867. Mrs. Amee was the only known woman to be paid for lighthouse duties in the Portsmouth area. In 1865, the White Island keeper asked to have his wife appointed assistant, but his request was shelved. Elsewhere there were a number of women who were paid assistants to their husbands, and there were widows of keepers who took the place of their husbands as keepers, but for the most part, and in particular at one-keeper, family lighthouses like that at Fort Constitution light, wives or daughters or sons who helped with lighthouses chores were not paid. After the raises for Whale's Back were approved, the keepers at the other local lighthouses wanted more money too, and solid raises were approved for them, but this extra pay did not come through until after the war was over.[88]

At war's end, the Light-House Board was confronted with the tremendous expense of rebuilding the many southern lighthouses destroyed or damaged in the war. New construction along the northern New England coast, begun with such energy by the Light-House Board's engineers in the years after the Board was established in 1852, resumed only gradually in the late 1860s, but picked up smartly in the 1870s.

XI Post-Civil War Developments: Replacements for Whale's Back and Fort Constitution Lighthouses and the Establishment of a Lighthouse at the Nubble

... it was pulled down, and a hideous iron tower took its place, which resembles nothing so much as a length of corpulent stove-pipe, set on end—and painted.

—John Albee, *New Castle Historic and Picturesque*, 1884.

THE LIGHT-HOUSE BOARD resumed the improvements to the U.S. lighthouse system that were interrupted by the war. Army and Navy officers were gradually reassigned to lighthouse duty as district engineers and inspectors, and in the First Lighthouse District by the beginning of the 1870s continued the rebuilding program begun by the board in the 1850s. The board, especially after Joseph Henry became chairman in 1872, devoted considerable attention to keeping abreast of the Europeans in construction and lighting technology and even achieved an international reputation for leadership in the development of fog signals.

In the two decades after the Civil War, shipbuilding in private shipyards and at the Portsmouth Navy Yard, historic mainstays of the Piscataqua region's economy, declined sharply, and in the private yards came to an end completely in the mid-1880s. In the immediate postwar years, barely one merchant ship was built each year, a construction rate that continued until the September 14, 1877, launching of the *Paul Jones,* the last square-rigged merchant vessel built on the Piscataqua.

The last of four schooners built on the river in the 1880s, the 185-ton *Lizzie J. Call,* was launched in 1886. The workforce at the Portsmouth Navy Yard was sharply reduced; most of theactivity was decommissioning surplus vessels to ready them for sale. A tiny handful of steam sloops were built at the yard in the 1870s.[1]

After the demise of the private shipyards, bricks manufactured in upriver yards in the last quarter of the nineteenth century were about the only locally produced items leaving the area by water. However, shipping into the harbor and upriver grew, mostly because of increasing demand for coal for both domestic and industrial use. Much coal was unloaded in Portsmouth, and large quantities were carried inland by rail, but a considerable amount went upriver on vessels. Robert A. Whitehouse and Cathleen C. Beaudoin, in their history of the Port of Dover at the tidal head of the Cocheco River in that textile-manufacturing town, observed that though the prewar development of railroad lines had the initial effect of taking away business from waterborne transport, high freight rates after the war brought demand for river transport. This development was abetted by dredging and blasting operations on the Cocheco River lasting from the early 1870s until the mid-1890s, and was sustained in large part by the factories' need for coal after conversion from waterpower to coal-fired steam, begun before the Civil War. Summer coastal resort development and seasonal yachting along the New Hampshire and Maine coasts were becoming a factor in the economies of these states. The owners of the passenger steamers that carried increasing numbers of vacationers along the coast of Maine and New Hampshire to summer resorts began to influence the federal government's decisions about aids to navigation around Portsmouth. However, the needs of yachtsmen were not deemed to require federal expenditures for aids to navigation until after the end of the century.[2]

Light-House Board Tenders

In the First and Second Lighthouse Districts, a second schooner named *Wave* was placed in service in 1861, to take the place of the one used by Lieutenant Franklin in the 1850s, and continued to ply Maine and New Hampshire waters until being condemned in 1879. Of unknown origin and specifications except for her 138-ton displacement, the second *Wave* was originally named the *Delaware* and was used from

1856-1861 in the Fourth and Fifth districts prior to being renamed and transferred to duty in the northeast.[3]

Gradually, through the remainder of the nineteenth century, the Light-House Board developed a fleet of vessels to serve its lighthouse construction and repair needs, to provide for buoy-laying and maintenance, and to perform systematic inspection of the lighthouses. In addition, they furnished far more reliable lifelines for offhsore lighthouse keepers and their families than had been the case before the creation of the board, when revenue cutters occasionally stopped at these lighthouses.

The aftermath of the war brought one benefit to the Light-House Board in the form of surplus Navy steamers. The board bought six small screw steamers in 1865 to use as lighthouse tenders to supplement its antiquated fleet of sailing vessels. Most of these steamers had been built for private purposes, and were acquired by the Navy for various wartime duties. For an unknown reason, the Navy gave these vessels the decidedly un-nautical names of flowers, shrubs, and trees—a practice perpetuated by the Light-House Board for both "pre-owned" vessels and those built especially for the board.[4]

Iris, a 281-ton vessel from the Navy's "flowerpot fleet," was assigned to the First District in October 1865. The first propeller-driven vessel acquired by the Light-House Board, *Iris* was a wooden-hulled tugboat, eighty-seven feet in length, with a draft of nine and a half feet, built in Brooklyn, New York, in 1863 and christened the *Willett Rowe*. Purchased by the Navy later that year and given her floral name, *Iris* served as an armed tug at Charleston, South Carolina until acquisition by the Light-House Board. In 1871, *Iris* was sent to a Camden, New Jersey yard to be rebuilt and lengthened to 115 feet and returned to the First District. This lighthouse tender, with a steaming speed of from seven to eight knots, was used as a buoy tender as well as an engineer's tender in the district until replaced in 1892 by *Lilac*.[5]

Iris's territory extended from Hampton, New Hampshire all along the Maine coast. Annual Light-House Board reports listed the projects undertaken by the tenders. In 1867, for example, *Iris* and her crew made repairs and delivered fuel and other supplies to the forty-six lighthouses in the district, repaired beacons, and replaced any of the 271 buoys that had been torn from place by heavy weather or ice. Around Portsmouth, Stone's Rock off the York coast was marked for the first time with a wooden spar buoy. At Boon Island, the lamps were given new plungers and valves, and a new smoke pipe was installed in

the lantern. Whale's Back light tower was re-pointed, the roof of the
woodshed repaired, and the revolving machinery for the lighting apparatus cleaned. The Portsmouth Harbor lightkeeper's house was painted outside and interior plaster repaired. At White Island, the bricks of
the lighthouse were re-pointed, repairs were made to the doors and
windows of the house and to the boathouse and boatways, and various
adjustments and repairs were made to the lighting apparatus. New
red glass panes for creating the red portion of the light characteristic
were supplied in the lantern. All the Fresnel lenses in the district's
lighthouses were provided with new protective linen covers. *Iris* probably included inspections of the lighthouses and keepers during the
post-war period before the board was able to assign both Army engineers and Navy inspectors to each district and could provide a vessel
for each of the military officers.[6]

In 1869, the Light-House Board adopted a flag to identify the vessels in its fleet of lighthouse tenders. It was a triangular pennant with
a red border and a blue lighthouse on a white field, and was flown on
either the fore or aft derrick mast.[7]

The lighthouse tender Iris *served in the first lighthouse district from 1865 to 1892. Built
as a tugboat in 1863, she was acquired by the Navy the same year and given the floral
name that was retained after transfer to the Light-House Board.* MM.

In 1872, another Light-House Board vessel began operation in the first district. She was the brand-new 348-ton screw steamer *Myrtle,* built especially for the service to carry the Navy inspectors to the lighthouses in both the first and second districts from her home port of Boston. *Myrtle* was built of oak in the Birely, Hillmand and Streaker shipyard in Philadelphia and was 140 feet in length with a draft of nine and a half feet. After the sailing vessel *Wave* was retired in 1879, *Myrtle* also took on the job of carrying materials for construction and repairs in the first district. *Myrtle's* complement was at first five officers and fourteen men until 1911 when there were four officers and sixteen men aboard. In 1914, *Myrtle* began service in other districts, was sold by the board in 1922, and began a career of twenty-one years as a merchant vessel.[8]

The lighthouse tender Myrtle *was not a Navy cast-off, but was built especially for the Light-House Board in 1872. She served in the first lighthouse district from 1879-1914. She was eventually painted black like most other lighthouse tenders.* NARG26.

New Fuels for Lighthouse Lamps

The cost of sperm oil had risen steadily during the war, and by 1867 the board had substituted lard oil in all lighthouse lamps. At the main depot on Staten Island, the Light-House Board's Committee on Experiments, chaired by Joseph Henry,developed elaborate testing procedures for the lard oil, subjecting samples from each barrel to temperatures between thirty and forty degrees and assessing the quality of the flame produced in a special black-walled chamber, using a Bunsen photometer.[9]

Lard oil was used for only ten or twelve years before it was supplanted by kerosene. Kerosene, or mineral oil, as it was then called, is a thin, volatile liquid distilled from petroleum. Since the major Pennsylvania oil strikes just before the Civil War, it had become cheap and plentiful, and had the important advantage of being free-flowing in cold weather. The United States had been exporting kerosene to Europe for use in lighthouses for years, and the Light-House Board had begun experiments with it as early as 1855. But concerns about the explosiveness of the fuel and the necessity to develop lamps especially for its use were a deterrent. In 1864, a Lake Michigan lighthouse keeper on his own initiative had tried substituting kerosene for lard oil with disastrous results. When he tried to put out the flame by blowing down the lamp chimney, it exploded, setting his clothes on fire. He had barely escaped from the lantern room when the lamp itself exploded, destroying the lantern and the costly Fresnel lens. The board also faced a long legal battle for the right to develop its own lamps to avoid the cost of using a patented burner developed by an American, Captain Doty, whose kerosene lamps were being used in Europe. In addition, it had been discovered that the quality of this fuel deteriorated when stored in the large tin butts used for the lard oil, and smaller storage cans would be needed to replace them. It was finally the dramatic economies possible with kerosene and the example of the Europeans that spurred the board to solve these problems.[10]

Introduction of kerosene in the United States began in the mid and late 1870s in the smaller, fifth-and sixth-order lamps. In 1878, Fort Constitution was one of the earliest fourth-order lighthouses to use kerosene, closely followed by Whale's Back and a new lighthouse built at Cape Neddick in 1879. By the end of 1882, the second-order lights at Boon Island and White Island lights had made the transition to kerosene.[11]

James C. Duane, Army Engineer for the First District

During the postwar years of rebuilding southern lighthouses, the civilian William Goodwin continued as acting engineer for the First and Second Lighthouse Districts, working out of Boston, until near the end of 1868. In the fall of 1868, the first Army engineer assigned to the First Lighthouse Districts since the start of the Civil War arrived at the district's Portland headquarters He was Lieutenant Colonel James

Lieutenant Colonel James C. Duane (1824-1897), the Light-House Board's Army engineer for the first lighthouse district, 1868-1879. He was responsible for the design of the still-standing Whale's Back, Fort Constitution, and Nubble lighthouses. Photo courtesy of the Office of History, U. S. Army Corps of Engineers.

Chatham Duane, of the Army's Corps of Engineers, and held the temporary rank of Brigadier General. For more than ten years (September 1868–July 1879) he was the Board's engineer for the district, and in addition was engineer for the Second Lighthouse District June 1870–June 1881. The combined extent of the two districts stretched from the south end of Massachesetts to the northeastern tip of Maine. Duane continued the rebuilding work begun by William B. Franklin before the Civil War, designing and supervising the building of many new and replacement lighthouses and lightkeeper's houses along this stretch of coast. Most of them still exist as familiar landmarks. Around Portsmouth, Duane was involved with the design of the present lighthouse on Whale's Back Ledge, the replacement lighthouse and keeper's dwelling at Fort Constitution, a new double lightkeeper's house at White Island (demolished), and the lighthouse and keeper's house for the light station established at the end of the 1870s at the Nubble in Cape Neddick, Maine.[12]

James C. Duane (1824-1897) graduated from West Point in 1848 as an officer in the Corps of Engineers, the branch of the Army that specialized in the building of fortifications and that absorbed the Topographical Engineers during the Civil War. After graduation, Duane combined engineering assignments with teaching at West Point, for which he wrote *Manual for Engineer Troops*. He gained experience with the Light-House Board as inspector-engineer in New York for nearly two years in the late 1850s, and designed at least two lighthouses. During the war he was much involved with building the bridges and roads crucial to the Union Army's efforts, and for three years after the war superintended the building of a fort in the state of New York.[13]

When he took on the first and second district Light-House Board engineering posts, Duane was also put in charge of Maine and New Hampshire forts, and superintended construction at Forts Preble and Popham in Maine. Duane was assigned to the Third Light-House District from late 1878 until near the end of 1886, and was engineer for a number of lighthouses and keeper's houses in that district, many of which resemble those he designed earlier for Maine, New Hampshire and Massachusetts. He was appointed chief engineer for the Army in 1886, and served as a member of the Light-House Board until his retirement from the Army in June 1888. After retirement he was a member and chairman of New York's Croton Aqueduct Commission.[14]

A New Lighthouse for Whale's Back Ledge

The first of the three lighthouses Duane designed for the waters around Portsmouth was the long-sought replacement lighthouse for Whale's Back Ledge. Throughout 1869, lighthouse keeper J. W. Varney kept track of passing vessels, and there is no doubt that this light was extremely important not only for vessels entering the harbor with cargoes but also for any needing to take shelter from storms in the lower harbor. Varney counted a total of 7,590 vessels: three ships, thirteen barks, 265 brigs, 220 sloops, 237 steamers, and 6,852 schooners. On a single day in September of the following year he counted 380 passersby.[15]

An undated photograph taken in the late 1850s shows this lighthouse as it looked about a dozen years before a new lighthouse rose beside it. (See chapter 6.) Perched on the foundation pier next to the entrance door is the flimsy-looking frame shed for the fog bell machinery. Running vertically up the sides of the foundation pier are the iron strapping bars intended to hold it together. The tiers at the mid-point of the pier show signs of patching: The mortar outlines the irregularity of the stones used for the masonry laid back in 1829 by Palmer and Haselton. In 1868, some of the vertical iron straps were rebolted to the foundation pier and the tower's masonry was pointed again. Nevertheless, it still leaked badly. Spring and fall gales in 1869 snapped the iron strapping; "the stones on the upper side are cracked and started out." To secure the structure for the winter, an encircling iron band was bolted in place around the upper course of the foundation pier masonry. The board cautioned, though, that "there can be no reliance upon this expedient for any length of time," and included an estimate of seventy-five thousand dollars for building a new lighthouse.[16]

Locally, it was rumored that the Whale's Back light was to be abandoned altogether, and a new one placed on Odiorne's Point—the site first proposed for a lighthouse back in 1742.[17] But in July 1870, Congress appropriated funds for a tower, to be constructed beside the old one, on Whale's Back, as reported in the Light-House Board's *Annual Report* for that year:

> The granite pier erected in 1829 on which the light-house tower now stands had become so much injured by the heavy seas, to which it is constantly exposed, that Congress, by the act of 15th of July, 1870, granted an appropriation of $70,000.[18]

The old lighthouse was to be left standing, in part so that the light could be maintained during building of the new lighthouse, and also because there were plans to use it to house a fog signal proposed to replace the existing fog bell. Duane's plans called for a new structure of dovetailed blocks of granite, supplemented by concrete. This still-standing lighthouse rises from a base twenty-seven feet in diameter, tapering slightly to rise more than sixty feet to a pronounced cavetto cornice of stone, virtually the only stylistic detail of the structure. The focal plane of the light in the new tower is sixty-eight feet above sea level, the same as it was in the old light.

Alexander Parris's proposal for Whale's Back called for a foundation base composed of a solid mass of dovetailed, closely fitted granite blocks, and the lighthouse at Minot's Ledge was constructed in this manner, but the description of the first twenty feet of the Whale's Back lighthouse emphasized its concrete core: Granite blocks would form "a facing for the interior mass of concrete which will be tied together by dovetail joints, as is usual in similar sea structures." Concrete was a mixture of Portland cement, an extremely hard mortar of sand and finely ground stones and clays, and larger chunks of stone that could be formed into a rigid mass Duane was evidently interested in the possibilities of concrete for building an entire structure; only two years after the construction of the Whale's Back lighthouse he unsuccessfully proposed a concrete lighthouse for Cape Elizabeth, Maine.[19]

One of the drawings for the new Whale's Back lighthouse shows the relationship of the old and new towers, and indicates that it was originally planned to place the fog bell atop the old tower once the lantern had been removed. Duane's plans called for joining the bases of the towers on the sea side with a wall of granite masonry. Above this wall was a bunkerlike mass of solid concrete sloping upward to a height of about five feet above the foundation pier of the old lighthouse. This was to provide shelter for the keepers when they went to activate the fog bell machinery, located on the foundation pier of the old structure. The hoisting equipment for supplies and the boat davits remained on the sheltered side of the old lighthouse on the platform created by its foundation pier.

Work began immediately after the appropriation was made, with leveling of the site underway in the summer and fall of 1870, and (in an echo of 1829), the board noted that the site was "one of the most difficult to work upon on the coast, as the rock is covered by the waves except at low water and is exposed to the full force of the Atlantic." The contract

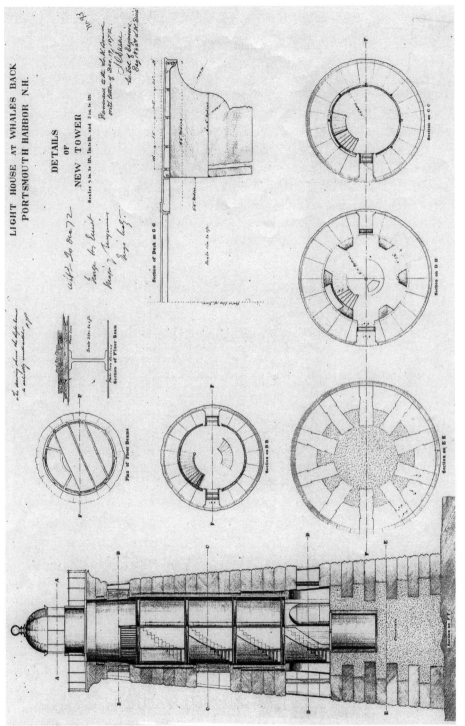

Cross-section plans of the 1871 Whale's Back lighthouse, showing the use of concrete for the core of the foundation. NARG26.

Plans for the Whale's Back lighthouse indicate that it was originally planned to place the fog bell on top of the old lighthouse on the right. NARG26.

for supplying the granite was awarded to partners Gooch and Haines of Biddeford, Maine, who were reported in December to have a large force of men working to cut and dress the granite quarried from Goodwin's Ledge. Completion of the lighthouse was scheduled for late 1871.[20]

In Spring 1871, loads of Biddeford granite began arriving on the freight steamer *Enterprise*. The construction supervisor was Captain A. J. Day, of Portland. The tower reached about twenty feet above the low-water mark by the end of June, and by mid-August most of the masonry for the new lighthouse was finished. The next step was to install the structural iron in the interior. Within the twelve-foot diameter of the

WHALE'S-BACK LIGHT.

Illustration from Samuel Adams Drake's 1875 Nooks and Corners of the New England Coast, *showing the old Whale's Back lighthouse still standing beside the new one.*

cylindrical space of the interior, horizontal I-beams provided the support for each of the four floors. Iron plates were used for the ceilings and
subflooring, with hard pine forming the floors themselves. Cast-iron
staircases curved around a segment of the circumference of the tower
to connect each of the floors. As at Boon Island, an inner wall of brick
lined the tower. The fog bell was not moved to the top of the old lighthouse after the lantern and lens were moved to the top of the new lighthouse, as the plans projected, but was kept in its original position in the
twenty-five-foot-high frame structure resting on the foundation pier on
the south side of the old lighthouse.[21]

Like the first lighthouse on the Whale's Back Ledge, the new one
provided living accommodations for the keeper and his assistant. By
November 1871, Whale's Back lightkeeper William A. Caswell and his
son Frank, his assistant, had the chance to compare the old and new
structures during a terrible gale during which "at times the water
completely covered the structure from sight." The new light was "perfectly safe," Caswell said. "The tremendous seas did not even make it
tremble." The old structure, however, gave off the sound of a discharging cannon every time it was struck by a sea. Lighthouse visiting had
become a holiday and vacation pastime, and on the fourth of July 1872
the new lighthouse drew a large number of sightseers.[22]

A New Lighthouse for Fort Constitution

In 1878 a new lighthouse replaced the cut-down 1804 wooden structure at Fort Constitution. Its outer walls were of cast iron, a building
material that was adopted for commercial buildings before the Civil
War and widely used in the decades after the war. Iron, cast in sections
that could be bolted together, had already proven a strong and econom-
ical material for both initial construction and later maintenance of several prewar U. S. lighthouses. One of the advantages of cast iron was
that the parts could be manufactured and transported by sea or rail to
remote sites, especially those where other building materials were not
readily available. Where erosion was a problem, a cast iron lighthouse
could be dismantled, moved back from the encroaching sea and rebuilt.
Cast iron was impervious to the ravages of wood borers, a particular
problem in the South, and provided a protective outer shell around
masonry inner walls, thus reducing the cost of periodic re-pointing.

According to lighthouse historian Francis Holland, two cast-iron lighthouses were built in the United States even before the creation of the Light-House Board. The earlier was built in the Gulf of Mexico, in Biloxi, Mississippi in 1848. By the summer of 1850 there was a lighthouse constructed of cast-iron plates at Monomoy Point on Cape Cod.[23]

The massive 1852 report of the Light-House Board recommended the judicious use of cast iron for "dry" lighthouse sites, but feared that a salty atmosphere would soften cast-iron into a "substance resembling plumbago," or lead. Too, there was concern that the bolted iron plates of the structure would "work" when stressed by wind and cause vibrations and wear that would open the seams between the plates. The board looked not to the early U. S. examples but rather to British colonial prototypes. In 1842 a lighthouse of cast-iron plates had been erected at Morant Point, Jamaica and another one in 1846 at Gibb's Hill, Bermuda. They were designed and built by Alexander Gordon of London. These

The 1804 wooden Portsmouth Harbor lighthouse at Fort Constitution, as it looked a few years after it was cut down in height in 1851. Photo courtesy of the Maine Historic Preservation Commission.

lighthouses were painted white, and "resisted the wet very well." Though the Board's report was cautious in its recommendation, well before the Civil War two more Gulf of Mexico cast-iron towers were built in Texas in 1852 at the entrances to Galveston and Matagorda Bays. A cast-iron Atlantic Coast light tower was begun at Cape Canaveral (Kennedy) in 1859, but construction was interrupted by the war. The tower erected in 1868 at this site was a tremendous 145 feet in height. Between 1872 and 1875, the board had built a number more, ranging from 120 to 165 feet in height, including three light towers on the South Atlantic and Gulf Coasts. [24]

Contrary to popular local belief that the lighthouse built at Fort Constitution in 1878 was erected one thousand feet south of the one it replaced, the new iron tower was actually constructed on the same site as the old wooden one. Because it was of smaller diameter than the broad-based old structure, its components were assembled and bolted together inside it, according to a contemporary account. The light of the old tower was exhibited in its lantern through a Friday night in mid-May. The next morning the old lantern was removed and the new one placed atop the cast-iron tower within the old wooden lighthouse. It was lit up the evening of the same day. [25]

The iron plates, cast in Portland, were shipped in numbered segments, each weighing about one thousand pounds. Each section of the five slightly tapered tiers of nearly equal height was cast with flanges for bolting the segments together on the interior. A final, shorter section of plates completed the structure below the lantern. The platform deck was supported by iron brackets. Cast-iron posts with ornamental finials were used for the iron railing circling the platform. Each facet of the lantern was glazed with single sheets of plate glass. The door and window openings feature arched tops; the enframements for the single window in each of the cast-iron tiers consist of projecting sills and Italianate hood-molds incorporating triangular pediments. In the topmost tier below the lantern platform, four small circular, or occulus, windows light the watch room just below the lantern.

In his design for Fort Constitution lighthouse, which is similar in its Italianate detailing to the lighthouses at Little River, in Cutler, and the twin towers at Cape Elizabeth, both in Maine, as well as the 1879 lighthouse at Cape Neddick, Duane exploited the fact that cast iron permitted the use of ornamental features that could be molded and replicated at low cost. Although cast iron was employed for lighthouses in many other districts, the Italianate details of the cast-iron lighthouses built in the first district and in the other districts where he served as engineer appear to be Duane's design signature. During his tenure as second district engineer, most of which overlapped his service in the first district, cast-iron lighthouses with similar Italianate detailing were built in Massachusetts, at Chatham, Falmouth, Nauset Beach, and East Chop on Martha's Vineyard. These features also appear on cast-iron lighthouses built during Duane's tenure as district engineer for the Third Lighthouse District in the 1880s.[26]

The interior of the new cast iron tower at Fort Constitution was lined with brick, with an air space between the iron and brick, and was fitted with a cast iron spiral staircase. The new lighthouse was not painted white as it now is, but a dark tone, described as red in lighthouse reports, and as brown in other descriptions. The color may have contributed to New Castle writer John Albee's harsh judgement on the appearance of the structure. In 1884 he described it as "hideous." It "resembles nothing so much as a length of corpulent stove-pipe, set on end..."[27]

When the new lantern was installed, lighthouse keeper Joshua Card was instructed in the use of a new fuel and new lamps. Card, a New Castle native, had seen a number of years of service at Boon Island before appointment as keeper of the lighthouse in his hometown

The 1878 cast iron Portsmouth Harbor lighthouse when it was still painted brown. SB

in 1875. He was to remain in this position until retirement in 1909 at the age of eighty-six. At Boon Island he must have struggled with the sperm oil used in the lamps when he began serving there in 1867, and later with lard oil, both of which tended to congeal in freezing weather. When the temperature dropped, keepers had to pre-warm these fuels before they were useable in the lamps. The new lamps at the Portsmouth Harbor light at Fort Constitution were fueled by kerosene, which had already been substituted for lard oil in the smaller fifth and sixth order lights operated by the government. The Portsmouth Harbor light was one of the first fourth order lights where kerosene replaced lard oil, and by November of 1878 the other local fourth order light, Whale's Back, was converted to kerosene. [28]

The Portsmouth Harbor lighthouse was painted white in 1902. NARG26.

The Cape Neddick "Nubble" Lighthouse

The last of the major lighthouses serving navigation in the waters around Portsmouth was built in 1879, and proved another boon for the iron founders of Portland. It was the lighthouse at Cape Neddick in York, Maine, and was the sixty-first lighthouse established along the Maine-New Hampshire coast. Cape Neddick is a promontory that juts from the coastline just north of York Beach. The Nubble is a small but bold, rocky island with a grassy crest a stone's throw from the mainland at Cape Neddick and is separated from it by a narrow gut that can be walked at full-moon low tides.

From as early as 1807 there had been petitions in favor of a light at the Nubble. But the government judiciously decided that the most important site for a lighthouse in these southern Maine waters was Boon Island. Periodic petitions met with no success until 1837, when proponents made the case that its prominent position made the Nubble a logical site for a light to guide vessels through the inner passage between York Ledge and Stone's Rock. Vessels sailing regularly between Portsmouth and Portland generally kept to the passage between Boon Island and York Ledge. It was argued that the proposed light would assist vessels using the more direct route inside York Ledge. [29]

In 1837, the twenty-fourth Congress appropriated five thousand dollars for a light at the Nubble, in an enactment that provided for many lighthouses and other aids to navigation. Probably because of the criticisms of the lighthouse establishment voiced by the Blunts and others, the bill stipulated that a commission of naval officers be sent to determine the importance of each before any of them was built.

The Nubble fell within the area that Captain Joseph Smith, of the Navy, was assigned to investigate in the Portland revenue cutter *Morris*. Bolstered by the opinions of men with local experience such as Lieutenant Green Walden, master of the *Morris,* and Nathaniel Baker, a pilot who was later lighthouse keeper at Boon Island, Smith recommended against a lighthouse at the Nubble, arguing that it would be foolish to encourage use of the inner passage, especially in an onshore wind, when it could be difficult to "haul off" the lee shore. During an offshore wind, which was generally accompanied by fair weather and good visibility, hazards could readily be seen, and Cape Neddick and the Nubble itself were said to loom up clearly at night from a distance of six miles. Smith thought it far more important to mark the York Ledge,

and recommended a harbor light for York Harbor. This harbor was useful as an emergency shelter for vessels, but its blind entrance was difficult to find at night. York Ledge was finally marked by an unlit beacon
in the early 1840s (see chapter 7), but there would be no York Harbor
light in the nineteenth century.[30]

In 1842, the brand-new, Kennebunkport-built bark *Isidore* was
wrecked near Cape Neddick in a late-fall, gale-driven snowstorm, with
the loss of Captain Leander Foss and his crew of fifteen young men
from Kennebunkport. And on April 6, 1852, the schooner *Georgianna* of
Phippsburg, Maine, was wrecked near the Cape. The crew was rescued,
but the *Portsmouth Journal* editorialized that "had there been a light
on the Nubble, as has several times been petitioned for, the vessel
would in all probability have made a harbor." [31]

Clifford Shattuck, in his book about the Nubble lighthouse, wrote
that it was the development of summer tourism and yachting that
brought about an 1850s appropriation of five thousand dollars for a
lighthouse on the Nubble, but that the year-round-resident mariners
had by then embraced Captain Smith's opinion as to the danger of
encouraging coast hugging along this stretch of shore. Even though
Lieutenant Franklin, the Light-House Board's first district engineer,
had already drawn plans for a lighthouse, local interests effectively
opposed construction. Any thoughts of new lighthouses anywhere were
put on hold during the Civil War. [32]

It may have been the post-war increase in the number of steamers
plying this shore, many putting into developing summer resorts and
not so completely at the mercy of onshore winds as sailing vessels, that
turned the tide in favor of a lighthouse on the Nubble. The *Portsmouth
Chronicle* reported in 1874 that companies operating coast steamers
were lobbying for it. Many sailing coasters also regularly passed
between Portsmouth and Portland, their masters so familiar with the
coast and tide conditions that with the addition of a light they would
more often take advantage of the opportunity to take a short cut. Some
did so even without a light on the Nubble. The Nova Scotia schooner
Emily S. was wrecked on the Nubble in September of 1874. Within a
year, Congress had appropriated $15,000 to build the lighthouse as
soon as the site could be acquired.[33]

But there was a new problem. A group, mostly Bostonians, had
bought the Nubble and land on Cape Neddick across the gut which separated them. They enjoyed making fall trips for shooting the waterfowl

that regularly gravitated to the Nubble. (The legacy of these hunters, in the form of birdshot strewn all over the little island, for years would make it impossible for lightkeepers to raise hens there, as the poultry died of lead-poisoning when they ate the shot, which they mistook for gravel.) The owners were at first not interested in selling the island. It took the threat of eminent domain to persuade them to part with it for fifteen hundred dollars in February 1879. In the meantime, Stone's Rock off York had been marked by the end of June 1876 with a wrought-iron spindle thirty-five feet high, topped by a black spherical cage four feet in diameter. This marker replaced the vulnerable spar buoy that had indicated this hazard since 1867.[34]

Once the Nubble was acquired, work began soon afterward. The new Nubble lighthouse was a shorter version of the one at Fort Constitution, being of three rather than four tiers of cast iron below the two short sections just beneath the lantern platform. By early April 1879 the cast-iron plates for the outer walls had been produced in Portland and loaded onto the Light-House Board's *Myrtle*. Accounts vary as to whether construction of the inner brick walls preceded or followed the installation of the iron plates of the outer skin of the structure; but because the cast-iron plates had to be bolted together from the inside, the inner bricks must have followed. It was predicted that bolting the prefabricated components in place would take only a matter of days. One novel feature was the use of bronze post finials in the form of light-houses for the railing of the platform encircling the lantern. Construction was finished by mid-June.[35]

A fourth-order fixed Fresnel lens manufactured by a French firm, Sauttier-Lemonnier of Paris, was installed in the lantern, with colored-glass panels to give the light its fixed red characteristic. Like the Fort Constitution lighthouse, its cast-iron exterior was painted reddish-brown and the dome of the lantern black. A three-hundred-pound fog bell mounted on the seaward side of the lighthouse was part of the original equipment at the lighthouse, and was to be hand-struck in response to signals from passing vessels. A small, barn-like storage structure on the Cape Neddick side of the Nubble is seen in early photographs of the Nubble; its building probably dates to the construction of the lighthouse itself.

The lighthouse was placed in service on July 1, 1879. The fog bell was soon replaced by a larger bell mounted on an open framework housing a clockwork mechanism for striking it. There is no written reference to building a boathouse or boatways until 1888, but these must have been part of the original lighthouse facilities.[36]

At the time, the new light fell under the jurisdiction of Portsmouth Customs Collector Alfred Howard, giving him the patronage prerogative of appointing a keeper. This job, at a spanking new lighthouse and keeper's dwelling at a station literally within a stone's throw of the mainland, must have been considered a plum. According to Shattuck, more than forty applied for the job, many of them experienced light-keepers. Collector Howard at first chose Leander White, who had been first assistant keeper at Boon Island, for the five-hundred-dollar-a-year job, but then decided to appoint him to the keepership at Whale's Back (a seven-hundred-dollar position) in place of Chandler Martin. Howard next picked Simon Leighton of York. Leighton had already begun work before the lighthouse was completed, and is said to have lit the lamp in a June trial. But he was in poor health and had to resign almost immediately. The final appointment went to Nathaniel H. Otterson, who was appointed June 29. Shattuck noted that Otterson was totally lacking in experience but had one advantage over all the other applicants—his

The Cape Neddick "Nubble" lighthouse not long after its 1879 completion showing an open framework support for the fog bell. NARG26.

cousin Natt Head had just been elected governor of New Hampshire! There is no evidence that Otterson did not perform his duties adequately. He remained in the post until 1885. [37]

The light at the Nubble apparently achieved one of the uses projected for it: to enable coasters and steamers to use it as a guide through the channel inside York Ledge, rather than the longer one between the ledges and Boon Island. But barely two months after the Nubble light was lit there were complaints from local fishermen. They had an advocate at the *Portsmouth Chronicle,* who reported that sometimes as many as a hundred small boats used the waters off York for fishing in this inner channel,

> many of which lay at anchor at night waiting for the earliest light to spread their trawls, and when one of the heavy lumber crafts, with their high deck loads, comes rocking and tumbling through the waves, and especially on dark nights, there is a general consternation among the smaller fry, and a feeling of insecurity in the watch kept aboard these visitors to their garden grounds, and they make every preparation to move... which is not always an easy matter, as the boats are oftentimes manned by only one man, who has to pull a heavy anchor up and perhaps hoist three sails.

The writer also urged a light for York Harbor to help these fishermen find their way home after dark and to mark the entrance for coasters in need of shelter in storms. [38]

With the completion of this new lighthouse, the principal lighthouses as they now exist in the waters around Portsmouth—at Fort Constitution, Boon Island, White Island, Whale's Back, and the Nubble—were complete. In the next decades the array of lesser aids to navigation (but not including a light for York Harbor) would be expanded.

New Houses for Lightkeepers

By the early 1870s, the Light-House Board had nearly recovered the momentum begun in the 1850s and virtually stopped in the war years by the loss of its engineering officers. And there was still much to be done locally. At Portsmouth Harbor light at Fort Constitution, a new keeper's house rose on the foundation of the old one near the War of 1812 period brick martello tower. Plans for the new house, a "neat cottage," were

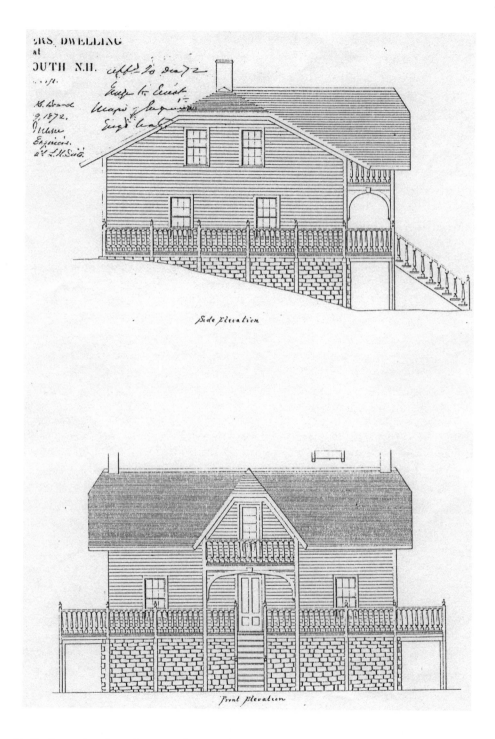

Preliminary drawings for a new keeper's house at Fort Constitution. NARG26.

prepared in Lieutenant James Duane's Portland headquarters. Preliminary drawings were made by H. D. Duane, and show a clapboarded, gabled house of two stories, with a central cross gable on the front façade. Projecting eaves, clipped gable ends and a second story balcony were features reflecting popular Cottage-style architecture. This is the structure that still stands just inside the walls of the fort, although it has been altered and twice moved since its building in 1871.[39]

In the summer of 1877, a new keeper's house was built at White Island. The plans show that the Light-House Board had taken an interest in providing comfortable houses, by now sensitive to the demoralizing frictions that could develop when people were forced to live in close proximity in isolated situations where they had only each other for company for long stretches of time. Before the creation of the Light-House Board, keepers could pick their own assistants, or have family members help them. Now, though some keepers managed to engineer appointments for friends or family as assistants, others

The 1871 keeper's house at Fort Constitution, shown at its original location near the War of 1812-era Martello tower. The porch extending across the front and sides shown in the drawing either was never built or had been removed. The man standing beside the house is probably the lighthouse keeper, Joshua Card.

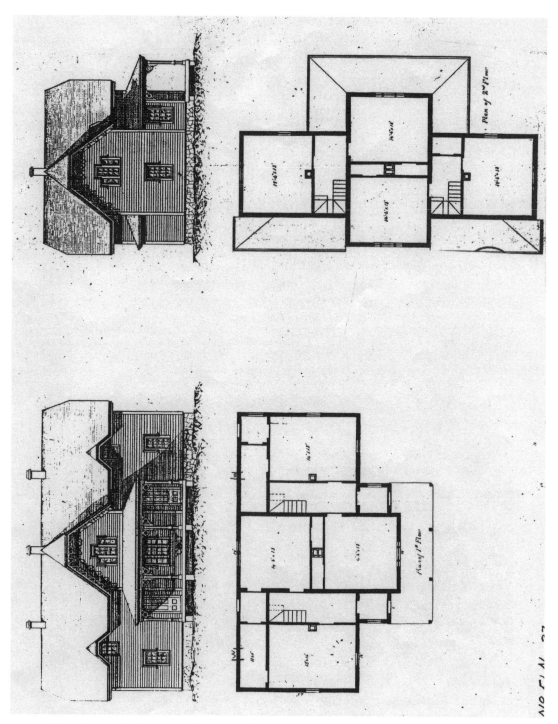

Plans for the double keepers' house built at the Isles of Shoals in 1877. NARG26.

found themselves having to share their living space with men not of their own choosing who often had families of their own.

The new house provided separate kitchens, pantries and living rooms on the first floor and two upstairs bedrooms for each family. Chimneys were built so that heating stoves could be installed in each of the living spaces in addition to the cookstoves in the kitchens. The plans were signed by James Duane, the engineer officer assigned to the first district. Duane may have been instructed to create a stylish aura for the house, located as it was in a spot frequented by so many summer tourists. Like the earlier house built for the keeper at Ports-mouth Harbor, it was of frame construction with clapboarded exterior, and a roof with clipped gable ends and a central, gabled bay at the front, also with a clipped gable roof. But the two-story White Island house was

Henry G. Peabody photograph of the new house at the Shoals. Celia Thaxter's childhood home was cut down to its high cellar walls and a new gable roof installed to protect the large water cistern in the basement. LC.

embellished with ornamental barge boards at the gable ends, and instead of single windows the front and side façades had tripartite windows headed by label moldings. Imparting a resort-cottage feel was a porch extending across the central bay. Light-House Board regulations for 1881 prescribed paint colors for the exterior: white, with lead-color trim. A photograph showing the house much as it must have looked when it was first built was taken in 1888 by Henry G. Peabody of Boston, a photographer who had already published two volumes of yachting and Maine coastal scenes. The photograph also shows the new, larger boathouse built that year.[40]

Behind the exterior boarding and clapboarding the house was bricked in between the studs of the house frame, with an airspace between the bricks and both the exterior boarding and the interior laths and plaster. The purpose was to provide a degree of insulation to the house, which was sited in a position more exposed to offshore gales than the old stone cottage, and perhaps to impart more "heft" and strength to the building on its wind-battered site. [41]

Another view, showing the rear of the new house and one end of the covered walkway altered to provide an entrance closer to the new house. NARG26.

Celia Thaxter's childhood home, the old rubblestone house built in 1820, was converted into a storage building. It was torn down except for the high cellar, which was given a new roof and clapboard sheathing. The new double house had no cellar to speak of except for an area excavated for a water cistern with a capacity of 40 barrels. According to the *Chronicle,* the reason for not tearing down the old house completely was to preserve its deep cellar which contained a much larger cistern. The writer thought, however, that with the removal of the thick stone upper walls, water and anything else stored in the cellar would freeze solid. In fact, the writer (probably Israel Miller who had until only recently lived there as lighthouse keeper) expressed, perhaps with tongue in cheek, considerable affection for the old house and regret that it had been torn down, even though it was, as he put it,

> cold as a barn in a winter nor'-wester; and about a quarter of its internal space was taken up by a fourteen-feet-square chimney of rocks... And thousands of summer visitors at the Appledore who in years past have gazed with wondering curiosity at the two-feet-thick walls of the old house, the small, old-fashioned windows, with their heavy protecting shutters of plank, and the massive rock chimney with a brick top; and the many others who have had a chance introduction to it through the medium of magazine articles, or who have become thoroughly acquainted with it through the graceful writings of Mrs. Thaxter, will regard the new house with much the same feelings as the "old families of Portsmouth" are said to entertain toward an interloper who finds a way within the sacred circle...they will cordially dislike the agency which substituted a modern house with big windows and a half-way French roof for the quaint old building of rocks that was the home of Hon. Thomas B. Laighton during the earlier years of his voluntary exile from the main land, and was the play-ground of Celia Thaxter and the present Lords of Appledore *[Oscar and Cedric Laighton]* during their childhood.[42]

At the Nubble lighthouse, the design for the 1879 keeper's house was also doubtless drawn in the office of first district engineer James Duane, where the earlier plans for the keepers' houses at Fort Constitution and White Island were produced. The Nubble lightkeeper's house was for a single family and consisted of a central block with projecting wing at the south end and a roofed porch at the north end of the front façade. Plans show that the porch was originally designed to extend along the north end of the house. At the rear was a one-story pantry with a shed roof and rear entry porch. In its detailing: porches, gingerbread bargeboards and tripartite windows with label moldings on the front and side elevations, it was very similar to the White Island keepers' double house. The principal stylistic difference was the elimination of jerkin-head gable ends at the Nubble house. It is probable that this house, like the one at White Island, was bricked up between its studs. Regardless of the *Chronicle*'s lament for the old White Island keeper's house, Arnold B. Johnson, in his 1890 book, *The Modern Light-House Service*, might have had in mind the keepers' houses at White Island and the Nubble when he wrote:

> As the dwellings of the light-keepers are often tastefully planned, well-built, and located on picturesque sites, people in search of summer quarters have so besought keepers for accommodation that the Board has been compelled to prohibit them from taking boarders under any circumstances. [43]

A Daboll Fog Horn for Whale's Back Ledge Lighthouse

In the late 1870s the local press agitated for an improved fog signal at the entrance to Portsmouth Harbor, and reported near-misses by vessels trying to thread their way in fog through rocks and ledges to a safe anchorage. In an on-shore wind and thick weather when most needed by vessels trying to make the harbor, the bell at Whale's Back Ledge was practically inaudible and was deemed no more useful "than a boiled carrot in a boot-leg." One newspaper proposed the installation of one of the new wave-activated whistle buoys off the dangerous Kitt's Rocks just outside the mouth of the river. Another suggestion was for a steam foghorn at the seaward extremity of Odiorne's Point. It was at first thought that it would be impossible to replace the Whale's Back bell with the bulky machinery required to operate a Daboll trumpet without the great expense of first taking down the old lighthouse. Congressman Frank Jones, a Portsmouth brewer and entrepreneur, was pressed to introduce a bill to provide for a fog signal of some sort for Portsmouth Harbor, and it was Jones who was responsible for the bill that finally funded a Daboll fog-horn for Whale's Back. [44]

In 1871, during his last year as chairman of the Light-House Board, Admiral Shubrick stated that the lighting apparatus used in the United States lighthouses was "equal to any in the world." This was the result of the Board's openness to taking advantage of European technology, particularly the French Fresnel lens that had been installed in all U. S. lighthouses. Fresnel lenses had the U. S. market to themselves until later in the 19th century, when English manufacturers began competing. In spite of abortive attempts to do so, no nineteenth century American manufacturer was able to equal the quality of the French and British lenses.[45]

When it came to fog signals, however, the United States made important contributions in the second half of the nineteenth century. Even before the creation of the Light-House Board, C. L. Daboll of New Haven, Connecticut developed a foghorn driven by compressed air. Later, substantial developments were achieved under the leadership of the scientist Joseph Henry, chair of the board's Committee on Experiments. He was at first frustrated in his desire to have fog signals

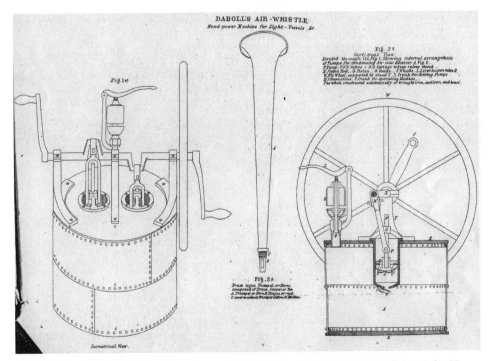

C. L. Daboll's hand-cranked fog signal, illustrated in the 1852 report of the Light-House Board. Daboll also produced a horse-powered fog horn. His cousin C. M. Daboll developed a hot-air engine that made the Daboll fog horn much more practical.

installed along foggy coasts by others on the committee who held that
they were not really necessary. Mariners could either feel their way
by taking frequent soundings or could anchor and wait for the fog to
dissipate as they had traditionally done, they said. Minds eventually
changed; it may have been the realization that to compete successfully with railroad transport, ocean-going freighters could not afford to
be so much at the mercy of the weather, especially if there was a way
to avoid delays caused by fog. In addition, Henry had considerably
more clout when he became chair of the entire board in 1871.

Celadon Leeds Daboll (1818-1866) of New Haven, Connecticut,
around 1850 invented a fog whistle using compressed air. One version,
for use on light-ships, had to be cranked by hand to operate. A horse-
powered version devised by Daboll had been placed by 1851 at Beavertail Light in Rhode Island at the mouth of Narragansett Bay. The sound
for these devices was created by air forced though a narrow opening to
vibrate a metal reed, or tongue, much as sound is produced when one
blows through cupped hands onto a blade of grass held tautly between
two thumbs. The sound passed out through a long trumpet with a clar-
inet-shaped bell. The initial, massive report prepared by the Light-
House Board before its permanent establishment in 1852 contained an
illustration of Daboll's horse-powered fog whistle. The need for manual
operation of the smaller version of Daboll's horn was a distinct drawback, especially in times of protracted fog. The much larger equipment
installed at Beavertail, though evidently successful, had the major
drawback that it was dependent upon horse-power and required sta-
bling for horses. It was C. L. Daboll's cousin, Charles Miner Daboll, who
developed another way to power the trumpet by using a hot-air Erics-
son engine. In 1864, the British government ran comparative tests of a
bell, a steam horn, and the Daboll equipment at the Dungeness Lighthouse in the English Channel. The Daboll fog horn was found so much
more effective than the other devices that the English purchased it in
order to keep it in operation there. [46]

Closer to Portsmouth, an air-driven fog signal of some sort had been
placed at the Thacher's Island twin light station off Cape Ann by 1859,
but by 1867 it had been supplanted by a hot air locomotive whistle. The
Light-House Board considered this signal too weak to be effective, however, as it did the hot air fog trumpet placed on West Quoddy Head,
Maine the same year. The Board admitted that the subject of fog signals
had been one of "much perplexity," and had been a matter of study by

the Committee of Experiments . Through his service on the Light-House Board, Joseph Henry became intrigued with the problem of fog signals and in the nature of sound and its transmission. In the mid-1860s he began experiments on the relative merits of various noise-making devices. When he became Chairman of the Light-House Board in 1871, he intensifiedexperimentation with fog trumpets, steam whistles and sirens. For measuring their effectiveness in a controlled way, he devised an "artificial ear" featuring a membrane with sand placed on it. When sound waves reached this device they vibrated the membrane and shifted the sand, enabling Henry to measure the range of the different signals. He enlisted the help of Army engineers like James Duane. When Duane was assigned to the first and second lighthouse districts, he lived in South Portland, Maine, within earshot of the steam whistle at Cape Elizabeth, and reported on its audibility in various weather conditions. Henry, until his death in 1878, included in many of the board's *Annual Reports* long accounts of his and others' experiments that read like papers for presentation to learned scientific bodies. [47]

As early as 1855, the board had commissioned experiments with steam-powered fog signals, but even in 1867 considered them impractical for many lighthouse situations because of the water needed for their operation, and the difficulty of keeping the water from freezing in winter. Cost was another factor; they consumed more fuel than the hot air horns, requiring either larger storage areas or more frequent deliveries of coal. Finally, in spite of improvements in the manufacture of steam boilers, there was apprehension about explosions if tended by lighthouse keepers lacking training in their operation. Though steam whistles and sirens had proven to produce a more powerful sound, the Daboll hot air fog horn was considered most appropriate for a situation like the Whale's Back lighthouse. [48]

In spite of local advice that it was foolish to place a Daboll horn in the disintegrating old Whale's Back lighthouse that had been left standing beside the new one built in 1872, the Board proceeded to do just that in the late summer of 1877. The trumpet installed was a third-class Daboll, with a duplicate hot air engine as a back-up. The horn was pronounced a vast improvement over the bell. The *Chronicle* in October reported that the "dulcet tones" of the horn must be very powerful since it could be heard near Portsmouth's North Mill Bridge several miles upriver, even though the horn trumpet was facing out to sea. Another report said that its "friendly boo-ing" could be heard several miles off shore in a moderate storm, and in light weather from outside the Isles of Shoals. At least one person was unaware of how the sound was produced, and exclaimed "What lungs that man must have, to blow that horn so loudly!" [49]

But in February 1878 the old stone light tower in which the Daboll horn had been placed began to present serious problems. A storm that smashed the keeper's dory also undermined the foundation stones in the wall connecting the two towers. This wall had provided protection from the storm seas that sometimes swept over the passageway between the two structures. The keepers found it impossible to get to the fog horn when seas were running high, with the result that it remained silent during an entire day of thick fog. The *Chronicle* was indignant, charging that placing the fog horn in the decaying old tower

> amounted to reckless and criminal trifling with the lives of the men whose duty it is to run it. How would it work, while the House committees are investigating everything else, for one of them to propound some conundrums to the engineer who ordered or allowed the fog-horn to be placed where it is?

At the end of April 1878, Congress made a special appropriation of $15,000 to correct the situation. The solution was to construct a new housing for the foghorn, in the form of a truncated conical cast iron tower immediately to the north of the 1872 lighthouse, with an iron bridge connecting them. The lighthouse, it was thought, would protect the fog tower from the full force of seas piling in from the open ocean in easterly and southeasterly gales. The old lighthouse was to be left standing until it collapsed, since demolishing it was considered too expensive. This economy was rationalized by the theory that this structure would serve in some way as a breakwater for the 1872 stone lighthouse and as a shelter for the keeper's boat which was hoisted up onto thefoundation pier of the of the old tower. [50]

Work began in mid-May. First the boat landing and stone steps on the north side of the 1872 lighthouse were torn down to make way for the new structure. Next, a granite and concrete base ten feet high was built. The fog tower itself consisted of two ten-foot-high cast-iron sections, each made of a number of plates bolted together to create a structure twenty-four feet in diameter and about two-thirds as high as the lighthouse. Work was delayed when three of the castings for the first section were smashed by high seas late in July, and replacements had

Whale's Back lighthouse in a dramatic storm, showing the remnants of the old lighthouse and the cast iron fog tower to the left of the 1872 structure. Print by Hendrick Hallett. PrC.

to be ordered from Portland. The lower section was partially filled with granite and cement. The work was completed in late November, when new engines and a third-class Daboll horn were installed and tested. The trumpet of the horn protruded above the top of the iron tube, with its bell flared seaward. The foghorn tower was painted reddish brown like the cast iron lighthouses of this period. At the *Chronicle*, a close and critical eye was kept on the situation, and even before the work was finished the paper criticized the decision to install another third-class trumpet instead of a more powerful one. During construction of the new fog tower, the old one was kept in operation. When the first fog horn was installed it was said to be audible off the Shoals, but when the case was being made for a first-class horn, the range of the third-class one suddenly became inadequate. And the *Chronicle* darkly predicted

problems landing a boat when seas funneled through the space
between the fog and light towers and swirled around the old tower and
sometimes poured over the barrier erected between the two stone
towers.[51]

XII *Some Late Nineteenth and Early Twentieth Century Lighthouse Keepers*

On the intelligence, fidelity, and experience of the keepers depend the thousands of lives and millions of property which are nightly approaching, leaving, or sailing along our eight thousand miles of sea, gulf, and lake coasts.

—Joseph Henry,
Annual Report of the Light-House Board, 1872

IN EUROPE, LIGHTHOUSE KEEPING could be a lifelong career. In the United States, however, the tenacious patronage system of lighthouse appointments, dominated by local customs collectors and their political leaders at the national level, endured until near the end of the nineteenth century. In the post-Civil War decades, the Light-House Board began paying more attention to the lightkeepers, who were, after all, essential to the success of the lighthouse system. By 1872 the board had managed to raise the average annual salary for keepers to six hundred dollars.

Although the Republican Party held the White House from 1861 to 1885, there were three different Portsmouth collectors of customs during this period and thus considerable turnover in lightkeepers. The board found the patronage system hard to live with, especially as more complicated and expensive lighting and fog signal equipment came into use. Joseph Henry, in his first annual report as board president, in 1872, made an especially strong argument for eliminating patronage appointments. He wrote that the nomination of a lightkeeper by a collector of customs virtually assured his appointment. At the very least, he urged, applicants for lighthouse jobs should be required to take written examinations similar to those by then required for other federal employees. Lightkeepers, he wrote,

> should have sufficient intelligence and skill to manage our delicate and costly lenses and the machinery connected therewith, as well as the steam machinery of our fog-signals. At many of our distant stations, if, through the carelessness or incapacity of a keeper, these are disarranged, the light may not be exhibited or the signal sounded for weeks before repairs can be made, and commerce can have that security which should be assured to it...

Henry continued:

> In the light-house service of other countries which have the same excellent system of illumination as our own . . . . the keepers when appointed are young men who have been required to pass medical and intellectual examinations, and they remain in service during good behavior. In Great Britain their moral character must be vouched for by the clergymen of their parishes. There is promotion for merit, and when superannuated they are pensioned.[1]

Major George Elliott, the board's engineer secretary, traveled to Europe in 1873, primarily to look into the equipment used in the British Isles and on the continent. He also reported on the management of lightkeepers, and substantiated Henry's observation that more attention was paid than in the United States to training and standards of behavior, as well as to factors like job security and living conditions that affected the morale and the performance of the lightkeepers. New keepers' houses built by the board in the mid-to late-1870s suggest that the European example had been taken to heart (see chapter 11)[2]

Something of a breakthrough occurred that year. The *Portsmouth Evening Daily Times* reported that promotions for assistant lighthouse keepers would come from the Light-House Board after an examination, rather than from collectors of customs: "If this reform is not a mere farce, the politicians will lose one of their list of perquisites. Heretofore they have managed to defeat all attempts to inaugurate any such reforms." Collectors continued to exercise their patronage over appointments of head keepers at lighthouses with only one keeper and also managed to bring in head keepers with no previous experience at other lighthouses, until 1896.[3]

Before the establishment of the Light-House Board in 1852, lighthouse keepers like Eliphalet Grover and John Thompson at Boon Island and Joseph L. Locke and Thomas Laighton at White Island could leave their lighthouses in the care of a paid hand or family member. The creation of the Light-House Board meant tighter controls on the comings and goings of the keepers. At Boon Island, by 1856 there were two government-paid assistants and at White Island, one and occasionally two. A paid assistant was added at Whale's Back during the Civil War. And head keepers were expected to share equally with their assistants in the actual work of maintaining the lights.[4]

Portsmouth Harbor light in New Castle, and the Nubble light in Cape Neddick were, and remained, "family" lights, with only a single lighthouse keeper whose wife or children were unpaid assistants. Even at potentially dangerous offshore lighthouse posts, keepers were permitted to have their families living with them. In spite of detailed regulations and instruction manuals formulated by the board and more frequent contact with inspectors, lightkeepers still had to be resourceful and able to cope responsibly with minimal supervision, especially at the offshore lights. Storms, accidents, and even death could call on them to improvise.

The year 1880 was the last during which local collectors of customs themselves actually disbursed pay to lightkeepers. This became the function of the district naval inspectors, and was symbolic of a steady erosion of local control of lighthouse patronage and the development of a more centralized bureaucracy administered locally by the executive officers of the Light-House Board and their subordinates in each district.[5]

Civil war labor shortages and competition with the Navy Yard had pushed pay for head keepers at such island posts as Boon and White Islands to eight hundred and twenty dollars and at Whale's Back to seven hundred dollars annually, with first assistants (who might be a family member) receiving as much as four hundred seventy dollars and second assistants four hundred and fifty. [6]

With postwar layoffs at the Navy Yard and the last of the merchant sailing vessels coming off the ways of privately owned Piscataqua shipyards in 1886, the local economy was less than robust. Breweries and factories took up some of the employment slack, but the lighthouse salaries for head keepers must have become very attractive during the 1870s and 1880s, and there were fewer men who resigned to look for greener employment pastures. This remained generally true even after pay for head keepers at Boon and White Islands was cut back to seven hundred and sixty dollars in 1886 as one of President Grover Cleveland's initiatives to decrease federal expenditures, although the resignation of Alfred Leavitt, who had been head keeper at Boon Island since 1874, was perhaps due to the pay cut. First assistants at these lighthouses were given a slight raise, to four hundred and eighty dollars.[7]

With increasingly elaborate instructions and regulations to read, costly equipment to maintain, and, frequently, engines to run, higher levels of literacy and mechanical aptitude became necessities. Belatedly, in 1896, the Light-House Board managed to bring its employees under Civil Service regulation, at last putting an end to the patronage system in the U.S. lighthouse system.[8]

Uniforms for Lighthouse Keepers

In 1883, the Light-House Board directed that all lighthouse keepers and assistants and all crews of lightships and of lighthouse tenders be measured for dress and fatigue uniforms. Uniforms were seen as a way to foster *esprit de corps* and to symbolize the authority and discipline that characterized the military branches of the government. At first, the uniforms were provided free, with the men expected to pay for replacements, but after 1886, all men new to the service were required to pay for their first uniforms as well.

Regulations published in 1884 described the dress uniforms as dark blue suits of kersey, a twilled woolen fabric (or of lighter flannel for warm climates), with double-breasted jackets, single-breasted vests, trousers cut "in the prevailing style," and blue caps with cloth visors. The jackets had regulation brass front and cuff buttons, lapel insignia, at first of metal but later of gold thread, with a *K, 1, 2,* or *3* designating head keepers and first, second, and third assistants; the cap had a yellow-metal lighthouse badge. Later, length of service was indicated by a gold stripe for each five years of service, or a star for twenty-five years, sewn on the lower left sleeve.[9]

Lightkeepers were expected to remove their jackets and don regulation aprons when they cleaned the Fresnel lenses, not so much to preserve the jackets as to protect the costly, highly polished lenses from being scratched by the jacket's rough cloth and metal buttons. In fact, aprons had been required before uniforms were prescribed, probably when Fresnel lenses were introduced into the U.S. lighthouse system in the 1850s. For doing chores outside, keepers were to wear a fatigue uniform. The cost of a lightkeeper's dress uniform in 1890 ran to almost thirty dollars; the fatigue uniform, or "working suit," cost only a dollar twenty-five. Somewhat different uniforms were prescribed for men on lightships and lighthouse tenders.[10]

Given the relatively high cost of the dress uniform, it would not be surprising if keepers at remote light stations wore their own work clothes, especially in the winter months, when no tourists or yachtsmen were likely to visit, and quickly changed into their uniforms when a lighthouse tender with an inspector aboard came into view. No illustration has been located of the fatigue suit.

William C. Williams, with a carnation in the buttonhole of his regulation uniform. The photo was probably taken in 1888 after his promotion from Boon Island's first assistant to head keeper (indicated by the letters "K" sewn in gold thread on his collar). KHNM

Nathaniel Hawthorne, on his late summer visit to the Isles of
Shoals and White Island lighthouse in 1852, wrote in his *American
Journal,* "A light-house nine miles from shore would be a delightful
place for a new-married couple to spend their honeymoon, or their
whole first year." He was probably influenced by his visits to the cottage
on Star Island where the young Celia Thaxter (whom he called an
island "Miranda") and her husband, Levi, were then living. Hawthorne
had not experienced the cold, stormy isolation of an island lighthouse
post in winter.[11]

Celia Thaxter—who had—wrote a poem about the tragic end to the
honeymoon year of one couple at desolate Boon Island:

The Watch on Boon Island.

They crossed the lonely and lamenting sea;
     Its moaning seemed but singing. "Will thou dare,"
He asked her, "brave the loneliness with me?"
     "What loneliness," she said, "if thou are there?"

Afar and cold on the horizon's rim
     Loomed the tall light-house, like a ghostly sign;
They sighed not as the shore behind grew dim,
     A rose of joy they bore across the brine.

They gained the barren rock, and made their home
     Among the wild waves and the sea-birds wild;
The wintry winds blew fierce across the foam,
     But in each other's eyes they looked and smiled.

       . . . .

Death found them; turned his face and passed her by,
     But laid a finger on her lover's lips,
And there was silence. Then the storm ran high,
     And tossed and troubled sore the distant ships

       . . . .

Still like a ghost she trimmed the waning light,
     Dragging her slow weight up the winding stair

       . . . .

Three times the night, too terrible to bear,
     Descended, shrouded in the storm. At last
The sun rose clear and still on her despair,

And all her striving to the winds she cast,
And bowed her head and let the light die out,
    For the wide sea lay calm as her dead love.

. . . .

Out from the coast toward her high tower they sailed;
    They found her watching, silent, by her dead,
A shadowy woman, who nor wept, nor wailed

. . . .

They bore the dead and living both away.
    With anguish time seemed powerless to destroy
She turned, and backward gazed across the bay,—
    Lost in the sad sea lay her rose of joy.[12]

Whether Thaxter's poem is based on fact is uncertain. It is possible that the keeper was Caleb Gould of Scarborough, Maine, appointed in April 1853, who married Sarah E. Williams of Kittery in July of that year.[13]

"A Beastly Outrage" at Whale's Back

Morgan Willis, as a Coast Guardsman in charge of Whale's Back lighthouse after World War II, recalled that the policy of the Coast Guard at that time was for men to serve at that light for only a year because of the stress of living in such cramped quarters. A man standing with outspread arms in the center of the kitchen at the lower level of the light house could almost touch the encircling walls, Willis remembered.[14] Under the Light-House Board, however, there was no time limitation on a keeper's tenure at a lighthouse, except for changes in personnel brought about by the old patronage system, which existed until 1896. Otherwise, unless he decided he'd had enough or was flagrantly derelict in his duties, a keeper could remain on the job—at least until the next presidential election.

Local newspapers were apt to describe the keepers at Whale's Back light, their assistants and their families as "inmates," and it is easy to see why. An undated photograph of Whale's Back light taken around 1858 shows two men, probably the keeper Reuben Leavitt and his unknown assistant, on the catwalk encircling the lantern of the white-washed masonry structure. Below, on the foundation pier which was their playground, two boys pose with a young woman near the small boat that linked the family to the mainland.

Tragedy befell one Whale's Back family during the 1860s. Gilbert Amee began service at Whale's Back as assistant in August 1864 and became head keeper that fall. His wife Mary was appointed assistant keeper in November. Elsewhere, quite a few women had paid light-house-keeping jobs, and a number became head keepers after their husbands died, but Mary Amee was the only woman in the Portsmouth area who is recorded on the rosters of lightkeepers and assistants. With wartime salary raises in effect, the couple's combined annual pay was a comfortable eleven hundred dollars per year. Their good fortune came to an end, however, when Mary contracted tuberculosis. Her health certainly could not have been improved by life in the dim, dank, leaking Whale's Back lighthouse. She was taken ashore and died at the age of thirty-two on December 18, 1867.[15]

Isaac Chauncy, of Kittery, took her place as assistant keeper and was officially appointed to the post on December 27, 1867. Also living at the lighthouse were Gilbert Amee's five-year-old son and his four-teen-year-old daughter, Lucy. Three months later, on March 30, 1868, the *Daily Evening Times* reported "A Beastly Outrage:" According the newspaper, Chauncy,

> a gray haired old sinner . . . . a married man about fifty-five years of age . . . .committed rape upon the person of a daughter of . . . . the light-house keeper . . . . it is reported that she is suffering from her injuries so severely that she will be unable to leave her bed for a fortnight. The miserable old biped who perpetrated the outrage is now undergoing an examination before Justice Dennett of Kittery.

Chauncy hired attorneys Albert Hatch, of Portsmouth, and M. N. Safford, of Kittery, the *Times* reported, and admitted to adultery, but not to rape. The preliminary hearing at Kittery Point drew a full house. Attorneys for the prosecution were W. H. Y. Hackett, of Portsmouth, and C. C. Hobbs, of South Berwick. Lucy herself was not present, although the defense lawyers successfully petitioned to have her testify in ten days' time when she was expected to have recovered from her experience.[16]

The *Times* reporter characterized Chauncy as a man whose "physiognomy indicates strong passions," but who would "pass in a crowd as an honest-looking, hardworking man." Amee was described as nervous and excitable. He "lost the confidence of the bystanders by his evidence of over anxiety to prejudice the Court against the accused and continual attempts to make special pleas to the sympathy of his hearers." Amee testified that his daughter and son slept in the room above his, where the only light came from a lamp at the top of the stairs. He described himself as a sound sleeper ("thunder would not wake me") and testified that he had been awakened, not by the screams of his daughter but by the voice of his dead wife. He then heard his daughter's stifled shrieks. Amee testified that he

> went up the stairs and found my assistant on the bed with her, she screaming and fighting him; they were both undressed, same as myself; they both rolled off the bed together, she under-neath; Chauncy rose up and met me; had it not been for the voice of my wife, I should have killed him; the girl and boy both went down stairs; I said, "Chauncy, what in God's name have you done?" He answered, "done? have not done anything, why, what is the matter?"

Amee said he began ringing the lighthouse bell to summon help. He was afraid Chauncy would kill him with a hatchet, he said, and that he spent the night outside on the foundation pier with a gun and a knife. It was not reported where Lucy and her brother—and Isaac Chauncy— spent this time. No one came until the next morning, and finally members of Amee's family arrived to take Lucy ashore. Amee said that his normally robust daughter had to be helped into the boat, that she had been "raising blood" and that he was afraid she was dying. Testimony by Dr. Edward T. Balch, of Kittery, who had examined Lucy Amee, and the cross-examination by Chauncy's lawyers reveal an attempt to depict the girl as having acquiesced to Chauncy's advances, in effect transforming her from victim to defendant. Dr. Balch testified that Lucy said she couldn't walk, but that he didn't believe she had been bleeding from the lungs as her father claimed. The *Times* reported that much of the doctor's testimony was "unfit for publication," but that the "substance of it was that the girl's person gave some slight evidence that she had been unfairly and harshly dealt with, but none that her person had been bruised. No marks of violence upon her body anywhere, such as might be expected from a struggle such as her father testified she had with a strong, muscular man like Chauncy." Testifying for the defense, John S. Safford contradicted Amee, stating that Amee had told him that his daughter "had never cried out at all, because, he said, she was afraid of her life," and that it was not the first time Chauncy had raped his daughter; "but he did not pretend that she had holloed on either occasion." [17]

Under cross-examination, Amee denied that his daughter had made no outcry, although he admitted that Chauncy had attempted to rape her previously. He also stated that Lucy, who had been at the light-house all winter, had been left alone with Chauncy for twenty-four-hour periods on more than one occasion. Amee testified that since the beginning of January, she had begged him to discharge Chauncy. But Amee said she gave as reasons that "he made too much work for her," and that he was incompetent. Her father admitted that she had never complained of "indecent behavior" by Chauncy. But one can imagine that Lucy may have been too ashamed or too afraid to tell her father what had happened but wanted desperately for Chauncy to be gone.

The *Times* reported no testimony by Chauncy, whose friends were out in force and claimed he could not have been guilty of rape. Bail, initially set at fifteen hundred dollars, was lowered to eight hundred, with three of his friends offering themselves as surety. The *Times* report concluded with the assessment that

> very few, if any, are inclined to believe that the old fellow has
> not been for some time rather more intimate with the girl than
> such aged, grandfatherly chaps are expected to be . . . .
> Whether the old man is guilty or innocent of the rape, he has
> got himself into a dirty scrape.[18]

The *Portsmouth Journal* carried no news whatsoever of the case, and the *Portsmouth Chronicle* printed only two short items when the incident first came to light.[19] The *Times*, after its detailed coverage of the preliminary hearing, published no follow-up stories. The case against Chauncy must have been dropped. No record exists of a Superior Court trial that was to have taken place at the county seat in Alfred, Maine, and no Light-House Board records at the National Archives have been located that refer to the case. And, incredibly, Chauncy was permitted to resign his post as assistant as of June 25, 1868, three months after the episode with Lucy Amee. It is not known whether Chauncy actually served those three months at the lighthouse. Gilbert Amee, however, was "removed" in September 1869.[20]

This incident brought no change in the Light-House Board's policy on families living at Whale's Back light. Civil War veteran Ferdinand Barr was appointed in June of 1868 to replace Isaac Chauncy as Amee's assistant. Barr became head keeper in March 1871 when the building of the replacement lighthouse was under way. He was doubtless looking forward to a more secure place to live and work. But in June, while out lobstering in a heavy sea, his boat overturned. The accident was witnessed by his three children, who had been left alone at the light, and they signaled for help. Two men tried to rescue Barr, who attempted to swim ashore, but by the time they reached the spot where Barr had last been seen, he had disappeared.[21]

According to the *Journal,* Barr's wife was in Portsmouth at the time. Barr had come to Portsmouth from Philadelphia by 1862, when he married Lucy A. Watkins of Portsmouth, daughter of a Navy Yard laborer. He had served in the war with the 13th New Hampshire Regiment; his hiring as a lighthouse keeper may have reflected a desire to give preference to veterans. But even after the alleged rape of Lucy Amee there had been no move by the Board to designate this confining lighthouse a "stag" light. The account of the tragedy made no reference to the whereabouts of the assistant keeper, Frederick Barr, who was perhaps Ferdinand Barr's brother, but before the end of the month he had been replaced as assistant.[22]

Israel Miller at White Island

In November 1874, a journalist with a sense of humor became keeper at White Island light. He was Israel P. Miller (1835–1906), son of Tobias H. Miller, a minister who became publisher and editor of the *Portsmouth Chronicle* and the *New-Hampshire Gazette.* His older brother, Frank Miller, became publisher of the papers and a prominent local politician.

The forty-one-year-old Israel Miller had been something of a rolling stone. He had tried his hand as a farmer, cabinet-maker, and Navy Yard clerk, and at the age of nineteen he shipped aboard a whaler, spending the years between 1857 and 1868 in the Pacific as a merchant sailor, a railroader in Australia, and a gold prospector and steamboat mate in New Zealand. But journalism was in his blood, and during his years away he sent periodic accounts of his experiences back to the *Chronicle.* Just before his appointment as keeper of White Island light he had been a compositor and writer at the family's *Chronicle.*[22]

The competing *Journal,* reporting his appointment, said, "May the music of the sea lend a charm to his pen as he seeks to complete certain labors of a literary nature on which he has for some time been engaged." The article, alluding to the late Thomas Laighton, hoped that "the new keeper of White Island can more easily find neighbors than did the sage of Appledore during his early self-banishment to those lonely isles . . ."[23]

Miller seems not to have completed his literary labors, or if he did, they were never published. But after only a week on duty at White Island, he sent ashore to the *Chronicle* a column signed "Pakeha," under the heading "Our Foreign Correspondent," describing the island and its buildings to "readers in the United States":

> The private residences are not numerous, being largely out-numbered by the public edifices, one of the latter being five or six times as high as it is wide . . . . the one in which your correspondent is domiciled is . . . . a solid old relic of antiquity with walls of stone about two feet thick, and so cool that I frequently have to get up in the night and go out doors to sit on the rocks to get warm. When it was built, insular tradition sayeth not; but the letters "C. C." cut deeply into one of the inner doors show which room Christopher Columbus slept in when he visited this island; and the recent discovery of a big pair of boots down cellar, marked "J. S.—his bootes," proves beyond cavil that Capt. John Smith occupied the house at a later date . . . .In the boat-house is the barge which carried Cleopatra on her visit to Senator Anthony; it was a royal craft in its day, but it now has two serious faults,—one is, it is too big and clumsy to be easily got afloat,and the other is that it will only stay afloat two minutes at a time after it is once got into the water.[25]

It is not known whether Miller himself—or a colleague at the *Chronicle*—wrote the following spoof on the boasts of various light-keepers as to the quality of the lights they tended:

> They say the new keeper of White Island light has his lamp wick so well trimmed . . . . that steamer Faraday's crew were enabled to see the bottom of the ocean, five hundred miles away, on dark nights . . . . Fishermen off the banks are obliged to wear green glasses when they look toward White island,— and passengers from Europe report that they have seen the light from mid ocean by the help of an opera glass.[26]

Miller, whose assistant keeper was Franklin Bragdon, had fun with the elaborate Light-House Board's "Instructions and Directions to Light-Keepers," which was furnished each keeper. "Catch-22" was not a twentieth-century phenomenon:

> My mate and I have come to the conclusion that we are in prison for the rest of our lives .... Light-keepers "are authorized to leave their stations to attend public worship on Sunday," to draw their salaries, get provisions, etc.; but further research has taught us that no keeper can leave his station until he has provided a substitute, (how one of us can get a substitute out here without first leaving is a puzzle to us,) and that "Keepers and assistants are not permitted to employ substitutes,"—the latter rule being emphasized by italics.

He also kept the folks ashore posted on the antics of two cats, Exodus and Sin (short for Abyssinia), who shared the island with him and his assistant.[27]

Miller also wrote, more seriously, of the problem created by the height of the new Oceanic Hotel, built on Star Island by Henry Poor. The hotel blocked the White Island light from view by vessels sailing from the eastward and passing outside Boon Island. There had been talk of making the White Island light tower taller so that its light would clear the hotel. Miller questioned the government's permitting this obstruction, asking if it was to be expected to raise the lighthouse every time Mr. Poor added a story to his hotel.[28]

Another article a year later reported a move to build another lighthouse on Star Island but recommended the low-lying Duck Island with its ring of treacherous ledges. Being the most easterly of the islands in the group it would be more useful " .... except as an attraction to summer travel." The one advantage to Star Island as a site, he wrote, was that the storm signals of the recently created U.S. Signal Service could be displayed from it and seen in all directions.[29]

The White Island lighthouse was not made taller, and no lighthouse was ever built on either Star or Duck Island, and when storm signals were finally displayed from the Shoals nearly twenty years later, they would be hoisted on Appledore rather than Star Island. But the problem of the looming Oceanic Hotel was temporarily removed in November 1875. While on night watch in the lighthouse during a violent northwest gale, Israel Miller saw the sky suddenly light up and the hotel ablaze. Because there was no way for him and his assistant to get over to Star Island to do anything about it, they could only watch as the building was spectacularly consumed by the gale-driven flames:

> At this time the wind was blowing a furious gale from the nor'west, catching the crests of the immense seas which were

rolling in from the southeast, and the vast masses of spray
which flew aloft from the rocky shores of the islands, and bearing them hundreds of feet higher in the air than I ever saw
spray go before; and the glare of the fire on the flying spray
brought out myriads of rainbows, which flashed into sight in
nearly all directions and instantly disappeared.[30]

Miller also wrote about the need for a buoy to mark Half-Way Rock,
a submerged hazard smack in the middle of the channel between
Lunging and Star Islands. But he couldn't resist submitting a comic
account of the scene created when an excursion steamer from Massachusetts ran into it on a calm July day in 1875:

> Handkerchiefs were waving, passengers cheering and music
> playing as the boat steamed rapidly past White Island, but the
> music dried up very suddenly and the chorus gave place to a
> grand chorus of shrieks when the boat bumped on the rock ...
> . The ladies were terribly frightened, and several of them
> begged piteously to be taken on board a racing-shell which was
> pulled up near at hand by a Portsmouth gentleman, they over-
> looking the facts that the flimsy cockle shell would capsize if
> the occupant should shift his cigar from one side of his mouth
> to the other, and that a man so reckless of his own safety as to
> pull from Portsmouth to White Island in such a craft wasn't a
> suitable custodian of the safety of other people, on deep water.
> The male passengers were not at all alarmed, and as soon as a
> big seine-boat which the steamer had towed astern was brought
> up alongside they showed their coolness and self-sacrificing
> gallantry by all crowding into it, and magnanimously leaving
> all the room on board the steamer to the women. One Spartan
> father calmly marched to certain safety in the seine-boat, leav-
> ing four beloved daughters behind on the steamer's deck.
> Ardent lovers and faithful husbands tore themselves from the
> arms of their sweethearts and wives and dashed alone into the
> boat, utterly regardless of best clothes and fish-scales.

All the passengers were eventually removed, and the steamer was
towed off the rock by a tugboat.[31]

Miller's stint at White Island, which lasted until February 1876,
seems finally to have satisfied his craving for new experiences. He
returned to stay and marry in Portsmouth. He worked as writer and
editor at the Miller papers and later for the *Portsmouth Times* and as
Portsmouth correspondent for the *Boston Globe,* until his death in

1906. Miller maintained his interest in White Island light and the Shoals. His years at sea and at White Island had given him a keen and knowledgeable appreciation of the power of the sea and for the aids to navigation which helped local fishermen and coasters. The *Chronicle* in the years after he came ashore contained a more than usual number of articles about them.

Edwin Hobbs

Just about when Israel Miller was deciding to turn to newspapering for good, a much younger voice was heard from the far bleaker, lonelier Boon Island. Annabelle, or "Annie," Lee Hobbs, daughter of assistant keeper Edwin Hobbs, wrote wistfully of her life in a letter published in the children's magazine, *The Nursery*.

> Out at sea, on a rock eight miles from the nearest point of land, and about nine miles east of the town of Kittery, is Boon Island, upon which I have been a prisoner with the privilege of the yard, for the past two years."

She described this yard as "made up of nothing but rocks, without one foot of ground for trees, shrubs, or grass." She went on:

> [The sails] dot the wide expanse, reminding me that there is a world beside the little one I dwell in, all surrounded by water. The inhabitants of this island consist of eight persons—just the number that entered the ark in the time of the flood.

They were her parents, her three-year-old brother Steven, head keeper Alfred Leavitt, and first assistant Leander White and his wife and four-year-old daughter. Annie wrote that her parents were her teachers.[32]

The story of Edwin Hobbs and his family and their lighthouse life suggests that a few of the men who took their families to isolated lighthouse posts were driven to leave mainland life by more than an interest in providing an essential service to mariners or in the romantic experience of tending a light, and that things did not always work out well for them. Edwin Hobbs (1826–1905) had varied experiences before becoming second assistant keeper at Boon Island in 1874. He came from a family of Hampton farmers who were also dedicated church musicians. Relatives report that he was a talented, conscientious, hardworking, mild-mannered man. He had become choir director for the Congregational church at the age of sixteen, and was involved in introducing musical instruments into the church services before organs were widely used. He himself played the violin and his father the viola da gamba.[33]

In 1849, while in his early twenties, like many other young men, Hobbs went to the West Coast in search of gold. He next shipped aboard clippers as a carpenter, sailing to ports all over the world. In the Civil War he served as sergeant in Company K, 16th New Hampshire Volunteers, and saw service under General Banks in New Orleans. He was wounded, and returned to Hampton with injuries that plagued him the rest of his life. He conducted a singing school in his parents' house.[34]

It may have been his marriage to a strong-willed, intense woman, Hannah Phelps, from neighboring Seabrook, that led him to seek a job as assistant lightkeeper at Boon Island. Family lore holds that Hannah, a student in Edwin's singing school, ordered at gun's point the upright Edwin to marry her. Traditionally strong antipathies between residents of Hampton and Seabrook, plus his wife's aggressiveness and eccentricities, must have made life miserable in Hampton.[35]

One would like to imagine that the family found some sort of happiness offshore, making music together, with Edwin crafting ingenious toys for his children, and reading together the books that the Light-House Board began distributing to offshore lighthouse families in 1876. But Hobbs's now lost journal indicated, according to relatives, that there was friction among the keepers' families. The patience of even the most congenial of families must have been taxed by the enforced togetherness in the cramped conditions in the half of the Boon Island house they shared with White and his family.[36]

Annie Hobbs wrote that in winter she yearned to go sleighing and that in summer there was more company, with visitors to the lighthouse coming from resort hotels and boardinghouses at the beaches ashore. Annie sometimes tired of leading these pleasure parties up the 167 steps to the top of the 123-foot tower.[37] She did not write, though, as her father evidently did in his journal, that the wife of one of the other keepers had taken an intense dislike to her, and had several times attempted to drown her![38]

In February 1876, Annie's father was made head keeper at White Island. The children must have enjoyed the slightly less barren surroundings of this island and the bustle of summer visitors who flocked to the Shoals in steamers and yachts. For these vacationers, a visit to the scene of Celia Thaxter's idyllic and romantic childhood lighthouse home had become almost obligatory; in 1873, the year of publication of *Among the Isles of Shoals,* an assistant keeper reported that eight hundred people had signed the lighthouse register that summer season. These sightseers may have presented something of a bonanza. Regulations by at least 1881 forbade keepers and their families from accepting money, but it would not be surprising if more than a few visitors slipped a coin or two to the keeper or family member who escorted them to the top of the tower.[39]

Lighthouse visiting by summer residents and tourists, who became more numerous every year along the New Hampshire and Maine coasts, reached troublesome proportions. In 1899, the *Portsmouth Herald* reported that the Light-House Board had instructed Atlantic Coast lighthouse keepers to permit visitors to the lighthouse towers only between the hours of two and four in the afternoon. "Of late years so constant has been the flow of visitors that the keepers have had little time for rest and sleep, and in consequence it has in many instances unfitted them for faithful vigil through the coming night."[40]

It must have been Annie Hobbs who organized the funeral, described in the *Chronicle,* for the mischievous White Island cat, Exodus. Israel Miller, who knew the cat well when he was keeper at White Island, may have been one of the mourners, and is the likely author of the piece "Exit Exodus":

> His obsequies were all that could be demanded for a high-toned cat of the greatest—though until he was dead to a great extent undiscovered—merit, the young folks of the island community officiating as mistress and master of ceremonies; he was honored with a coffin, a wreath, and the stars and stripes to cover his bier; and the entire resident population of the island and several visitors joined in the funeral procession, each of the mourners dropping a sprig of green into the grave, which was duly marked with head and foot stones. Many a poor sailor, or worn out human being on shore, has a less imposing funeral and goes to his final rest less sincerely mourned than the old white cat of the light-station, Exodus. **Requiescat.**[41]

The Hobbs children had the excitement of seeing a new keepers' house built during the warm months of 1877. The *Chronicle* noted that "the old rubblestone house, though picturesque and romantic looking, is miserably uncomfortable in the winter and too small to accommodate more than one family." The new house was to be a double one, so that the families of Hobbs and his assistant, Alden White, could have separate quarters. Brick for the inner walls and the chimneys arrived at White Island by March 22.[42]

The steamer *Appledore* made daily summer trips to the Shoals with hundreds of tourists. They came by train from inland New Hampshire, and excursion steamers from Portsmouth and as far away as Boston regularly steamed past White Island, from which Annie Hobbs hailed them on the high, rocky knob at the east end of the island. In August 1879, as she waved to the steamer *Empire State* from this vantage point, she fell and broke her right arm. In winter an accident of this sort would have posed a problem, but during the summer a doctor was available for guests at the Oceanic and Appledore hotels, and was sent for to set the bone.[43]

This was Annie Hobbs's last summer at White Island. In the spring of 1880, her father was replaced by Captain David Grogan, a former seafaring man who had been an assistant at Boon Island for several years. Edwin Hobbs, perhaps dreading life ashore and the loss of a steady income, protested his removal, and asked for an investigation. But the lighthouse service would not be placed under civil service regulations until 1896. Hobbs was evidently a victim of the patronage system, unless the difficulty of his wife's personality was the reason for his replacement. The *Chronicle* reported that the wounded war veteran Hobbs had been "summarily bounced to make room for a civilian," in spite of his good record as a keeper.[44]

Hobbs, who never recovered from the traumas of war, found life back in Hampton discouraging. He built a house for his family and began teaching music again. But his disabilities apparently demoralized him. He was plagued by depression and was hospitalized in Boston; in 1896 the *Chronicle* reported that he had attempted suicide by cutting his throat, and he finally ended his life in 1905. According to relatives, his children, who had spent six of their young years at island lighthouses, found the transition to life ashore difficult; Annie was reputed to be a shy eccentric and Steven took to drink.[45]

In 1879, the Light-House Board's naval secretary informed the board of "troubles existing in several isolated light-houses, owing to the presence of women and children." We do not know if the troubles the secretary had in mind were those caused by personality conflicts like those related by Hobbs's relatives or were of the sexual variety such as occurred at Whale's Back in 1867, but the naval secretary presented a resolution: "At isolated stations where there are two or more keepers, no women or children will be allowed to reside unless special permission of the light-House Board is previously obtained." The board adopted the resolution, but it is not clear to what degree it was enforced. Permission must have been readily given, because families with children continued to live at offshore lighthouses.[46]

David Grogan

David Grogan, who took Edwin Hobbs's place at White Island in 1880, had, like Hobbs, begun as an assistant at Boon Island, in 1877. He remained at the Shoals station until poor health forced him to retire in 1894.

A native of Kittery, Grogan had a long career at sea beginning when he was a teenager, and as a seaman shipped aboard the Piscataqua-built clipper *Midnight* on her maiden voyage in 1854. He eventually became a ship's officer of vessels in the European and West Indies trade and finally a master of coasting schooners.[47]

Grogan owned a large, handsome dog, a cross between a Newfoundland and a Collie, who became a well-known fixture at White Island. "Mr. Doggy's" barks were credited with warning the steamer *John Brooks* from going aground in the summer of 1891, and Grogan had him photographed on the rocks of White Island. Light House Board regulations against commercial undertakings by lighthouse keepers did not dampen Grogan's entrepreneurial spirit. The *Chronicle* wrote that the pictures of the dog "found a ready sale" to visiting tourists at the island.[48]

Light-House Board regulations stipulated that "it is the duty of light-keepers to aid wrecked persons as far as lies in their power," but there were instances when they even attempted to save the vessels themselves from destruction. Keeper Grogan, a well-seasoned master seaman, was involved in saving an endangered vessel in December During a Christmas Eve storm, the schooner *Elizabeth Foster* went aground off the Shoals. The heavy seas pounded her on the rocks, putting a hole in her hull. The vessel floated off at high tide and was anchored, but then began to fill. Her master signaled for help, and Grogan rowed out to her, got her under way, and beached her next to the wharf at Star Island, where she was patched up and eventually towed into New Castle.[49]

William C. Williams of Boon Island

William C. Williams (1845–1939), a native of Kittery, spent the years 1885–1911 at Boon Island, racking up three more years than Eliphalet Grover had earlier at this bleak and dangerous outpost. He began as second assistant at the age of forty, was promoted to first assistant keeper in 1886, and became principal keeper in 1888 after Orrin Lamprey's resignation. There is little information about how he made his living before he took the lighthouse job. He married a Kittery Point woman, Mary Abbie Seaward, with whom he had three children (one of whom died at an early age), and. had been owner of a small, 6.85-ton, schooner, the *Clara Bella*, which he sold in 1882, and in which he doubtless fished the local waters.[50] His use of the phrase "cotton-mill din" to describe the noise experienced in the Boon Island lighthouse lantern suggests the possibility that he had worked for a time in a textile mill in the area, though the phrase may have been common usage during this period.

Interviewed when he was ninety by Robert Sterling, Williams talked about what it was like when he first went to Boon Island:

> I could not get away from the idea that I was the same as locked up in a cell . . . When rough weather came we didn't know as it would make much difference as to whether we went into the tower or not, for a safe place. The seas would clean the ledge right off sometimes. It was a funny experience to be on a place and know you couldn't get off if you wanted to . . . . Take it with me, I was a young fellow and had never been placed in such a situation. When the terrible seas would make up and a storm was in the offing, I was always thinking over just what I would do in order to save my life, should the whole station be swept away. I believe it is these little things that gradually wear on the mind and finally upset the brain.[51]

Williams recalled that when he and the other keepers took their turns at watching the light, it made more sense to stay in the watch room just below the lantern than to make the trip up and down the iron spiral staircase that "winds you up dizzy as you go" to the top of the high tower.[52] In severe storms the tall granite shaft swayed and shuddered alarmingly:

> There was no lounging place at the top of the tower, only an old soap box or camp stool...As you set there just watching your

light, all the enjoyment you got was hearing the wind making
a cotton-mill din around the lantern.[53]

The disturbing swaying and tremors were doubtless due to the lighthouse having been "strained" by the battering storms that periodically
swept across Boon Island, hurling around huge boulders. In 1888, the
Light-House Board attempted to solve the problem with struts and
bracing cables that extended from the top of the lantern to a point forty
feet below it, but the vibrations continued, and in 1902 added more
struts and cables to extend farther down the exterior of the tower.(See
chapter 11.) Wind blowing across these cables produced a "strange,
musical cadence." Sometimes this sound was punctuated by the thud of
birds crashing into the plate glass of the lantern, and after a storm it
could take a good part of a day to clean the glass of the feathers and
salt spray that caked it.[54]

James Burke, an enterprising assistant of Williams, took some of the
most attractive and least damaged birds killed against the lantern glass
into Portsmouth to be mounted by a taxidermist. On one occasion, when
provisions were low, the fatal attraction of the light for birds provided
the lighthouse families with a Thanksgiving banquet of black ducks.[55]

Over the years at Boon Island with his wife, who rarely spent time
ashore, Williams evidently came to relish the interest of mainlanders
and summer visitors in the difficulties and dangers of his work, and
devised ways to improve life for the island families. He brought soil
from the mainland so the women and children at Boon Island could
have gardens, even though he knew that, even in summer, storm seas
could sweep them away, and he would have to begin the process over
again the next year. For a time, carrier pigeons provided a means of
keeping in touch with the mainland, and not just for emergencies.
Pigeons may have brought news of the end of the Spanish-American
War to Boon Island in July 1898, and in anticipation of the McKinley-
Bryan presidential election of 1900, Williams took some pigeons ashore
and left instructions to have them sent out to the island as soon as the
results were known. It is probable that the pigeons were part of a four-
year joint experiment begun in 1897 by the Navy and the Light-House
Board to facilitate communication between offshore lighthouses and
government vessels and the mainland.[56]

Williams enjoyed his contacts with the summer visitors who called
at the island during the summer months. And there were many of
them: In 1885, the *Portsmouth Journal* noted, "The solitary(?) Boon

Island Light had 215 visitors during the month of August."[57] Williams
and his wife often provided fish chowder for them, beginning a tradition followed by families that succeeded the Williamses. He loved to
recount dramatic stories of the rigors of life at Boon Island and the
wrecks that occurred there. In fact, the *Portsmouth Herald* reported:

> Captain Williams . . . loves to be asked if there were any severe
> storms during the winter. He will stop work, even if he is pack-
> ing a kit of mackerel, and give a graphic account of the waves
> dashing against the house that he feared would be swept away.
> He will tell about seeking refuge in the lighthouse and remain-
> ing there several days, without food, while a storm raged. It is
> a good story and the old captain looks very picturesque, stand-
> ing on the summit of a knoll, and stretching his sun burned
> arm toward the giant shaft. But as surely as the red [sic] star
> revolves there tonight he has been telling this same story, in
> the same graphic way, more than ten years.[58]

A tale Williams enjoyed telling was of the wreck of the ninety-six-ton
Nova Scotia schooner *Gold Hunter*, bound in December 1892 for Boston
with a load of hardwood. It was after dark, during a gale wind, when the
vessel ran onto Boon Island Ledge, three miles northeast of the island.
The master and crew of seven struggled for three hours to lower a boat
in the heavy seas before escaping the sinking schooner. They reached
Boon Island at one A.M. It was a freezing night (four below zero), and
Williams and his assistants Walter Amee and Leonidas Sawyer used
lanterns to guide the men of the *Gold Hunter* around to the lee shore of
the island for a landing. By this time the wreck survivors, including a
young, lightly dressed cabin boy, were frozen to the thwarts of the dory
and practically helpless. Williams and his men grabbed the boat as it
came ashore on a sea, while the island dog took the boat's painter in his
teeth and ran it ashore. The crew of the schooner were taken into the
house, where the keepers and their wives "had a desperate task for the
next few hours to resuscitate the almost lifeless men."[59]

The next day Williams and his son Charles, using two open boats,
headed to Portsmouth with the crew of the *Gold Hunter*. They were
spotted, picked up, and taken to Portsmouth by the crew of the brand
new lighthouse tender *Lilac,* which had just finished setting a can
buoy off the rocks and ledges of the Triangles near the Kittery shore.
One of the lightkeepers commemorated the wreck of the *Gold Hunter*
by creating an ingenious painted wood model, now owned by the
Portsmouth Athenæum.[60]

The late Beulah Quinn, whose father, Charles Allen, was an assistant keeper at Boon Island under Williams, recalled in 1986 something of Boon Island from a child's perspective. The family was deposited on the island by a lighthouse tender in the late spring of 1907, when Beulah was an infant. Their belongings included her mother Minnie's piano, which was hoisted ashore by the island derrick (and later traveled with the family to two other island light stations). Both her parents were musical and—as with many other lighthouse families—music was an important part of their home-grown entertainment. Her father played the harmonica, and during his hours on duty in the lantern room at night taught himself to play a mail-order cornet. Her mother—when her cooking, cleaning, and laundry chores were done—knitted, crocheted, and tatted.[61]

The Allens shared the old stone keeper's house with first assistant Mitchell Blackwood until Williams retired and Blackwood replaced him as head keeper and moved into the 1904 house Williams, his wife and daughter had occupied. Fuller Larrabee then came to the island as second assistant, with Allen moving up to become first assistant.[62]

While the Allens were at Boon Island, two more children were born, and Mrs. Allen traveled to Lubec, Maine to be with hometown family and friends during their births. Beulah Quinn recalled that there could

Beulah Allen Quinn, holding a photograph of her father, Charles Allen, an assistant keeper at Boon Island. Peter Ralston photo.

be as many as ten children at the island at one time, depending on the size of the keepers' families. She remembered the Williams's Boston Terrier Tiny and cats owned by Mitchell Blackwood.[63]

Mrs. Eunice Lewis Evans, a great-granddaughter of the Williamses, wrote in 1998 of the stories her mother, Mary Luther Lewis, told her about the summers she spent on the island with her grandparents. The children were all given chores, which might be salvaging usable chunks of coal from the ashes of the wood cookstove, dusting, and polishing brass in the house, killing flies, or picking caterpillars off the flowers grown outside. The pennies they earned went into savings accounts. Their grandmother made cloth dolls with hair made from unraveled rope. She taught the girls to embroider placemats made from the discarded linen covers that protected Fresnel lens from dust during the day time, and to make rugs from cut up pieces of their grandfather's worn out blue uniforms.[64]

The children were expected to take part in evening prayer services held regularly at Boon Island, and like everyone else were in bed by eight o'clock and up at five in the morning. Older children—if they had been good—were rewarded with a trip to the top of the lighthouse with

William C. Williams with his wife Mary Abbie Seaward Williams. OYHS.

their grandfather when he had the first watch, which began at sunset. After climbing the 167 steps to the lantern, they were allowed to stay exactly a half an hour.[65]

There was one occasion when the island children were expected to be absolutely silent. This was the annual painting of the exterior of the lantern and its dome, which was, keeper Williams recalled, "truly scary." The adults stopped whatever work they were doing, so as not to disturb the painter. Everyone watched anxiously as whichever keeper had volunteered to do this chore, hung by a rope secured to the lantern railing and slung over the top of the lighthouse and looped around the ventilator ball.[66]

Each spring and fall the keepers made trips to town to stock up on provisions, returning with barrels and cases of flour, sugar and canned goods. Most of the keepers fished in the vicinity of the island, and fish, fresh and salted, was an important part of their diet as well as a source of income. Mrs. Quinn remembered catching cunners with periwinkles for bait, and roaming around the rocks and tide pools, and using a common pin to pry loose and collect in a matchbox the embedded translucent shards of isinglass that glistened on the rocks. Memorable occasions were the periodic arrivals of a lighthouse tender with coal for the stoves and kerosene for the lamps of the lighthouse and the houses. The supplies were hoisted ashore by a derrick installed at the island. Coal was toted in canvas bags by the crew of the tender. The tender's crew used shoulder yokes to carry the metal containers of kerosene for the lamps to the oil storage house.[67]

Williams family albums of undated photos give us unusual glimpses of the lighthouse families in a festive summer mood, of the children and grandchildren who summered on the island and the toy boats and dolls made for them by the adults, of the men fishing with nets off the island. These photographs convey the sense of a close-knit group of people who have endured terrible, often dangerous living conditions and long separations from their mainland families and friends—and triumphed. One feels their pride in their resourcefulness in a situation that must have tested them all.

A BOON ISLAND PHOTO ALBUM

assembled from Williams family photograph albums

The Williamses in their "yard," with what appear to be healthy clumps of flowers grown in earth which must have been imported by Williams from the mainland almost annually to replenish the soil swept away by periodic storm seas. OYHS.

Williams, with the 1904 head keeper's house and part of the lighthouse visible behind him, posing by a huge boulder. The sign documents that it was "thrown up by the sea March 13, 1888. 80 tons" OYHS.

Two views of the second order Fresnel lens in the lighthouse lantern. OYHS..

The spiral iron stairs of 167 patterned steps that the keepers had to climb to tend the lighthouse lamp. OYHS.

Lighthouse tender crew members using yokes to carry supplies (probably kerosene containers) to the oil house. OYHS.

Fishing off Boon Island. PA.

Fishing off Boon Island. PA.

Keeper Williams holding up one of the salted codfish set out to dry on wooden "flakes."
OYHS.

"Free-range" Boon Island poultry. OYHS.

The Williams's granddaughter Myrtis with her dolls, some "store-bought" and others handmade by her grandmother. OYHS.

A display of large and small toy boats, most probably made by the keepers for their sons or grandsons. OYHS.

Two of the island boys with a handsome model sloop in a tide pool. PA.

One of the boys rowing a tiny square-ended punt. PA.

This posed "rescue" of a drowning man documents a bit of adult fun at the island. PA.

Picnicking beside the boatways in front of the boathouse. It is not known if these water-melon-eaters were visiting daytrippers or family members. PA.

Keeper Williams and his wife posing with a group of visitors. PA

Joshua Card

At Fort Constitution, Joshua Card became keeper in 1875. He had started out his lighthouse career in 1867 as head keeper at Boon Island, at an annual salary of $860, and served there about eight years before taking the job at Fort Constitution lighthouse. The compensation of living near relatives and friends in his native New Castle and at a much safer location must have been worth the cut in annual pay to five hundred dollars. Card did not retire until 1909 at the age of eighty-five, after more than forty years as a lighthouse keeper, one of a handful of local lighthouse keepers who served forty years or longer.[68]

Card and his family moved into the keeper's house built by the Light-House Board in 1871 close to a War of 1812-era stone martello tower. This house replaced one that had been moved to this site to put distance between and minimize friction with the military men stationed at the fort and the lightkeeper. However, friction did arise in 1881 when keeper Card's cow provoked the rage of the ordnance sergeant at the fort. Captain J. S. Skerrett, the Light-House Board's Navy officer for the First Lighthouse District, reported to the chair of the board, Rear Admiral John Rodgers, that Card had "been deprived of the privilege of pasturing his cow on Government Grounds in the vicinity

Joshua Card, standing in front of the Portsmouth Harbor lighthouse. SB.

of the keeper's residence" and enclosed a threatening letter from Sergeant Adolph Franz. The letter, preserved in the National Archives, is charred at the edges, suggesting that Card may have thrown it into the fire and then retrieved it. It reads:

To Mr. J. K. Card May 30, 1881

Sir:

Are you aware that you disobey an order of Col. Blunt's in relation to your pasturing a cow on the reservation [burnt] allow me to repeat it to you, and if you continue [burnt] another day I will prosecute you for Trespass. I wish you to understand that you can do nothing without legal authority you must obey the [burnt] Adolph Franz

Ordinance Sgt. U.S.A.
In charge[69]

The Colonel Blunt referred to in Franz's letter was Charles E. Blunt (ca. 1823–1892) of the Army's Corps of engineers, a Portsmouth native and 1846 graduate of West Point who was much involved in work on harbor defenses during the Civil War; he retired from active service in 1889. In 1881, Blunt had multiple assignments: He was in charge of fortifications in Maine and New Hampshire and of river and harbor improvements and surveys in those states, and was also First Lighthouse District engineer. No resolution of the problem of Card's cow is recorded in the Light-House Board's files, but the episode hints at "turf" issues and a degree of friction between the two branches of the military.[70]

During Joshua Card's long career as lighthouse keeper, he witnessed many changes: the switch from sperm oil to lard oil at Boon Island, and from lard oil to kerosene at Fort Constitution; the building of the new cast-iron lighthouse in 1878 and the change of its color from reddish brown to white; the rebuilding of the walkway and bridge to the lighthouse in 1879 and 1889; the removal of the snow-catching upper balcony of the keeper's house in 1889; the construction of a wooden oil storage house in 1892 replaced by a brick one in 1903; the installation of a fog bell and its housing in 1896; and the moving of the keeper's house in 1897 to make way for Battery Farnsworth. The house was moved again in 1906, when Battery Hackelman was constructed, to its present location just inside the walls of Fort Constitution and much closer to the lighthouse the octogenarian Card continued to tend until his retirement three years later.[71]

Brackett Lewis

Brackett Lewis (1848-1931) was a native of Kittery, Maine. At the age of just fifteen he enlisted in the 27th Maine Regiment and was taken prisoner by the Confederates at Cemetery Hill in Virginia two months later. By December 1864 he was in the 31st Maine Regiment and was mustered out of the Army in June of 1865.[72]

Lewis's lighthouse keeping career did not begin for nearly twenty years. In 1883 he was appointed Leander White's assistant at Whale's Back lighthouse, and in 1885 he began nineteen years as keeper at the Nubble light.

After Whale's Back, Lewis must have enjoyed the relative spaciousness of the Nubble post, the house in which his family could live with him, and the closeness to the shore. Except in rough weather, it was a short row ashore, and at extreme low tides could be walked in boots. Lewis tried raising hens, but soon found they mistook the gunshot left by hunters of sea fowl over the years for gravel and died of lead poisoning. He raised hogs instead.[73]

Lewis encouraged his sociable daughter Hattie to invite her friends to the island. One party was described in the *Chronicle* in May, 1893:

> A party was given by Miss Lewis of the Nubble Lighthouse .... last week, and those who had the honor of an invitation were treated to a novel and unique experience by a voyage in boats to the island, where entertainment of the most hospitable nature, such as music, trips to the top of the tower, games of the good old-fashioned order, where post office, etc., were not left out, and a bountiful supper was served. Although one young lady from the beach was said to have lost her supper on the way home, and a young man took a sudden foot bath, all voted it the best time of the season.[74]

Hattie Lewis's marriage to Charles Billings was the first of several weddings to take place in the lantern of the lighthouse, according to Clifford Shattuck's history of the Nubble lighthouse.[75]

Going Ashore

Island lighthouse families took advantage of every opportunity to restock their larders. While some very remote U.S. lighthouses were provided with food rations, none in the Portsmouth area were, and it was up to the lighthouse keepers to lay in enough provisions, not just for themselves and their families, but also for repair crews and lighthouse inspectors, as well as shipwreck survivors, whose arrivals were unpredictable. When Light-House Board work crews came to make repairs, the keepers (or more likely their wives) were expected to provide their meals. They were reimbursed for this service at a set daily rate, but the unexpected arrival of workmen or wreck survivors could rapidly deplete their stores. William C. Williams of Boon Island recalled:

> . . . . we keepers always layed in enough stores so if we had callers in the dead of night who were cold and hungry we could feed them up well. You know that one could never tell when I was on Boon Island when a call might come from poor shipwrecked sailors for food and plenty of it. All the sailors around Kittery and York knew where to come if they were off on the fishing grounds and got out of food."[76]

When inspectors were making the rounds of local lighthouses, keepers could sometimes hitch a ride into Portsmouth on a Light-House Board vessel, and White Island keepers could take advantage of the steam packets that made daily runs to the Shoals during the summer tourist season. But for Boon Island keepers these provisioning trips were generally made in the open sailboat provided each light station by the board. (Motors were not provided for lighthouse boats until around 1910.) These trips could become dangerous when there were sudden weather changes.[77]

Leander White, an assistant keeper at Boon Island, endured a hairraising experience in the spring of 1875 when he sailed ashore for provisions. The wind was favorable when he set out, but at dusk died down before he could make Portsmouth Harbor, and then after dark breezed up so strongly that he had to sail offshore. The beach stone ballast in the boat continually shifted, the boat was in danger of swamping, and he was almost run down be a large vessel which finally heard his shouts and changed course in the nick of time. By dawn, White had been swept to Ipswich Bay. He sailed back to Portsmouth, arriving "wet, hungry and tired, but not at all discouraged." His wife must have been glad to have him assigned the next year to Whale's Back, where at least she could see him as he rowed the mile and a half to New Castle for supplies.[78]

In May 1885, Boon Island keeper A. J. Leavitt had just been to Portsmouth for coal and provisions and was heading down the river on his way back to the island when the current swept his boat against a diving stand at Gangway Rock, where divers were working on blasting the ledge. The boat was overturned and swept downstream, with Leavitt clinging to it, finally sinking and leaving Leavitt floundering in the water. The exhausted keeper was picked up by a boat sent out by the diving party and was taken aboard the schooner *Yankee*. The Boon Island boat popped up bow-first near the narrows at Henderson Point, "with the snort of a puffing pig," but the supplies were lost.[79]

Keeper William C. Williams, his wife, his son Charles, and three men who had been making repairs at Boon Island had a frightening experience in April 1890 while sailing ashore in the open lighthouse boat, two of them riding in a dory towed behind it. In the sailboat, Mrs. Williams had covered herself with an old sail to keep from being soaked by spray. About two miles off Gerrish Island, the sailboat overturned in a sudden powerful gust of wind, throwing everyone into the freezing water. The dory in tow might have capsized as well, but Charles had the presence of mind to cut the towline. Mrs. Williams was finally extricated from under the heavy canvas, and all four passengers were hauled into the dory. Within a half hour, they had been sighted and picked up by the schooner *Portland Packet* and the sailboat and dory taken in tow. The master of the packet, apparently not wanting to put into the harbor, signaled for a tow to take the Williamses in. At Jerry's Point Life-Saving Station, the men started off in the oar-powered surfboat, boarded a tug at the harbor entrance, and were towed out to the packet. The lighthouse people were taken aboard the tug and made the rest of the trip to town in it.[80]

For the keepers at White Island, the simple act of returning from a social call at one of the neighboring islands could be dangerous because of the ledges off the steep boatways there. In June 1891, assistant keeper Thomas Barber and his wife were overturned fifty yards offshore on their way back from a visit to Star Island. Mrs. Barber managed to grab an oar and kick her way back to the dory where both the Barbers clung until Keeper Grogan came to their rescue. Mrs. Barber was congratulated for her coolness in "trying circumstances" which must have been exacerbated by the voluminous long skirts women then wore. But this experience may have had something to do with Barber's resignation within six weeks. Later the same year he became a surfman at the Jerry's Point Life-Saving Service station, in Rye.[81]

XIII *The Light-House Board, 1880–1910, and Harbor and River Improvements, 1880–1915*

> *The* Iris *... was bought from the Navy Department in October, 1865. It is not known when, where, or by whom she was built. She was rebuilt in 1871, and has been in steady service ever since. It is probable that if she were caught in a storm, or if she touched the bottom, she would become a complete wreck.*
>
> —Light-House Board *Annual Report*, 1889

PRIVATE SHIPYARDS CEASED ACTIVITY after the launch of the schooner *Lizzie Call* in 1886, and the Navy Yard continually struggled to justify its existence and to upgrade its facilities in the hope of competing more effectively with shipyards elsewhere. Its civilian payroll (1,861 in 1865) sank to just seventy-one in 1877, and never rebounded to above a thousand until World War I.[1]

A big event at the yard was the arrival of the *U. S. S. Constitution* in 1882. The venerable warship was turned into a receiving vessel for new recruits and also became something of a tourist attraction until being towed back to Boston in 1897. On October 11, 1904, in Bath, Maine, the twin-screw, first-class battleship *Georgia* was launched. On the same day, all Portsmouth turned out to celebrate the launch of the *Boxer* at the Navy Yard. Compared to the *Georgia*, she was something of an anachronism—a wooden-hulled sailing brig of 350 tons, intended as a training vessel.[2]

Portsmouth breweries and the textile mills, both in Portsmouth and in communities upriver along Piscataqua tributaries, were mainstays of the economy. Maritime activity in the harbor and river was steady, though not exactly robust. The Portsmouth Board of Trade kept track of it as means of bolstering the case for river and harbor improvements. Its statistics for 1888 showed:

> Four steamboat lines and five tow boats run in and about Portsmouth harbor; and in 1888 thirty-nine steamers, with a net tonnage of 33,406 tons, and carrying 702 men, arrived here; this was exclusive of tow boats and excursion steamers. There arrived during the year 871 sailing vessels, with a registered net tonnage of 206,756 tons, and carrying 4,858 men; also several United States vessels ... The only articles of any note exported are bricks, of which 15,000,000 went out during the year. There arrived at this port .... 310,909 tons of coal, 3,850,000 feet of lumber, 200,000 railroad ties, 42,500 barrels of lime, 15,000 boxes of salt, 6,000 barrels of plaster, 2,000 bushels of potatoes, 5,950 bushels of oysters, 1,590 tons of moulding and building sand, 300 tons of phosphate, 1,850 tons of pig iron, 745 tons of stone, 600 cords of wood, 175 tons of ashes, 100 tons of asphalt, 310 tons of pavings, 1,096 tons iron water pipe, and 1,500 tons miscellaneous merchandise. There was no shipbuilding during the year. There are sixty-three vessels owned here, with a tonnage of 10,198.87 tons[3]

As was the case earlier, the waters off Portsmouth were full of coastwise schooners from Maine ports that often put into Portsmouth to shelter from storms. Along with the locally owned fishing vessels that had always been a part of the maritime scene, steamboats and pleasure boats associated with the growing summer population along the New Hampshire and Maine coasts were also much in evidence. Local maritime interests counted on reliable aids to navigation, especially if they could help better compete with the railroads, and lobbied for more of them as well as for projects to physically remove obstacles to navigation.

The Spanish-American War

The blowing up of the *U. S. S. Maine* in Havana Harbor on February 15, 1898, and the subsequent declaration of war against Spain in April of that year spawned the fear that the Spanish fleet might attack anywhere along the coast. The naval cruisers *Columbia* and *Minneapolis* began patrolling the New England coast early in May. There was panic up and down the Atlantic seaboard. Coastal resort hotels reported widespread cancellations for the summer season. Four men from each of the life-saving stations at Jerry's Point, Jenness Beach and Wallis Sands (normally closed during the summer months) were called to duty in June to watch the New Hampshire coast.[4]

The Navy Yard was considered to be a potential target, and in early May, the Light-House Board's tender *Lilac* spent two days setting out buoys to mark the locations of the twenty-one underwater mines subsequently laid by a variety of government craft. The river's channel could be safely navigated during the daytime, but between the hours of eight P.M. and four A.M. the river was closed to all navigation: During those hours, the electricity to trigger the mines was turned on. And from Portland, First Lighthouse District inspector Commander Perry announced on May 9 the suspension of the lights and fog bell at Portsmouth Harbor lighthouse and of the Seavey's Island range lights for the duration of the war. It was reported that the lighthouse tender *Myrtle* was laying telephone cables to first district offshore lights, from which word could be sent of the approach of suspicious vessels.[5]

Even Boon Island was expected to be connected to the mainland. A cable was laid to the Nubble lighthouse (and removed after the war), but before any telephone line to Boon Island was accomplished, the war came to an end with the destruction of what was left of the Spanish fleet off Cuba on July 3. The only members of the Spanish navy seen by Portsmouth area people were the some sixteen hundred Spanish prisoners interned for a few weeks in a hastily assembled camp at the Navy Yard. They were sent back to Spain in September 1898.[6]

A brief note in the *Portsmouth Chronicle* for July 10, 1898, headlined "Fire at Boon Island," reported that those aboard a yacht returning to York Harbor in the evening said they had seen the buildings at the island on fire, and rockets being sent up to call for assistance. There were no later confirming stories and no Light-House Board reports of fire damage at Boon Island. A possible explanation is that the inhabitants were celebrating the end of the Spanish-American War with a bonfire and fireworks. Word may have come to them via homing pigeon (see chapter 12).[7]

In 1903, the Light-House administration was transferred from the U. S. Treasury Department, where it began in 1789, to the newly established Department of Commerce and Labor. The existing Light-House

Board administrative structure remained the same, however, and military men continued to serve as district engineers and inspectors, and to make their rounds aboard vessels acquired by the board.

Light-House Board Tenders

The Light-House Board's fleet consisted principally of antiquated steam-powered Civil War era cast-offs that gradually replaced the sailing vessels in use previously. The first district's Army engineer officer's territory—the Maine and New Hampshire coasts—usually also included the Massachusetts coast in the second district. The work of the board's inspector's and buoy tender was confined to the First Lighthouse District.

Although some of the tenders started out with white-painted hulls, by the late 1890s black became the standard color for hulls, stacks, and deck machinery—far more practical for the rough work done by these vessels. White was reserved for deckhouses and railings; decks were painted gray and derrick masts and booms tan. Each tender carried a miniature brass lighthouse on her bow, and brass letters spelled out the tender's name on the stern.

District Engineer's Tenders

The sailing vessel, *Wave,* continued in use through 1879, delivering building materials and carrying work crews to lighthouses in both first and second districts. *Myrtle* was a 140-foot-long single propeller, coal-fired steamer with an oak hull, built especially for the Light-House Board in Philadelphia in the winter of 1871 for fifty thousand dollars. (See Chapter 11) She remained in service in the first and second districts 1872–1914—an impressive forty-two years. Her deckhouse had to be extended when the total number of officers and crew aboard was expanded from fourteen to nineteen. Specialized machinery installed in her hold took up more and more space, reducing her coal carrying capacity and leaving her able to carry enough fuel for only one and a half weeks—a real disadvantage for work along the eastern Maine coast, where coaling facilities were inadequate. It was not until 1908 that the board's pleas for a replacement for *Myrtle* were finally answered when Congress passed a bill appropriating two hundred thousand dollars apiece for the design, building and fitting-out of new tenders.[8]

District Inspector's Vessels

In addition to carrying the Navy officer on his quarterly tour of inspection of each lighthouse and delivering routine supplies such as heating coal for stoves, and wicks, chimneys, and fuel for the lighthouse lamps, the crews of the inspector's vessel placed and maintained of a variety of floating and stationary aids to navigation: buoys, spindles, and fog signals.

The wooden-hulled screw steamer *Iris* had been in Light-House Board service since shortly after the Civil War (see chapter 11). When not transporting the inspector on his rounds, delivering coal and lamp fuel, setting buoys in new locations, or replacing markers that had been wrenched from their moorings or struck by passing vessels, the crew repaired and painted wooden and iron navigational markers and made new ones at the district's buoy depot in Portland's Casco Bay. By the end of the nineteenth century other depots had been established farther along the Maine coast, at Mount Desert Island and Whitehead Island in Penobscot Bay.[9]

Help was sometimes provided by supply tenders from other districts. The 160-foot-long, steel-hulled *Fern*, built in 1871 and assigned to the third district in 1873, was in Portsmouth Harbor in August 1882. The *Chronicle* reported that she had been on her "annual cruise" along the Maine coast supplying lighthouses, had just supplied Whale's Back and Fort Constitution lights, and would next proceed to White Island.[10]

For a time around the turn of the century, the 201-foot-long *Armeria*, a steel-hulled, twin-propeller steamer built in 1890 Camden, New Jersey and assigned to the third district, was brought in as a supply tender for "outside," or offshore lighthouses in the first and second districts. She loaded up at the principal Light-House Board supply depot on Staten Island with specialized lighthouse needs. She generally made her appearance in the first district in July or August and operated out of the depot on Little Diamond Island in Casco Bay. At 1,052 gross tons, *Armeria's* large capacity for coal and materials let her steam longer distanes between fuelings than the *Iris*. She was accompanied by a small steam yacht for landing supplies at the lighthouses. *Armeria* was assigned elsewhere in 1903 and in 1912 was wrecked on an uncharted ledge on the Alaska coast.[11]

By 1889, *Iris* was showing her age. According to the board's reports, she had a new boiler installed in 1888 and a new propeller in 1889, but her hull was "rough and battered," and it was feared that if "she were caught in a storm, or if she touched the bottom, she would become a complete wreck."[12] In spite of her fragility, in 1888 the *Iris* steamed 16,055 miles, and landed 312 tons of coal at lighthouses; her crew made and "ironed" two hundred buoys, painted 727, and placed thirty-one new ones. After years of pleading, the Light-House Board was finally provided funds to replace *Iris*, which was sold and lived out her life as a merchant vessel in Texas waters until around 1910.[13]

Her replacement, *Lilac*, was one of two steel-hulled seagoing tenders built in Cleveland in 1892 especially to meet the needs of the Light-House Board. Built at a cost of ninety-two thousand dollars, she was a screw steamer of 434 gross tons, 145 feet long, with a draft of fifteen feet. *Lilac* boasted electric lights, cherry-paneled quarters for the master and mates, and a large cabin and stateroom on the aft upper deck for the Navy officer who was the Light-House Board's inspector. A derrick boom was mounted on the fore-mast for hoisting buoys from the deep forward hold, and she carried a searchlight. *Lilac* was manned by a crew of sixteen, including two engineers. She made her first appearance in Portsmouth Harbor in November 1892.[14]

Lilac evidently performed well. In 1897, for example, in the course of steaming 14,245 miles, her crew replaced 112 buoys, changed 154 and painted 251, and painted twelve spindles and tripods. She also delivered 120 tons of coal to light-stations. She spent some thirty-eight days at district buoy depots while the crew made and "ironed" sixty-six

Lighthouse tender Lilac. *MM*

new buoys.[15] But because of her fifteen-foot draft she could not get as close to some of the sites for laying buoys as desired, so another tender, *Geranium,* a side-wheel steamer drawing only a little more than twelve feet was brought into service in the first district temporarily in 1896 and was assigned permanently to it the next year. *Lilac* was assigned to Puerto Rico around the turn of the century.[16]

Geranium was another Civil War veteran of the "flower pot fleet," built as the 128-foot-long commercial tug *John A. Dix* in 1863, acquired that year by the Navy, and given her floral name. She served as an armed tug off the South Carolina coast during the war and was acquired by the Light-House Board in 1865. Her first assignment was as an inspector's tender out of New Orleans in the eighth district. She was rebuilt and lengthened to 156 feet in 1879, and subsequently served in the third and second districts before moving to her new home port in Portland. By 1909, *Geranium*'s age had caught up with her, and when the weather was considered too stormy for her to venture out, her crew kept busy at the buoy depots making and repairing buoys. She was to be auctioned off in Portland at the end of that year. A writer for the *Portsmouth Herald* wrote a valedictory piece, "Goodbye Geranium," hoping that the "staunch craft," with her history of service in the Civil War and more than forty years with the Light-House Board, would find a buyer appreciative of her heritage.[17]

Lighthouse tender Geranium. *MM*

To take *Geranium*'s place until the completion of a new $200,000 tender authorized by Congress in 1908, another side-wheeler, the iron-hulled, 167-foot-long *Wistaria,* (later spelled *Wisteria*), with a draft of only ten feet, was brought into the district in 1910. She was built in Wilmington, Delaware in 1882 for the board, and was stationed in Charleston, South Carolina before arriving in the first district in 1910, where she was in service for only a year before being decommissioned.[18]

During the last two decades of the nineteenth century and the first decade of the twentieth, the Light-House Board's officers continued to grapple with structural and equipment problems at existing lighthouses and tried to improve poor living conditions endured by many keepers and their families. The board also responded to demand for more and better navigational aids, and the officers assigned to the first district kept an eye on the harbor and river improvements increasingly called for by local interests, and that often required added aids to navigation. Light-House Board Army engineers designed and oversaw the building of new lighthouses farther east along the coast.

Locally, the focus was on the maintenance and refinement of existing structures and equipment and the building of ancillary structures like buildings to store the kerosene used to fuel lighthouse lamps. Whale's Back and Boon Island lighthouses required the lion's share of attention during this period.

Lighthouse tender Wisteria. *MM*

Solving Problems at Whale's Back Lighthouse

James C. Duane's successors as First Lighthouse District engineer and the men who served under them spent much time on Whale's Back lighthouse problems during this period. In the dark, predawn hours of February 3, 1880, Whale's Back's head keeper, Leander White, made his way from the lighthouse across the open bridge into the iron foghorn tower to start the fire for the horn's engine. Drenching spray already was cascading across the slippery bridge, and snow was thickening in the intensifying wind. White knew hat visibility would soon be almost zero and that the foghorn would be needed. Fishermen, groping their way that morning into the harbor, peered into what had become a blinding gale-driven snowstorm. But they heard no reassuring blasts from the foghorn at Whale's Back telling them they were at the mouth of the river. In the nearly three years since its installation, they had come to depend upon it at times like this.

Inside the fog tower, White and his assistant, George Leavitt, were trying frantically trying to get the horn to sound, stoking the fire with coal and heating the air in the pressure tank well beyond the usual level needed. They checked the reed of the horn and every part of the machinery that might be causing the problem. Finally, in desperation, they boiled kettles of water, climbed up the outside of the iron tower, and poured the water into the mouth of the trumpet. Out came a choked blast, along with the chunks of ice that had clogged the throat of the trumpet. During the storm that day, seas had smashed against the connecting bridge, dislodging one end of it. Bolts snapped that held the heavy, inch-thick iron band around the base of the 1829 stone lighthouse which had been left standing beside the new tower, and spray from the heavy seas breaking against the old structure were thrown into the foghorn trumpet, periodically cutting off its voice.[19]

To eliminate the cause of the spray that went into the fog horn trumpet during storms, board workmen in the summer of 1880 took down Palmer and Haselton's 1829 lighthouse tower, leaving the foundation pier in place. The twenty-foot-high high pier was expected to break the force of the waves that swirled between the fog and light towers. The lighthouse boats had formerly been hauled up on the pier on the lee side of the old tower. To provide a new, sheltered location for them, the men attached wrought-iron boat davits to the west side of the iron fog tower and cut a door through the tower so the keepers could get at the block and tackle for raising and lowering the boats. Finally, to protect them from the breakers that sometimes crashed onto the bridge between the 1872 lighthouse and the fog tower, the workmen built a covered passageway between them.[20]

The gray granite of the lighthouse was left unpainted, with annual paint jobs required only for the lantern and its dome and the window frames. But like the iron Fort Constitution and Nubble lighthouses, Whale's Back's iron fog tower and the tall tube housing the trumpet above it required regular painting to protect it from rusting. This was a job assigned to the lighthouse keepers, and it was while doing this job in the summer of 1882 that assistant keeper, John Lewis, of Kittery was fatally injured, falling from near the top of the tube to the roof of the fog tower. The tug *Naumkeag* was sent out with a doctor, and Lewis, with a broken hip and other injuries, was taken home to Kittery, where he died two weeks later.[21]

The 1880 alterations at Whale's Back were not effective, and storm seas continued to plague the keepers. In an early-January 1884 gale, Leander White and his assistant, Brackett Lewis, had an especially rough experience. First the tremendous volume of spray dumped into the mouth of the fog trumpet poured into the engine room and made the horn inoperable. Green seas broke over the foundation of the old lighthouse and well up the side of the new lighthouse, with spray shooting up over its lantern. On the ocean side of the lighthouse, where the lowest window had already been blocked in, a sea smashed the next highest window. Tons of water poured in and cascaded into the spaces below, flooding the basement freshwater tanks with seawater. When the tide ebbed, White and Lewis frantically blocked the window opening against the next high tide as best they could with boards and coal sacks. The boat hanging on the davits off the fog tower was smashed, leaving the men no means to get ashore to report the damage. They waved a blanket to signal for help, and a boat was finally sent out from New Castle.[22]

A March 1888 gale demolished much of the foundation pier of the 1829 lighthouse. Using a derrick, lighthouse construction crews began in late summer to build a heavy timber-and-plank bulkhead between the now exposed bases of the fog and light towers, and to fill the space between the bulkhead and the towers with dry masonry. The work was nearly finished when the violent two-day gale of November 25 and 26 hit, carrying away more of the foundation pier of the old lighthouse, and the derrick and rigging, and heaping about two thousand tons of stone from

1885 View of Whale's Back after construction of the cast iron fog tower and the removal of the old lighthouse tower. The foundation pier was left in place. NARG26.

the old lighthouse in front of the access ladder to the fog tower, which had become the main entrance to the lighthouse. At the same time, gravel and concrete were swept away from the base of the fog tower, threatening to undermine it. By the end of June 1889, Light-House Board crews had repaired the base of the fog tower, and broken up tons of stone from the old lighthouse to form a base for a boat slip. They built a roof above the boat davits to keep the boats from filling with sea spray and rain.[23]

The optic at Whale's Back was changed in 1898, with a new fourth-order Fresnel lens with flash panels installed on a revolving pedestal or "chariot" with ball bearings. The result was a fixed light varied by an intense flash every minute and a half. [24]

The Whale's Back foghorn was upgraded in the spring of 1899, when a new second-class Daboll trumpet and a new Clayton air compressor were put in place. Duplicate oil-fueled two-horsepower Hornsby-Akroyd engines were installed along with a tank for water to cool them. In place of the four to seven tons of coal needed annually, about two hundred gallons of oil were consumed. The new trumpet emitted a five-second long blast every twenty-five seconds.[25]

The first-class fog signal sought by local interests back in 1878 was finally installed in 1902, along with more powerful four-horsepower horizontal engines, which consumed four hundred to eight hundred gallons of oil annually. An eighteen-hundred-gallon water tank was needed to cool these engines. The substitution of oil for coal must have been welcome for the men who operated the foghorn. In the more than usually foggy year of 1907, when the horn was sounded for 1,150 hours, keeper Walter Amee and his assistants, John Wetzel and John Brooks, were almost drowned by a deluge when the water tank burst and put the foghorn out of commission. There was still no telephone connection to the mainland even though phones were widely used there, and Amee had to row ashore to send a telegram to the first district headquarters about the situation.[26]

Living and working with the foghorn was doubtless the most difficult aspect of duty at Whale's Back. It was probably similar to conditions described in a 1957 magazine article. Sleeping within a few feet of a horn meant to be heard from four or five miles away was just about impossible, and even during the daytime it was nerve-wracking for the men cooped up in the cramped lighthouse. Windows rattled every time the horn blasted. And working on the machinery in the iron fog tower was hellishly hot; the temperature generated by the engines could reach 145 degrees.[27]

A March 1888 storm destroyed most of the foundation pier of the 1829 lighthouse. Using stone from the old structure, Light-House Board crews created a landing slip off the fog tower. They also built a roof above the boat davits to keep water from accumulating in the keeper's boat. Photo courtesy of Peter Narbonne.

Boon Island Light

The Light-House Board made many changes, repairs, and improvements at Boon Island during these years. The board had made annual appeals for funds to build separate structures for storage of the substantial quantities of the highly flammable kerosene that was used in all lighthouses by 1883. One of these, an eleven-by-fifteen-foot building, was completed at Boon Island in the summer of 1887.[28]

By then, serious structural problems with the lighthouse tower had become evident. In high winds, the tower would vibrate. The iron-framed windows leaked, and could not be opened to help dry out the damp interior of the tower. During high storm tides, water flowed in to the floor at the base of the tower. Major repairs were begun in the early summer of 1888. New wooden double-hung windows were substituted for the iron ones, and a layer of concrete was applied to the floor at the base of the tower to raise it a foot and a half. To stabilize the top tiers of masonry, six sets of iron ties with struts were attached to the top of the lantern and fastened to the masonry of the upper forty feet of the tower.[29] The vibrations continued. Assistant keeper Charles Williams, who had been on watch duty in the lantern during a December 1900 gale, told a local reporter:

> it seemed to him that the tower would topple over. The huge granite shaft shook constantly with a tremulous, vibratory motion that would cause one's teeth to chatter involuntarily. A pail of water stood on the floor at the top of the tower—he was obliged to keep wiping up the water that came in around the windows—and by the shaking of the lighthouse the surface of the water in the pail was so agitated that it formed ripples fully an inch high.

Rods extending still farther down the side of the tower were added in 1902.[30] Similar rods were installed at Petit Manan lighthouse, another tall granite lighthouse for which Lieutenant Franklin drew the plans, strongly suggesting a flaw in the design.[31]

The board's Annual Report for 1888 noted the poor condition of the keepers' house and the crowding endured by the three keepers and family members who lived in space originally intended for two families: "The keepers have had to store their vegetables and provisions in the halls adjoining their bed-rooms." The solution was not another house, but a twelve-by-twenty-foot clapboarded and plastered structure for storage of the provisions.

Boon Island lighthouse after rods and struts (barely visible) were installed in 1888 to stabilize the lighthouse tower. (Additional stabilizers were added in 1902.) The photo also shows a crowd of people on the island, probably including visitors as well as the keepers and their families, on a good day for drying the laundry. NHHS.

Twelve workmen were still at Boon Island in November 1888 when
the great gale of the twenty-fifth and twenty-sixth broke. William C.
Williams, just promoted to acting head keeper, had gone ashore, perhaps to see about filling the vacant position of second assistant, leaving
behind his wife and teenaged daughter, assistant keeper James Burke,
and the workmen. By midnight of the second night of the storm, the
seas mounted to the point where it was apparent that at high tide the
new storage building would be threatened. The men moved all the provisions back into the house. The gale winds subsided, but the seas continued to pile onto the island. The next night, waves undermined the
small building in which the workmen were staying, and all twelve of
them crowded into the keepers' house. When Burke and one of the
workmen went through the covered passageway to the lighthouse to
see to the light at three A.M., a tremendous sea smashed doors and windows and filled the passageway to a depth of three feet. A barrel of lamp
chimneys was smashed.[32]

Inside the house, Mrs. Williams and her daughter, who had stayed
fully dressed since the storm began, could hear the terrifying sound of
water swirling beneath their feet in the fifteen-inch space between the

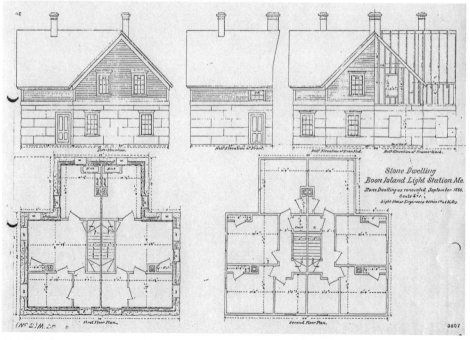

*1888 Light-House Board plans for enlarging the Boon Island keepers' house. The roof of
the old stone house was removed and a wood frame second story added.* NARG26.

double floors of the first story. Burke was about to order everyone into the lighthouse for safety when the tide began to draw down. Outside, the schooner *Teal,* which had been heaved onto the island in a February 1883 storm, was swept off again; the underpinnings of the boathouse were washed out, and a tremendous boulder landed between the boatways. Salt from the spray, which shot up 133' to the lantern of the lighthouse, encrusted the glass.[33] The oil house, just built in 1887, had to be replaced, this time with a structure of brick and stone. The twelve-hundred-pound fog bell, which was hand-struck in response to signals from vessels groping their way in fog, was badly damaged and had to be recast. It was reinstalled on top of the new oil house.[34]

The Board finally came to grips with the serious crowding of the keepers' families in the stone one and-a-half-story house built back in 1854. The solution, accomplished during the first half of 1889, was to remove the roof, gut and re-plaster and rearrange the interior spaces and add a wood-frame second story and new roof.[35] The board, knowing this would still not meet the needs of the number of people living at the island, in 1891 began to make annual requests for funds for another keeper's house. In the meantime, a telephone connection between the lighthouse lantern and the keeper's house was installed in 1902, a convenience that must have been very welcome, considering the many steps needed to get to the lantern of the lighthouse.[36]

The enlarged house is shown in this undated photograph. Also visible is the brick and stone oil house built to replace an earlier one destroyed in an 1888 storm. The hand-struck fog bell was placed on top of this structure. NARG26.

Congress finally granted the request for an additional keeper's house in 1904 with an appropriation of four thousand dollars. Because there was only a scant single acre above water at high tide, the house was built as close as possible and to the south of the lighthouse. Keeper Williams, ashore in mid-October of 1904, reported that the new six-room house was almost finished. He and his family would occupy it, leaving the other house for the first and second assistants. The house no longer exists. It was a wooden structure of one-and-a-half stories.[37]

The hand-struck fog bell at Boon Island had long been considered inadequate. The Light-House Board, echoed by the local press, made annual requests for a more effective fog signal. A foghorn was recommended in 1901, at a projected cost of about ten thousand dollars. The board cited the thousands of people carried by the Boston–Bangor passenger steamers that ran for Boon Island on their passage. The board was still making the recommendation in 1910, by which time the price tag had doubled. Perhaps the only person who was pleased when Congress continued to deny funding was keeper Williams. The *Portsmouth Herald* reported that the veteran of twenty-five years on the island considered that the "lonely rock is not big enough for both him and this noisy aid to navigation" and that he hoped to retire before its approval.[38]

He need not have worried. A hand-struck fog bell was still the only fog signal at Boon Island in the 1920s, and it may have been decided that the whistling buoy activated by the motion of the sea that had been placed off the south end of Boon Island Ledge in 1882 was adequate.[39]

According to Light-House Board reports, the lighthouse was painted (probably whitewashed) in 1906, apparently to increase its usefulness as a daymark. The cast-iron lighthouses at Fort Constitution and Cape Neddick, originally painted brown, had been painted white in 1902. The board's *List of Lights, Buoys and Day Marks in the First Light-House District* for 1909 indicated that Boon Island lighthouse was still white. No photograph of Boon Island lighthouse in this whitened state has been discovered, though. If it had indeed been whitewashed, the cost of whitewashing this, the tallest, lighthouse in the first district, may have proven too much (to say nothing of the dangers involved in doing the work), and nature was evidently permitted to wash away the whitewash and restore it to its original grey granite color.[40]

The 1904 head keeper's house is seen beyond the masonry oil house and a storage building. OYHS.

Work at White Island

The violent gale of November 1888 that swept the wrecked schooner *Teal* off Boon Island carried the vessel to the Isles of Shoals where the wreck lodged briefly on the east side of the remains of the stone breakwater between Cedar and Smuttynose Islands. A tremendous sea then lifted her up and over the line of stones and she finally landed on Lunging Island where she was pounded to pieces. The storm blew over a fifteen-foot-high stone monument to John Smith on Star Island, but relatively little damage was done at White Island. Assistant Keeper Elias Tarlton's henhouse and hens were blown away, and some rotted wooden bracing legs of the covered way to the lighthouse were washed away. These were replaced during the next year by Light-House Board workmen, who also reshingled the walkway. A brick oil house was built in 1892, and in 1902 board workmen installed a telephone connection between the keepers' house and the lighthouse. A machine-struck fog bell was placed at the island in 1906, set to strike two blows at twenty-second intervals.[41]

Fort Constitution Light

The lighthouse at Fort Constitution suffered no spectacular damage during the great gale of 1888, but the 320-foot-long bridge from the keeper's house to the lighthouse was in bad shape because of rotted wood. Apparently a favored vantage point for summer residents, as well as the lightkeeper's means of getting to the lighthouse, it was rebuilt in 1889. Light-House Board workmen also removed the snow-catching second story open balcony of the keeper's house and built a roof over the open porch at the first story.[42] As part of the board's efforts to provide separate storage for the kerosene for the lighthouse lamps, workmen in 1892 built a small wooden structure, twelve by eighteen feet, but replaced it eleven years later with a more suitable brick oil house, twelve by fifteen feet in plan, which still stands on the sea side of the fort's walls, near the walkway to the lighthouse. The year 1896 saw the installation of a fog bell atop a flat-roofed structure housing a clockwork mechanism for striking the bell, which was cast by the Blake Company of Boston.[43]

The 1872 keeper's house had been built on a rise to the west of the lighthouse, near a War of 1812 Martello tower, on the foundation of the earlier keeper's house which had been moved to this location to put distance between the military and the lighthouse operations at the fort. The needs of the military required the moving of the 1872 house two times: first in 1897 to make way for Battery Farnsworth and then in 1906, when the War Department installed Battery Hackleman and the house was moved to its present location inside the walls of the fort. The color of the cast-iron lighthouse was changed from reddish brown to white in 1902. Records are not consistent as to whether the use of brown paint for the lighthouse was resumed for a time after this date.[44]

Cape Neddick (Nubble) Lighthouse

Work at the Nubble lighthouse after its completion in 1879 included modifications to the fog bell and its means of operation. The original hand-struck fog bell was replaced by a slightly larger one suspended from the sea side of the light tower in 1880, but soon thereafter an open, wooden framed bell tower with a mechanical bell striker was built just to the southeast of the light tower. In 1890 a larger bell, weighing close to a ton, was placed in the bell tower, which had been strengthened to sustain this greater load. This bell had an outside rather than an inside striker. A rebuilt striking machine was installed and was set to deliver one blow to the bell every fifteen seconds, twice as frequent as the previous setting. A boarded-in, metronome-shaped housing was provided for the clock-work. Covered walkways were added between the house and the lighthouse and between the lighthouse and the fog bell structure. A brick oil house was constructed in 1902. Outbuildings for storage and workshops were built, repositioned, or rebuilt from time to time.[45]

Oddly, there is no record of construction of a boathouse and boatways when the lighthouse was first built, though a boat for access to the island must have been part of the original equipment at the Nubble. The clipping files show the building of a boathouse and boatways in 1888 (perhaps to replace ones damaged by a storm), and the next year the lengthening of the boat house and extension of the landing slip by sixty-four feet to permit its use at lower tides. Wooden stairs for the steep climb from the boat house to the keeper's house were rebuilt periodically.[46]

The Nubble lighthouse file at the National Archives also has a notation of work done in 1881: "The exterior walls of the light-tower and dwelling were re-painted two coats white…" This suggests that white paint was applied over the original reddish brown paint of the light tower as well as to the house; but the board's List of Lights for 1889 shows the tower to be the original color, which was evidently the prescribed color for cast-iron lighthouses until after the turn of the century.[47]

Spindles, Buoys, Post Lights, and Floating Fog Bells

Spindles and Buoys

The Light-House Board's work to maintain and adjust the positioning of existing aids to navigation and place new ones demanded by maritime interests all along the New Hampshire and Maine coasts was never-ending. Storms, unpredictable but inevitable, often complicated matters. The great storms of March and November 1888, for example, made a lot of work for the crews in the First Lighthouse District. Locally, a thirty-foot-high iron spindle marking Anderson's Rock, about a mile southeast of White Island at the Isles of Shoals, only recently placed, was destroyed by storms, and in July 1889 it was replaced it with a more substantial marker. This required drilling a hole in the rock three feet deep to receive a new iron spindle, thirteen inches in diameter and thirty-five feet high, with an iron cage at its top to make it identifiable from a distance.

Also at the Shoals, the crews re-positioned a horizontally-striped spar buoy marking Half-Way Rock, situated in the channel between Star and Lunging Islands. In Portsmouth Harbor, off the south side of Noble's Island, a black buoy was moved to a position thirty yards from the end of the wharf there. These changes and the many others that occurred almost annually, and the numbered charts affected, were duly noted in "Notices to Mariners" published in the local newspapers, with reference to the notices regularly produced by the U.S. Coast and Geodetic Survey. It was a far cry from the early-nineteenth-century period when information about such changes was not at all well publicized. The *Chronicle* reported less than a month later that the Half-Way Rock buoy had been carried away by a heavy sea in early December 1889, warning that until the Light-House Board could replace it, "seamen using that channel should not forget that an unmarked danger exists there." The tender *Iris* by February had put in place a new spar buoy at Half-Way Rock and another at the ledge off Frost's Point at the entrance to Little Harbor.[48]

Floating Fog Whistles and Bells

Between 1880 and 1910, in addition to hand-or machine-struck fog bells and foghorns attached to lighthouses, numerous floating fog signals activated in various ways by the surge of the sea were put in place by the Light-House Board. Fogs off Portsmouth were not as frequent or

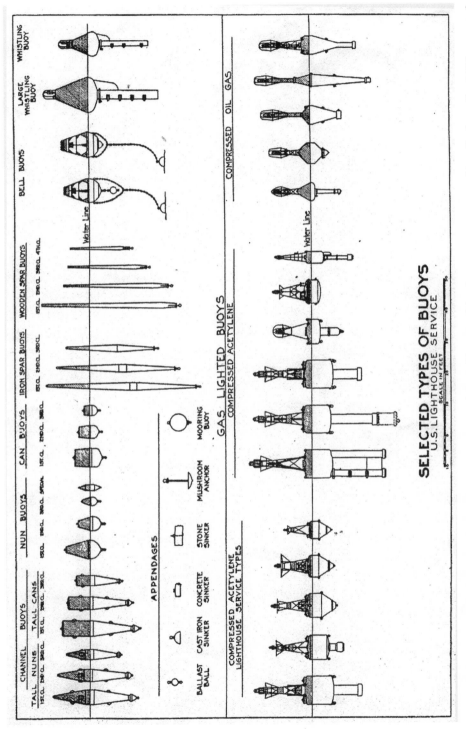

Types of buoys used by the U. S. lighthouse service. Most of those illustrated in the top row were used locally from the 1880s onward. Many of the others were introduced in the early decades of the twentieth century.

as prolonged as they were off the coasts of Down East Maine and the Pacific northwest, but were far more often a problem than along the South Atlantic and Gulf Coasts. Whale's Back's Daboll horn was in use every year for an average of 875 hours, or the equivalent of a solid month. But Seguin Light Station, at the mouth of the Kennebec River in Maine, one year clocked a total of 2,734 hours, and off San Francisco, the lightship there once racked up 2,221 hours.[49]

A relatively new device, a whistling buoy, was placed in the waters off Portsmouth in the spring of 1882 by the lighthouse tender *Iris*. The buoy was the 1876 invention of J. M. Courtenay, and consisted of a pear-shaped iron bulb, twelve feet in diameter, through which a tube nearly three feet wide and forty feet long descended to a depth of thirty-two feet. When the sea caused the rising and falling of the buoy, air pressure was built up through an arrangement of holes, tubes, and valves to activate a locomotive whistle.

On May 1, 1882, one of these buoys was set in the waters off the treacherous Boon Island Ledge. Like the first-class nun buoy it replaced, it was painted with red and black horizontal stripes, and the letters *B I L* painted in white across its midsection. It may have been Israel Miller of the *Chronicle* who saw and heard it at the Navy Yard before its offshore installation. It would give "blasts at short intervals," he wrote, "its shrieks, howls and yells, and other noises, if there are any more, increasing in volume with the increasing violence of the sea. It will be a boon indeed to the mariner."[50]

At the end of July 1882, another whistling buoy was placed off Kitt's Rock near the entrance to Portsmouth Harbor to take the place of the second-class can buoy there. It was painted red with a white *P* to mark it as right hand entering buoy for the harbor. The *Chronicle* dubbed it the "Jersey Bull" and predicted that when there was a southeasterly wind, its persistent, irregular voice would provoke negative comment from summer visitors at the Wentworth Hotel at Little Harbor. And in fact the Jersey Bull met the fate of other whistling buoys that had been placed within earshot of summer vacationers. Before a year had passed its caterwauling was replaced on June 1, 1883, by the much mellower— and far less useful—tones of a bell buoy. This featured a three-hundred-pound bell mounted atop a nine-foot-high tapered iron framework affixed to an iron half-sphere designed to roll in slight swells. Suspended below the buoy by a chain was a spherical weight intended to lower the center of gravity of the buoy to keep it from rolling over completely.

The bell sounded when it was struck by an iron cannonball that rolled around in a grooved framework set at the level of the bell's mouth.[51]

The *Chronicle* took up the cudgels for the fishermen who sorely missed the Jersey Bull, complaining that they often could not hear the bell buoy until they were dangerously close to it. They proposed that the "Bull" be set off Kitt's Rock during the stormy fall, winter, and early-spring months when it was most needed, and in the tourist season to replace it with the bell buoy. This is exactly what was done in a similar situation off Eastern Point, Gloucester, Massachusetts in 1884, for the benefit of "summer butterflies .... who think their pleasure is of more consequence than the lives of many fishermen." But is seems the fishermen of Portsmouth had less clout than the Gloucester men, and a bell buoy, later relabeled *2KR*, remained off Kitt's Rock until 1911, when it was announced that a whistling buoy was finally to be put in place by the lighthouse tender *Myrtle*.[52]

In 1894 a whistling buoy labeled *W I* was placed about two miles south of White Island. It remained there until 1906, when a machine-struck bell was installed on White Island itself. Its machinery was enclosed in a structure mounted on top of the cut-down 1820s lighthouse structure.[53]

Lights, Private and Public

Even before the advent of electric lighting in Portsmouth, local mariners had made private arrangements for lights to help them into their home berths at night. Fishermen paid to fit up with red glass the gas streetlight at the corner of Court and Water Streets as a guide in to Commercial Wharf. And in December 1887, an electric light on a sixty foot pole was erected on this wharf as an aid to the fishing vessels that tied up there. But within weeks, they urged a return to the old gaslight, complaining that the electric light was too high to be useful, and furthermore that the power was not maintained all night long.[54]

Lights were kept on the Portsmouth–Kittery toll bridge as well, with a night watchman keeping an eye on them. When they were first installed is not known, but it was probably after a congressional act of 1882 required owners of bridges over waterways to maintain them. They may have been similar to the lanterns carried by railroad men, and easily pilfered. On one occasion of a bridge lantern theft, a local newspaper predicted that next people would be "stealing cracks in the sidewalk."[55]

There were doubtless other privately installed lights along the waterfront, of use principally to local masters comfortable with the

idiosyncrasies of the harbor. But until 1893, the Light-House Board
made no attempt to assist vessels arriving at night at Portsmouth
wharves. Coasters had to wait in the lower harbor not only for slack
tide but also for daylight before proceeding upriver. Railroads not only
did not have to wait for favorable wind and tide conditions, but also
were not dependent daylight for operation. "Time" was increasingly
"money" for merchants, who wanted reliable deliveries of goods.

The problem in 1893 finally drew the attention of the Light-House
Board and its ex officio chairman, the Secretary of the Treasury, and on
June 19, acting Navy Secretary McAdoo responded to his request and
authorized the Light-House Board to use Henderson's Point on
Seavey's Island (Navy Yard turf) for a post light.[56]

A post light was nothing more than a kerosene lantern, often with
a pressed-glass, Fresnel-type lens, mounted on a pole. Post lights were
used in waterways where powerful lights were not needed. Beginning
in the mid-1870s, the Light-House Board began providing hundreds
of them on the busy Ohio, Mississippi, and Missouri Rivers to mark
the navigable channels. By 1890, there were more than fifteen hundred on inland waterways and coastal estuaries, each tended by a
Light-House Board employee.[57]

At Henderson's Point, the work of drilling holes for iron supports for
the post was accomplished within a few days in late September 1893.
Two kerosene lanterns with tubular red glass chimneys were hung, one
above the other, from a red-painted post to mark the right side of the
channel ("red right returning") and were lit for the first time on September 25, 1893. It is not clear whether these lanterns were of the
eight-day variety fueled by storage tanks mounted atop each lantern.
Joseph Pruitt, of Kittery, was given the job of tending the lights, succeeded briefly by John Wetzel in 1897 and then by Frederick Stone
when Wetzel was assigned to Whale's Back as an assistant keeper.[58]

In April 1894, the post lights were converted into range lights for
vessels passing into the treacherous channel between the Goat Island
ledge and Henderson's Point, by the addition of another post light ninety feet east of the existing lights. The idea of using two existing natural
or man-made landmarks in alignment to set a course to steer toward an
objective or through a channel is an ancient one. Sixteenth-century
European navigational charts illustrated the practice of placing unlit
beacons, monuments, or poles as leading marks for existing landmarks
like church steeples, and windmills. Seventeenth-century English coast
maps show pairs of vertical poles placed to establish bearings.[59]

The use of lighted range markers for nighttime navigation was a logical next step. A nearby early American example was the pair of lighthouses built in 1794 at the north end of Plum Island at the entrance to Newburyport Harbor, a mile or so south of the New Hampshire border with Massachusetts. *The American Coast Pilot* of 1800 gave instructions for lining up the two lights to steer a safe course into the mouth of the Merrimack River between the often fatal south and north breakers, and in 1804 illustrated their use as range lights. Because constantly shifting sand shoals at the river's entrance continually altered the safe channel, these wooden lighthouses were constructed so they could be moved as needed to provide the proper alignment.[60]

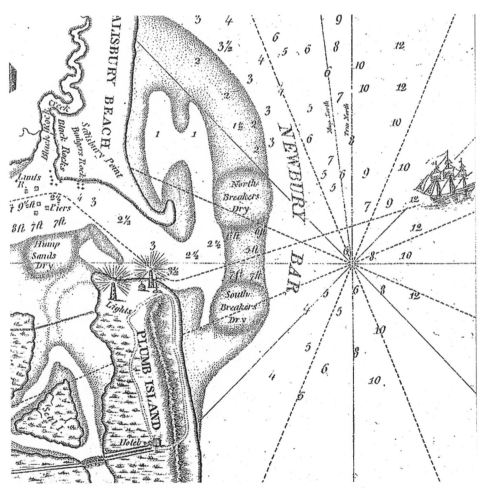

American Coast Pilot *chart of the entrance to Newburyport, showing a sailing vessel using the two Plum Island lighthouses to set a safe course into the river. These lighthouses were movable, to accommodate the shifting channel, and were in use as early as 1794.*

A one-story, two-room shed was built at Henderson's Point to accompany the post lights. One room was for oil storage; whether the other one was intended as a place to sleep for John Wetzel or Frederick Stone, who succeeded him in 1897, is not clear. By the end of the century, the Light-House Board evidently decided that the man responsible for the range lights should have a decent place to live within sight of his responsibilities. Plans drawn for a house for the Seavey's Island Light-station, as it was called by the board, called for transforming the existing shed into a Colonial Revival style cottage. The design included a gambrel-roofed addition built above a cellar, and encompassed four more rooms and a porch. This was completed in 1900, but would become obsolete within five years because of an ambitious river improvement project already in the works.

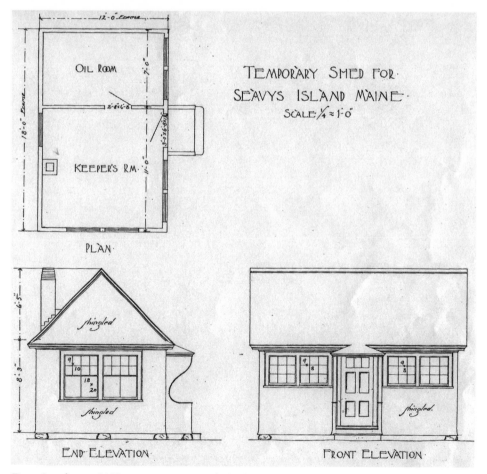

Drawing for an 1890s temporary post light keeper's and oil shed at Henderson Point on Seavey Island. NARG26.

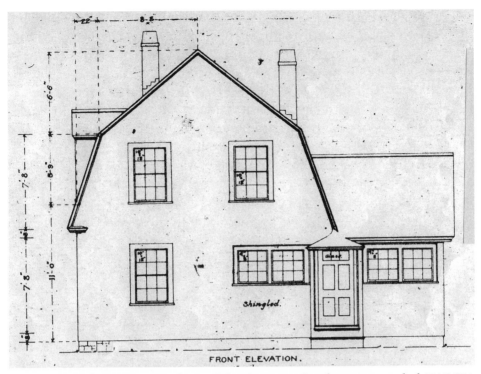

FRONT ELEVATION.

Plan for a keeper's house at Henderson Point, incorporating the temporary shed. NARG26.

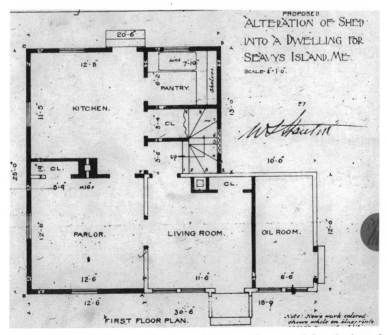

PROPOSED
ALTERATION OF SHED
INTO A DWELLING FOR
SEAVYS ISLAND, ME.

FIRST FLOOR PLAN.

First floor plan of the Henderson Point keeper's house. The second floor had two bedrooms.
NARG26.

Other post lights were established at Little Harbor in the 1890s in conjunction with an important harbor improvement project. In late May 1896, a kerosene lantern with a red lens, was placed on a white wooden post at the end of a breakwater running south from Jerry's Point to mark the entrance to this harbor. At the end of another breakwater off Frost's Point on the other side of the harbor entrance, two white lens lantern lights were hung on a post, one above the other. The job of tending the breakwater lights went to Henry Becker Jr. of New Castle. He began work on May 25, 1896 at an annual salary of five hundred and twenty dollars.

This 1902 view shows the two range lights and the keeper's house. Plans were already underway to demolish Henderson's Point. PA.

NOTICE TO MARINERS.

(No. 73 of 1896.)

UNITED STATES OF AMERICA—NEW HAMPSHIRE.

FROSTS POINT BEACON LIGHT.

Notice is hereby given that, on or about May 25, 1896, two fixed white lens-lantern lights will be established on the northeasterly end of the breakwater making off from Frost's Point, southerly side of the entrance to Little Harbor. Each light will illuminate the entire horizon.

The focal planes of the lights will be 22 feet and 30 feet, respectively, above mean high water.

The lights will be shown, one vertically above the other, from a white wooden post on the pier at the end of the breakwater.

The approximate geographical position of the lights, as taken from Chart No. 329 of the U. S. Coast and Geodetic Survey, will be:

Latitude, North, 43° 03′ (19″);

Longitude, West, 70° 43′ (03″).

Whaleback Light House, E., nearly $\frac{15}{16}$ mile.

This Notice affects the LIST OF LIGHTS AND FOG SIGNALS, ATLANTIC AND GULF COASTS, 1895, *page* 26, *after No.* 66, *and the* LIST OF BEACONS AND BUOYS, FIRST LIGHT-HOUSE DISTRICT, 1895, *page* 105.

BY ORDER OF THE LIGHT-HOUSE BOARD:

JOHN G. WALKER,

Rear Admiral, U. S. Navy,

Chairman.

OFFICE OF THE LIGHT-HOUSE BOARD,

Washington, D. C., May 19, 1896.

1896 notice of the establishment of Frost's Point post light. A single red post light was put in operation at Jerry's Point at the same time. NARG26.

Becker's nephew Frederick S. White said that Becker was the son of Henry Becker who lived on Smuttynose Island and worked for Thomas B. Laighton's Isles of Shoals fishing enterprise, and had come ashore to live in New Castle after the Civil War. One of the Beckers briefly tended White Island light after Laighton temporarily relinquished it in 1841. Henry Becker Jr. was the off-season caretaker for families summering in a house on Wild Rose Lane, which leads to Jerry's Point. At first he lived in a building on this property but he later moved to the Niles family's caretaker's cottage on the other side of the road. The lights Becker tended were of the five-day variety with a tank holding three gallons of kerosene mounted on top of them, according to his nephew. The kerosene for these lights had been stored with the kerosene for the Fort Constitution lighthouse, in a wooden structure built there in 1892. In 1903 the Board's work crew built a brick, gable-roofed oil house on Jerry's Point for the Little Harbor lights, like the one constructed that year at Fort Constiution to replace the previous structure.[61]

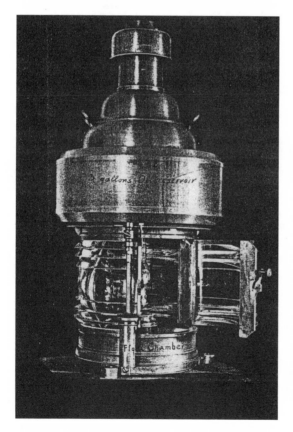

A brass five-day lens lantern of the type used at kerosene-fueled post and range lights of this era. The reservoir on top held three gallons. From a U.S. lighthouse service instruction manual.

Becker's job required him to take a boat across the entrance of Little Harbor to the Frost's Point breakwater to fuel the lanterns and trim their wicks, and he may have tended the Jerry's Point light by boat, as well, rather than by walking across the irregular stones of the breakwater. In February 1909, Becker nearly lost his life when he went in a small motorboat in rough weather to adjust one of the lights. On his way back to shore the boat filled and capsized, and Becker had to swim for it in the freezing water. He managed to pull himself, exhausted, onto one of the breakwaters. It was two hours before he was observed by a guard patrolling at Fort Stark on Jerry's Point. The closest U.S. Life-Saving Station, then located on Wood Island, was informed, and the U. S. Army tender *Hayden* towed the station's surfmen in a dory to the breakwater, where they had a difficult time in the choppy seas rescuing Becker from his rocky perch.[62]

Becker may have decided he'd had enough. The Light-House Board's register of keepers shows that A. B. White was appointed keeper of these lights in November 1909, though Becker was continued on the rolls through early 1910.[63]

The oil house with the Jerry's Point breakwater in the background. Author's photo.

1903 brick oil house at Jerry's Point. Author's photo.

Harbor and River Improvements

The Little Harbor breakwaters and their lights were the products of a long campaign to dredge Little Harbor. Through the 1880s and 1890s, local citizens struggled to maintain the viability of the Port of Portsmouth and the Navy Yard. They fought off an early-1880s move to close government shipyards in favor of contracting with private yards elsewhere with superior facilities for building ever larger iron-and steel-hulled vessels. As part of this effort, the Portsmouth Board of Trade lobbied Congress for river and harbor projects to improve the quality of navigation in the Piscataqua for both naval and commercial vessels, and thus contribute to overall prosperity. To help bolster its case, this board published annual reports of the movement of vessels carrying both cargo and passengers in and out of the port, and these statistics were published in the local press. Most of the proposed improvements had implications for the Light-House Board.[64]

Locally, the earliest federally funded engineering projects in aid of navigation were two breakwaters at the Isles of Shoals, the larger of which was the unsuccessful one built 1822–1823 between Cedar and Smuttynose Islands, which did not survive intact for a year. (See chapter 5.) In the 1870s, merchants in Dover, an important textile mill town, had managed to loosen governments funds to begin a substantial project to dredge and blast obstructions in the Cocheco River, a tributary to the Piscataqua. Elsewhere, millions of dollars were spent to accommodate the increasing size and quantity of vessels berthing in major ports like New York and Boston.[65]

Little Harbor Improvements

Proponents of dredging Little Harbor argued that it would benefit small commercial vessels by serving as a harbor of refuge. The dredging began in 1887. The project's goal was to create a forty-acre basin with a depth of twelve feet at mean low tide. The Jerry's Point breakwater and another running north from Frost's Point on the other side of the harbor entrance were finished by the end of 1895, before the dredging was completed. The Jerry's Point breakwater incorporated the red-painted iron daymark with a distinguishing cagelike "perch" placed there in 1850 (see Chapter 10), and was constructed with a built-up pier where the Jerry's (sometimes called Jaffrey's) Point post light was installed.

The Light-House Board in May 1896 announced the placement of seven numbered red and black spar buoys within Little Harbor to mark the channel, which by then extended a little more than half a mile from the two new breakwater post lights.[66]

It is interesting that while local movers and shakers struggled in the 1880s for improvements to navigation in Portsmouth Harbor and the Piscataqua River channel leading to the Navy Yard and the wharves of Portsmouth itself, the Little Harbor project, serving a much smaller need, gained the support and funding it achieved. Although most projects were initiated by local interest groups, the approval of the Army Corps of Engineers, which oversaw river and harbor projects, was crucial to obtaining appropriations from Congress and calls for bids from contractors to do the work. The annual reports of the engineer corps always included information about customs revenues collected and statistics about commercial shipping activity in the areas being considered for improvements as part of their analysis of the cost benefits of a particular project. (In 1880, revenues collected in Portsmouth amounted to only $17,972, compared to $348,288 in Portland.) In the 1880s, several projects were accomplished in the Piscataqua. Based on an 1878 survey, the Corps' Portland-based district engineer recommended three projects: the construction of a breakwater to close the turbulent channel between Great Island (New Castle) and Goat Island; the removal of Gangway Rocks between the South Beacon Shoal and the Navy Yard; and the removal of a ledge at the southwest point of Badger's Island. The work was done in small increments based on congressional appropriations parceled out throughout the 1880s, and several other small Piscataqua River projects were put forward as these neared completion.[67]

The crucial ingredient in the successful advocacy for and completion of the Little Harbor project was without a doubt the clout of Portsmouth politician and entrepreneur Frank Jones. Jones, who made an impressive "rags-to-riches" climb to power and wealth, has been described as Portsmouth's own robber baron, with a Portsmouth brewery, railroad holdings, and involvement in a variety of other enterprises. He acquired the Wentworth (later known as Wentworth-by-the-Sea) Hotel at the head of Little Harbor in 1879. He soon thereafter began to lobby behind the scenes for dredging the harbor for the benefit of his hotel enterprise. Tourism was not at this time considered in the Corps of Engineers assessments of commercial activity, perhaps because Congress did not consider it either. Jones, who had just completed two terms in the U.S. House of Representatives (1875–1879), was probably well aware of this.

The Little Harbor project first surfaced in a small way in the 1882 report of First District Engineer Major General George Thom of the Army Corps of Engineers, titled "Shoal in Channel of Harbor of Refuge Near Jerry's Point." Thom had prepared a survey and recommended approval of the project, which he estimated would cost twenty thousand dollars for dredging and ten thousand for a single breakwater off Jerry's Point. He suggested that seventeen thousand dollars earmarked for continued work on the Gangway Rocks project could be applied to begin the work.[68]

Thom's successor, Colonel Charles E. Blunt, however, thought that Little Harbor was not a priority, and not worth the "expenditure of the national treasury." He recommended that consideration of the project be deferred until the Piscataqua River projects already approved and under way were completed. Furthermore, he wrote that if Little Harbor were to be made into an effective harbor of refuge for small draft coasting vessels and fishing boats unable to make it in to Portsmouth Harbor when the wind was from the northwest, it would need to be deeper and wider than first proposed. In addition, not one but two breakwaters would be needed to funnel the tides in and out of Little Harbor to produce the scouring action that would keep it from filling in again with silt, at an estimated total cost of $154,000. In response to more pressure, Blunt wrote in August 1884 to his superior, Brigadier General John Newton, Chief of Army Engineers, that his "recommendations in this regard were *intentionally* made, knowing that improvements outside of the approved projects were talked about in certain quarters."[69]

Frank Jones, receiving no satisfaction from Blunt, swung into action with a September 1884 letter to Blunt's boss, General Newton, outlining the advantages of a harbor of refuge for commercial vessels (with no reference to the project's benefit for yachts, passenger steamers, and his hotel). At the same time, an 1884 Wentworth Hotel brochure illustrated a variety of pleasure craft in the harbor below the hotel, including a schooner that probably could not have made it that far into Little Harbor at the time. Letters written in July 1884 by the president of the Portsmouth Board of Trade and several other local men had been sent to Blunt and were forwarded by him to Washington. Blunt was ordered to substantiate his view that a harbor of refuge at Little Harbor did not warrant the expense. He was apparently unable to find anyone willing to provide compelling evidence to support his view, and in October was inundated by a barrage of twenty-eight more letters of support for the harbor improvements. One was written to Jones himself by Jesse Frisbee of Kittery Point, listing the thirteen schooners wrecked on Gerrish Island over a ten-year period and stating that "all of these, or nearly all, would have been saved if Little Harbor had been accessible." The others were handed to Blunt by Frank Jones, and all in more or less detail reiterated the case made by Jones for the Little Harbor improvements. They included a "Who's Who" of Portsmouth: the mayor, the president of the Board of Trade, the collector of customs, prominent local businessmen and lawyers, several masters of local vessels, Whale's Back lighthouse keeper Leander White, former White Island keeper Israel Miller, who was then editor of the *Portsmouth Daily Chronicle*; and Silas Harding keeper of the Life-Saving Station at Jerry's Point. One letter-writer referred hopefully to Blunt (a Portsmouth native) as "a son of old Strawberry Bank."[70]

Blunt, forwarding the letters to General Newton, wrote that he was not persuaded, and "it seems to me most extraordinary if the improvements ....would be so desirable .... as the writers ....represent, the district engineer should have been from 1865 to 1882 wholly ignorant of the fact." All this paper landed on the desk of Robert Lincoln, Secretary of War, and

Frank Jones the politician and entrepreneur who owned the Wentworth Hotel and skillfully maneuvered the federal government into appropriating funds for dredging Little Harbor. PA

This illustrated 1884 Wentworth Hotel brochure somewhat misleadingly and prominently shows a small schooner in Little Harbor, where at the time it would doubtless have grounded out at low tide. The brochure stated "An appropriation has been asked, and will probably be granted, for the purpose of dredging Little Harbor to a depth sufficient for the largest yachts." PA.

in January 1885 made its way to the House of Representatives. General Newton recommended Major Thom's more modest proposal of 1882, and Congress approved it. It was a foot in the door.[71]

Blunt, who also served as First Lighthouse District engineer 1879–1883, was replaced as District Engineer for the Corps of Engineers by Major Jared Smith. Smith prepared a map of the project and, after the project was adopted in 1886 with an initial appropriation of $10,000, requested bids to begin the dredging operation. Work was under way by spring 1887 and continued through 1903. More lobbying resulted in expanding the project in 1888 to pretty much what Charles Blunt (with the apparent goal of having it rejected because of the high cost he projected) had considered necessary for an adequate harbor of refuge. The size of the area to be dredged was expanded, and the depth of dredging increased from nine to twelve feet. A second breakwater was added. The estimated price tag was $235,000. The scope of the dredging operation was scaled back in 1894, with the final cost of the entire undertaking projected at about $150,000. By 1890 the Corps' District Engineer could report "small steamers have made regular trips to the landing and a regular passenger steamer has now been provided to and from that place during the summer season." Jones and his hotel were the obvious beneficiaries.[72]

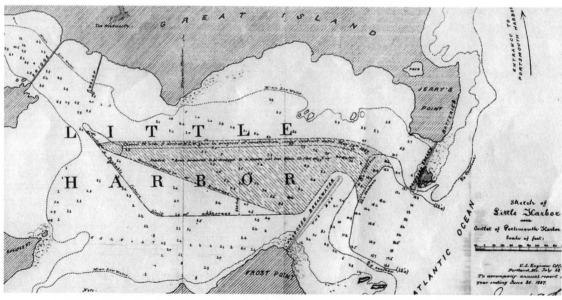

Major Jared Smith's June 1887 sketch for improvements to Little Harbor, showing the proposed two breakwaters and the area to be dredged. Dredging had begun in May, and Smith duly noted on the sketch the work already accomplished. The Wentworth Hotel and its wharf are shown at the upper left. From the 1887 report of Chief of Engineers, U. S. Army.

The Frost's Point breakwater was finished in October 1893 and the one at Jerry's Point two years later. The old iron multi-legged unlit beacon of 1850 was incorporated into this breakwater, to be retained until post lights could be installed and maintained. At the outer end of each breakwater a built-up granite pier was constructed for the projected lights. The Light-House Board installed them in May 1896, and announced their lighting on the twenty-fifth. The next year's report of the Corps of Engineers included statistics produced by Alpheus Mayo, then keeper of the Jerry's Point Life-Saving Station, who stated that during the remainder of 1896 the lights had helped two coasting vessels, nine yachts, and eleven fishing vessels to take refuge from storms in Little Harbor.

Soldiers and lady friends on a holiday outing, posing on the granite pier at the end of the Jerry's Point breakwater. The brass lens light is hanging from a post. In the foreground, part of a steam-powered hoisting device can be seen, suggesting that the photograph was taken before completion of work on the breakwater. The visitors blithely ignored the signboard that reads: "Keep Off the Ladder. U.S.L.H. E." (for U. S. Light-House Establishment) Bolling Smith Collection.

By 1903, the project was considered complete, with a small surplus applied to repairing storm damage to the breakwaters. The charade of statistics on vessels seeking storm refuge was more or less dropped in early-twentieth-century compilations of statistics by the Corps of Engineers. The report for 1901 said that 290 vessels "frequented" the harbor, many more of which were pleasure yachts than commercial vessels: "Seventy-seven schooner yachts, 84 steam yachts, 75 sloop yachts, 37 fishing vessels, 11 tugboats, and 6 barges." Average tonnage was one hundred and fifty and average draft was eight feet.[73]

Frank Jones died in 1902. In the summer of 1905, negotiations to end the Russo-Japanese War took place at the Portsmouth Navy Yard and culminated with the Treaty of Portsmouth on September 5. Jones would have

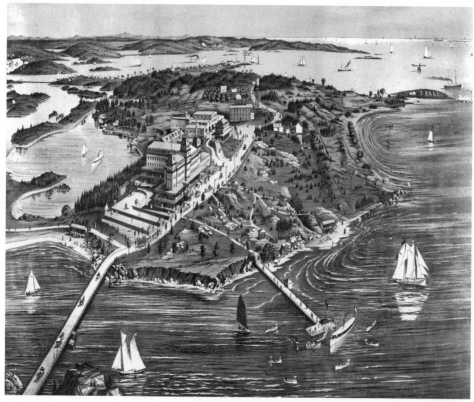

An 1890s view of the Wentworth Hotel shows what must have been one of the "largest yachts" in Little Harbor, made possible because of the dredging operations, and also the substantial expansion of the hotel's facilities by that time. From John Albee's *New Castle Historic and Picturesque. The Jerry's Point breakwater, completed in 1895, is not in evidence in the upper right distance. The view was included in a 1970s reprint edition of John Albee's 1884* New Castle Historic and Picturesque.

been gratified that the Japanese and Russian participants stayed at the Wentworth Hotel, and (weather permitting) made the trip to and from the navy yard in launches that passed in and out of the deepened Little Harbor between the breakwaters that Jones had browbeaten the Corps of Engineers and the federal government into approving and funding.[74]

Little Harbor is used year around by local lobster and fishermen and has proven to be an important attraction for pleasure boaters of all stripes. Franklin D. Roosevelt, an avid yachtsman, brought the yawl *Myth* to anchor there in 1932, the year before he became president. The next year, as president, Roosevelt entered the harbor at the helm of the schooner *Amberjack II,* with a small flotilla of press boats. Two accompanying destroyers were positioned outside the harbor's entrance.[75] The anchorages in the harbor never lack takers, and the 168 berths at the marina created by the owners of the Wentworth hotel in May of 1988 were quickly snapped up.

Participants in the summer of 1905 negotiations to end the Russo-Japanese War stayed at the Wentworth Hotel, and when the weather was good were transported from the hotel by launch like the one in this photograph to the Navy Yard where the peace discussions were held. PHC

Henderson's Point

Henderson's Point, a five-hundred-foot-long ledge of rock, popularly known as "Pull and be damned" Point, had always been a major impediment to navigation in the Piscataqua River. The point jutted into the river off Seavey's Island, the location of the Portsmouth Navy Yard, and since 1893-94 had been marked by the Light-House Board's post and later range lights. The point constricted the river's channel, creating a sharp bend, and forced the tides to funnel through at the rate of seven knots. Instead of risking Henderson's Point, many of the increasingly large warships entering Portsmouth Harbor to refuel anchored in the lower harbor, where coal and supplies had to be brought to them by lighters.

With a massive new stone dry dock under construction upriver from the point, the Navy asked the Army Corps of Engineers to approve a project to remove Henderson's Point—and got a cold shoulder. Evidently the Navy had argued only its own case for getting rid of the point and had neglected to mention that the project would also be of tremendous benefit to commercial navigation as well. This should have been obvious to the Corps, of course, but its report stated that this "improvement was not worthy of being made by the United States for the benefit of the commercial interests of the port." New Hampshire's Senator Jacob Gallinger by-passed the Corps, however, and managed to get a bill for the project approved by Congress in 1902. The massive work required building a cofferdam, excavating ledge behind it and drilling holes for some thirty-six tons of dynamite charges; the work involved hundreds of workers over a three-year period. It culminated on July 22, 1905, when thousands lined the opposite shore of the river to watch, with a mammoth explosion that threw an estimated seventy thousand tons of rock and a huge spout of water high into the air. It was considered at the time to be the world's largest man-made explosion. The result was a channel widened by four hundred feet to a depth of thirty-five feet.[76]

To make way for the excavations, the lightkeeper's house for the Seavey's Island range lights was moved to a nearby site and in 1903 four large red lights were placed on a wharf built in connection with the Henderson Point project. Light-House Board records show that a brick oil house was built to serve these lights in 1904. Lightkeeper Stone was on the payroll through March 1904, and it may be that after that the Navy maintained the lights until the big explosion of 1905. The Board as early as 1903 proposed acquiring a strip of land on Pierce's Island on

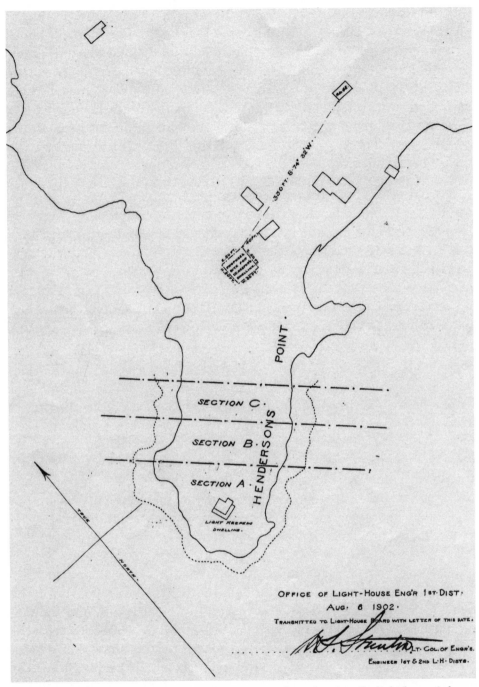

Light-House Board tracing of a Navy Department plan, showing the light keeper's house on Henderson's Point and the site proposed for the re-location of the house after the point was demolished. NARG26.

the other side of the river for range lights there, but none were put in place until considerably later.[77]

Modernization efforts at the Navy Yard and the blasting of Henderson Point apparently paid off for the yard. In 1909, some of the battleships in President Teddy Roosevelt's "Great White Fleet" came to the yard for minor and major overhauls after the fleet's worldwide show of the United States' naval might ended; the payroll at the yard almost doubled from 440 to 840 between 1908 and 1909 and climbed steadily upward thereafter.[78]

Pepperrell Cove Improvements

For the pleasure boats of the booming colony of summer residents at New Castle and Frost's Point, for the guests at the Wentworth Hotel, and for cruising yachtsmen, the deepened Little Harbor and its buoys and the lighted breakwaters at its mouth were a decided boon. In 1910, however, a writer for the *Portsmouth Herald* wrote that as a harbor of refuge for small coasting vessels Little Harbor had "proven a dismal failure," with fewer than six using it annually over the previous ten years.

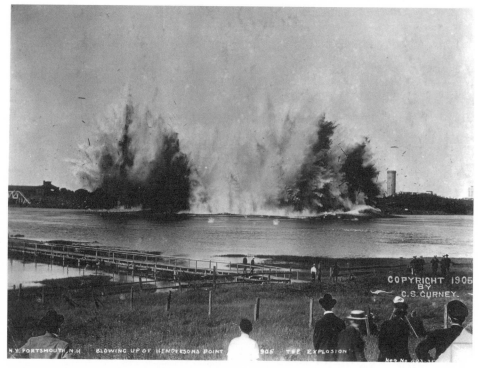

The blowing up of Henderson's Point in August 1905. PA.

He listed the many wrecks that might have been avoided if Pepperrell's Cove had been available as a harbor of refuge, and suggested that unused Little Harbor funds be allocated to remove Logy Ledge at the entrance to Pepperrell's Cove on the north side of Portsmouth Harbor, "which has already stranded more coasters than ever will enter Little Harbor from now till the crack of doom."[79]

The 1910 critic of the Little Harbor project may have been expressing the frustration of those who had tried unsuccessfully to get approval for dredging this shallow harbor and removing Logy Ledge from its entrance. A proposal for Pepperrell's Cove was rejected by the Army Corps of Engineers in 1901, based on the statement of district engineer Colonel Jared Smith that the only active proponents of the project he could find were the proprietor and some guests of a summer hotel at Kittery Point, adjacent to the cove. Local mariners he talked to could only say, with not much urgency, that "it would be a good thing if the cove could be dredged" and did not make a strong case for making the cove more useful as a harbor of refuge. Given the propensity of the Corps at this time to take seriously only the needs of commercial vessels, based on the tonnage of waterborne goods that went in and out, and its lack of interest in tourism as a creditable component of economic activity, this rejection is not surprising.[80]

On January 6, 1909, the *Gettysburg,* a large, 150-foot-long steel tug, with coal-laden barges in tow, ran aground on a shoal at the entrance to Pepperrell's Cove while trying to avoid heavy seas outside. Though the tug was floated the next day with little apparent damage, the *Portsmouth Herald* took the opportunity to enumerate the other sizable vessels that had come to grief recently on this shoal, and reiterated its plea for dredging the cove. The climate for improvements had changed by 1910. In spite of the use of the words to describe the cove as having "no commerce worthy of consideration as such," the purpose of the project was "to increase the anchorage area for craft entering Portsmouth Harbor," which did have commerce worthy of consideration, amounting to 429,000 tons of coal incoming and 62,500 tons of bricks outgoing.[81]

Congress approved the dredging of forty-one acres of the cove to a depth of twelve feet at low tide and removal of the ledge to a depth of twelve and a half feet, with an estimated cost of $158,000. Dredging began in spring 1911 and was nearly done in 1912. Drilling and blasting of Logy Ledge and other ledges uncovered during dredging was finished in March 1916, almost exactly within the cost projected in 1910.[82]

Breakwaters at the Isles of Shoals

The 1821–23 breakwater between Smuttynose Island and Cedar Island that was mostly demolished soon after its completion was rebuilt between 1903 and 1904 at a cost of thirty thousand dollars. The Corps approved the project , despite its finding that there was no commercial activity of significance. This the Corps measured in tonnage of coal and groceries brought in by boat, rather than by the amount of money spent at the thriving summer hotels on Appledore and Star Islands. However, it reported that one thousand schooners and small steamers "frequent- ed" the Isles of Shoals harbor. To complete the protection of the harbor from easterly storms, in 1910 a breakwater between Cedar Island and Star Island was approved. It was begun in 1912 and completed in 1914 at a total cost of $80,691. Storm damage repairs to the Cedar–Star Island breakwaters were undertaken in 1916.[83]

A Rejected Plan to Dam the Piscataqua River

A Portsmouth booster claimed in 1909 that even the *Titanic,* then being built in a Belfast, Ireland, shipyard, would find the waters of this ice-free port deep enough.[84] But in spite of all the work done to improve navigation, there were still serious drawbacks. The blasting of Hender- son's Point both gave more turning room for large vessels and eased the bottleneck through which the tides roared. However, tidal eddies still had enough force to sweep vessels onto the still-problematic Gangway Rocks

Aerial view of the breakwaters at the Isles of Shoals. Peter Randall photo.

and the other hazards remaining in the waterway. The Navy Yard commandant wrote in 1909 that it was still necessary to wait for slack tide before large battleships could enter for repairs. This was true as well for any sizable vessel going upriver to berth at the wharves on the Portsmouth side of the river. This delay was considered the reason it cost five cents a ton more to ship coal into Portsmouth than into Boston and Portland, and one of the reasons Boston–Portsmouth water freight rates were no longer competitive with rail rates.[85]

It was reported that many ship masters if given a choice preferred charters into ports like Boston. In the early 1900s, Portsmouth was third in New England in coal imports, behind Boston and Providence, with 429,000 tons entering in Some of it sailed into port in the holds of coasting schooners but still more had been loaded aboard former sailing vessels with their masts chopped down and ignominiously towed as barges behind tugs. However, Portsmouth could boast favorable rail freight rates to such New Hampshire cities Manchester, Concord and Dover where textile mills and coal gassification plants consumed enormous amounts.[86]

The advent in Boston of huge new colliers, each of which could carry as much tonnage as eight good-sized schooners, caused anxiety that Portsmouth harbor would be at a disadvantage, and could be in danger of losing out to Boston, where these vessels could dock at any tide.[87]

With vessels increasing steadily in size and heated battles for freighting contracts, competition for federally funded harbor and river improvements was fierce, and spawned the creation of lobbying groups such as the New England Waterways Association and the Atlantic Deeper Waterways Organization, both of which had representation in Congress's River and Harbors Committee. Locally active on behalf of navigation were the Board of Trade, the Harbor Improvement Association, and the Masters, Mates, and Pilots Association's local chapter, Piscataqua Harbor, No. 83. These groups also worked for new or improved buoys and fog signals, as well as for a lighthouse on Duck Island at the Isles of Shoals. They were united in promoting a massive project to actually do away with the problem of tides in the river. The proposal was for locks and dams intended to create slack water at all times in the harbor and adequate water on those tributaries to the Piscataqua where there was still significant waterborne activity.

The proponents of the project revived a proposal to dam the Piscataqua River at Frank's Fort just below Dover Point, first aired back in

1882 when extensive engineering solutions to navigation problems began to be applied more and more nationwide. A bill authorizing a new Army Corps of Engineers study of the lock and dam project was included in the River and Harbor Act passed by Congress on March 3, 1909.[88]

Lieutenant Colonel George Zinn, U.S. Army Corps of Engineers District Engineer at the time, prepared a detailed report weighing the potential economic benefits against upriver damage to water-power production, to fishing and salt-hay harvesting in Great Bay, and to private property along the waterways that would be affected. Perhaps the most powerful argument he made in opposition to the project was that creating slack water was likely to cause ice to form, eliminating one of the most touted advantages of the harbor, which was that only very rarely was it iced in. Further, Zinn noted, shoaling was likely to occur both above and below the proposed dam and would cause new difficulties to navigation.[89]

At a public hearing held in Portsmouth in June 1910 by a panel of Army engineers from Washington, local testimony in favor of the project was extensive and almost unanimous. One of the two dissenting voices was that of Albert H. Adams. He delivered a paean to the beauty of Great Bay and its tides, and to the birds that abounded there, the nutritious seaweed that was harvested for farm fertilizer, and the joys of saltwater bathing. He ended by questioning this massive project to alter nature and man's right to do so. His arguments probably had littleimpact on the Corps of Engineers, who were accustomed to altering nature. The Board of Engineers for Harbor and River Improvements did, however, support Colonel Zinn's conclusion that this project was not a good idea, and it failed to achieve congressional approval.[90]

The local view that without a slack tide harbor the port's profitable coal business would be doomed proved not wholly true. Cut down schooners and specially-made barges, and finally steam-powered colliers brought thousands of tons of coal into the port annually through the next decades, and finally favorable rail freight rates even made it possible to capture lucrative contracts in the important textile mill city of Lowell, Massachusetts. A tremendously destructive March 1896 flood in Dover, that undid much of the Cocheco River improvement work of the previous decades, had already brought river freighting to that town to a virtual standstill, but the closing of inland textile mills in the 1930s probably had more to do with the eventual dwindling of water freighting of coal that entered the Port of Portsmouth than the deficiencies of its harbor.[91]

Maritime interests along the Piscataqua's tributaries and in the small harbors to the south and north of Portsmouth also contended for the federal river and harbor improvement dollar, not always successfully during the late-nineteenth and early-twentieth centuries. Among projects approved and accomplished were various small ones to improve the Bellamy and Exeter Rivers. Dredging to deepen and widen the tortuous entrance to York Harbor, and blasting a portion of Stage Neck where it protruded into the channel were done in 1889 and 1890.[92] But in 1909, Colonel Zinn, of the engineer corps, recommended against a 1909 proposal to improve Rye Harbor by dredging it and constructing a breakwater. The harbor was a man-made creation of the late eighteenth century. It was a community effort by forty-six men, fueled by ten gallons of rum, who with their teams of oxen dug out a small harbor in 1792. Zinn described it as a "small indentation in the coast" with a depth of only two and a half feet of water at low tide. He noted that only eight small motorboats used it for landing fish, lobster, and sea moss, in addition to the boats of summer residents. He pointed out other nearby harbors that could serve their needs, the trolley and railroad services that made land transportation into Portsmouth convenient, and advocated against the expenditure of federal resources for a project that would benefit so few people. His position was upheld by the board of the Engineer Corps. Another proposal to improve Rye Harbor was rejected in 1930, but Rye citizens finally prevailed with a project to dredge the harbor and build two jetties, jointly funded by the state and federal governments, that finally got under way in the summer of 1938.[93]

Local groups continued to press for whatever they could get to enhance the Port of Portsmouth, and in the first decade of the twentieth century continued to ask the Light-House Board for more and improved aids to navigation. The voices of the Kittery and Portsmouth Yacht clubs, established towards the end of the nineteenth century, also began to be heard and heeded. Though the desired lighthouse at Duck Island at the Isles of Shoals never materialized, minor but nonetheless important new or improved buoys, fog signals and other markers were put in place or authorized by the end of the decade. These included, off or along the York shore: a whistling buoy for York Ledge, five spar buoys to mark the entrance to York Harbor and a previously-dredged channel, and a cask on a spindle on a ledge a sixth of a mile northwest of Boon Island. Off the Kittery shore: a second-class nun buoy on Murray Rock and a red spar buoy for the West Sister. For Portsmouth

Harbor: a second-class nun buoy on Wood Island ledge, a second-class nun buoy on Stileman Rock, and an unlit stone beacon (approved though never built) for Hick's Rock opposite Jamaica Island near the entrance to the back channel on the Kittery side of Seavey's Island.[94]

The End of the Light-House Board

There had been attempts by the Navy to take over the Light-House Board in 1862 and again in the early 1890s, but these were successfully rebuffed by the board. However, it was increasingly evident that the board as it had been constituted in 1852 was not suited to meet the new demands upon it. The coasts, rivers and lakes where its services were needed had expanded by leaps and bounds with settlement of the western coasts and the growth of commerce on inland waterways and the Great Lakes. Its responsibilities became even more far flung with the acquisition of Alaska in 1867 and in the empire-building aftermath of the Spanish-American War when territories in both the Caribbean and the Pacific were acquired by the United States. When the board was created, there were barely three hundred lighthouses, located on the Atlantic coast, in the Great Lakes, and on the Gulf coast. By 1910 the numbers had more than quadrupled and included many Gulf and Pacific coast lights. In addition, more inland waterways were being lit with post lights, considered minor, but as important to waterborne commerce as coastal sea and harbor lights. The total of unlit aids (buoys and floating and land-based fog signals) had reached 6,507, or more than six times the number in 1850.[95]

President William Howard Taft, in an address to Congress in December 1909 recommended an overhaul of the U.S. lighthouse administration. Taft marveled that the Light-House Board had accomplished so much in the fifty-seven years of its existence, especially without a single full-time executive at its head. Meeting together only four times a year, and without pay, the five military men and two civilian members of the Board elected their own chairman and divided responsibility for the work of finance, engineering, lighthouse, lighting, and experiment committees. Executive functions were split between one Navy officer and one Army Engineer Corps officer detailed to the board as secretaries in charge of the work of each district's Navy inspector and Army engineer. Both the Navy and Army men assigned to Light-House Board districts were frequently reassigned, and during war time could be called to war duty. Often, by the time one of these men became familiar with the needs of the district he'd been assigned to, orders came for duty else-where. Further, the Army officers who were lighthouse district engineers were also given responsibilities related to fortifications and government buildings in their districts and frequently were also district engineers for harbor and river improvements for the Army Corps of Engineers. Maintaining one fleet of lighthouse tenders for the inspectors and another for the engineers created inevitable inefficiencies. Except for the seven and a half years of Joseph Henry's chairmanship of the board back in the 1870s, the position had been held by an officer of the Navy, and frictions between the two military branches were reputed.[96]

In spite of these difficulties, the Board successfully tackled many of the problems resulting from Fifth Auditor Stephen Pleasonton's penny-pinching and defensive management style. The strongly military cast of the Light-House Board was probably what was needed when it was created, in spite of the frictions and inefficiencies that resulted. Trained civilian engineers were not widely available when the Light-House Board was formed and were best supplied by the Army's corps of engineers and its topographical engineers; and the more rigorous management of lighthouse personnel by officers of the Navy was a needed antidote to the sketchy supervision provided during Pleasonton's long tenure. The five existing lighthouses around Portsmouth were built during the Light-House Board years, and still stand. The determination to use the best possible lighting apparatus brought the wholesale adoption of the Fresnel lens in lighthouse lanterns. The conversions first from sperm oil to lard oil and then to kerosene for the lamps were undertaken after careful experiments in the board's laboratories, and the knotty problem of fog signals received similar attention, thanks to the board's civilian scientist, Joseph Henry. Detailed instructions and more rigorous standards for keepers were spelled out, and control over lighthouse personnel was gradually wrested from the patronage of collectors of customs even before the merit system was formally applied in 1896. Government-paid assistants replaced the helpers paid by the keepers themselves, though unpaid family members continued to assist at lighthouses with no assistant keepers assigned to them, like the Fort Constitution and Nubble lights, which remained "family" lights.

In 1910 Congress abolished the Light-House Board and replaced it with the Lighthouse Bureau under a civilian commissioner.

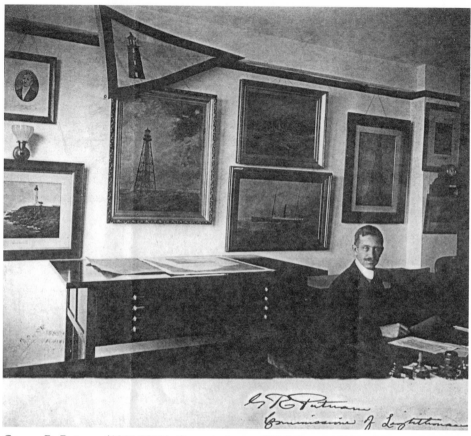

George R. Putnam (1865-1953), Commissioner of Lighthouses 1910-1935, in the Washington office of the Lighthouse Bureau. Among the photographs hanging on the wall is that of Fifth Auditor Stephen Pleasonton, to the left of one of the ensigns flown by lighthouse vessels. LC

XIV *The Bureau of Lighthouses, 1910–1939, and Some Lighthouse Keepers of This Period*

The building and the keeping of the lights is a picturesque and humanitarian work of the nation. But this work is not all romance, as, unseen by the passing mariner, and back of the lighthouse and ship and buoy, there must be a great engineering and businessmachine with its endless contracts, plans, specifications, the routine of office and depot and ship and light-station. Scarcely a day passes, however, that there does not gleam in the mass of dry routine a fact of interest, an act of bravery, a risk cheerfully taken to aid another, a record of long and faithful service, an improvement of light or of fog signal, of vessel or of lighthouse, an historic record of the past, or a photograph of the present.

—George R. Putnam,
Lighthouses and Lightships of the United States, 1932

The Bureau of Lighthouses

THE *PORTSMOUTH HERALD* OF JULY 23, 1910, reported a major change in the management of the lighthouses and other aids to navigation in the United States. All employees of the Light-House Board were to be transferred to a newly created Lighthouse Bureau within the Department of Commerce and Labor. The new bureau was to be supervised by a full-time commissioner of lighthouses, assisted by a deputy commissioner, a chief constructing engineer, and a superintendent of naval construction. At the discretion of the commissioner, the number of lighthouse districts could be increased from thirteen to as many as nineteen, with a civilian inspector (later named district superintendent) in place of the Navy and Army officers who had served as inspectors and engineers in each district. There would be a three-year transition, beginning on July 30, 1910, with a military man in charge of each district's operations until a civilian could be appointed. The new agency eliminated Army-Navy rivalries and the dual structures of support personnel, equipment, and vessels that had become costly and inefficient. The Lighthouse Bureau existed until 1939, when its operations were absorbed by the U.S. Coast Guard, an agency of the Department of Treasury that was the result of the merger of the Revenue Marine and Life-Saving services in 1915.[1]

In the Portsmouth area during the years of the Lighthouse Bureau, summer resort development and sail- and powerboat yachting increased steadily, but a 1914 conflagration on Appledore Island at the Isles of Shoals destroyed the Laightons' Appledore House and many cottages, including Celia Thaxter's.

After the 1904 launch of the anachronistic training brig *Boxer,* the only new vessels built at the Navy Yard until 1917 were the tug *Patapsco* (1908) and a ferryboat to carry shipyard workers across the river (1912). In 1915, the hull of the first government-built submarine was laid, and the building and repair of submarines became the yard's mainstay through the rest of the century. The civilian payroll there expanded dramatically to a high of 5,500 in 1918, fell off after the war and began to climb again in the prelude to World War II. World War I brought lighthouse personnel and vessels into the military for the duration, and a damper on tourism, but there was a booming revival of shipbuilding on the Piscataqua, with two new upriver yards established to produce merchant vessels, though these endeavors were abandoned after the war.[2]

In the 1920s, a gypsum plant established just below the present I-95 bridge over the Piscataqua brought freighters upriver with regular shipments of Nova Scotia gypsum, and other freighters carried Labrador seashells to a poultry feed plant, the Sunrayed Lime Products Company. Coal continued to arrive in substantial quantities, some unloaded at the power generating plant on the Portsmouth waterfront, some at the Consolidation Coal Companies facility there, from which it was shipped out by rail, with some going farther upriver by boat to towns on Piscataqua tributaries. The building of the toll-free Memorial Bridge across the Piscataqua at the end of Daniel Street to Badger's Island in Kittery in the early 1920s eased communication between Portsmouth and Kittery but complicated river navigation. The loss of brewery jobs with the advent of Prohibition and the Great Depression that followed brought hard times to the Portsmouth area.[3]

George R. Putnam

The commissioner of the new Lighthouse Bureau was appointed at the end of July 1910. He was George R. Putnam (1865–1953). He was a wise choice, and held the job for the next twenty-five years, retiring in 1935 at the age of seventy, just a few years before the merger with the Coast Guard. In a memoir written in retirement, Putnam wrote of his childhood far from the ocean on the outskirts of Davenport, Iowa, and his teenaged adventure paddling a canoe with a friend four hundred miles down the upper Mississippi River. He worked as a stake man for a railroad survey in the Midwest, studied law briefly and then engineering at the Rose Polytechnic Institute in Indiana.[4]

After graduation, Putnam spent twenty years with the U.S. Coast Survey, surveying the coasts of Alaska and the Philippines, taking part in a Greenland expedition to explore the Arctic ice cap with Robert Peary, and making astronomical observations to establish triangulation points in many parts of the United States. By the time he became commissioner he had wide experience and knowledge of coastal navigation conditions.[5]

His memoir, and *Lighthouses and Lightships of the United States*, written when he was still at the Lighthouse Bureau, reveal that he was something of a romantic about the role of lighthouses and lightships in the nation's maritime history and that he knew and appreciated the difficult lives of the people who tended them. However, he embraced new technologies for improving aids to navigation and was tough-minded about implementing their adoption, even though in the long run many would lead to the obsolescence of manned lighthouses. Putnam was a big supporter of the merit system, an ardent opponent of bureaucratic sprawl, and a believer in decentralization.[6]

Lighthouse keepers from the ranks of Light-House Board personnel continued in the new service, and for district superintendent positions Putnam found as many men as he could among the civilian employees of the Light-House Board, with a few coming from the Coast Survey where he'd previously worked.

In the First Lighthouse District, the Navy inspector, Commander C. M. Fahs, was retained for a year, working out of the Portland office. The Army engineer's office in Boston, which had served both the first and second districts, was closed and its workforce transferred to Portland, supervised by a construction superintendent. In 1911, Carl T. Sherman took over from Fahs. Sherman had begun as a fourteen-year-old light-house tender messboy, gradually working his way up to the command of tenders. He remained First District Lighthouse Superintendent until his death in 1933. His successor was Charles C. Brush, who had worked as a designer in the Bureau's Washington naval construction office.[7]

For the district's construction superintendent, Putnam chose Royal Luther, a civilian veteran of twenty-six years with the Light-House Board in the district. He had been involved with fog signal experiments back in the 1890s. For the next seventeen years, he was considered the district's expert on fog signal installations. He retired in 1928, having served an amazing fifty-three years in the district. Men such as these provided the continuity and commitment that had been impossible with the frequently reassigned military men previously posted to oversee the operations the First Lighthouse District.[8]

Improvements around Portsmouth

The transition from the Light-House Board to the new Lighthouse Bureau was remarkably smooth. Improvements requested by local interests or already in the pipeline moved forward quickly. With engines steadily replacing sails, louder fog signals were needed so they could be heard over the roar of motors, and the proliferation of street and domestic electric lights along the shore made it difficult to make out the white lights at Whale's Back and Fort Constitution lighthouses. In November 1910, the local branch of the Masters, Mates and Pilots organization joined forces with the Boston Chamber of Commerce to petition the new Lighthouse Bureau in the hope that some of the improvements they'd lobbied for previously would get a more favorable reception. The petition requested a gas whistling and light buoy for Kitt's Rock, the moving of the Kitt's Rock bell buoy to Gunboat Shoal, a bell buoy for Wood Island, increased intensity for the light at Whale's Back lighthouse and a louder fog signal there, and a change in the white light at Fort Constitution. A little more than a month later, word came from the Lighthouse Bureau that almost all of these needs were to be met.[9]

In January 1911, only a few months after the petition by local and Boston interests, the lighthouse tender *Myrtle* arrived with a whistling buoy to replace the bell at Kitt's Rock. The change was much appreciated by mariners who remembered how much more effective the "Jersey Bull" buoy had been during its brief tenure there during the 1880s. The bell buoy was moved to Gunboat Shoals to replace the can buoy there, and a larger can buoy replaced the one previously marking Wood Island.[10]

In February 1911, the *Portsmouth Herald* announced that Fort Constitution lightkeeper Leander White would begin presiding over a fixed red light to contrast with the street lights, in place of the white light there. Because of the light-absorptive character of the red-glass panels that created the red light, a more powerful light source was needed to make it visible from a useful distance. It was made possible by a new, more intense light source—the incandescent oil vapor, or "i.o.v." lamp, as it was generally called. Like the Fresnel lens through which the light shone, the use of this new illuminating device was pioneered by the French and first used off the French coast in 1898, and subsequently in the United States at a lighthouse off the New Jersey coast.[11]

Keeper White was shown how to light the new lamp, which was fitted with a fuel nozzle instead of a wick. Above this a cone-shaped fiber mesh mantle was suspended. The mantle, which became incandescent when heated, was similar to the mantle used in "Aladdin" kerosene lamps for household lighting.[12]

The process of lighting these new lighthouse lamps was more complicated and time-consuming than for the old wick lamps, and was described in detail by Constance Small in *The Lighthouse Keeper's Wife*. First, kerosene was pressurized by pumping it into a tank below the lamp. Next, wood alcohol was poured into a small cup below the mantle, then lit and allowed to burn until the mantle reached white heat. Finally, the kerosene flow was turned on, with the heated mantle vaporizing the pressurized kerosene. The flame rose from the fuel nozzle to keep the mantle brilliant. This process required keepers to start the operation a half hour before sundown "lighting-up" time. The new lamps could increase brilliancy by as much as eight times, and had the further advantage of sharply reducing kerosene consumption. In 1912, the intensity of Whale's Back light was increased by one of the new i.o.v. lamps, and by mid-June 1914 there were i.o.v. lamps at Boon Island, White Island, and Cape Neddick lighthouses.[13]

Along with the i.o.v. lamp, Whale's Back was fitted out with a new fourth-order Fresnel lens. This lens created a new characteristic for the light in place of the white light varied by a flash every ninety seconds that had emanated from the lighthouse since 1898. From the deck of a vessel pitching in rough seas it could be difficult to identify Whale's

The new Whale's Back lighthouse lens installed after this March 1912 photograph was taken, probably at the Staten Island buoy depot. NARG26.

Back light because it took a minute-and-a-half to determine the characteristic that differentiated it from other lighthouses in the area. The new lens, manufactured by the French firm of Barbier, Benard and Turenne in 1911, had on each of its two principal faces two circular "flash panels" made up of concentric rings of prisms surrounding a central, circular lens section that intensified the light for the observer as the lens rotated on its pedestal. A new pedestal, or "chariot," on which the lens was kept in motion by a clockwork mechanism, held a mercury-filled grooved channel, or "float," that reduced friction to a minimum and let the apparatus revolve at a far greater speed: twenty seconds for a single rotation, during which time two flashes were displayed. With this new "quick-flashing" characteristic, Whale's Back light could be positively identified much faster. The mercury float also permitted a clockwork mechanism of lighter weight, needing to be wound up less often than the old carriage set on ball bearings.[14]

The main buoy depot at Staten Island, where equipment was assembled and repaired, fuels were tested, and vessels serviced. NARG26.

There had been plans to replace the first-class Daboll foghorn at
Whale's Back with the more penetrating sound of a siren. But just as
opposition by summer residents prevailed against the whistling buoy
off Kitt's Rock back in 1883, Kittery Point opponents defeated its installation. They may have recalled an article from the *Washington Star*
published in a Portsmouth newspaper in 1894 that described the
sounds of various fog signals:

> Worst of all are the steam sirens, which are truly a diabolical
> invention from any other point of view than that of utility.
> Theyutter an unearthly series of whoops which ascend the
> scale, note by note, until the unwilling listener feels as if, in
> case they should go a few notes higher, he would become sud-
> denly insane.[15]

A more colorful account of the sound of the fog siren described "a
screech like an army of panthers, weird and prolonged, gradually lowering in note until after half a minute it becomes the roar of a thousand
mad bulls, with intermediate voices suggestive of the wail of a lost soul,
the moan of a bottomless pit and the groan of a disabled elevator."[16]

The summer hotel interests at the Shoals evidently had less clout
than the Kittery Pointers. The siren's new destination was to be White
Island. It was rumored among anxious hotel owners and summer vacationers that it would be audible for fifty miles and would shatter the
relaxing quiet they prized. First District Superintendent Sherman hastened to reassure them:

> Nothing of the sort is contemplated, and a whistle large
> enough to be heard 50 miles would be an absurdity . . . it would
> mean that it would be heard beyond Boston . . . . it will be at
> least half a mile from the nearest hotel . . . and will be pointed
> seaward. It will be practically like the one at the Portland
> headlight and will be heard about 10 miles off thecoast, and of
> course will be in use only during foggy weather. When the sum-
> mer guests of the Isles of Shoals sit on the verandas . . . . and
> hear the siren they will have the satisfaction of thinking that
> the sailors out on the water are safer because of it. [17]

The fog siren was an American invention that underwent modifications after the first steam-powered one was placed off the New Jersey coast in 1868. Its components included perforated hollow tubes,
one of which rotated inside the other. The alternate stopping and

release of either steam or compressed air forced through the tubes created vibrations that produced the penetrating sound that emerged through a trumpet. Installation of the White Island fog siren was under way in December 1911, with a crew of seven at work on the island. It was of the compressed-air variety, favored because there was no need to build up a head of steam before it could be sounded. White Island lighthouse keeper James Burke reported in June 1912, a few months before he was transferred to the Nubble lighthouse, that the siren was almost ready to begin its work. The new fog signal was placed in its own structure adjacent to the lighthouse, and when in operation sounded for three seconds every thirty seconds. The fog bell was retained as a backup. Superintendent Sherman had evidently inoculated the Lighthouse Bureau against complaints: None has been found, and we must imagine the guests sitting in the rockers on the hotel porches at the Shoals nodding in appreciation of the safety the siren afforded mariners in the vicinity.[18]

Because of the labor involved in operating the machinery for the new fog siren, another assistant keeper was added at White Island, and a new keeper's house was built from plans prepared in 1913. The house was built on the foundation of the original 1820 stone house, which had been torn down to the cellar and roofed over to protect the water cistern there when the double keeper's house was built at the end of the 1870s. The new house was a one-and-a-half-story wood frame, clapboarded building with shed dormers, more or less approximating in scale and form Celia Thaxter's childhood home.

The fog siren at White Island was replaced in 1932 by a "typhon"—a type of fog signal developed in Canada and then so widely adopted in the United Statesthat the deep *bee-ohh* tones these foghorns emitted are now the ones most often associated with foghorns.[19]

A New Lighthouse Tender for the First District

Eight new steel-hulled lighthouse tenders were authorized near the end of the Light-House Board's existence, and were built and launched in Camden, New Jersey, in 1908 at a cost averaging $200,000 per vessel. Originally two of these lighthouse tenders were slated for the First District, but only one of them, *Hibiscus*, was assigned to the First District. She arrived in Portland in August 1908. Each of the tenders in this class

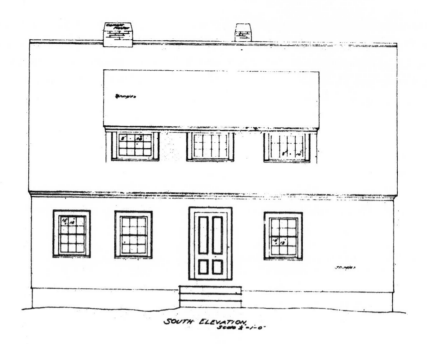

SOUTH ELEVATION

EAST ELEVATION

Plans drawn in 1913 for an additional keeper's house at White Island. The date of its actual construction on the site of the original rubblestone house is not entirely clear. NARG26.

served the Lighthouse Service well: All were in use until the end of World War II. *Hibiscus* remained in the First District until being decommissioned in 1946 and sold the next year. Like the others in her class, she was 173.6 feet in length, with a draft of sixteen feet and beam of thirty feet, and featured steel rather than wooden derrick masts and booms and wire rope instead of manila lines. She was powered by two coal-fired steam engines that delivered 1,000 horsepower to her twin propellers; she was considerably larger and far more powerful than *Myrtle* and *Lilac*, both of which continued active in the district until assignments elsewhere by 1914. Over her long career, *Hibiscus* carried between four and seven officers and from twenty-three to twenty-nine crewmen.[20]

The lighthouse tender Hibiscus, *one of eight brand-new steel-hulled vessels built in 1908 specifically for use by the Light-House Board. She arrived in Portland that year to begin service in the first district that lasted through 1946. NARG26.*

Another tender, *Ilex,* was built as the minelayer *General Edmund Kirby,* one of nine 172-foot-long steel-hulled vessels with a draft of eleven-and-a-half feet, fitted with steel derrick booms, oil-fired engines and twin propellers in a class of vessels built at a cost of $540,000 each in a Milwaukee shipyard. They were designed for World War I use but with peacetime conversion to use as lighthouse tenders in mind. They were not finished in time for war service, and in 1922 six were transferred from the Army to the Lighthouse Bureau, at no cost; the bureau converted each of them to its purposes as funds became available. The *Ilex* was converted at a cost of $44,000, and in 1924 was placed in service in the First District to take the place of *Zizania,* and worked out of Portland until 1942. She was commanded during much of her career by Captain O. C. Faulkingham, who earlier had served aboard *Hibiscus.*

A not very imaginatively named tender, the *Shrub,* was sometimes brought from the Second District for buoy work, probably because at 107 feet in length and a draft of only six feet nine inches, she was more suited to working around ledges than the longer and deeper tenders in service in the district. The wooden-hulled craft, with coal-fired engine and single propeller, was built in 1912 as a commercial freighter, purchased by the Navy in 1917, and acquired by the Lighthouse Bureau in 1919. She was commissioned as the *Shrub* the next year. On August 6, 1931 she came to grief on Bridge's Rock off York Harbor while placing buoys in the area. A gash was torn in her side and she flooded and sank. The crew of fifteen escaped safely but it took weeks of efforts by various salvage vessels to get her to Portland and then to Staten Island for repairs.[21]

The tenders' principal functions were lighthouse inspection and supply and buoy maintenance, and lighthouse construction, maintenance, and repair. They also carried reassigned lighthouse keepers, their families, and belongings from one station to another. But almost every year they were involved in rescues, as were many lightkeepers. The Lighthouse Bureau's annual reports devoted a section summarizing their activities, and Commissioner Putnam initiated a monthly "Lighthouse Service Bulletin", to report on new or improved lighthouses and aids to navigation, personnel changes, retirements, and deaths, as well as acts of unusual dedication or heroism by lighthouse service people. For example, a 1914 bulletin noted that *Hibiscus* was involved in pulling two stranded vessels off the rocks, and that *Zizania* towed to safety a schooner that had anchored during thick fog in a dangerous spot. The same bulletin reported that at Boon Island, Keeper Mitchell

Blackwood and his second assistant Charles Radley put a boat off to rescue two men in a disabled power boat, while James Burke, who had become keeper at the Nubble light, towed a launch to the lighthouse and put up its occupants overnight; he also saved Samuel L. Lewis from drowning and supplied him with dry clothes.[22]

Buoys and Floating Fog Signals and Lights

The Lighthouse Bureau began setting out more and more floating and land-based aids to navigation that required minimal maintenance, thus allowing the use of more of them. A kerosene-fueled lighted buoy had been placed experimentally by its manufacturer in 1881 near the entrance to New York Harbor and was adopted by the Light-House Board three years later, but this type of floating buoy was problematic and was superseded in 1904 by buoys based on European models, fueled by acetylene gas. The gas was produced through the reaction of water with calcium carbide, but the mixture was dangerously explosive. The Nobel Prize-winning Swedish physicist Gustav Dalen (1869–1937) between 1905 and 1907 developed a safer technology as well as an ingenious, light-sensitive "sun valve" that shut off the gas-feeding mechanism during daylight hours and thus enabled a cylinder of gas to remain as long as twelve months in service before a replacement was needed.[23]

Offshore, on Boon Island Ledge, one of the First District tenders placed a lighted whistling buoy. Land-based lights using acetylene gas technology were also installed in locations too difficult for manned lighthouses. Whether the Boon Island Ledge buoy was of the new variety is not clear. It was carried away by a storm and was replaced in February 1916 by "one of the latest types of converted Wilson gas and whistling buoys," weighing fourteen tons. It was seen by a reporter at the Customs House wharf in Portland before being taken to the ledge for installation by the crew of the tender *Hibiscus:*

> Unless carried away by the elements it will be left to its own care for the next 12 or 18 months. This gas buoy is a sort of a mechanical lighthouse as it provides a powerful gas light operated mechanically by acetylene gas generator and a strong whistle . . . Like a mammoth iceberg only about half the combination buoy appears above the water.[24]

The *Herald* credited the lobbying efforts of the local chapter of the Masters, Mates and Pilots Association for two acetylene gas–fueled lights in the Piscataqua River for nighttime navigation. In January 1915, a buoy with a light flashing for ten seconds at ten-second intervals was put in place by the crew of the *Hibiscus* off the New Castle end of Goat Island opposite the landing for the naval prison which had been built in phases between 1903 and 1912 on Seavey's Island. The lighted buoy replaced a can buoy; the local press praised the new buoy for the way it defied the forceful river current that had pulled down previous buoys there, by standing upright, and pronounced it to be of "great advantage to deep water vessels coming in at night." Six months later a flashing post light was placed on Pumpkin Island, a tiny islet of rock farther upriver between Badger's and Seavey's Islands. (This rocky hazard to navigation has long since been obliterated by Navy Yard expansion. The shipyard's Pier Number 2 now covers the site.)[25]

Upriver Navigational Lights

Privately installed and maintained lights were being used more frequently to mark the wharves of Portsmouth, and by the early twentieth century congressional enactments regulated their use and required that information about them be provided to the lighthouse administration. The lights on the Noble's Island–Kittery toll bridge continued to attract miscreants. In May 1913 one of the lights, a red one on the second span of the Portsmouth end of the bridge, was stolen. It was the "line light, for navigation." The *Herald* cautioned that the ongoing theft of bridge lights "may some time lead to serious trouble for river craft and for the party who is engaged in such mean work."[26]

In 1914, the U.S. Coast and Geodetic Survey produced a new survey of the Piscataqua River above the Noble's Island–Kittery bridge. The next spring First Lighthouse District Superintendent Carl Sherman arrived in Portsmouth aboard the *Zizania* and then proceeded upriver by motor launch with local pilot Captain Burton Hoyt into Little and Great Bays to decide on locations for the first-ever federal government buoys in these waters.. In June 1915, a total of seven black and red spar buoys were put in place in the Piscataqua above the bridge, and two more were installed in Little Bay and one in Great Bay to mark the entrances to the tributaries leading to Exeter and Newmarket.[27]

The *Herald* viewed these new buoys as benefiting principally summer pleasure boaters. The great deluge of 1896 had undone much of the dredging work on the Cocheco, bringing almost to a standstill commercial freighting on that river. Some remedial dredging was done but by then rail and truck transport had became the dominant means of carrying goods, and the bricks still manufactured at the yards in Dover and in Eliot, Maine, were increasingly shipped out by rail and truck rather than by water.[28]

World War I

In May 1915, the ocean liner *Lusitania,* with 128 Americans aboard was sunk by German submarines. The U.S. government was urged to construct a system of antisubmarine nets to protect U.S. dockyards from German subs that were increasingly considered a threat not only to shipping at sea but to the North Atlantic coast as well. In August 1916, Congress gave President Wilson authority to transfer to the War Department any Lighthouse Service vessels, stations, equipment and personnel that might be needed in the event war threatened American shores. The threat was real. In October 1916, the Nantucket Shoals lightship picked up some 115 survivors of three vessels torpedoed by the Germans. [29]

After the United States entered the war in April 1917, President Wilson issued executive orders transferring fifty lighthouse tenders (practically the entire fleet), four lightships, and twenty-one light stations to the War and Navy Departments, and their 1,120 personnel were transferred to the Navy. Lighthouse Service vessels were involved with laying mines, placing defensive entrance nets at some harbors, and setting out floating targets for the military's artillery practice. No nets were placed at the entrance to Portsmouth Harbor, though they were in World War II, but mines evidently were during the first world war. Just as during the Spanish-American War, for the duration of World War I no navigation into or out of the harbor was permitted between sunset and sunrise, strong indication that mines had been laid to protect the harbor and the Navy Yard. Lighthouse visiting was banned for the duration, lightkeepers were instructed to keep an eye out for suspicious activity, and some lights were doused or lit only sporadically. A telephone line was installed at the Nubble in 1917, perhaps in part in response to a petition by citizens of York, who must have argued that they would be safer if the lighthouse keeper could warn the townspeople of threatening offshore activity.[30]

It is not clear which of the lighthouses around Portsmouth were taken over by the military during the war, though all would have been logical candidates. At the Nubble lighthouse James Burke, who had become keeper there, was sworn into the Navy. Clifford Shattuck wrote in his book about the Nubble that soldiers were assigned sentry duty there and that the light was "alternately dimmed and extinguished on successive nights 'to confuse any possible submersibles.'" [31]

To supplement the meager U.S. fleet of destroyers, submarine chasers—110-foot-long boats capable of high speeds—were hastily built by the hundreds at various shipyards (though not in Portsmouth). Some were sent to Europe and others began patrolling the Atlantic coast in 1917. They were sometimes sighted from local beaches: The *Herald* of August 14, 1917, commented on "these long, lean, greyhounds of the sea, who appear off Boar's Head near the Isles of Shoals, and in an incredible short space of time have disappeared in the mists of Cape Ann." There were many U-boat sightings around Portsmouth, most perhaps imaginary, but apparently only one known encounter with one, thirty or so miles along the coast, off Cape Porpoise, Maine.[32]

The war came to an end in November 1918, but the Lighthouse Service was not returned to civilian status until April 1919, probably to allow the service's tenders and crews to assist with removing the nets and mines that were placed at harbor entrances. A lasting change was introduced during the war: Many of the tenders were fitted with radios, beginning a trend to supply them all with this means of communication with other vessels and with district headquarters. In the First Lighthouse District, the *Zizania* and the *Hibiscus* were equipped with radios.[33]

* * *

Commissioner Putnam took advantage of the excellent wartime service of the men of the Lighthouse Bureau to mount a successful campaign for pensions for Lighthouse Service personnel similar to those provided in the regular military services. Even before war's end, the Lighthouse Retirement Act of June 20, 1918, was enacted by Congress, providing for retirement pay after thirty years: three quarters of the pay averaged during the last five years of service. Retirement was made optional at age sixty-five and mandatory at age seventy.[34]

Near the end of 1922, the *Portsmouth Herald* announced a unique situation: For fifteen days, no vessel with tall masts or stacks would be allowed to pass upriver beyond Court Street. This was because of the imminent installation of the draw span of a new bridge under construction across the Piscataqua between Portsmouth and Badger's Island in Kittery This bridge, the long-sought toll-free bridge across the river, was named Memorial Bridge in honor of the men killed during World War I, and was opened to automobile traffic on August 17, 1923.[35]

Regulations promulgated by the War Department regarding opening the draw for river traffic were published in the *Herald,* and called for the draw to be opened on demand between April 1 and November 30 between the hours of four A.M. and eight P.M., and between six A.M. and six P.M. during the rest of the year. The draw could be opened at other hours, but only with six hours' written or telephone notice. Vessels were to give four blasts of a horn to request the opening of the draw, to be answered by three blasts from the bridge. Boards painted white with black figures at least six inches high showing the headroom under the bridge at all stages of the tide were to be placed on the bridge, to be visible to both upriver and downriver traffic. There would be periodic changes in the timing and arrangements for opening the draw, based on lobbying by both maritime and land-based interests.[36]

An Invisible Aid to Navigation

One of Commissioner Putnam's proudest—but least romantic—achievements was the Lighthouse Bureau's adoption of a largely invisible aid to navigation: the radiobeacon. This device was at first of most use to the large vessels, especially ocean liners and other transoceanic vessels, whose owners could afford to install the necessary radio direction finders to receive the signals sent from transmitters placed at intervals along the coasts in the 1920s. The first transmitters were installed on lightships for the benefit of vessels making for New York Harbor in 1921, and others were later placed on lightships and selected lighthouses on all the coasts. To the northeast of Portsmouth there was a transmitter on the lightship off Portland Harbor, and to the south one was installed on the lightship off the entrance to Boston Harbor, each with a designated frequency and distinctive signal (long, short, long for the former and long, long, short, short for the latter) that could be picked up from great distances.[37]

The last span of the Portsmouth-Kittery bridge being put in place, December 20, 1922. PA

Advantages were several: Radiobeacons worked regardless of visibility and, unlike foghorns, whistles, and sirens, the signals could be picked up regardless of the noise made by engines or storm seas; once installed they could be operated by regular lighthouse and lightship personnel with far less labor and much smaller cost than it took to run fog sirens, horns, and other such devices; and, as Putnam pointed out, "they did not disturb people's slumbers or nerves."[38]

Eventually, LORAN (Long Range Aids To Navigation) and SHORAN (Short Range Aids to Navigation) and more recently Global Positioning Satellites have made not only the radiobeacon obsolete, but also the complicated, labor-intensive noise-making fog signals installed at most local lighthouses in the late nineteenth and early twentieth centuries. These have now been phased out in favor of solar-or electric-powered electronic "pure tone" devices. In spite of an International Association of Lighthouse Authorities statement that fog signals "are no longer necessary for the needs of navigation," these fog signals are still in use locally, and are helpful to small boats without location-finding devices.[39]

Most of the vessels coming into the Port of Portsmouth in the 1920s and 1930s were not equipped to take advantage of radiobeacon signals, and the lights, fog signals, and buoys maintained by the Lighthouse Bureau remained crucial aids to navigation. At many lighthouses, especially those designated "sea lights," like White Island lighthouse, the Lighthouse Bureau moved steadily to eliminate light characteristics with red or green elements, as their range was far less than white, and at lights where a color, usually red, was alternated with white, confusion arose because the white sectors were visible from a much greater distance. At White Island in March 1931, the panels that produced the red sectors of the light, which gave out only seventeen thousand candlepower, were removed, giving the light a characteristic of white flashes of equal sixty thousand candlepower at fifteen-second intervals.[40]

The requirements for harbor and river lights were different, however. In December of the same year, the Portsmouth Harbor light was substantially increased in intensity from twenty-three hundred to seventy-four hundred candlepower with the removal of the red panels in the lighthouse lantern, but the light must have been difficult to distinguish from streetlights because not long afterward, a green shade was installed and a two-hundred-watt electric light bulb replaced the i.o.v. lamp, providing a green light of thirty-two hundred candlepower. At any rate, the green light made more sense than the red one; the lighthouse marked the port side of the entrance to the harbor. The *Herald* reported on May 22, 1931, that Boon Island light was to be electrified as well, enabling an increase in candlepower from seventeen thousand to seventy-five thousand, to make it the most powerful light between Cape Elizabeth, Maine and the Graves, outside Boston Harbor.[41]

The Beginning of the End of Manned Lighthouses

Although the lighthouses in the Portsmouth area would remain manned for decades more, the technology embraced by Commissioner Putnam was having an impact. A 1925 article in the *Portsmouth Herald,* headlined "Science Ends Hero Role of Lightkeeper," announced the change of 114 manned lighthouses to the automatic variety, using batteries, acetylene gas, or electric cables. In a report to President Hoover, Putnam pointed out the saving of federal dollars automation afforded. Aware of the potential public outcry, he stated:

> There is no present prospect, however, of making the primary
> lights and fog stations or outside lightships entirely automat-
> ic or unattended . . . . These stations require high power, com-
> plicated machinery and apparatus—the immense value of
> property and lives depending upon their reliable operation
> renders the substitution of wholly automatic stations out of
> the question for the present.

He added that the personnel at automated facilities would be transferred to light stations where vacancies occurred in the normal course
of events, thus minimizing hardship for these men.[42]

River and harbor entrance lights were the most likely to be automated. In 1928, for example, in New York Harbor and its approaches
there were twenty manned lighthouses but twenty-five automated
lights on fixed foundations and fifty automatic lighted floating buoys. It
would have been logical to automate Portsmouth Harbor lighthouse at
this time, and in fact in 1933 a rumor that this light was slated for
automation prompted the state legislature to prepare a resolution opposing automation of the Fort Constitution light and the elimination of the
fog bell there and to lodge a protest with Commissioner Putnam.[43]

The resolution and protest were presented by New Hampshire Senator Henry W. Keyes. Putnam's response was diplomatic but noncom-
mittal. He wrote to Keyes that there were no immediate plans to
automate the lighthouse, but that economies dictated by reduced appropriations for the service required careful study to determine which
manned facilities might be automated and "which are more urgently
essential to the safety of navigation." Further efforts by the New Hampshire delegation to Congress pointed out the historic nature of the
Portsmouth lighthouse as one of the oldest in the nation and asserted
that "the whole state would suffer if the light was operated any other
way than at present." Putnam's response was similar to his previous one
to Senator Keyes, but the *Herald*'s headline was: "Lightkeeper At Newcastle To Be Retained," and so he was until 1948, when the personnel at
the Coast Guard Station in New Castle took over maintenance of the
light—a task that by then consisted mainly in flipping a light switch.
Operation of the lighthouse was automated in 1960.[44]

Lightkeepers during the Lighthouse Bureau Era

When the Light-House Board was supplanted by the Lighthouse Bureau in 1910, there was no wholesale replacement of lighthouse keepers. The careers of many keepers that began under the Light-House Board's authority ended under the Lighthouse Bureau's. Likewise, later lightkeepers who started out with the Lighthouse Bureau continued to serve after it was absorbed by the Coast Guard in 1939. Thirty and even forty years' service was not unusual, although many keepers served at several different lighthouses, unlike William C. Williams of Boon Island, whose entire lighthousekeeping career was spent at Boon Island (see chapter 12). The improved attention to living conditions begun during the Light-House Board years and continued when the Lighthouse Bureau was established, the end of the patronage system in 1896, and the establishment of pensions in 1918 were all contributing factors.

The Lighthouse Bureau also tried to address the problem of schooling for children of keepers of offshore lighthouses with a policy that whenever possible keepers with children between the ages of five and sixteen would be transferred to lighthouses on the mainland where the children could attend public schools. The State of Maine even provided traveling teachers, who were transported by lighthouse tenders to island lighthouses where there were school-aged children. The teachers stayed at each lighthouse for perhaps a week, unless bad weather prolonged their visits, and laid out work for the parents to supervise after the lighthouse tender picked them up and took them to another lighthouse. The success of this arrangement depended a great deal upon the parents themselves, not all of whom were cut out to be teachers.[45]

One of these itinerant teachers was Lilla Severance, whose island lighthouse teaching career began in June 1915, just after graduation from the normal school in Castine, and lasted about four years. Eva Philbrick, whose father Roger was first assistant keeper at Boon Island 1913-1918, recalled that her father left that island post so that she could go to school ashore, but that the head keeper who followed Mitchell Blackwood had fifteen children, and the two assistants each had two, making the Boon Island families conspicuously eligible for a teacher. One of the teachers who taught these children may well have been Lilla Severance, although, given the number of children involved, a full-time teacher might have been provided.[46]

Another link to the mainland world for island lighthouse families began in 1929. William Wincapaw, an airplane pilot who provided emergency transportation services to people at remote locations in the Penobscot Bay area, decided to repay the lightkeepers whose lighthouses had provided crucial guidance when he flew during heavy weather. On Christmas day he flew over a dozen lighthouses, and tossed out of his plane packages containing coffee, candy, magazines, and newspapers. The grateful response to this first delivery convinced him to continue and expand his Christmas deliveries. Eventually, with the assistance of his son, Wincapaw (who came to be known as the Flying Santa) delivered Christmas packages to ninety-one lighthouse and Coast Guard families from Maine to Connecticut.[47]

Lighthouse historian Edward Rowe Snow joined the Flying Santa project, and was involved with the holiday flights for forty years. Dropping a package at lighthouses like Whale's Back could be an uncertain proposition. Snow recalled circling around Whale's Back to drop a second bundle after missing his target on the first try. The package that landed in the ocean turned up a couple of weeks later on the Cape Cod shore.[48]

The security of a lighthouse job must have been particularly attractive during the high unemployment years of the Depression era. In addition, unlike the situation during the early years of U.S. lighthouses when many men appointed to these jobs were landlubbers, most of the keepers came from seafaring backgrounds, were less likely to be daunted by storms, and were more adept at small-boat handling—a necessity for offshore keepers.[49]

James Burke

James Burke (1848–1935) began his lighthouse-keeping career in 1887 and served for thirty-two years, until his retirement in 1919. He was born in Portsmouth and at the age of fourteen went to sea, first as a fisherman and then aboard coasting vessels. Boon Island was something of a training ground for new lighthouse keepers, and Burke's first lighthouse jobs were as second and then first assistant under William C. Williams. He was transferred and made head keeper at Burnt Island light in Boothbay Harbor in 1890 and then at White Island 1894–1914. His last lighthouse assignment was to the Nubble light.[50]

During Burke's time at Boon Island, he was involved in an effort to save a wrecked vessel that went well beyond the call of duty. The schooner *City of Ellsworth* went aground on ledges off Boon Island at high tide at one A.M. on November 27, 1889. Burke, hearing the shouts of the four men aboard, rowed out to bring them ashore to the island. Early the next morning he set out for shore in his dory with the schooner's master, rowing the six miles to the Nubble in York and then taking the trolley to Portsmouth Navy Yard in search of a tug to haul the vessel off. No tug was available there, and in Portsmouth they found that the tug *Cocheco* had gone upriver with tows to Dover; they had to wait for its return. The next day the *Cocheco,* with Burke and the master of the wrecked vessel aboard, set out for Boon Island. They got no farther than the Sisters when they had to turn back because of high seas. They finally reached Boon Island the next day aboard the steamer *Undine,* only to find that the *City of Ellsworth* had gone to pieces, with only part of her deck house remaining and her cargo of thousands of shingles strewn over the island. The *Undine* took Burke and the vessel's crew to Portsmouth, leaving Burke to retrace his journey to York to retrieve his dory and row the long miles back to Boon Island.[51]

In 1911, when he was head keeper at White Island, Burke was the subject of a story in the local press headlined "Heroic Devotion to Duty." He and his wife had become very ill with what the newspaper described as "grippe" while his assistant Gordon Sullivan was on shore leave. Burke's attempts to signal for help from the Life-Saving Service crew on Appledore Island went unnoticed, and for six days he steadfastly continued to tend the light, according to his wife crawling on his hands and knees up the spiral staircase to the lantern. When Sullivan returned and discovered how sick the couple were, he rowed over to the Life-Saving Station to ask the crew to take the Burkes ashore. The seas were high, and Mrs. Burke, by then sicker than her husband, refused to be taken in the station's small powerboat. Joseph Staples, keeper of the Life-Saving Station, tried unsuccessfully to intercept the Revenue Cutter *Gresham* passing nearby, and finally took the station's boat to the Wood Island Life-Saving Station, where he used the telephone to call for the sturdy tug *M. Mitchell Davis*. By then it was too rough even for the tug, and the rescue mission was postponed until the next morning. Burke was laid up ashore for two weeks before he was well enough to return to White Island, where Sullivan had tended the lighthouse by himself during Burke's absence.[52]

In 1912, Burke took over the Nubble keepership from William Brooks. Brooks had been forced to resign after the district inspector discovered that he was not only running a business, charging ten cents to ferry visitors to the island where he had fishing poles and bait available, but was advertising his services with a sign placed on the shore opposite the lighthouse; his wife had been giving tours of the house for a nickel. James Burke may have been relieved not to have the responsibility for the newly installed fog siren at White Island, and was definitely looking forward to his new job at the Nubble, much closer to the mainland and his daughter Lucy's school. A covered walkway between the house and lighthouse and another between the lighthouse and the bell tower had been built the year before his arrival, providing welcome protection from stormy weather.[53]

Clifford Shattuck's book contains an interesting reminiscence by Burke's daughter, with many details of their life at the Nubble. She recalled that when the tide was low enough, her father, in hip boots, would carry her across the gut to the island, and at other times picked her up in the island's rowboat. Sometimes visiting friends had to spend longer than planned when it turned too stormy to put them ashore. There was a parlor organ in the house, and singing by family and friends, and an outhouse behind the house. The family kept a cow and chickens, and her father set up flakes to dry the fish he'd caught offshore and salted. Like other lighthouse families, the Burkes worked hard to keep everything in spotless and polished readiness for the inevitable but unpredictable visits of the district inspector.[54]

Even when in his late sixties Burke remained ready to go to the rescue of people in trouble. The Lighthouse Commissioner's annual report for 1914 referred to his towing a disabled launch to the lighthouse and taking care of its occupants overnight. On another occasion that year, a Mr. Lewis credited Burke with saving his life by pulling him out of the water and then providing him with dry clothes. The next year's report noted that Burke had saved another man from drowning.[55]

At the outbreak of World War I, Burke, like most other island lighthousekeepers, received a telegram from the district inspector on April 18, 1917, notifying him that he and the lighthouse and all its equipment were transferred to the Navy Department. A telephone line to the mainland was installed and a sentry station constructed on the sea side of the lighthouse where soldiers did sentry duty. Burke was ordered to dim and extinguish the light on alternate nights to confuse the enemy submarines that might be lurking offshore. When Burke retired in 1919, he was among those eligible for the pensions for lighthouse personnel voted by Congress in 1918.[56]

Walter S. Amee

Walter Amee, of Kittery, had been owner and master of several fishing schooners before he became second assistant at Boon Island in 1891. He served briefly at White Island and then was assigned to Whale's Back light in 1893. Amee was head keeper for an amazing twenty-seven years at this cramped post with its noisy fog signal. He and his assistant must have had mixed feelings when oil replaced the coal they had shoveled to fuel the foghorn machinery when a new—and louder—second-class Daboll foghorn was installed in 1899, to give a five-second blast every twenty-five seconds during fog. A second assistant was added in 1901, probably in preparation for the installation of an even more powerful—and even louder—first-class fog horn in 1902. With a third man at the lighthouse, each of the three men worked at the lighthouse four days and then took two days off. These would have been very welcome during a foggy period. The horn was operated for 1,150 hours in 1907. During that year, Amee and his assistants were inundated when the 1,800 gallon tank of water for cooling the engine burst (see chapter 12).[57]

In July 1911, Amee rescued two men who were going out of the harbor at full speed in a motor boat, anxious to get to York before dark, when they ran hard aground onto a rock to the east of the lighthouse. One of the men was thrown overboard by the impact and was pulled back into the boat by the other, but the boat was sinking fast. Amee heard their shouts, lowered the lighthouse boat, and, just as their boat sank, pulled them out of the water and took them back to the lighthouse. Walter Amee retired in 1921, having racked up a total of thirty years of service.[58]

John W. Wetzel

John Wetzel's 1924 obituary said that he had entered the lighthouse service in 1889; he was briefly keeper of the Seavey's Point range lights established in the 1890s (see chapter 13), and became assistant at Whale's Back in 1897. At the time of his sudden death at the age of only fifty-seven, his twenty-seven years at Whale's Back matched Walter Amee's tenure there.[59]

Leander White

Leander White ended his forty-one year career as a lighthouse keeper at Fort Constitution light in his native town of New Castle. He began as an assistant keeper at Boon Island in 1874, and in 1875 had a frightening experience while sailing ashore for provisions (see chapter 12). He was assigned to Whale's Back in 1878 as acting and then head keeper. From 1887 until 1909, he was keeper at lighthouses at Goat Island at Cape Porpoise and then at Cape Elizabeth, both in Maine. After Joshua Card's retirement in 1909, White came home to New Castle to tend the light at the fort. He retired in 1915, when his son-in-law Henry Cuskley took his place.[60]

Arnold B. White

Arnold White's last lighthouse assignment was also as keeper at Fort Constitution light, where he took the place of Henry Cuskley in 1942. His lighthouse service began around 1908, and included twenty-one years at Whale's Back. A 1939 article in the *Herald* by a visitor to Whale's Back described in detail the well-ordered, spotless lighthouse he kept with his two assistants, Maynard Farnsworth and Warren Alley. White gave a tour, starting with the cellar where equipment and cupboards of supplies were neatly arrayed. A large tank for storage of the Sebago Lake water that was delivered regularly to the lighthouse was kept in this space. Above this was the simply furnished kitchen that also served as a living room, with a well-polished Queen Atlantic stove, a telephone connected to the mainland, a clock, lamp, and shining brass implements. White shared his recipe for dumplings, and told the reporter that each of the men cooked his own meals. They had tried taking turns cooking for each other but found that their food preferences were incompatible.[61]

On the floor above was White's room with bunks and a table and chair where he filled out a weather log every four hours and recorded wrecks in the vicinity as they occurred in the volume that had been kept at the lighthouse since 1855. The room contained a barometer, a radio, and a medicine chest. White recalled being iced in for two weeks during the bitter winter of 1924. Lighthouse regulations by that time permitted only the lighthouse personnel to live permanently at Whale's Back, though they were allowed to have visitors, and Mrs. White often spent several days at a time there with her husband. In 1938, White earned the distinction of being the district's only lightkeeper west of Maine's Kennebec River to be awarded the Lighthouse Bureau's coveted and hard-won efficiency pennant, based on an almost microscopic, white-glove inspection of the living and working quarters, the fog and lighting equipment, and the records keepers were required to maintain.[62]

Henry M. Cuskley

Leander White' son-in-law Henry Cuskley, who took over the keep-ership at Fort Constitution in 1915 when White retired, was a seasoned lighthouse keeper. He had already been a keeper at Maine lighthouses for nineteen years, first at Cape Elizabeth, and then at island posts on Libby Island at the entrance to Machias Bay, and on Seguin Island, off the mouth of the Kennebec River. He remained keeper at Fort Consti-tution for twenty-five years until his retirement in 1941; his service as a lighthouse keeper totaled an impressive forty-four years.[63]

Cuskley's duties as keeper were considerably simplified when elec-tricity was substituted for kerosene in the mid-1920s. Instead of spend-ing a half hour with the incandescent-oil-vapor-lamp to ready it for lighting, he had merely to flip the light switch to *ON*. The replacement of the kerosene-fueled i.o.v. lamp and chimney by an electric light bulb also eliminated one of the many cleaning tasks lightkeepers were expected to do daily.

However, one of the tasks that remained a constant at all light-houses involved the brass implements and containers that abounded in every lighthouse and which were to be kept shining at all times. The complaints of a lighthouse keeper to the visiting district machinist, Fred Morong, inspired Morong to write a poem of fourteen stanzas, entitled "Brasswork," which was widely distributed and became very popular with lightkeepers and their wives. [64]

It begins,

> O what is the bane of a lightkeeper's life
> That causes him worry, struggle and strife
> That makes him use cuss words, and beat at his wife?
>> It's Brasswork.

And ends:

> And when I have polished until I am cold
> And I'm taken aloft to the Heavenly fold
> Will my harp and my crown be made of pure gold?
>> No, Brasswork.[65]

Cuskley's wife and two daughters lived with him in the keeper's house. A friend's amusing reminiscence described the frenzy of cleaning and polishing that occurred when word reached them that the inspec-tor's arrival was imminent:.

> Mrs. Cuskley was a spotless housekeeper, but all the same
> when the inspector was coming, all Hell broke loose. She flew
> around throwing things out the portholes and I'd run out and
> catch what I wanted as it flew by. I have a small table today
> that I caught on the fly. The Cuskley kids holed up at such a
> time and read while the cleaning storm raged. Mr. Cuskley was
> nervous too but went about spit and polishing in a calmer way.
> I'd do the fetching, for I loved the excitement as the storm
> increased. There was a room downstairs where Mr. Cuskley and
> the girls would go, but I stayed upstairs where the fun was.

The Cuskleys were sociably involved with the New Castle community. He was an active member of the school board, and she was remembered for her Sunday dinners and elegant raspberry tarts.[66]

A new chore was added to Cuskley's duties in 1938. The U.S. Department of Agriculture transferred its storm signal flags and lanterns, formerly displayed at various Portsmouth locations, to Fort Constitution, where the lightkeeper was given the responsibility for running them up a pole when needed. A single triangular red pennant (for daytime) or a red light above a white one (for nighttime) was a small-craft warning, indicating winds of between eighteen and thirty-three knots; two red pennants or a white light above a red one was a gale warning for winds of from thirty-four to forty-three knots; a square red flag with a black square in the middle or two red lights was a storm warning for winds above forty-eight knots; two of the square flags or red, white, and red lights displayed one above the other was for hurricane winds over sixty-four knots. The flags were sizable: eight by fifteen feet for the pennant and eight by eight feet for the square flags. Elson Small, who was keeper of Fort Constitution light in the late 1940s after a long career at several Maine coast lighthouses, gave his wife Connie the job of hoisting the flags. She recalled that the flags had to be replaced when they became tattered, which happened after a few exposures to high winds, and she used salvaged sections of the flags to make quilts.[67]

Some of the brass implements that lighthouse families had to keep gleaming, in the collection of the Maine Lighthouse Museum, Rockland, Maine. Author's photo.

Herman Ingalls

Records of long and loyal service with the Lighthouse Bureau were by no means confined to lighthouse keepers. The monthly bulletin published by the bureau regularly reported retirements and deaths of men (and a rare woman) who had twenty, thirty, and sometimes even more than forty years of service aboard lighthouse tenders, or as engineers, draftsmen, technicians, clerks, or administrators in the central and district offices of the bureau. Many of them began in lowly jobs as civilian employees of the Light-House Board, and as they gained experience worked their way up to positions of great responsibility.

A case in point was Herman Melville Ingalls (1875–1965). He grew up in coastal Washington County, Maine, where many men made their living at sea fishing or lobstering or aboard coasting vessels. A considerable number went into government service at regional life-saving stations and lighthouses, or aboard lighthouse tenders; it was not unusual for more than one family member to enter one of the maritime-related services. Herman's father was a master of coasting vessels. In 1890, after eight years of schooling Herman (then fifteen) went to sea himself. Over the next three years he shipped aboard seven different coasting vessels as a seaman.[68]

In 1893 he began forty-seven years of lighthouse service, starting at age eighteen as an able seaman aboard the Light-House Board's First District lighthouse tender *Lilac* for thirty dollars a month plus rations. He ended his career with the district's top job: First District Lighthouse Engineer and Superintendent, at an annual salary of $5,600. Most of his service was in the First District, aboard lighthouse tenders that made regular appearances in the waters around Portsmouth.[69]

His progress up the ranks was steady. In 1895 he was promoted to quartermaster aboard *Lilac;* two years later he became mate of the side-wheeler *Geranium*. In the summers of 1901 and 1902, his intimate knowledge of the Maine coast was put to good use: He was detailed to serve as pilot aboard *Armeria* when that Boston-based tender supplied First District lighthouses; in 1903 he was transferred back to *Lilac* as mate, becoming first mate and finally master. He was master of *Zizania* from 1912 to 1924—a period when many automatic lights and range lights were installed along the coast. In 1924 he was named captain in command of *Hibiscus*, a position he held until his appointment as district superintendent in 1937.[70]

*Herman M. Ingalls (1875-1965) served aboard lighthouse tenders from 1893-1937, and was superintendent of the first district from 1937 until his retirement in 1940.*Courtesy of his grand-daughter Prudence Heard.

Both of Herman Ingalls's younger brothers were in lighthouse service. Frank Ingalls had a forty-six-year career, first on the lighthouse tender *Geranium* and then as keeper of a number of Down East Maine lighthouses.[71] Eugene Ingalls followed his brothers into the lighthouse service and became keeper of the light at Petit Manan Island off the coast from Millbridge, Maine. His career—and his life—were cut short when he was only thirty-four. Early in January 1917, he disappeared after leaving for the mainland in the lighthouse powerboat during a heavy northwester. Herman Ingalls, in command of *Zizania*, joined *Hibiscus* in what must have been a grim and disheartening search for his missing brother, while along shore beaches, coves and inlets in the area were scoured by searchers. Eugene was never found. Part of the lighthouse boat was later discovered by a lobsterman in Machias Bay.[72]

During Herman Ingalls's long career he was involved in more than twenty successful rescues, a number of them around Portsmouth. In January 1923, while master of *Zizania,* he towed the coal schooner *Ada McIntyre* to safe anchorage in Portsmouth Harbor. In March 1932, on an inspection of a new fog signal at the Isles of Shoals, an auxiliary fishing sloop was observed displaying a distress signal five miles southwest of the islands. She was the *Marguerite McKenzie,* of York, with a disabled engine. Ingalls and his *Hibiscus* crew towed her fifteen miles into York Harbor. Two years later, *Hibiscus* went to the rescue of the lumber schooner *Margery Austin,* in distress four miles south of Whale's Back lighthouse. The Nova Scotia vessel, with torn sails and much of its deck load gone, had the captain's wife and children aboard, along with three crewmen. In June 1936, *Hibiscus* rescued two men and a woman and their small sailboat when they were in trouble off York Ledge.[73]

While serving as district engineer and superintendent from 1937 until his retirement in 1940, Ingalls supervised a staff of about a hundred engineers, draftsmen, technicians, and clerks. He was responsible for the thousands of buoys and other aids to navigation in the district, and inspected its 131 lighthouses to make sure all was well with the keepers and their families and that the lights, fog signals, and buildings were properly maintained.[74]

Among Ingalls's last assignments was assisting with the months-long efforts to salvage the Portsmouth-built *Squalus* after the submarine went to the bottom during a test dive off the Isles of Shoals in the summer of 1939.

The End of the Lighthouse Bureau

George Putnam, after twenty-five years as commissioner of the Lighthouse Bureau, retired in May 1935 at the age of seventy. When he began work at the newly created bureau in 1910, he inherited from the old Light-House Board a staff of fifty-four in the Washington office. Twenty-five years later there were only forty. System-wide, the number of employees had been reduced from 5,778 in 1910 to 4,940 when Putnam retired. Because of Putnam's embrace of new technologies, the number of aids to navigation had more than doubled, from 11,713 to 24,000. These efficiencies and economies were doubtless appreciated by Congress, with whom Putnam had a good working relationship.[75]

Putnam's successor was Deputy Commissioner Harold D. King, who had twenty-four years of service with the bureau. He was one of the men Putnam brought in from the Coast and Geodetic Service, where King had worked for nine years on surveys on the Atlantic and Pacific coasts, in Alaska, and the Philippine Islands and had commanded survey vessels.

The first district's buoy depot on Little Diamond Island in Casco Bay. This is where buoys were stored and where crews cleaned and painted buoys that had been pulled. NARG26.

His first assignments with the Bureau of Lighthouses were as superintendent of three different districts and, like Putnam, he had been involved in efforts to achieve international uniformity in aids to navigation.[76]

On the occasion of the 150th anniversary of the lighthouse service of the United States in the summer of 1939, the accomplishments of the Lighthouse Bureau received an excellent press. Nevertheless, at end of June came the announcement that the existence of the bureau was to end on July 1, 1939.[77] The Treasury Department's U.S. Coast Guard on that day took over the responsibilities of the bureau under the command of Rear Admiral Ronald R. Waesche. The 4,119 full-time and 1,156 part-time personnel of the lighthouse service would be transferred into the Coast Guard, which then numbered 10,164 officers and civilians.[78]

The idea for this consolidation had been in the air for years. The merger of the Revenue Marine and Life-Saving Services to create the Coast Guard in 1915 was one step toward reorganizing and streamlining federal services, promulgated by a commission appointed by President William Taft five years earlier. The plan evidently called for including the lighthouse service in the merger, to unify all three of these maritime services under one administrative roof. Robert Erwin Johnson, in his history of the U.S. Coast Guard, has theorized that Commissioner Putnam had the political skills and clout needed to successfully head off the absorption of the service by the Coast Guard. Though Putnam had decentralized the administration of the service by giving the district superintendents considerable control over their domains, there had been no sacrifice of high standards of performance and he had taken advantage of new technologies to increase and improve aids to navigation while achieving striking economies. Johnson suggests that Putnam's successor did not have enough time to develop the support of Congress and other Washington insiders to succeed in making the case for maintaining the lighthouse service as a separate civilian entity.[79]

The merger did achieve the intended goal of economy, and was doubtless inevitable regardless of who was commissioner. It came during the Depression, when federal dollars had to be spread as widely as possible. The seventeen lighthouse districts and the existing Coast Guard districts were to be consolidated into thirteen. Maine, New Hampshire, Vermont, Massachusetts, and Rhode Island would comprise a new First Coast Guard District with headquarters in Boston.[80] In 1940 the Coast Guard claimed that the consolidation of district offices, supply depots, and administrative personnel had saved one million dollars, or about one-tenth of what the Lighthouse Bureau had spent annually. And it was expected that there would be additional savings when and if the more highly-paid civilian lighthouse personnel, who were Civil Service employees, joined the ranks of the Coast Guardsmen, who were not.[81]

The merger was not without friction. Most lighthouse service personnel were given the option of continuing as civilians or becoming part of the Coast Guard's military structure. For those who chose the military route, Coast Guard–appointed boards in each district determined rank, usually based on years of service. Lighthouse keepers could become chief or first class petty officers; masters of tenders and chief engineers could be warrant boatswains and machinists; district superintendents could be commanders or lieutenant commanders. Those deemed eligible to become Coast Guardsmen would have to accept being junior to those already serving in the Coast Guard—an arrangement that did not appeal to some veterans of the lighthouse service. In fact, of the 4,119 full time lighthouse personnel only 103 chose to accept commissions when they were offered and only 466 accepted petty officer ratings, preferring to remain civilian employees.[82] Ten years after the consolidation, one retired southern lighthouse keeper wrote:

> ... how the Commission had the heart to think we civilian personnel would ever blend with 15 & 16 year old Coast Guard men, 'is a huckleberry away above my persimmon' no good blood ever existed between or with either group. The Coast Guard & Rear Admirals to[o] brassy for we common Sailors, Fishermen Oystermen & what have you.[83]

It is not clear how many of the keepers at Portsmouth area lighthouses opted to remain civilians, how many decided to become Coast Guard petty officers, or how much pressure there was for them to do so. It is known that keepers Arnold White, Maynard Farnsworth (who moved up from assistant keeper to keeper in charge at Whale's Back), and Elson Small, who followed White at the Fort Constitution light became chief boatswain's mates.[84]

For others in the lighthouse service, the decision was not theirs to make. Herman Ingalls, with an unblemished record of forty-seven years of service and broad experience with lighthouse and buoy tenders as well as administrative responsibilities as district engineer and superintendent, applied for a Coast Guard commission as an officer but was informed by Admiral Waesche that he was not eligible.[85] The reason was not spelled out, but it seems likely that his lack of formal education beyond eighth grade was a factor. He retired in April 1940, just ten months after the U. S. Coast Guard took over the Lighthouse Bureau.[86]

Eventually all the men who chose to remain civilians reached retirement age. Because the Coast Guardsmen who replaced them drew shorter lighthouse assignments interspersed with other duties that might be aboard Coast Guard cutters, rescue boats, or tenders servicing buoys, careers devoted solely to lighthouse keeping came to an end, and so did this fascinating chapter of maritime history.

XV *Afterword*

OF COURSE THE HISTORY OF LIGHTHOUSES and aids to navigation in the Portsmouth area does not end in 1939, and lighthouse keepers, whether as civilians or as Coast Guardsmen, continued to serve with dedication. Amenities such as electricity, telephone lines, and indoor plumbing made their lives more comfortable; nearby Coast Guard station crews and their powerboats ready to assist and eventually helicopter pads at offshore stations made them safer. But keepers still faced dangers during major storms like those that struck and devastated Boon Island in the mid-1940s and again in 1978.[1]

The adoption of new technologies pursued so vigorously by the Lighthouse Bureau and diminishing coastwise shipping along the New England coast by the 1930s resulted in the closing and auctioning off of a number of lighthouse properties in this region. In 1934, nine Maine lighthouses were sold, mainly to summer residents. In 1935, the acreage surrounding or associated with another thirteen New England lighthouses went on the auction block, some of it acquired by communities for public parks.[2]

Under the Coast Guard, the process of automation continued after World War II, gradually completely eliminating the need for manned lighthouses.[3] In 1960 Fort Constitution light was the first of the Portsmouth-area lighthouses to be automated. Whale's Back was next in 1963 after the laying of power cables from the mainland.[4] In the late 1960s, the Coast Guard announced its Lighthouse Automation and Modernization Project (LAMP), with the goal of automating all U.S. lighthouses. Automation of Boon Island light came in 1978, as it did to White Island and Cape Neddick lights in 1986 and 1987 respectively. By 1995, all U.S. lighthouses were unmanned with the exception of Boston Harbor light. This light, the first established in the nation, is to be permanently manned, thanks to a 1989 act of Congress [5]

In the early years of the Coast Guard's lighthouse automation program, a few of the old lighthouses were demolished, sometimes with bare-bones steel structures put in their place to elevate new automatic lighting and fog signal equipment; in other cases the old lighthouses were left standing, but the buildings associated with them—keepers' houses, oil houses, and boat houses—were demolished. At other lighthouses where these buildings had been left in place they suffered from neglect and vandalism.

It was not long before people realized how painful it was to see the deterioration and potential loss of these iconic structures. The Coast Guard confronted the problem of how to accomplish its mission as efficiently and economically as possible in the face of a rising tide of concern for these beloved, familiar, and picturesque elements of the coastal scene. They had become in many ways emblematic of the romance and dangers of the seagoing life and of the faithful and courageous lives of the human beings who maintained these "friendly edifices."

With the approach of 1989 and the U.S. lighthouse bicentennial, and the automation of the majority of lighthouses already accomplished, there was a great deal of activity by people who cared about lighthouses and all they represented. There was a blizzard of books about the lighthouses in virtually every region of the United States where there were lighthouses. From coast to coast, organizations were formed to preserve lighthouses and the buildings and artifacts associated with them and to gather the histories of the keepers and families who spent years at usually isolated and frequently dangerous stations.

Federal grants to state historic preservation offices provided for documenting and establishing the historic importance of the various states' lighthouses with National Register of Historic Places nominations. Local governments and non-profits negotiated with the Coast Guard ways of taking on responsibility for maintaining individual lighthouses and the buildings associated with them, often through lease arrangements. To standardize the process, and to make it possible for these organizations to acquire lighthouses when feasible, Congress in 2000 passed the National Lighthouse Preservation Act, setting out procedures for the transfer of lighthouse properties at no cost to state and local governments or to qualified non-profit entities

The American Lighthouse Foundation of Wells Maine (www.lighthousefoundation.org) is one of these non-profits, with more than twenty lighthouses under its stewardship umbrella. The foundation also operates The Museum of Lighthouse History and a shop selling lighthouse-related items to benefit the foundation's work. The museum is open seasonally and by appointment. (207) 646-0245.

Fortunately, in the Portsmouth area, all five of its nineteenth-century lighthouses survive today and still serve as Coast Guard aids to navigation, though some, particularly Boon Island lighthouse, have lost structures associated with them.

Portsmouth Harbor Lighthouse has been adopted by the Friends of Portsmouth Harbor Lighthouse, a chapter of the American Lighthouse Foundation. (ALF). In 2000, ALF was issued a license to care for the light tower, oil house, and wooden walkway, and later obtained funds for the restoration of that lighthouse's brick oil house from a group called New England Lighthouse Lovers. The Friends of Portsmouth Harbor Lighthouse welcomes new members, opens the lighthouse for periodic open houses, and maintains an excellent website containing a history of the lighthouse, a bibliography, a list of lighthouse keepers, and many illustrations: www.portsmouthharborlighthouse.org.

White Island Lighthouse is now owned by the Department of Parks and Recreation of the State of New Hampshire. The "Lighthouse Kids" are a group of North Hampton school children who started raising money to help correct the severe structural problems at White Island lighthouse. They were instrumental in obtaining a federal grant to match their fund-raising efforts, and welcome donations. Their web site is at www.lighthousekids.org.

Cape Neddick ("Nubble") Lighthouse was leased to the Town of York, Maine, in 1989, and ownership was transferred to it in 1998. The town and an active group of friends have been able to fund the restoration of the buildings and create a visitors center on the mainland across the gut from the Nubble. Each December the lighthouse and its buildings are decorated with holiday lights. The friends, always looking to add to their membership rolls, may be reached at a website maintained by the Town of York: www.parksandrec.yorkmaine.

Whale's Back (now commonly known as Whaleback) **Lighthouse** was licensed to the American Lighthouse Foundation late in 2005. The

U.S. Coast Guard retains ownership; ALF plans to undertake maintenance and repairs of the structure. The foundation contemplates educational activities to help build financial support and is developing a
partnership with the Town of Kittery, owner of the nearby Wood Island
Life Saving Station, to preserve these important landmarks of the
area's maritime heritage. (www.lighthousefoundation.org)

Boon Island Lighthouse was licensed to the American Lighthouse Foundation in 2000. Its second-order Fresnel lens was replaced
by the Coast Guard in 1993 with a more modern light, now solar-powered. As of this writing in 2005, the Fresnel lens is on loan to the Kittery (Maine) Naval and Historical Museum, which is open seasonally
and by appointment: (207) 439-3080. Afficionados of the lighthouse
formed The Republic of Boon Island in 2003 and schedule cruises to the
lighthouse and other Boon island-related events. For more information
see the Lighthouse Foundation website. (www.lighthousefoundation.org)

The Maine Lighthouse Museum Preserving the magnificent
Fresnel lenses that were being replaced by more modern lights, as well
as obsolete buoys and other artifacts associated with lighthouses and
aids to navigation became a passion for Ken Black, a Coast Guardsman. After his retirement in 1971, he established the Shore Village
Museum in Rockland, Maine. The museum moved in 2005 to new quarters in Rockland, to become the Maine Lighthouse Museum. It, too, has
a website: www.mainelighthousemuseum.com.

Finally, an active website, www.lighthouse.cc, is devoted to the lighthouses in all the New England states. It contains a wealth of information: histories, bibliographies, information about the current status of
each lighthouse, lists of lighthouse keepers, and excellent contemporary
photographs as well as historic images. It is maintained by Jeremy D'Entremont, who has begun publishing books about the lighthouses in each
New England state. Volumes about New Hampshire and Maine lighthouses are in the offing, and will fill in gaps, correct whatever errors
there may be in this book, and cover the history of the Coast Guard years
of responsibility for them that has not been attempted here.

Notes

Chapter I: Introduction

1. William Hubbard, *A General History of New England, 1680*. Boston, 1848, cited 1n William G. Saltonstall, *Ports of Piscataqua* (Cambridge, Mass.: Harvard University Press, 1941), 3.

2. Jeremy Belknap, G. T. Lord, ed., *Belknap's New Hampshire: An Account of the state in 1792*. Facsimile edition of volume 3 of *The History of New Hampshire* (Hampton, NH: Peter E. Randall, 1973), 145–146.

3. Ibid., 145.

4. John Smith, *A Description of New England, 1616* (Boston: William Veazie, n.d.), 22–23.

5. Saltonstall, 42.

6. Richard Candee, "William and John Godsoe," in Peter Benes, ed., *New England Prospect: Maps, Place Names and the Historical Landscape* (Boston: The Dublin Seminar for New England Folklife Annual Proceedings, 1980), 13–14,dates the map based on the building types represented.

7. "A Chart of Ye Coast of New England, New York & Long Island," (London: Sellers & Price, 1703).

8. Walter W. Ristow, *American Maps and Mapmakers. Commercial Cartography in the Nineteenth Century*. (Detroit: Wayne State University Press, 1986), 221–222; Nathaniel Bouton, compiler and editor, *New Hampshire State Papers* (Concord, NH: various printers and dates.) (hereafter NHSP), vol. 3, 766–767; Sinclair Hitchings, "Guarding the New England Coast: The Naval Career of Cyprian Southack," in *Seafaring in Colonial Massachusetts* (Boston: The Colonial Society of Massachusetts, 1980), 43–64; Karen Alexander, "Charting the Piscataqua," in *Cross-Grained & Wily Waters: A Guide to the Piscataqua Maritime Region*, W. Jeffrey Bolster, editor. (Portsmouth, NH.: Peter E. Randall Publisher, 2002), 57, 61.

9. William P. Cumming, "The Colonial Charting of the Massachusetts Coast." *Seafaring in Colonial Massachusetts*, 90–91.

10. Willis Chipman, "The Life and Times of Major Samuel Holland, Surveyor General, 1764–1801," in *Papers and Records of the Ontario Historical Society*, Volume 21 (1924), 14, 15, 18–19; Ristow, 27–28; Cumming, 99–100; Grace S. Machemer,

461

"Headquartered at Piscataqua: Samuel Holland's Coastal and Inland Surveys, 1770–1774," *Historical New Hampshire,* volume 57, Nos. 1 and 2 (Spring/Summer 2002), 6–7.

11. Portsmouth Tax Lists and Accounts (Portsmouth, N.H. City Hall), for 1771 show James Grant, Samuel Holland and Thomas Wheeler on pages 261, 262, and 268 respectively. Charles Basquette, possibly a corruption of Charles Blaskowitz, another deputy, appears on page 259.

12. Chipman, 24-27 (on *Canceaux*). Grant first visited St. John's Lodge in December 1771, and was present at least eight times in 1772. Charles Blaskowitz, another deputy, was at the lodge a number of times over a period of several months beginning in October 1771; Deputy Thomas Wheeler visited the lodge twice in November 1772. George Sproule, another deputy, was in Portsmouth in April 1774. Gerald D. Foss, "DesBarres Atlantic Neptune," in "The Trestle Board," January 1969, published by St. John's Lodge, Portsmouth, N.H.; Machemer, 11–22.

13. G. N. D. Evans, *Uncommon Obdurate: The Several Public Careers of J. F. W. DesBarres* (Salem, Mass. and Toronto: Peabody Museum of Salem and University of Toronto Press, 1969), 3, 7. 33; Ristow, 222–224; Cumming, 101–102; Machemer, 6.

14. Ristow, 30, 222–224; Evans, 8, 20–24.

15. Ristow, 224; Cumming, 104–105.

16. Ristow, 228–233.

17. Ristow, 233, 234; Hitchings, 63.

18. John Deane, *A Narrative of the Shipwreck of the Nottingham Galley in Her Voyage from England to Boston.* Reprint of the fifth, 1762 edition.(Portland, Maine: The Provincial Press, 1968),1.

19. Deane's account is the basis for Kenneth Roberts's historical novel *Boon Island.*

20. Major English-language sources on the history of European lighthouses: John Naish, *Seamarks, Their History and Development* (London: Stanford Maritime, 1985); Douglas B. Hague and Rosemary Christie, *Lighthouses: Their Architecture, History and Archaeology.*(Llandysel, Wales: Gomer Press, 1985); D. Alan Stevenson, *The World's Lighthouses Before 1820.* (London: Oxford University Press, 1959).

21. Stevenson, 122. Smeaton's lighthouse was replaced by a taller structure built in 1882 by Sir James Douglas at a site near Smeaton's. Smeaton's iconic structure was dismantled and the upper portions re-erected on the mainland. Stevenson, 124.

22. Arnold B. Johnson, "Lighthouse Establishment, The United States," *The Annual Cyclopaedia,* 1880, vol 5, 430. Typed copy of the entry in the author's possession, kindness of Rita F. Conant.

23. Naish, 17.

24. *New Hampshire Documents in the British Archives,* vol. 14, 241–249, and vol. 15, 252, 254. (at the New Hampshire Historical Society, Concord, N.H.) Nelson Lawry kindly provided these references to the Muscovy lanterns at the fort.

25. Abraham Rees, *Cyclopaedia; or Universal Dictionary of Arts, Science, and Literature.* First American edition, 42 vols. of text and 6 of plates. (Philadelphia: Samuel F. Bradford and Murray, Fairman and Co., 1806–1820), q.v. "mica."

26. NHSP, vol. 3, 821; vol. 4, 31, 55, 97, 357, 446.

27. Ronald H. Quilici, "A Voyage to Antigua, A Social and Economic Study of the Maritime Activities of Colonial Portsmouth, New Hampshire" (Masters thesis, Department of History, University of New Hampshire, 1973), 92; Charles E. Clark, *The Eastern Frontier* (Hanover, N.H. and London: University Press of New England, 1983), 98.

28. *Laws of New Hampshire, including public and private acts and resolves . . .* 10 vols. By the State, 1904–1922 (hereafter N.H. Laws), 2:695–701.

29. Quilici, xvi.

30. Ibid., 93; NHSP vol. 13, 269-271. The signers included merchant/shipbuilder George Boyd, Mark Hunking Wentworth (brother of Governor Benning Wentworth and father of future Governor John Wentworth), Daniel Warner, and John Penhallow. Others were King's Attorney Wiseman Clagett, Postmaster Eleazer Russell, nautical instruments manufacturer William Hart, and innkeepers James Stoodley and John Stavers. Twenty-two of the names appeared under the heading "Members of the Marine Society." All of these, except for Collector of Customs James Nevin, were ship owners or shipmasters, or both, including Samuel Moffatt, James McDonough, Nathaniel Adams, Woodbury Langdon, William Whipple, Titus Salter, Gregory Purcell, and Nathaniel Sherburne. Charles W. Brewster, *Rambles About Portsmouth* (First Series), [hereafter Brewster I] (Portsmouth, N.H.: C. W. Brewster, 1859), 165, lists principal taxpayers in 1770. Ronald H. Quilici, "The Portsmouth Marine Society: Social Diversity in a Colonial Maritime Community," *Historical New Hampshire,* vol. 30, no. 2 (Summer 1975),101–111, analyzes the membership of the society.

31. NHSP vol. 7, 295.

Chapter II: The First Portsmouth Harbor Lighthouse

1. Paul Wilderson, "Protagonist of Prudence: A Biography of John Wentworth, the King's Last Governor of New Hampshire," (Ph.D. diss., University of New Hampshire, 1977), 53.

2. Ibid., 53; Benjamin Franklin Parker, *History of Wolfeborough, N.H.* (By the Town, 1901), 63.

3. *New-Hampshire Gazette,* 16 December 1768.

4. *New-Hampshire Gazette*, 16 June 1770; George R. Putnam, *Lighthouses and Lightships of the United States.* (Boston and New York: Houghton Mifflin Company, 1933), 11–12, 14–15.

5. NHSP vol. 3, 279.

6. Ibid.

7. NHSP vol. 3, 555.

8. Wilderson, 305.

9. Ivan Meloon, compiler. "Correspondence with Washington. Lighthouse, Fort, Coast Guard." Undated typescript (Portsmouth Athen-æum), 30.

10. Chipman, 20,21,27,33; Robert Dishman kindly provided the reference to Holland's "elegant plan" for a combined courthouse and jail in Haverhill for the recently created Grafton County: *New-Hampshire Gazette*, 24 December 1773, 3.

11. P. A. Penfold, ed. *Maps and Plans in the Public Record Office. 2. America and West Indies* (London: Her Majesty's Stationery Office), 447, lists the plan of "Lake Winipissiokee, including the new settlements" by Thos. Wheeler, February 1770. Holland was to receive one hundred guineas upon presentation of copies of the map resulting from his survey of the province to the governor, council, and assembly. NHSP vol. 7, 264, 268, 293, 294. According to one source, Holland's New Hampshire surveys were done in 1773 and 1774 although the map was not published in

England until 1784. Belknap, 12; Chipman, 82, publishes a letter written by Wentworth in 1785 in which he recalls the 1772 favorable decision of the province's judges and attorney general on the legality of Holland's marriage to his common law wife; Machemer, 19–20, discusses the relationship of Holland and Wentworth.

12. Portsmouth Tax Lists and Accounts for 1771 list Charles Basquette (possibly a garbled rendition of Blaskowitz, 259; James Grant, 261; Captain Samuel Holland, 262; and Thomas Wheeler, 268. None is listed the next year, but Grant is shown in 1773, 1774, and 1775, on pages 379, 434, 484.

13. *New England Historical and Genealogical Register,*(Hereafter NEHGR) (Boston: New England Historic and Genealogical Society, April 1896), 167.

14. Putnam, 22, 24, 25.

15. James L. Garvin, "Academic Architecture and the Building Trades in the Piscataqua Region of New Hampshire and Maine, 1715–1815," (Ph.D. diss., Boston University, 1983),11, 55–56. Two brick houses were built in Rockingham County in the first quarter of the eighteenth century: the Weeks house in Greenland and the MacPheadris-Warner house in Portsmouth. The masons for the latter almost certainly came from Boston.

16. Charles W. Brewster, *Rambles About Portsmouth, Second Series* [hereafter Brewster II], (Portsmouth, NH: Lewis. Brewster, 1869), 99; NHSP vol. 34, 253–254; Parker, 332. David married the sister of George Gaines, another joiner, and by 1766 had built a house for himself in Portsmouth. Garvin, 76.

17. Treasury Papers, Box 9 (hereafter N.H. Treasury Papers), New Hampshire Division of Archives and Records Management, (hereafter NHDARM), Concord, N.H.

18. Wilderson, 311–333, writes of Wentworth's absorption with western boundary problems during this period and with his Wolfeborough estate where he spent much time.

19. N.H. Treasury Papers; NHSP vol. 7, 294–295.

20. N.H. Treasury Papers.

21. Julian D. Fischer, "Shipbuilding in Colonial Portsmouth: The *Raleigh*," in *Historical New Hampshire*, vol. 42, no. 1, Spring, 1987, 34,17,13. Fischer writes that Noah Parker supplied nails, Moses Noble masts, and Joseph Simes paint. Furnald was employed as a tinsmith.

22. N.H. Treasury Papers; Inventory of Estate of Thomas Bell, Probate Docket 4075, Rockingham Registry of Deeds and Probate, Brentwood, N.H.

23. N.H. Treasury Papers; Fischer,13; Saltonstall, 60, wrote that "as a rule, these spars were as many yards in length as they were in diameter:" Thus, the "kink post" would have been about seventy feet long; Gershom Bradford, *The Mariner's Dictionary.* New York, Weathervane Press, 1952, 143; René de Kerchove, *International Maritime Dictionary.* New York: Van Nostrand Reinhold Company, 1961, q.v. King Post.

24. N.H. Treasury Papers; William Doak may have been the son of the Boston mason William Doak who worked on the brick MacPheadris-Warner house, a rare exception to the wood construction norm, back in 1716. Or he might even have been the same man, who lived to then astonishing age of ninety-eight and would have been eighty-three in 1771. A Captain William Doak was listed on the 1770 Portsmouth tax list (as was the other mason on the job, William Caverly). Garvin, 55–56, writes that the William Doak who worked on the MacPheadris-Warner house sometimes

worked as a mariner in the Boston area, and presumably he or a son of the same name combined the two professions in the Piscataqua region.

25. N.H. Treasury Papers.

26. Ibid.; Saltonstall, 42, identifies three pilots, including Briard, in 1760; Abraham Rees, *The Cyclopaedia*, q.v. "Lighthouse."

27. N.H. Treasury Papers.

28. N.H. Treasury Papers.

29. Parker was paid by the province for cleaning and repairing guns, 1768–1771, and making a stove for the assembly room in 1773. NHSP vol. 7, 186, 228, 283, 319; Adoniram J. Patterson, "Historical Address," in *Centennial Anniversary of the Planting of Universalism in Portsmouth, N. H.* (Portsmouth: Wm. A. Plaisted, printer, 1874),18; George A. Nelson, compiler, "U. S. Customs Records and History, Portsmouth, N. H." typescript in six volumes, Portsmouth Athenæum, Portsmouth, N. H., volume 1, "Joseph Whipple" (hereafter Nelson I), 151, provides the dimensions of the lantern; Garvin, 13, notes that though iron was being smelted locally, through the eighteenth century most was imported.

30. N.H. Treasury Papers; Furnald was listed as a "brazier" in the 1771 Portsmouth tax list; Garvin writes that Germans had set up a glass manufactory in Braintree near Boston in 1752 but had stopped production by 1769. The lead and sheet copper would also have been imported; the first copper rolling mill in America was not established until the late 1790s, when Paul Revere opened one. Margot Gayle and David W. Look, *Metals in America's Historic Buildings.* (Washington, D.C.: U.S. Department of the Interior, Heritage Conservation and Recreation Service, Technical Preservation Services Division, 1980), 8, 23.

31. N.H. Treasury Papers; *New-Hampshire Gazette,* 21 June 1771.

32. Nelson I, 153. In 1804, Collector of Customs Joseph Whipple referred to the new replacement lighthouse's greater height, "now 80' to the lantern" as a justification for increased pay for the lightkeeper.

33. N. H. Treasury Papers; Wilderson, 335 and 371 (note 50). Wentworth was in Wolfeborough most of July, evidently, and wrote from there on the twenty-third to Lord Rockingham about a doe he had captured and sent to a relative in England.

34. The French built a lighthouse at Louisbourg, Nova Scotia, in 1733. Dudley Witney, *The Lighthouse* (Boston: New York Graphic Society, 1975. Reprint edition, New York: Arch Cape Press, 1989).17.

35. NHSP vol. 7, 287–288.

36. N.H. Treasury Papers.

37. Ibid.

38. NHSP vol. 3, 572-573; N.H. Treasury Papers: The record of payments for oil from December 18.1771–December 19, 1772 lists fourteen suppliers of fish oil: Henry Card, James Neal, William Gilbert, John Talton (Tarlton, probably), Thomas Bell, Esq., Thomas Bell, Jr., James Hickey, Nathan White, Pettiah Weeks, Jeral Stone, Stephen Chace, William Vennard, Samuel Wallace, and John Davidson.

39. N.H. Treasury Papers.

40. Lorenzo Sabine, *Biographical Sketches of Loyalists of the American Revolution,* vol.1. (Boston: Little, Brown and Company, 1864.), 320; NHSP vol. 14, 28–30.

41. NHSP vol. 7, 9–10.

42. *Laws of New Hampshire* vol. 3, 594–595.

43. NHSP vol. 18, 651.

44. N.H. Treasury Papers; *Laws of New Hampshire*, 3:623–624.

45. "Port of Piscataqua Colonial Customs Records 1770–1775 Ports-mouth NH," Facsimile, unpaged. Portsmouth Athenæum. This document gives a partial picture as it includes only commerce with the West Indies and southern Europe. Activity with the Canadian provinces, England, northern Europe, and the other American colonies would have been substantial.

46. Ibid.

47. "Port of Piscataqua Colonial Customs Records 1770-1775 Portsmouth NH,"; Saltonstall, 51–53.

48. *New-Hampshire Gazette*, 25 November 1774, 4.

49. Raymond A. Brighton. *They Came To Fish.* (Portsmouth N.H.: Randall/Winebaum Enterprises, 1979), 50–54; Saltonstall, 85–87. A later shipment of tea, early in 1775, was publicly burned. *New-Hampshire Gazette,* 20 January 1775.

50. Wilderson, 404, 405.

51. Brighton, 57, 58.

52. Paul Wilderson, "The Raids on Fort William and Mary: Some New Evidence," *Historical New Hampshire,* vol. 30, no. 3, Fall, 1975, 186–202.

53. Ibid., 194–195.

54. Brighton, 61, 62.

55. Charles L. Parsons, "The Capture of Fort William and Mary," (The William and Mary Committee of The New Hampshire American Revolution Bicentennial Commission, 1974.) Reprint from *Proceedings of the New Hampshire Historical Society,* vol. 4, with additions of letters from New Castle selectmen and Governor. Wentworth, 30, 31; Sabine, 320, 321.

56. John Wentworth to Earl of Dartmouth, 12 September 1775. Transcript of Wentworth Letter Book, NHDARM, Volume 3, 152.

57. Records of the Committee of Safety, NHDARM, 88.

58. *New-Hampshire Gazette,* 15 August 1775; William H. Emery, *The Salters of Portsmouth* (New Bedford, Mass.: New Bedford Print Co., 1986).

59. Brighton, 64, 65.

60. Harriet S. Lacy, "A Postscript: Fort William and Mary Becomes Fort Constitu-tion," in *Historical New Hampshire*, vol. 29, no. 4, Winter, 1974, 284; Emery, 36, 37; vol. 8, 92.

61. Records of the Council, Book 7, NHDARM, 90.

62. *Laws of New Hampshire* vol. 4, 557– 558.

63. N.H. Treasury Papers.

64. NHSP vol. 20, 234.

65. Ibid., 105, 251.

66. *Laws of New Hampshire* 5:35, 36.

67. NHSP, vol. 20, 328, 385; vol. 21, 13, 155, 166; Lacy, 285.

Chapter III: The Federal Government Takes Over

1. Nelson I, 45.

2. Charlene Bangs Bickford and Helen E. Veit, Editors. *Legislative Histories, Volume 5.* (Baltimore and London: Johns Hopkins University Press, 1986), 1255.

3. Naish,117; Hague and Christie, 27, 46, 56.

4. Hague and Christie, 44.

5. "A History of Enforcement in the United States Customs Service 1789–1875." (San Francisco: Department of the Treasury, 1998), vii.

6. Ibid., 13–14.

7. Ibid., 4, 25 (note).; Thomas L. Tullock, "Presidential Appointments at Portsmouth," in *Granite Monthly* (vol. 6, no. 4, January 1886), 111.

8. NHSP vol. 20, 572; Nelson I, 1–26; NHSP vol. 23, 270–271.

9. Jefferson is now in Coos County. Nelson I, 1-6; Benjamin G. Willey, "Incidents in White Mountain History." (Boston: Nathaniel Noyes, 1856), 70–72.

10. Fischer.

11. Jere Daniell, "Frontier and Constitution: Why Grafton County Delegates Voted 10 to 1 for Ratification," *Historical New Hampshire* (vol. 45, no. 3, Fall 1990), 215, 219.

12. NHSP vol. 18, 811–812.

13. Nelson I, 34, 35.

14. Ibid., 155.

15. Ibid., 37, 38.

16. *American State Papers* (hereafter ASP), Miscellaneous Volume I. Washington, D.C.: Gales & Seaton, 1834), 67.

17. Ibid., 60.

18. Carl E. Prince, *The Federalists and the Origins of the U. S. Civil Service* (New York: New York University Press, 1977), 45–66; Richard E. Winslow, III, *Wealth and Honor.* (Portsmouth N.H.: Portsmouth Marine Society, 1988), 84, 85.

19. Prince, 14, 50–53.

20. Ibid., 53, 54.

21. *New-Hampshire Gazette*, 16 October 1798; *Oracle of the Day* (Portsmouth NH), 3 November 1798; *A Biographical Directory of the United States Customs Service, 1771–1989,* compiled by the Information Services Division Office of Logistics Management Comptroller's Office, United States Customs Service, second volume, March 1986, *q. v.* Thomas Martin. Martin died in 1805.

22. Prince, 55.

23. Until 1820, responsibility for the federal lighthouse system alternated between the Treasury Secretary (1789–92 and 1802–1813) and the Commissioner of Revenue (1792-1802 and 1813-1820). Arnold Burgess Johnson, *The Modern Lighthouse Service* (Washington, D.C.: Government Printing Office, 1890), 8.

24. Lighthouse Deeds and Contracts, Book A (hereafter Lighthouse Deeds and Contracts). Record Group 26, National Archives, Washington D.C. (hereafter NARG26), 3; NHSP vol. 18, 817,822. The President most likely signed the contracts

because the enactment preceded by two months the September 2, 1789 creation of the Treasury Department. Washington appointed the first secretary, Alexander Hamilton, later that month. "A History of Enforcement in the U. S. Customs Service 1789–1785, 13.

25. Nelson I, 45, 49, 57, 60.

26. NHSP vol. 22, 127, 131,145,179; Putnam, 32.

27. Lighthouse Deeds and Contracts, 3; NHSP vol. 18, 817,822.

28. Nelson I, 81–82.

29. Ibid., 66, 68.

30. Ibid., 85.

31. Francis Ross Holland, Jr. *America's Lighthouses: An Illustrated History.* (New York: Dover Publications, 1988), 14.

32. Nelson I, 87, 88, 100, 101

33. Ibid., 91, 92.

34. Meloon, 94–95.

35. Ibid.

36. Putnam, 27; Nelson I, 82, 83.

37. Nelson I, 93, 100,101, 109, 119.

38. Meloon, 100, 102. It is not clear when the fort was garrisoned. Construction continued off and on; the phase begun in 1794 was finished in 1796. Lacy, 288. Further work was done near the end of the century because of the Quasi-War with France, according to unpublished research by Nelson Lawry.

39. Putnam, 214–217.

40. Ibid., 215.

41. Phineas Merrill, "Plan of the Town of New Castle,1806" and Mason H. Stansbury, cartographer, U.S. Coast Survey, "Preliminary Chart of Portsmouth Harbor, New Hampshire, 1842, 1843, 1844" both in the collection of the Portsmouth Athenæum.

42. Nelson, 98–99.

43. Ibid., 103–104, 108.

44. Ibid., 108–109, 126–127.

45. Nelson I, 8. The U.S. Life-Saving Service was created as a branch of the Revenue Marine in 1871 and was made a separate agency in 1878. Both maintained individual identities until 1915. In that year the Revenue Marine and the Life-Saving Service were re-united as the U. S. Coast Guard, and in 1939 the Lighthouse Service, the senior member of this maritime triumvirate, was merged with the Coast Guard.

46. Gerald Foss, "Hopley Yeaton and the Revenue Marine," *The Trestle Board,* August 1965 and May 1975; Walter H. Fentress, *Centennial History of the Navy Yard at Portsmouth, N. H.* (Portsmouth, N.H.: O. M. Knight, Publisher, 1876), 82.

47. Horatio D. Smith, Elliot Snow, ed., *Early History of the United States Revenue Marine Service, 1789–1849.* (A Coast Guard Bicentennial Publication, Washington, D.C., 1989), 7; Nelson I, 51, 57, 59.

48. Nelson I, 121; Richard E. Winslow III, *"Wealth and Honor": Portsmouth During the Golden Age of Privateering, 1775–1815* (Portsmouth, N.H.: The Portsmouth Marine Society, 1988), 93; The *Oracle of the Day* (Portsmouth, N. H.) 11 August 1798, 3.

49. Nelson I,128–133; Smith, 17, 18, 21; *Record of Movements. Vessels of the United States Coast Guard. 1790-December 31, 1933. (*Washington, D.C.: United States Coast Guard, 1933), 110, 93, 310; Irving H. King. *The Coast Guard Under Sail: The U.S. Revenue Cutter Service, 1789-1865* (Annapolis, Maryland: Naval Institute Press, 1989), 20, 22–33.

50. King,122.

51. Joseph Whipple letter to John Langdon, January 31, 1793. Portsmouth Athenæum MS 50, Box 4A.

52. Nelson I, 94–95, 110–111; Coxe to Whipple. Lighthouse Letters, volume 1, NARG26,118.

53. Nelson I, 97–98.

54. Ibid. Mr. Clifford was probably Ebeneezer Clifford (1746–1821), who was active as a designer-builder in Exeter and Portsmouth and is discussed in Garvin, 262–269, 309–354, 435–457.

55. Nelson I, 98, 99.

56. Saltonstall, 128–129; *New-Hampshire Gazette*, 23 January 1799.

57. Meloon, 99, 100, 102.

58. Ibid., 99, 108, 108A.

59. *New-Hampshire Gazette*, 16 August 1802.

60. *New-Hampshire Gazette,* 31 August 1802.

61. Meloon, 103. There was still a shortage of workmen in town, because of rebuilding activity as late as April 1804, according to the *New-Hampshire Gazette,* 3 April 1804.

62. Meloon, 103; Franklin O. Spinney, "An Ingenious Yankee Craftsman," *The Magazine Antiques*, vol. 44 (September 1943), 116–119; *The Oracle of the Day*, 3 November 1798.

63. Lighthouse Contract Files, NARG26.

64. Ibid.; Putman, 22–23.

65. Lighthouse Contract Files ; Meloon,106.

66. *New-Hampshire Gazette*, 13 August 1803.

67. Timothy Upham to Stephen Pleasonton, 3 November 1820, Lighthouse Letters, Box 17E, NARG26 (hereafter Lighthouse Letters); *Portsmouth Herald,* 6 March 1909; Portsmouth Harbor Light-station Clipping File, NARG26, 1.

68. Meloon, 106, 108, 110,111.

69. *New-Hampshire Gazette*, 31 December 1805.

70. John Albee, writing in 1884 about the cast-iron lighthouse that replaced this one, evidently thought that it was the structure built by Governor Wentworth in 1771. John Albee, *New Castle Historic and Picturesque.* Hampton, NH: Peter E. Randall, 1974 (facsimile reprint of 1884 publication), 25.

71. Nelson I, 93.

72. *A Record of the Services of the Commissioned Officers and Enlisted Men of Kittery and Eliot, Maine.* (Boston: Alfred Mudge & Sons, Printers, 1901), 86; Chandler E. Potter, *The Military History of the State of New Hampshire 1621–1861* (Baltimore: Genealogical Publishing Co., Inc., 1972), 290–291, 302; Hazel Standeven, compiler, "Brown-Duncan Genealogy," 1981 typescript, (New Castle, N.H. Public Library), 33-34.

73. Nelson I, 91, 100–102.

74. Ibid., 100; Lacy, 191–192.

75. Nelson I, 105, 109, 112, 119.

76. Ibid., 112, 117, 121. Coxe wrote that at Cape Henlopen light there were more lamps of the same type, without mentioning whether this keeper was disabled. NARG 26, 211.

77. Ibid., 153.

78. Ibid., 154–155, 162.

79. Lacy, 290; Nelson I, 183.

80. *New-Hampshire Gazette*, 11 July 1809; Meloon, 183.

81. David Duncan to Joseph Whipple, 9 April 1813, transmitted to Washington, Lighthouse Letters.

82. Colonel H. Walbach to Timothy Upham, 10 February 1810; Upham to Wm. H. Crawford, Secretary of the Treasury, 14 March 1820, Lighthouse Letters.

83. Timothy Upham to Stephen Pleasonton, 19 April 1820, Lighthouse Letters.

84. Walbach to Upham, 10 February 1820 and Upham to Crawford, 14 March 1820, Lighthouse Letters.

85. Probate Docket 11288, Rockingham County Registry of Deeds and Probate, Brentwood, N.H.

Chapter IV: Boon Island Lighthouse and the Rise of Winslow Lewis

1. Clark,145–146.

2. Joyce Butler, "Rising Like a Phoenix: Commerce in Southern Maine, 1775–1830," in Laura Fecych Sprague, editor, *Agreeable Situations: Society, Commerce, and Art in Southern Maine, 1780–1830* (Kennebunk, Maine: Brick Store Museum, 1987),18.

3. William H. Rowe, *The Maritime History of Maine: Three Centuries of Shipbuilding and Seafaring* (Freeport, Maine: The Bond Wheelwright Company, 1966), 66.

4. Seguin Island light at the mouth of the Kennebec River was built 1796; Franklin Island light in Muscongus Bay and Whitehead Island light in Penobscot Bay were built in 1807. Holland, 80–85. The 1796 edition of *Blunt's American Coast Pilot*, 33, shows that Seguin light was in existence a year before the 1797 date cited by Holland. "Buoy List. Maine and New Hampshire" (Washington, D.C.: Government Printing Office, 1923), 61 gives the date of the building of the Wood Island light.

5. Deane,1.

6. Edward C. Moody, *Handbook History of the Town of York*. (York, Maine: The York Publishing Company, ca. 1914), 196–197.

7. Deane, 3.

8. *The American Coast Pilot*, 1800 edition, 38.

9. Lighthouse Letters, microfilm M63, roll 2, 80, 101, William Miller to Benjamin Lincoln; Edward Rowe Snow, *The Lighthouses of New England*. (New York: Dodd, Mead and Company, 1973), 94, 95.

10. Snow, 95.

11. Ibid., 95; Eliphalet Grover, "Logg Book (1825–1839), (hereafter Eliphalet Grover Log), Old York Historical Society, York, Maine. In his entry for May 11, 1839, Grover wrote, "Taking up the Bones of two people that were Drowned heare When

the first monement was Erected heare," but the bones are evidently those of men who build the second monument.

12. *New-Hampshire Gazette*, 29 May 1810, 1 January, 1811.

13. *New-Hampshire Gazette*, 19 February, 12 March and 16 April 1811; Land Cessions, Commonwealth of Massachusetts, NARG26 (Massachusetts to the United States); *Annals of Congress, 11th Congress, 3rd Session* (Washington: Gales & Seaton, 1853) 347.

14. Lighthouse Contracts File, NARG26 (unidentified, probably Boston, newspaper clipping); Christopher Hall, compiler, *Boston Architects and Builders compiled from the Boston Directory 1789–1846* (Cambridge, Mass.: Massachusetts Committee for the Preservation of Architectural Records, 1989), *q.v.* Porter and Heath. Porter was listed as a mason in Boston directories, 1796–1846, Heath in the years 1798–1813.

15. Lighthouse Contracts File, NARG26.

16. Ibid.

17. Stevenson, 287–288; Sarah C. Gleason, *Kindly Lights. A History of the Lighthouses of Southern New England* (Boston: Beacon Press, 1991), 20; *The American Coast Pilot*. (Newburyport, Mass.: Edmund March Blunt and Angier March, 1796), 33; Putnam,195; Winslow Lewis, "Description of the Light Houses on the Coast of the United States. (Boston: Thomas G. Bangs, printer [1817]), 4, shows Wood Island lighthouse with a revolving light, perhaps installed by Winslow Lewis to replace an earlier installation of an eclipser.

18. Lighthouse Contracts File.

19. Ibid.

20. Ibid.

21. *New-Hampshire Gazette*, 5 November 1811; Snow, 96–97.As recently as 1978, during the Groundhog Day storm, the two-man crew at Boon Island was evacuated by the Coast Guard. That battering February storm washed away the boathouse, boat and boatways; water five feet deep in the house forced the men to retreat to the light tower. The light was automated soon afterwards. *Portsmouth Herald*, 7 February 1978.

22. Winslow J. Lewis, "Remarks on Lighthouses," unpaged manuscript, ca. 1820. Lighthouse Letters, box 17e, NARG26.

23. Gleason, 39–60, describes many of Lewis's questionable dealings. Richard W. Updike, "Winslow Lewis and the Lighthouses," in *American Neptune,* vol. 28, no. 1, 47, offers a slightly less critical appraisal.

24. Naish, 105; *Appleton's Dictionary of Machines Mechanics, Engine-work and Engineering* (New York: D. Appleton & company, 1852), 54.

25. Updike, 32–35.

26. One of the 1810 observers of a demonstration of the lights described the lamps themselves as "fountain Argand lamps, of the size commonly used in dwelling places." ASP, Volume 7, Commerce and Navigation, volume 1. (Washington, D. C.: Gales & Seaton, 1832), 879; Arthur H. Hayward, *Colonial and Early American Lighting* (New York: Dover Publications, Inc., 1962); republication of the second, 1927 Little, Brown edition), illustrates opposite page 92 a number of metal reflector sconces for candles, including a concave reflector made up of pieces of reflective glass, and discusses, pages 41–42, oil lamps with magnifying lenses in use before the end of the eighteenth century, illustrated opposite pages 32, 44, and 55.

27. Updike, 34–36; ASP, 879–886.

28. ASP, 880.

29. Ibid.

30. Ibid., 881–883.

31. Updike, 35–37, 50.

32. *Boston Gazette*, 12 August 1811, 1.

33. Updike, 36–37; Lewis; Eliphalet Grover Log. The Fifth Treasury Auditor in charge of lighthouses wrote in 1838 that no lenses had been used after he took office in 1820. *Lighthouses. Fifth Auditor on Execution of Act of July 7, 1838*. 25th Cong., 3rd Sess., 1838-39, H. Doc. 24 (Serial 345).

34. Lewis; David Duncan to Joseph Whipple, 9 April 1813 and Joseph Whipple to Albert Gallatin, 4 May 1813. Lighthouse Letters.

35. Updike, 37; *War Journal* (Portsmouth N.H.), 26 March 1813, 3.

36. Meloon, 152, 153.

37. Updike, 40–44.

38. Nelson I, 22–26. Winslow, *"Wealth and Honor,"* 238.

39. Winslow, 172–173.

40. Robert Fraser, "Scituate Lighthouse," in *The Keeper's Log*, vol. 3. no. 2 (Winter 1987); Nelson I, 214–215.

41. Joseph Whipple to Samuel Smith, 21 February and 9 March 1815, Lighthouse Letters; Nelson I, 214; *Niles' Weekly Register* (Baltimore, Md.) October 6, 1814, 55, reported that orders had been given for dismantling all the lighthouses on the coast.

42. Joseph Whipple to Samuel Smith, 9 March 1815. Lighthouse Letters. Whipple received another estimate for repairs from William Marshall, a carpenter and housewright; New Hampshire Lighthouse Contracts File, NARG26.

43. *New-Hampshire Gazette*, 2 September 1817; The *Massachusetts* was sold two months later and was wrecked off the New Jersey coast on the way to new owners in the south. Paul Forsythe Johnson, *Steam and the Sea* (Salem, Mass.: Peabody Museum of Salem, 1983), 36–38.

44. Nelson , 44–45.

45. James Ladd to Winslow Lewis, 3 April 1816, Lighthouse Letters; *A Biographical Directory of the U. S. Customs Service, 1771–1989* (Washington, D.C.: U.S. Customs Service, Department of the Treasury, 1984), *q.v.* Timothy Upham.

Chapter V: The Fifth Treasury Auditor and White Island Lighthouse

1. Putnam, 52.

2. Updike, 40–44.

3. Holland, 32.

4. Henry Adams, *The Life of Albert Gallatin* (Philadelphia: J. B. Lippincott & Co., 1880), 277; William James Morgan, et al., eds. *The Autobiography of Rear Admiral Charles Wilkes* (Washington, D.C.: Naval History Division, Department of the Navy, 1978), 317–318; Anthony S. Pitch, "The Burning of Washington," The White House Historical Association website: www.whitehousehistory.org.

5. *The report of the general superintendent of the light-house establishment,* 31st Cong., 2nd sess., H. Ex.. Doc.14, 1850,131.

6. Putnam, 42; Dennis L. Noble, *Lighthouses & Keepers. The U. S. Lighthouse Service and Its Legacy.* (Annapolis, MD: Naval Institute Press, 1997), 7.

7. William H. Pierson, Jr., *American Buildings and Their Architects. The Colonial and Neo-Classical Styles* (New York: Anchor Books, 1976) 337–372.

8. Michael Fazio, "Benjamin Latrobe's Designs for a Lighthouse at the Mouth of the Mississippi River," *Journal of the Society of Architectural Historians,* vol. 48, no. 3, (September 1989), 232–244 and 241, note 42. A lighthouse for the Mississippi was approved by Congress shortly after the Louisiana Purchase. Due to delays in site selection and the War of 1812, final plans, specifications, and funding were not in place until 1817.

9. Ibid., 245–246; Updike, 43.

10. Fazio, 245.

11. Ibid., 245.

12. Todd Shallatt, "Building Waterways, 1802-1861: Science and the United States Army in Early Public Works," *Technology and Culture,* vol. 31, no. 1 (January 1990), 18–25, 32–34, discusses French models for engineering training contrasted with the more pragmatic British building traditions and U. S. suspicion of foreign models.

13. Fazio, 245–247, writes that this lighthouse was used from 1823 until 1856 when it was superceded by a lighthouse at another site. Holland, 145.

14. Ray Brighton, *Port of Portsmouth Ships and the Cotton Trade* (Portsmouth, N.H.: Portsmouth Marine Society, Peter E. Randall Publisher,1986), 13–55; Nelson, 44–46.

15. ASP, *Documents, Legislative and Executive, 1815-1823*, Vol. 2, 14, 518.

16. *Annals of Congress,* 16th Cong., 1st Sess. (Washington, D.C.: Gales & Seaton, 1855), 2622–3.

17. Lyman Rutledge, *The Isles of Shoals in Lore and Legend.* (Boston: The Star Island Corporation, 1971) and John Scribner Jenness, *The Isles of Shoals: An Historical Sketch* (Boston: Riverside Press, 1873).

18. Clark, 65,115; Blunt, 1804 edition, 37–38.

19. *New-Hampshire Gazette*, 18 April 1798.

20. Rutledge, 47–48, has one of the many retellings of this wreck, and gives evidence for its being *Conception;* Joseph Whipple reported that a letter found on one of the bodies identified the vessel as *Conception*, bound from Cadiz to New York. Nelson I, 208; Ray Brighton, "Shipwrecks Were His Business," in *Portsmouth Herald,* 14 June 1958, quotes at length from Samuel Haley's accounts of these rescues, for which he expected to be paid by the Commonwealth of Massachusetts.

21. Timothy Upham to Stephen Pleasonton, 28 June 1820, Lighthouse Letters; *Portsmouth Oracle,* 17 June 1820.

22. Lighthouse Letters.; *Laws of New Hampshire*, 8:898.

23. Lighthouse Letters.

24. Wayne Wheeler, "A Lighthouse for Bell Rock," *The Keeper's Log,* Summer 1988, 24–25; Hague and Christie, 171.

25. Upham to Pleasonton, 28 June 1820, Lighthouse Letters; Putnam, 228.

26. Upham to Pleasonton.

27. Garvin, 484–504.

28. John F. Parrott to Stephen Pleasonton, 12 May, 1821, Lighthouse Letters; Garvin, 504; Bryant F. Tolles, Jr., with Carolyn K. Tolles, *New Hampshire Architecture. An Illustrated Guide* (Hanover, N.H.: University Press of New England, 1979), 235; B. T. Whitehouse, collector, "Dover Cotton Factory #1" Pamphlet. (Dover, N.H. Public Library), 4; Robert A.Whitehouse and Cathleen C. Beaudoin, *Port of Dover: Two Centuries of Shipping on the Cochecho.* (Portsmouth: The Portsmouth Marine Society, Peter E. Randall Publisher,1988), 12. No William Palmer was listed in Dover or Portsmouth in the U.S.Census for 1820, but two—perhaps a father and son who were both masons—were listed in Dover in 1830.

29. Levi Woodbury, *Statement of Contracts authorized in 1834.* 23rd Cong., 2nd Sess., 1835. H. Doc.161; Betsy H. Woodman, "A Customhouse for Newburyport (1834–1835)," *Essex Historical Collections,* July 1985 reprint, 2.

30. *Report of the Officers Constituting the Light-House Board,* 32nd *Cong.,* 1st sess.,1852, S. Exec. Doc. 28, 114–116, quotes at length from an 1843 statement by Pleasonton in which he makes a case for using salt water and salt sand in mortars.

31. New Hampshire Lighthouse Contract File, NARG26.

32. Ibid.

33. Ibid.

34. Ibid.

35. *Portsmouth Chronicle*, 21 August 1877, described the house, when it was being drastically altered into a storage building, as having walls 2 feet thick, with the massive 14 foot square chimney taking up nearly a quarter of the interior space.

36. New Hampshire Lighthouse Contract File.

37. Ibid.

38. The contract filed in the National Archives, was dated 17 August; Folsom and Palmer's ad was published in the *Portsmouth Oracle* on the 12th of August.

39. Reference to teams of oxen used for the seawall construction is in Upham to Pleasonton, 16 July 1823, Lighthouse Letters.

40. Timothy Upham to Stephen Pleasonton, 3 November 1820, Lighthouse Letters, refers to Marston's work as master carpenter at White Island; the *Portsmouth Herald* of 6 March 1909 contains a long article about White Island light and appears to have been written by someone who researched customs house records no longer in existence. The author refers to the subcontractor having been paid nine hundred dollars, and mentions that he had built the lighthouse at Fort Constitution. The Portsmouth Directory for 1821 lists "Nathaniel Marstin, joiner."

41. Upham to Pleasonton, 23 August 1820, Lighthouse Letters.

42. New Hampshire Lighthouse Contracts File contains the receipt signed by Marston.

43. Ibid., "Mr. Willard" was probably the Boston clockmaker, Simon Willard, who never took out patents for his lighthouse clockworks, although his son Benjamin did in the 1830s. It is not clear whether Willard himself provided the light-rotating and bell-striking machinery. Benjamin manufactured a device installed in the Boston Harbor lighthouse in 1828 and in 1839 patented a quick-flashing device for light-houses. John Ware Willard, *Simon Willard and His Clocks.* (New York: Dover Publications, Inc., 1968), 36, 75–78.

44. New Hampshire Lighthouse Contracts File.

45. Meloon, 114, 115, 118, 119.

46. *The Oracle* (Portsmouth, N.H.) 1 December 1820.

47. New Hampshire Lighthouse Contracts File.

48. Ibid..

49. *Oracle of the Day* (Portsmouth, N.H.), 1 December 1820; *New-Hampshire Gazette,* 5 December 1820.

50. Ibid.

51. Ibid.

52. Upham to Pleasonton, 3 November and 23 December 1820, Lighthouse Letters.

53. Upham to Pleasonton, 12 June 1821, 14 June 1824, Lighthouse Letters. The civil engineer John Smeaton, cited in Andrew Ure, *A Dictionary of Arts, Manufactures, and Mines,* London: Orme, Brown, Green, & Longmans, 1840, 867–869, had before the end of the eighteenth century written on mortars using lime with properties that made them suitable for wet sites. But as late as the second decade of the nineteenth century, engineers trained at West Point used a textbook that deemed Thomaston lime best for hydraulic works. In use at West Point in 1823 for training Army engineers, this work was first translated from the French in 1826 with additions pertinent to the United States. M. L. Sganzin, *An Elementary Course in Civil Engineering,* Third edition. (Boston: Hilliard, Gray & Co., 1836), 22; D. H. Mahan's *An Elementary Course of Civil Engineering for the use of the Cadets of the U. S. Military Academy,* second edition, (New York: Wiley and Putnam, 1838),15, revised this opinion, stating that mortar using Thomaston or other common limes "will never harden underwater or in very moist places."

54. *Portsmouth Herald,* 6 March 1909; Upham to Pleasonton, 12 June,1821 and 14 June 1824, Lighthouse Letters.

55. Upham to Pleasonton, 5 October 1823, Lighthouse Letters. There is an account in the *Portsmouth Herald* of 6 March 1909 that the bell fell because the chain holding it broke and damaged some machinery which had to be repaired by a Portsmouth clockmaker named Gaines.

56. *American Coast Pilot,* 1827 edition, 45; 1833 edition, 164.

57. John P. Decatur to Stephen Pleasonton, 1 December 1829 and 10 April 1830, Lighthouse Letters; Blunt's *American Coast Pilot,* 1837 edition, 158.

58. *Portsmouth Journal,* 23 April and 5 May 1827.

59. ASP, *Class 4, Commerce & Navigation,* vol. 2. 505–506; Brighton, 45; George Nelson, compiler, "Early Portsmouth U. S. Customs House Records and History," Volume 3 of 6 (Hereaftrer Nelson III), 200.

60. Celia Thaxter, *Among the Isles of Shoals.* Boston: James R. Osgood & Co., 1873, 35–37; for reference to Haley's request for reimbursement see Lighthouse Letters, 1792-1809, NARG26 microfilm M 63, roll 2,168, 182, 215. Whether his request was granted has not been determined; *American Coast Pilot,* 1804, 138. In this and in the 1800 edition, 40, reference is made to a grist windmill on the north side of the island that could serve to identify the location for mariners. Upham to Pleasonton, 21 November 1821, Lighthouse Letters, reports the completion of the Malaga-Smuttynose seawall.

61. New Hampshire Lighthouse Contract File, copy of an Act ceding to the United States a place called sunken rocks in Portsmouth Harbor; Upham to Pleasonton, 21 November 1821, Lighthouse Letters.

62. Jonathan Folsom and Thomas Haven to Timothy Upham, 16 Nov-ember 1821 and Upham to Pleasonton, 21 November 1821, Lighthouse Letters.

63. Ibid.

64. New Hampshire Lighthouse Contract File.

65. ASP, *Class 4, Commerce & Navigation,* vol. 2, 505.

66. Ibid. Gundalows were evidently not taxable property, and thus do not appear on Portsmouth tax rolls, although Thomas Haven during this period was sole or part owner of several vessels. In 1813, he had bought from Folsom a remarkable, speculatively-built brick house with features suggesting the influence of William Thornton's "Octagon House" in Washington, according to Garvin, 488–490; *Portsmouth Journal,* 5 June 1822 published the request for proposals and on 6 July 1822 the Folsom-Haven ad for laborers.

67. *Portsmouth Journal,* 1 November 1823; ASP, 506; Upham to Pleasonton, 16 July 1823, Lighthouse Letters.

68. *Portsmouth Journal,* 1 November 1823; ASP, 506; Lighthouse Letters, 4 August 1823. The contractors were allowed another $1,500 to complete the project.

69. Upham to Pleasonton, 11 February and 14 June 1824, Lighthouse Letters.

70. *Portsmouth Herald,* 11 January 1909 describes the extensive 1823 damage to the seawall and the re-building of 1903-1904; *Portsmouth Chronicle* 5 December 1888 reported on the *Teal's* being swept over the seawall.

71. *New-Hampshire Gazette,* 7 February 1826.

72. Ibid.; Upham to Pleasonton, 15 February 1826, Lighthouse Letters.

73. Upham to Pleasonton, 15 February 1826; George A. Nelson, "Lighthouse at Newcastle was 7th Built in U. S.," *Portsmouth Herald,* 13 May 1933.

74. *Register of Officers and Agents in the Service of the United States,* (Hereafter Register of Officers) (Washington, D.C.: publisher varies.) 1824:, 20, 27–29, 32, 47; 1832, 27–32.

75. Ibid..

Chapter VI: Whale's Back and Boon Island

1. *Portsmouth Journal,* 19 May and 15 September 1827.

2. For example, the *Portsmouth Journal,* 14 July 1827 reported the arrival of the Ship *Hitty* in forty-two days from Liverpool with a consignment of salt, iron and coal to Portsmouth merchants, and "24 passengers—to be employed in the Calico Printing establishment at Dover;" Saltonstall, 187.

3. *Portsmouth Oracle,* 28 April 1821.

4. Timothy Upham to Stephen Pleasonton, 16 March 1827, Lighthouse Letters.

5. *Annals of Congress, Nineteenth Congress, Third Session* (Washington, D.C.: Gales & Seaton,1829), xvii; *Portsmouth Journal,* 3 March 1827.

6. Upham to Pleasonton, 16 March and 10 April 1827, Lighthouse Letters, discusses 1826 wrecks and the petition asking Maine legislature to cede sites to U.S.

7. Ibid.

8. Nelson I, 110.

9. Upham to Pleasonton, 16 March and 10 April 1827, Lighthouse Letters.

10. Some of the 1820s lighthouses where a keeper's house had a lantern mounted on top of the roof already built or underway were at Fog's Point in Chesapeake Bay

(1827), Sandy Neck in Cape Cod Bay (1827), Long Point in Provincetown, Massachusetts (1827), and Matinicus Island, Maine, where the stone keeper's house had a lantern at each end of the roof (1827). In Stonington, Connecticut and Warwick Neck, Rhode Island, lighthouses had been built in 1823 and 1826 with the light tower built directly against the wall of the keeper's house. "List of Light-Houses, Lighted Beacons, and Floating Lights, of the Atlantic, Gulf, and Pacific Coasts of the United States."(Washington, D,C.: Government Printing Office, 1862), 42–43, 18–19, 12–13, 26–27.

11. *Portsmouth Journal,* 27 October 1827, 23 February 1828.

12. New Hampshire Lighthouse Clipping File; Updike, 43–44, writes of Lewis's standardized specifications.

13. Upham to Pleasonton, 4 June 1828, Lighthouse Letters.

14. Ibid.

15. Ibid.

16. Ibid. Upham was a Proprietor of the Athenæum, which by the mid-1820s had acquired *Rees's Encyclopaedia.*

17. *Portsmouth Journal*, 7 March 1829; Charles Lanman, *Dictionary of the United States Congress.* (Philadelphia: J. B. Lippincot & Co., 1859), 42.

18. *New-Hampshire Gazette*, 31 March, 7 and 14 April 1829.

19. Winslow Lewis claimed design credit for the very similar 1839 Robbins' Reef lighthouse off Staten Island in New York Harbor, for which Daniel Haselton was contractor. Winslow Lewis, "A Review of the Report of I. W. P. Lewis on the State of the Light Houses on the Coasts of Maine and Massachusetts . . . " (Boston: Tuttle and Dennett, 1843), 6; Robert G. Bachand, *Northeast Lights.* (Norwalk, CT: Sea Sports Publications, 1989), 312–313.

20. Andrew Ure, *A Dictionary of Arts, Manufactures, and Mines* (London: Longman, Green, & Longman, 1840), 867–869.

21. *New-Hampshire Gazette,* 25 March 1829; New Hampshire Lighthouse Contracts File contains the articles of agreement with the contractors.

22. Ibid.

23. Robert Fraser, "Scituate Lighthouse," *The Keeper's Log,* vol. 3, no. 2 (Winter, 1987), 4; *Report of I. W. P. Lewis, Civil Engineer* 27th Cong., 3rd sess., 1843, H. Doc.183, CS 422.

24. *New-Hampshire Gazette,* 25 March 1829.

25. *Portsmouth Journal,* 8 November 1828, 9 May 1829, 18 April 1829; Donald B. Cole, *Jacksonian Democracy in New Hampshire, 1800–1851* (Cambridge: Harvard University Press, 1970), 88.

26. Lighthouse Letters and New Hampshire Lighthouse Contract File.

27. Rachael Wolford, Cathlamet, Washington, descendant of Daniel Haselton, letter to Jane Porter, undated (1986); Garvin, 399, 429, 470, 483; Bachand, 313.

28. *New-Hampshire Gazette*, 2 June 1829. Three spar buoys were installed: one on the west edge of Logy Ledge at the entrance to Pepperrell's Cove; another on the eastern edge of Stielman's Rock off the Portsmouth Harbor lighthouse (painted black with a black ball on the top); the third was a replacement marker for Kitt's rock just off the mouth of the river (painted black with a white ball on top). Decatur also requested bids on repairing the boatways at White Island.

29. John Decatur to Stephen Pleasonton, 5 June 1829, Lighthouse Letters.

31. *Portsmouth Journal*, 14 November 1906; Petition of William Palmer and Daniel Haselton, 22nd Cong., 2nd sess., 1832, H.Rep. 343, CS226. The identity of Mr. Rogers was not been determined. Conceivably he was architect Isaiah Rogers, whose influential Tremont Hotel was just being completed in Boston. Rogers, who married a Portland woman, conceivably stopped in Portsmouth on his way there for a visit; however there is no documentation for this, according to leading Rogers expert Denys Peter Myers of Alexandria, Virginia. Telephone conversation with the author, April, 1991. "Mr. Blasdell" was referred to in 1830 as having been appointed to keep an eye on the work. William Pickering to S. Pleasonton, letter of 14 August 1830 and John P. Decatur to Samuel D. Ingham, Secretary of the Treasury, 28 November 1829, Lighthouse Letters.

31. John Decatur to Samuel Ingham, 28 November 1829, Lighthouse Letters.

32. Daniel Haselton and William Palmer to John P. Decatur, 17 September 1829, Lighthouse Letters.

33. *New-Hampshire Gazette*, 10 November 1829, 3.

34. Extract, Ezra Young and Thomas B. Laighton to Samuel Ingham, 27 October 1829 and John Decatur to Samuel Ingham, 28 November 1829, Lighthouse Letters; Cole, 88.

35. Cole, 88; *New-Hampshire Gazette*, 5 January, 23 March and 6 and 20 April 1830.

36. William Walker to Stephen Pleasonton, 4 June 1830 and William Pickering to Pleasonton, 3 August 1830, Lighthouse Letters.

37. New Hampshire Lighthouse Contracts File; Decatur to Pleasonton, 12 June 1829, Lighthouse Letters.

38. *Portsmouth Journal* 11 September 1830.

39. William Pickering to Stephen Pleasonton, 14 August 1830, Lighthouse Letters.

40. John P. Decatur to Pleasonton, 3 August 1830, Lighthouse Letters.

41. Petition of William Palmer and Daniel Haselton, 22nd Cong., 1st sess., 1832, H. Rep. 343, CS226; 22nd Cong., Relief of Daniel Hazleton and William Palmer, 2nd Sess., 1833, H. Rep., 74, CS236. David Goodman kindly provided references to these documents; "Statement of Appropriations," Whale's Back Lighthouse Clipping File, NARG26.

42. Charles H. Bell, T*he Bench and Bar of New Hampshire* (Boston and New York: Houghton, Mifflin and Company, 1894), 567–77; William Pickering to Stephen Pleasonton, 11 August 1830, Lighthouse Letters.

43. *Portsmouth Journal*, 29 January 1831, reported on the act authorizing offshore winter cruises; Kensill Bell, *Always Ready* (New York: Dodd, Mead & Company, 1931), 56–57.

44. Eliphalet Grover Log, entries of 9 June, 19 September 1828, 7 October 1829 (Portland Cutter), 2 and 5 August, 19 September 1830 (Portsmouth Cutter).

45. *Record of Movements,* 340 for the cutter *Portsmouth* formerly *Hiram*. King, 80–81 for Shaw's problems with iced-up rigging; *Record of Movements,* 307 for cutter *Madison;* King, 93-97 for discussion of the Morris class of revenue cutters.

46. Eliphalet Grover Log; Correspondence of the Treasury Secretary with Customs Collectors, 1789-1833, NARG26, Microfilm M178, Roll 25, 89.

47. Maine Lighthouse Contract File, NARG26.

48. Ibid.

49. Ibid.

50. Ibid.

51. Eliphalet Grover Log; *Report of I. W. P. Lewis, Civil Engineer,* 131.

52. Eliphalet Grover Log, June and July 1831; 27th Cong., 3rd sess., 1843, H. Rep. 282, 1; Maine Lighthouse Contracts Folder.

53. Maine Lighthouse Contract Folder; Eliphalet Grover Log.

54. Eliphalet Grover to Stephen Pleasonton, 8 August 1831, Lighthouse Letters, Box 24.

55. John Chandler to Pleasonton, 7 September 1831, Lighthouse Letters, Box 24; Eliphalet Grover Log, 19, 26 October 1831; 19 January, 26 February, 3, 6, 10, 29 April, 7, 12, 20 May, 9, 28 June, 18 July, 20 August, 3, 12 September, 3, 12 October, 3, 25 November 1832, 7 January, 22 March, 3 May, 5, 16 July, 26 August, 7, 12, 25, September, 7 October, 11 November, 6 December, 1833, etc.; *Record of Movements, Vessels of the United States Coast Guard,* 507.

56. *Extracts from Congressional Documents Relating to Lighthouses, &c, &c., &c.*24th Cong., 2nd sess., 1833, S. Doc. 138, reprinted as Appendix O. in *Report of the . . . Light-House Board,* 1852, 493.

57. Ibid.

58. New Hampshire Lighthouse Contract File: 10 July 1836 request for proposals for replacing White Island lighthouse lantern and 18 August 1836 contract with Winslow Lewis.

59. *Portsmouth Journal,* 12 August, 12 September, 15 and 22 October 1836; New Hampshire Lighthouse Contract File; *Report of the . . . Light-House Board,* 494–509.

60. *Portsmouth Journal,* 12 August, 1836.

61. *Report of the . . . Lighthouse Board,* 498.

62. *Documents on the light-house establishment of the United States,* 25th Cong.,2nd sess.,1838, S. Doc. 258, CS316; *Report of I. W. P. Lewis, Civil Engineer,* 26.

63. Arnold Burgess Johnson, *The Modern Lighthouse Service.* (Washington, D.C.: Government Printing Office, 1890), 15-16; Clifford Shattuck, *The Nubble: Cape Neddick Lightstation, York, Maine* (Freeport, Maine: The Cumberland Press, Inc., 1979), 12–15.

64. *Lighthouses. Fifth Auditor on Execution of Act of July 7, 1838.* 25th Cong., 3rd sess., 1838. H. Doc. 24,CS 316.

65. Ibid.

66. Eliphalet Grover Log, entries of 8–15 August 1838. *Portsmouth Journal,* 18 August and 8 September 1838.

67. *Lighthouses. Fifth Auditor on Execution of Act of July 7, 1838.*

68. Ibid.

69. Ibid.

70. *Portsmouth Journal,* 14 August 1841. This factory did not provide oil for lighthouses. Whale oil for household lamps had been coming into Portsmouth for decades by the time a group of local entrepreneurs formed the Portsmouth Whaling Company in 1832, and C.H. and A. H. Ladd started a whale oil factory in a stone building at the end of Market street. By the early 1840s it was processing some 3,000 barrels of sperm oil annually. The *Journal* called it the only such factory east of Salem and boasted that "its products not only enlighten our own section of the country, but shed their beams in some of the principal hotels, etc. in New-York and Philadelphia."

71. *Lighthouses. Fifth Auditor on Execution of Act of July 7, 1838.*

72. Ibid.

73. Ibid.

74. Ibid.

75. Ibid.; *Report of the . . . Light-House Board* (1852).

76. Kenneth Sutton-Jones, *Pharos: The Lighthouse Yesterday Today and Tomorrow* (Salisbury, England: Michael Russell, Ltd., 1985), 96–97.

77. *Report of the . . . Light-House Board,*(1852). 557–584.

78. John O. Sands, "The U. S. Light House Board: Progress through Process," in *American Neptune*, vol. 47, no. 3 (Summer 1987), 175, quotes from Captain M. C. Perry, *Light-Houses of Great Britain and France,* 26th Cong., 1st sess., 1840, S. Doc. 619, CS361, 3–4. See also Captain M. C. Perry, *Communication,* 25th Cong., 2nd sess.,1838, S. Doc.159, CS316.

79. *The Sailor's Magazine and Naval Journal,* December 1838, 122 and January 1839, 156.

80. New Hampshire Lighthouse Clippings File; Documents Relating to Lighthouses, 1789–1871, NARG26, 304.

81. *Report of I. W. P. Lewis, Civil Engineer.* 27th Cong., 3rd sess., 1843, H. Doc. 183, CS 422, 206–207.

82. *Dictionary of American Biography*, 1936 (hereafter DAB), q.v. "Sylvanus Thayer."

83. Ibid., q.v. "Alexander Parris;" Garvin, 420; Fentress, 58–61.

84. Edward Zimmer, "The Architectural Career of Alexander Parris (1780–1852)," vol. 1, (PhD. Diss., Boston University, 1984), 593; Sutton-Jones, *36.*

85. Documents Related to Lighthouses, 1789-1871, 304

86. *Portsmouth Journal,* 28 August, 4 and 11 September 1852.

87. Zimmer, 593–594; Bachand, 196.

88. *Portsmouth Journal*, 9 February 1839.

89. Ibid.

Chapter VII: Eighteen-Forties Improvements at White Island

1. Thomas B. Laighton, Journal 1839-1840, 1846-185?, Barbara Durant Collection, Portsmouth Athenæum, unpaged. (Hereafter TBL Journal.)

2. New Hampshire Lighthouse Contract File, NARG26.

3. *Light-Houses. Letter from the Secretary of the Treasury transmitting the report of the general superintendent of the light-house establishment, December 20, 1850.* 31st Cong., 2nd sess., 1850, H. Ex. Doc. 14, CS 598, 69.

4. Ibid.

5. Stephen Pleasonton claimed in 1852 that the installation of French plate glass and improved reflectors were part of a systematic program of improvements. *A communication from the Fifth Auditor of the Treasury reporting the light-house system of the United States, in reply to a report made to Congress by the Light-House board.* 32nd Cong., 1st sess., 1852. H. Ex. Doc. 88, CS 644, 3; *Report . . . of the Light-House Board* (1852) 551, 529.

6. *A communication from the Fifth Auditor of the Treasury,* 1852, 55, prints Pleasonton's 28 December 1841 letter on the Fresnel lenses.

7. Ibid., 25.

8. TBL Journal; *Portsmouth Journal,* 16 October 1841.

9. *Report of I. W. P. Lewis, Civil Engineer,* 1843, 141; *Portsmouth Chronicle,* 18 December 1890 identified Pendexter as the builder of the covered way.

10. New Hampshire Lighthouse Contract File: 10 August 1842 contract for painting.

11. *Record of Movements, Vessels of the United States Coast Guard,* 307–308.

12. *Portsmouth Journal,* 28 November 1840.

13. Nelson II, Builders, Masters, Owners and Importers, 152-153.

14. *Portsmouth Directory,* 1834, 70; *Portsmouth Directory,* 1839, 96.

15. *Portsmouth Journal,* 13 June 1840, 12 December 1841, 19 November 1842; Whitehouse and Beaudoin, 29.

16. *Portsmouth Journal,* 9 May 1840.

17. *Portsmouth Journal,* 24 July and 21 August 1841.

18. Rowe, 315; *Portsmouth Journal,* 15 November 1845 noted forty-five coasters entering the lower harbor to shelter on a single day.

19. *Portsmouth Journal,* 9 and 16 October 1841.

20. *Portsmouth Journal,* 16 October 1841.

21. *Portsmouth Journal,* 21 November 1840.

22. *Portsmouth Journal,* 24 December 1836.

23. *Portsmouth Journal,* 9 October 1841.

24. Ibid.

25. DAB, q. v. "Gridley Bryant."

26. *Portsmouth Journal,* 9 October 1841.

27. Ibid.

28. Ibid.

29. Ibid.

30. Ibid.

31. Ibid.; *Report of I. W. P. Lewis, Civil Engineer* (1843), 62.

32. Updike, 46.

33. *Condition of the light-houses on the Eastern coast.* 27th Cong., 3rd sess., 1843, H. Rep. 282, CS 428,12.

34. Ibid., 2–5.

35. *Report of I. W. P. Lewis, Civil Engineer* (1843), 6, 42. Adams, whose previous experience was with railroads, later became president of the American Society of Civil Engineers. *Appleton's Cyclopaedia of American Biography.* (New York: D. Appleton & Co., 1887), q. v. J. W. Adams. Boutelle at one time worked as an engineer for the U. S. Coast Survey.

36. *Report of I. W. P. Lewis, Civil Engineer* (1843), 9.

37. Ibid., 9, 4, 215–218.

38. Ibid., 19, 20.

39. Ibid., 22–23.

40. Ibid., 52–53.

41. Ibid., 51–55.

42. Ibid., 146.

43. Ibid., 145–147.

44. Ibid., 146; TBL Journal, January, February entries.

45. *Report of I. W. P. Lewis, Civil Engineer* (1843),130-131.

46. Ibid., 58, 130–131.

47. Ibid., 25, 26, 131.

48. Ibid., 145.

49. Ibid., 145; 24th Cong., 1st sess., 1836, H. Doc. 66, 12.

50. *Report of I. W. P. Lewis, Civil Engineer* (1843), 9, 67. Lewis listed the spar buoys at Kitt's Rock, off Whale's Back; Stielman's Rock, off New Castle light; at the east end of Amazeen's (now Goat) Island; Jamaica Island, at the mouth of Spruce Creek (now incorporated by filling into the multiple island s that form the Portsmouth Naval Shipyard; Sunken Rocks, east of the stone beacon; Logy Ledge; Cod Rock, just north of the New Castle light; Hick's rock, on the east side of the entrance to Spruce Creek; and Seaword's (or Seaward's) Rock, on the Portsmouth side of the river, just downstream from the present Memorial bridge. Two beacons were listed: Sunken Rocks and at Pumpkin Island, a tiny islet between Badger's and Navy Yard islands—long since obliterated by Navy Yard filling.

51. Ibid., 62.

52. *Fifth Auditor's report relative to light-houses and lights, January 19, 1844.* 28th Cong., 1st sess.,1844, H. Doc. 62, CS 441,23–24, 28–30.

53. Ibid., 23–24, 28–30.; Nelson II (Builders, Masters, Owners and Importers), was consulted for information about the activity of the Portsmouth, New Castle and Kittery signatories of the testimonial Pleasonton received from Portsmouth. These included Christopher Amazeen and Thomas Frost of New Castle; both of whom were shipmasters in the West Indies trade; Samuel Batson and Daniel Frisbee of Kittery, both of whom were owners of small schooners likely to have been employed in the West Indies and coasting trade, and who had each served as customs inspectors by 1843, according to the *Official Register* of federal employees, 39.

54. Winslow Lewis, *A Review of the Report of I. W. P. Lewis* (Boston: Tuttle and Dennett, printers, 1843).

55. *A communication from the Fifth Auditor of the Treasury reporting the light-house system of the United States, in reply to a report made to Congress by the Light-House board,* 1852, 3.

56. Ibid.; *Report of I. W. P. Lewis, Civil Engineer,* 1843.

57. *Report of the Secretary of the Treasury on Improvements to the Lighthouse system and collateral aids to navigation.* 29th Cong., 1st sess., 1846, S.Doc. 488, CS 478; *A communication from the Fifth Auditor of the Treasury reporting the light-house system of the United States, in reply to a report made to Congress by the Light-House board,* 1852, 8–82.

58. Holland, 33.

59. Frank N. Schubert, ed., *The Nation Builders, A Sesquicentennial History of the Corps of Topographical Engineers,* (Fort Belvoir, Virginia: Office of History, United

States Army Corps of Engineers, 1988), 19–51; Aubrey Parkman, *Army Engineers in New England: The Military and Civil Work of the Corps of Engineers in New England 1775–1975.* (Waltham, Mass: U. S. Army Corps of Engineers, New England Division, 1978), 42.

60. *Light-house establishment.* 30th Cong., 1st sess., 1847, H. Ex. Doc. 27.

61. Arthur Schlesinger, Jr., *The Age of Jackson* (Boston: Little Brown and Company, 1946), 427, on John L. O'Sullivans's 1845 statement of manifest destiny.

62. *Portsmouth Journal,* 12 February 1848 quotes and debates the *New-Hampshire Gazette* on internal improvements.

63. *Portsmouth Journal,* 17 February 1848; Hague and Christie, 135–137.

64. George W. Cullum, *Biographical Register of the Officers and Graduates of the U.S. Military Academy at West Point, N. Y. , Volume 1.* (Boston & New York: Houghton, Mifflin and Company, 1891), 239–240.

Chapter VIII: Lighthouse Keepers: Fort Constitution and Boon Island

1. NHSP vol. 7, 288; *New-Hampshire Gazette*, 9 April 1814.

2. *Portsmouth Journal,* 24 July and 11 August 1838. The steamer *Huntress* offered a Boon Island excursion in 1841, and trips to the Isles of Shoals and other scenic coastal locations were also available during this period. *Portsmouth Journal,* 24 and 31 July 1841.

3. *Portsmouth Journal,* 19 August 1843.

4. *Portsmouth Journal,* 20 February 1847 reprints this article, signed "J. E." from the *Boston Evening Gazette,* written from Rye Beach, N.H. 25 January 1847. The visitor who wrote the piece was possibly Levi Thaxter.

5. *Report of I. W. P. Lewis, Civil Engineer,* 1843, 57–59; *Report of the Secretary of the Treasury on Improvements to the Light-house system and collateral aids to navigation,* 1846, 52.

6. Treasury Papers.

7. "Report of the Light-House Board," *Report on the Finances.* (Washington, D. C.: U. S. Treasury Department, 1855), 296. Under the Lighthouse Board created in 1852, Franklin was the first inspector for the Maine and New Hampshire coasts.

8. Town of New Castle Records, New Castle, New Hampshire, Public Library.

9. *Portsmouth Journal,* 23 September 1843.

10. John W. Chadwick, "White Island Light-House," reprinted from *Harper's Magazine, Portsmouth Chronicle,* 17 September 1874.

11. Snow, 96; J. Candace Cliffor and Mary Louise Clifford, *Maine Lighthouses. Documentation of Their Past.* (Alexandria, Virginia: Cypress Communications, 2005), 35-37.

12. Thaxter, *Shoals,* 149-150.

13. John E. Frost, "York (Maine) Record Book," Typescript, 1943, Old York Historical Society, 23; Portsmouth Tax Lists, 1801-1811. Portsmouth, N.H. City Hall, 120, 174,132; Nelson III, 118, shows Edmund Grover, whose relationship to Eliphalet is unknown, as master of Portsmouth vessels during the years 1800 to 1804; Records of St. John's Church, Vol. 1. Typescript, Portsmouth Athenæum, 13; York County Deed 83/73, Registry of Deeds, Alfred, Maine.

14. George Ernst, "Grover Family Genealogy." Typescript. Old York Historical Society; *Boston Weekly Messenger*, 24 April 1817.

15. Eliphalet Grover Log. A 1991 transcription of this manuscript by Susan L. Toll.is at the Portsmouth Athenæum, Portsmouth, NH; in October 1832 young Eliphalet Grover went to Mr. Pillow's in Portsmouth and in August 1833 he "commenced trade with Mr. John Colcot with four hundred Dollars"; Mark Dennett, Collector of Customs for York, *et als*. Letter of 15 July 1839 to Levi Woodbury regarding Samuel Grover, Correspondence Concerning Keepers and Assistants, 1821-1902, NARG 26.

16. Eliphalet Grover letters of 29 July 1839 to Levi Woodbury, in Correspondence Concerning Keepers and Assistants, refers to his wife's being "stupified" and 20 January 1841 to Stephen Pleasonton mentions his 84-year old mother.

17. Mary Ann Lowdar, deposition 30 April 1838 to Solomon Brooks, Justice of the Peace, York County, Maine, in Correspondence Concerning Keepers and Assistants; Charles Edward Banks, *History of York, Maine* (Boston: 1935, Vol. 2), 356–357 discusses provisions made for the poor in York. Lester MacKenzie Bragdon and John Eldridge Frost, transcribers, *Vital Records of York, Maine*. (Camden, Maine: Picton Press, n.d.), 265, 270, 368 shows a certificate formarriage of Miss Mary Ann Lowden to Benjamin Avery, both of York, issued on August 24, 1846; the solemnization of the marriage of Benjamin Avery and Mrs. Mary Ann Lowder on October 15, and the death of Mary Ann, wife of Benjamin Avery on March 13, 1863.

18. Laura Fecych Sprague, editor, *Agreeable Situations: Society, Commerce, and Art in Southern Maine, 1780–1830*. (Kennebunk, Maine: The Brick Store Museum, 1987), 45–46. Thanks to Sandra Armentrout for calling my attention to these pieces. Edward Wall, "Abraham Prescott: Bass Viol Maker," *Historical New Hampshire*, vol. 42, no. 3, Summer, 1987,102–104, discusses Prescott's manufacture of stringed instruments and the introduction of violincellos or "bass viols" as they were then known in churches before organs were widely used.

19. Clifford and Clifford, 2.

20. Winslow Lewis to Jeremiah Bradbury, 14 November 1817. ALS. Portsmouth Athenæum, Portsmouth, N.H.

21. Clifford and Clifford, 37,38.

22. Susan L. Toll's unpublished 1991 introduction to her transcription of Grover's log makes the comparison between the log and rural diaries, and quotes an article analyzing the latter: Marilyn Ferris Motz, "Folk Expressions of Time and Place," in *Journal of American Folklore,* vol. 100, 131–147. It is presumed that Grover was paid extra for maintenance tasks because in his 1840–1841 lighthouse journal Keeper Mark Dennett made notations of the amounts he was paid for similar work. "Daily Journal kept by Mark Dennett, Keeper of the Light House at Boon Island." Unpaginated manuscript, Maine Historical Society, Portland, Maine.

23. Eliphalet Grover to Stephen Pleasonton, 8 August 1831, Lighthouse Letters, Box 24.

24. Horatio Davis Smith, (Elliot Snow, 1923 editor), *Early History of the United States Revenue Marine Service 1789-1849*. (Washington, D.C.: A Coast Guard Bicentennial Publication, 1989), 47; Office of Assistant Commandant, U. S. Coast Guard, compiler, *Record of Movements, Vessels of the United States Coast Guard 1790–December 31, 1933*. (Washington, D. C.: Treasury Department Bicentennial publication, 1990), 80.

25. Eliphalet Grover to Stephen Pleasonton, 8 August 1831, Lighthouse Letters.

26. Deeds 124/104 and 133/1554, York County Registry of Deeds, Alfred, Maine, record the purchase and sale of the farm land.

27. Correspondence Concerning Keepers and Assistants, NARG26, Deposition of Daniel Nason, Jr. taken by Portland Customs Collector at Kennebunk, 10 April 1838.

28. *Portsmouth Chronicle,* 5 November 1836

29. Correspondence Concerning Keepers and Assistants, Joshua Herrick to Levi Woodbury, letter of 24 February 1838.

30. Ibid. Samuel Grover and Joel Newell, 10 April 1838 sworn statement to John Anderson.

31. Ibid. George Davis, Daniel Murphy, Stephen Ward, Solomon Brooks, andDaniel Nason, 10 April 1838 sworn statements to John Anderson.

32. Ibid. Eliphalet Grover, 25 April 1838 and John Anderson, 21 August 1838 letters to Levi Woodbury.

33. Grover's account of the storm, considerably tidied up, was published in the *Portsmouth Journal, 9 February 1839.*

34. *Registers of Light-house Keepers.*

35. Mark Dennett, "Sketches of Life." Manuscript. 23 pages. Collection of Armistead Dennett, Kittery, Maine; photocopy at the Portsmouth Athenæum.

36. Mark Dennett, "Daily Journal . . . ," Maine Historical Society, Portland, Maine.

37. Mark Dennett, "Sketches of Life."

38. Betsey Dennett to Alice Dennett, letter of May, 1841, Collection of Armistead Dennett.

39. *Portsmouth Jounral*, 23 October 1841.

40. Snow, 98–99.

41. Ibid.

42. Ibid.

43. All that could be learned of Fletcher is that he was born around 1791. His accidental death on May 30, 1855 at the age of 64 was recorded in the town of York's miscellaneous death records. John E. Frost, *Vital Records of York,* 435.

44. *Portsmouth Journal,* 8 September 1849.

45. Ibid., 24 November 1849.

46. *New-Hampshire Gazette,* 7 May 1850.

Chapter IX: Lighthouse Keepers: White Island and Whale's Back

1. An account of White Island light in the *Portsmouth Herald*, 6 March 1909, states that Jackson died in Rochester, N.H. in 1844 at 78; Portsmouth Tax assessment from 1795 to 1801, when his tax of $46.34 indicated he was making a comfortable living. Over the next four years, his tax declined, dropping suddenly to only $1 in 1805. In the years after this his tax never rose higher than $2.44 and during many years he was assessed only a poll tax. *U. S. Oracle of the Country* (Portsmouth, N.H.), 5 April 1803 contained a notice of his bankruptcy.

2. Timothy Upham to Stephen Pleasonton, 3 November and 23 December 1820, Lighthouse Letters, Box 17E.

3. Timothy Upham to Stephen Pleasonton, 10 July 1823; Clement Jackson to Wm. H. Crawford, 2 December 1823 and Upham to Pleasonton, 17 September 1824, Lighthouse Letters; *Portsmouth Herald*, 6 March 1909.

4. *New-Hampshire Gazette*, 16 June 1829; *Portsmouth Journal* 13 June 1829.

5. John P. Decatur to Samuel Ingham, Secretary of the Treasury, 31 September 1829, Lighthouse Letters; *New-Hampshire Gazette*, 14 July 1829.

6. William Pickering to Stephen Pleasonton, 11 August 1830, Lighthouse Letters.

7. William Pickering to Stephen Pleasonton, January 10 and April 30, 1833 and Joseph L. Locke to William Pickering, 1 January and 13 April 1833; John M. Parsons to William Pickering, 12 April 1833, Lighthouse Letters.

8. *Report of the . . . Light-House Board* (1852), 498 reprints the 30 November 1837 letter from E. and G. W. Blunt to Levi Woodbury.

9. Cole, 88. Collector John P. Decatur was a member of the Isaac Hill faction of New Hampshire Democrats with whom many Portsmouth Democrats were feuding, and it would appear that Locke was a member of the Hill branch of the party; Langdon B. Parsons, *History of the Town of Rye, New Hampshire* (Concord NH: Rumford Printing Co., 1947), 437.

10. Lyman Rutledge, T*he Isles of Shoals in Lore and Legend. . .* (Boston: The Star Island Corporation, 1971), 61–63; Ray Brighton, "Laighton Exiled Himself tothe Isles of Shoals," in the *Portsmouth Herald*, 7 January 1990.

11. Rosamond Thaxter, *Sandpiper. The Life and Letters of Celia Thaxter.* Reprint, edition of a 1963 publication. (Hampton, NH: Peter E. Randall, 1982), 1-8.

12. *Portsmouth Journal*, 18 January 1840.

13. Peter E. Randall and Mary Ellen Burke, editors. *Gosport Remembered: The Last Village at the Isles of Shoals.* (Portsmouth, N.H.: Portsmouth Marine Society, Peter E. Randall, Publisher, 1997), 120.

14. Ibid., 122-127.

15. *Portsmouth Journal,* 18 January 1840. It is not clear how Laighton won re-appointment, though the disarray of the Whig party after John Tyler became president may have been a factor.

16. Rosamond Thaxter, 16–17; Rutledge, 132–133; TBL Journal.

17. Rosamond Thaxter, 15–18, 24, 35.

18. TBL Journal.

19. Ibid.

20. Ibid.

21. Ibid.; Celia Thaxter, *Shoals,* 132–133; Oscar Laighton, *Ninety Years at the Isles of Shoals.* Andover, Mass.: The Andover Press, 1929.

22. TBL Journal; Rosamond Thaxter, 14.

23. *Portsmouth Journal*, 16 July and 10 December 1853.

24. Rosamond Thaxter, 10.

25. Celia Thaxter, "Land-Locked," in *Poems* (Boston: Houghton Mifflin and Company, 19th edition, 1893), 9–10.

26. Celia Thaxter, *Shoals,* and *An Island Garden. (*Boston: Houghton Mifflin and Company, 1894, 1988).

27. Sharon Paiva Stephan, *One Woman's Work. The Visual Art of Celia Laighton Thaxter* (Portsmouth, N.H.: Peter E. Randall Publisher, 2001) contains an extensive bibliography of Thaxter's publications, and books, articles, and dissertations about her life and work.

28. Celia Thaxter, *Shoals,* 120–121.

29. Ibid., 110–111.

30. Ibid., 122, 138.

31. *A communication from the Fifth Auditor of the Treasury of the Treasury reporting the light-house system of the United States, in reply to a report made to Congress by the Light-House board.* 32nd Cong, 1st sess., 1852, S. Ex. Doc. 88, CS 644, 294; Single ledger sheet, Isles of Shoals Collection, Portsmouth Athenæum, lists supplies left; Celia Thaxter, S*hoals*, 133–134.

32. Ibid., 139–140.

33. Celia Thaxter, "Wreck of the *Pocahontas"* in *Poems,* 18–19.

34. *Portsmouth Journal*, 28 December 1839 and 17 July 1841; Rutledge, 64, conjectured that the *Pocahontas* was a vessel of which Thomas Laighton's brother Mark was master, but this was evidently not the case.

35. Rosamond Thaxter, 63.

36. L. H. D. Shepard to Lory Odell, April 23, 1851. MS S-549, Portsmouth Athenæum, Portsmouth, N.H.

37. Nathaniel Hawthorne, *Passages from the American Notebooks of Nathaniel Hawthorne* (Boston: Houghton, Mifflin and Company, 1880), 208.

38. Ibid.

39. R*eport of I. W. P. Lewis*, *Civil Engineer,* 1843, 25.

40. Hascall may have come from Cumberland County, Maine, where a man of his name was listed in the census index in 1820, and after he left the lighthouse a Samuel Hascall was listed in Portland in the 1840 census. No Hascalls or Haskells were recorded in New Hampshire over this period.

41. *Register of Officers,* 1831, 1832, 1838.

42. *Portsmouth Journal,* 9 February 1839.

43. Robert G. Bachand, "Whalesback Lighthouse," *The Keeper's Log*, vol. 9, no. 2, Winter 1993, 3; *Portsmouth Journal*, 1 February 1839.

44. Bachand, 4; Parsons, 214; Letters Received by the Secretary of the Treasury from Collectors. National Archives Microfilm M174, Roll 31, 113–114.

45. *Portsmouth Journal*, 9 February 1839.

46. Ibid., 9 October 1841 and 4 December 1841; *Report of I. W. P. Lewis, Civil Engineer*, 36.

47. *Portsmouth Journal,* 10 and 17 November 1849.

48. *Portsmouth Journal*, 10 November 1849.

Chapter X: The Light-House Board

1. *Portsmouth Journal,* 11 February 1849.

2. Ray Brighton, *Clippers of the Port of Portsmouth and the Men Who Built Them* (Portsmouth, N.H.: Portsmouth Marine Society, Peter E. Randall Publisher,1986) and *Tall Ships of the Piscataqua 1830-1877* (Portsmouth, N.H.: Portsmouth Marine Society, Peter E. Randall Publisher, 1989).

3. *Portsmouth Morning Chronicle,* 18 November 1854.

4. Fentress, 80, 58, 67, 68; Ray Brighton, *They Came to Fish,* Vol. 1, 166.

5. *Report of the general superintendent of the light-house establishment.* 31st Cong., 3rd sess, 1850, H.Ex. Doc. 14, 66.

6. Ibid., 71.

7. Ibid., 69-71.

8. *Report of the . . . Light-House Board* (1852), 3.

9. Ibid., 189.

10. Ibid., 196.

11. *Portsmouth Journal*, 1 November 1851; *Portsmouth Chronicle*, 18 December 1890; the lantern was manufactured in Portland by blacksmith Stephen Emerson.

12. *Report of the . . . Light-House Board* (1852), 127, 133.

13. Ibid., 232–233.

14. Ibid., 107.

15. Parkman, 43; *A Communication from the Fifth Auditor of the Treasury reporting the light-house system of the United States, in reply to a report made to Congress by the Light-House Board,* 1852, contains Pleasonton's defense.

16. *Report of the . . . the Lighthouse Board* (1852), 64-65.

17. Robert V. Bruce, *The Launching of American Science, 1846-1876* (New York: Alfred A. Knopf, 1987), 17, 171–172.

18. Ibid.. 15–17, 160.

19. K. Jack Bauer, "Samuel Francis Du Pont: Aristocratic Professional," in James C. Bradford, ed., *Captains of the Old Steam Navy.* (Annapolis: Naval Institute Press, 1986), 145–147. *Appleton's Cyclopaedia of American Biography*, q.v. William B. Shubrick; *Annual Report of the Light-House Board*, included in the Treasury Department's *Report of the Finances, 1853* (Hereafter LHBAR, followed by year of publication), 194.

20. *Appleton's Cyclopaedia of American Biography*, q.v. Joseph G. Totten; Frank N. Schubert, ed., *March to South Pass: Lieutenant William B. Franklin's Journal of the Kearny Expedition of 1845.* (Washington, D.C. Historical Division Office of Administrative Services Office of the Chief of Engineers, 1979), 31, 44.

21. George Weiss, *The Lighthouse Service: Its History, Activities and Organization.* (Baltimore, Md.: The Johns Hopkins Press, 1926) 14-15; Sands, 175.

22. For Thornton Jenkins, see www.arlingtoncemetery.net/tajenkins.htm; For Edmund Hardcastle, see Henry P. Beers, *A History of the U.S. Topographical Engineers, 1818-1863.* www.topogs.org/history2.htm.

23. *Portsmouth Journal*, 28 August, 4 and 11 September 1852.

24. *Portsmouth Journal*, 19 April 1851 reported on the loss of the lighthouse and keepers.

25. *Report of the . . . Light-House Board* (1852), 196; George W. Callum,*Biographical Register of the Officers and Graduates of the U. S. Military Academy at West Point. N.Y.* (Boston: Houghton Mifflin and Co., 1891),240–241 contains a description of the structure and Swift's chilling defense of his design. The nine iron piles were inserted five feet deep into holes drilled on a surface only twenty-five feet in diameter in a situation that called for at least forty, with the keepers' dwelling and lantern resting at the top of the skeleton at the height of only sixty feet above low water level— not nearly tall enough toraise the solid part of the structure above

the level of the mountainous storm seas at this exposed site. In his report, Swift blamed the lightkeeper for the disaster because he had fastened a wooden platform at a lower level on the skeleton for the storage of water barrels and had attached a hawser to the lantern deck, anchored in the water below, for running supplies up to the lighthouse lantern; Holland, 97.

26. *Appleton's Cyclopaedia of Biography, q.v.* Franklin, William B.; "William B. Franklin's Military Record." Typescript. Office of History, U. S. Army Corps of Engineers, Ft. Belvoir, VA; Schubert, 1–36, publishes a transcript of Franklin's journal during Colonel Stephen W. Kearny's 1845 western expedition.

27. "William B. Franklin's Military Record," shows that he went to Washington as Engineer Secretary late in 1857, and the Light-House Board's Letters to Engineers, Vol. A (NARG26), 89, note that he was still assigned to this post in December 1859. For almost two years he was superintending engineer for the construction work on the Capitol, including its dome. Mark A. Snell, *From First to Last. The Life of Major General William B. Franklin.* (New York: Fordham University Press, 2002), 41–52. This biography touches only briefly on Franklin's lighthouse work, but is detailed in its description of his Civil War record and its account of the scapegoating that clouded his reputation. After the war he became vice president in charge of manufacturing for the Colt firearms company in Hartford, Connecticut.

28. Quoted in Snell, 33; Light-House Board Letters to District Engineers, Indexes to Minutes of the Light-House Board, Minutes of the Proceedings of theLight-House Board, and the Journals of the Light-House Board (all NARG26) contain references to Franklin's design work for the Board. The published Annual Reports of the board during Franklin's time were incorporated into the Secretary of the Treasury's reports, and contain notes of the year's work in each lighthouse district.

29. *Portsmouth Morning Chronicle*, 18 November 1854, contains an article about the 1851 storm and its effects on Boon Island.

30. Lighthouse District One Clipping File, NARG26.

31. Letters to District Engineers, Book I (31 December 1851 to 23 December 1852), NARG26, 50, 51; Journal of the Lighthouse Board, 9 October 1852—11 August 1854, NARG26, 133 (22 February 1853 entry).

32. Letters to District Engineers, 310 (12 November 1854 entry); Franklin's plans for Boon Island lighthouse have not been located, but his designs for many other Maine lighthouses and keeper's house have. Copies, gathered by Kirk Mohney of the Maine State Historic Preservation Commission, are filed at the commission office in Augusta, Maine.

33. *Eastern Argus* (Portland, Maine), 20 November 1854; "Introduction to Biddeford History." Typescript, c. 1944 (McArthur Public Library, Biddeford, Maine), 37–38 lists other projects for which Biddeford granite was used: the Saco River Breakwater, Portland Harbor fortifications, Brooklyn and Harlem River bridges, and a new Whale's Back lighthouse, in 1871.

34. *Eastern Argus*; Lighthouse Board Journal Abstracts, NARG26, Vol. 2, 155, 277, 419, indicate friction between Keeper Bowden and J. B. Leonard, the foreman of the woks, and that a lawsuit was filed against Leonard by Bowden in 1855.

35. *Appleton's Dictionary of Machines, Mechanics, Engine-Work*, 2 vols. (New York: D. Appleton & Company, 1852). vol. 2, 572.

36. Boon Island Lighthouse Clipping File, NARG26.

37. Kirk Mohney of the Maine Historic Preservation Commission kindly shared his extensive research on other Maine keeper's houses designed by Franklin.

38. Celia Thaxter, *Shoals,* 149–154.

39. *Portsmouth Chronicle,* 6 January 1855; the Fresnel lens in place at Fort Constitution in 1935 was manufactured by L. Sautter, according to the Lighthouse Service "Description of Portsmouth Harbor Light Station" (NARG26) for this year. It is possible that it was the lens originally installed. The present lens does not have identifying marks.

40. *Portsmouth Chronicle,* 2 January 1855.

41. "Illuminating Apparatus from H. Lepaute," NARG26, 1, records the Whale's Back lighting apparatus and its $6,391 cost; *List of the Light-Houses, Lighted Beacons, and Floating Lights, of the Atlantic, Gulf, and Pacific Coast of the United States* (Washington, D.C.: U. S. Lighthouse Board, 1862), 10–15. lists the other new Maine lighthouses equipped in 1855 with fixed lights varied by flashes: Little River at the entrance to Cutler Harbor; Petit-Manan Island, Baker's Island at the entrance to Frenchman's Bay, and Franklin Island, off Thomaston.

42. Lighthouse Clipping File, NARG26; *Report of the Light-House Board,* 1858, 442–443. The description of the Fresnel lighting apparatus comes from "Description of Light-House Tower, Buildings, and Premises at Isles of Shoals Light-Station, N. H., January 12, 1909," NARG26, It is possible that this was the lens originally installed.

43. John S. Conway, compiler, *The U. S. Lighthouse Service.* (Washington, D.C.: U.S. Department of Commerce, 1923, 51; *Report of the Secretary of the Treasury on Improvements to the Light-house system and collateral aids to navigation.* 29thCong., 1st sess., 1846, S. Rep. 488, 44–45.

44. *Portsmouth Journal*, 12 October 1850 and 16 October 1841.

45. *Portsmouth Journal*, 1 November 1851; U. S. Coast Survey. Preliminary Chart of Portsmouth Harbor 1854", Collection Portsmouth Athenæum ; Blunt's *American Coast Pilot*, 1857, 241.

46. *Portsmouth Journal*, 12 October 1850; 19 July 1851.

47. Ibid., 19 July 1851. The newspaper may have been in error as to the month when the York Ledge beacon was destroyed; it is possible that it was the same April storm that destroyed the Minot's Ledge lighthouse.

48. *Portsmouth Journal,* 12 October 1850; Letters to District Engineers, vol. 1 (NARG26), 50, entry for 14 March 1852; *Portsmouth Journal,* 26 March 1853;Blunt's *American Coast Pilot,* 1857, 242. Both beacons were probably provided by Portland partners Coburn and Emerson. A notation on one of two drawings of the Willey's Ledge beacon says that a letter from Joseph W. Coburn accompanied the drawings when they were sent to Washington. Letters to District Engineers, vol. 1 (NARG26), 71, 120.

49. No Navy Yard records or maps have yet been located showing the site of the buoy depot, and the precise dates of its opening and final closure have not been found. Geo. H. Preble, *History of the United States Navy-Yard, Portsmouth, N.H.* (Washington, D.C.: Government Printing Office, 1892), 82 writes that the Navy granted permission to the Light-House Board for storage of buoys in October 1852; Putnam, 43.

50 Douglas Peterson, *U. S. Lighthouse Service Tenders 1840-1939..* (Annapolis & Trappe, Maryland: Eastwind Publishing, 2000), 4.

51. LHBAR 1855, 293, 296.

52. Bachand, 161–162; *Report of the Secretary of the Treasury on Improvements to the Light-house system and collateral aids to navigation*, 44–46; *Portsmouth Journal*, 16 April 1853; LHBAR 1855, 197.

53. LHBAR 1853, 193; LHBAR 1855, 254, 277.

54. First Lighthouse District loose papers, NARG26; Register of Letters Received from the Engineer of the First Lighthouse District, E42, NARG26, 60, shows W. A. Goodwin, Acting Engineer 26 September 1858); *Portsmouth Journal*, 18 June 1859; Lighthouse Clipping Files, Box 1, NARG26.

55. *Portsmouth Journal*, 21 January 1860.

56. LHBAR 1855, 296

57. Ibid., 291.

58. Ibid., 270, 413–415.

59. Putnam, 201–205; Holland, 55–57.

60. *Report of the . . . Light-House Board* (1852), 35–36, 50–52.

61. Ibid., 51–52.

62. Putnam, 55–57, 201–202; *Report of I. W. P. Lewis, Civil Engineer,* 1843, 13–14.

63. David Boyd, compiler. *History of the U. S. Navy Yard, Portsmouth, N. H.* (N.p., 1930, unpaged); Putnam, 56; Holland , 57–61.

64. "Log of the U.S. Navy Yard, Kittery Maine," December 5, 1854–December 7 1855 and December 1856. Portsmouth Naval Shipyard Archives.

65. Willard Flint, unpaged typescript on the history of U. S. lightships, Coast Guard Academy Library, New London, Conn.

66. *Portsmouth Morning Chronicle*, 28 January 1856.

67. Flint.

68. Gustav Kobbe, "Life on the South Shoal Lightship." *The Century*, vol. 42, no. 69, August 1891, 540–542.

69. Flint; Putnam, 57–59; Holland, 59–60; Kobbe, 544–545.

70. Flint.

71. Louise Tallman, compiler, "Families of Gosport." Typescript, unpaged, Portsmouth Athenæum); Registers of Lighthouse Keepers, 1845-1912, National Archives Microfilm #1373, Roll 1 for dates of Richard and Otis Haley's appointments.

72. Letters to District Engineers, Book 1, NARG26, 58: Letters to Engineers, Vol. A, NARG26, 89. A note inserted into this volumes says that Goodwin looked after things when Franklin departed, and that he and Franklin corresponded by private, unrecorded letters about First District engineering matters.

73. Thaxter. *Shoals,* 134.

74. *Portsmouth Journal,* 6 October 1860.

75. *Portsmouth Journal,* 10 June 1860.

76. *Portsmouth Journal,* 16 June and 6 October 1860.

77. Register of Letters Received from the Engineer of the First Light-House District, NARG26. vol. 114, 205; vol. 115, 247;) *Report of the Light-House Board,* 1861, 205–206; *Appleton's Cyclopaedia of Biography, q. v.* William B. Shubrick, Joseph G. Totten.

78. Fentress, 75, 69, 71–73, 80.

79. *Portsmouth Morning Chronicle*, 7 October 1861.

80. Letters to District Engineers, Vol. A., NARG26, 89, 101.

81. *Portsmouth Chronicle,* 6 November 1861; *Report of the Light-House Board,* 1863, 153.

82. Meloon, 163.

83. Ibid.

84. Meloon, 163; Registers of Lighthouse Keepers.

85. *Portsmouth Chronicle*, 17 and 21 February 1863. The *Rouser*'s master was named Crafts, but neither he nor his papers were found. It was conjectured the schooner had first run onto the Sisters, the rocks sprinkled off Gerrish Island, and had then been blown in onto the Whale's Back reefs.

86. Meloon, 165–167; Registers of Lighthouse Keepers.

87. *Portsmouth Chronicle,* 8 August 1863.

88. Meloon, 166; Registers of Lighthouse Keepers; Index to Minutes of the Light-House Board, vol. 3, 509, 515. The registers of keepers show pay for Boon Island and White Island at $820 by 1867 (up from $600) and assistants at $460 (up from $300); at Fort Constitution the keeper's pay was raised from $350 to $500.

Chapter XI: Post-Civil War Developments

1. Richard E. Winslow III, *"Do Your Job!"* (Portsmouth, NH: The Portsmouth Marine Society, Peter Randall Publisher, 2000), 247, 249 for number employed at the yard and vessels built); Fentress, 71-73, 80 for vessels built at the yard.

2. Whitehouse and Beaudoin, 29–30 for postwar revival, rail freight rates.

3. Peterson, 10.

4. Peterson, 2.

5. Peterson, 20.

6. Putnam, 212; LHBAR, November 2, 1867, 3–5 (re *Iris*, repairs, etc.)

7. Putnam, 212.

8. Peterson, 36; LHBAR 1872, 476 and 1888, 38; *Portsmouth Chronicle,* 9 May 1889 (*Myrtle* carries construction materials)

9. Putnam, 185.

10. Hague and Christie, 156 (re Penn oil strike, Doty lamps); Johnson, 54-57 for kerosene, explosion Lake Michigan.

11. Lighthouse clipping files, NARG26 for kerosene in use, local lighthouses.

12. *Portland Daily Press*, 23 March 1896 for Wm. A. Goodwin obituaty; James C.Duane biographical information. Typescript. U. S. Army Corps of Engineers Office of History, Fort Belvoir, Virginia, courtesy Dale E. Floyd, Reference Historian.

13. James C. Duane biographical information typescript.

14. James C. Duane biographical information typescript.; *Dictionary of American Biography.* (New York: Charles Scribner's Sons, 1959), q. v. James C. Duane.

15. *Portsmouth Morning Chronicle*, 7 January 1870 and 21 September 1879 for Keeper Varney's shipping statistics.

16. Whale's Back Lighthouse Clipping File, NARG26, 1867–1870 entries.

17. *Portsmouth Journal*, 28 August 1869 for rumor about abandoning Whale's Back and placing a lighthouse at Odiorne's Point instead.

18. LHBAR 1870, 331.

19. Whale's Back Clipping File, 1871 for concrete core sheathed with granite.

20. Whale's Back Clipping File, 1870 for difficulty of site, 1871 for progress to twenty feet.

21. *Portsmouth Journal*, 19 April, 19 August 1871 for Biddeford granite, steamer *Enterprise*.

22. *Portsmouth Journal*, 25 November 1871 for storm, Caswells and 6 July 1872 for 4th of July visitors.

23. Holland, 145, 149 for cast iron lighthouses in Biloxi and Texas, 126 for Cape Kennedy; *Report of the general superintendent of the light-house establishment,* 1850, 59, for Monomoy Point cast-iron lighthouse.

24. "On the Construction of Iron Lighthouses," *Journal of the Franklin Institute,* vol. 61, March 1856, 148 for Morant Point & Gibbs Hill cast-iron lighthouses; *Report of the . . . Light-House Board* (1852), 461-463 for Morant Point andGibbs Hill, 109 for drawbacks of cast-iron; Holland, 149, 126 for more about; Johnson, 28 for 1870s southern cast-iron lighthouses.

25. *Portsmouth Chronicle*, 14 May 1878 for construction inside old lighthouse and new lantern installed the same day; LHBAR, 1878, 12.

26. F. Ross Holland, *Great American Light-Houses,* (Washington, D.C.: The Preservation Press, 1989), 79, 90,102,108,113,116, describes and illustrates cast-iron lighthouses; Bachand, 25, 40–41, 70–74, 92, 125, 188, 205–207, 307-308, 312-313, 326-327 for some of the lighthouses built or rebuilt, mostly of cast iron, during Duane's tenure as Third Lighthouse District Engineer.

27. Albee, 25.

28. Lighthouse clipping files, for new use of kerosene at local lighthouses; Registers of Lighthouse Keepers, for Joshua Card's service at various lighthouses.

29. Clifford Shattuck, *The Nubble. Cape Neddick Lightstation, York, Maine.* (Freeport, ME: The Cumberland Press, Inc., 1979) 11-14 for 1807 and 1830s request for lighthouse at Nubble.

30. Ibid., 12-13 for Smith's report.

31. Snow, 92, for 1842 wreck of *Isadore*; *Portsmouth Journal*, 17 April 1852 for wreck of *Georgianna*.

32. Shattuck, 15-16.

33. *Portsmouth Chronicle*, 16 September 1874 for steamers asking for light; *Portsmouth Daily Evening Chronicle*, 3 December 1874 for wreck of *Emily S.*; Shattuck, 16, for Congress appropriating $15,000 in 1874; also LHBAR, 1875-1876, 752.

34. *Portsmouth Journal* 18 October 1873 for shooting at Nubble; *Portsmouth Chronicle,* 6 December 1888 for bird shot killing hens; Shattuck, 16-18 for Boston and other owners and sale of land for $1500; LHBAR 1876, 14 for Stone's Rock spindle installation.

35. *Portsmouth Times*, 9 April 1879 for iron loaded on Myrtle and 19 June 1879 for work on lighthouse

36. LHBAR 1879, 12 for fourth-order Fresnel lens, fixed red characteristic, 300-pound bell, lighting 1 July 1879.

37. Shattuck, 25-26 for keeper appointment; Registers of Lighthouse Keepers for Leander White's lighthouse assignments, pay.

38. *Portsmouth Chronicle*, 16 September 1879 for problems for York fishermen; need for light for York Harbor entrance.

39. LHBAR 1872, 11 for keeper's dwelling, Portsmouth Harbor.

40. *Portsmouth Chronicle,* 21 August 1877 for keeper's house at White Island; "General Instructions to All Light-Keepers," 1881, 1885 insert facing 27 for paint colors.

41. *Portsmouth Chronicle* 21 August 1877.

42. Ibid., for new and old houses, tearing down old one above high foundation, etc. sentiment about old house.

43. Johnson, 103 for attractiveness of keepers houses for summer dwellings, etc.

44. *Portsmouth Chronicle*, 28 September 1876 for need for automatic fog whistle for Kitt's rock; 28 December 1876 for near misses; 12 June 1877 for Odiorne's Point as alternative foghorn site; urging Frank Jones's action.

45. The U. S. failure to produce lighthouses lenses equal to those manufactured by the French may have been due to the advanced state of French glass manufacture, and the use of "Crown Glass" by French Fresnel lens manufacturers. Produced by the Royal Glass Works at St. Gobain, near Paris, it was harder, though less dense, than "flint" glass and less reactive with atmospheric contaminants, according to a fact sheet produced by the U. S. National Park Service. Copy at the Kittery Historical and Naval Museum.

46. Hague and Christie, 190 notes pioneering U. S. fog signals; Putnam, 24 calls Beavertail the first fog-whistle; *Appleton's Cyclopaedia of American Biography, q. v.* Celadon Leeds Daboll and Charles Miner Daboll; *Report of the . . . Lighthouse Board* (1852), 180 for Beavertail fog signal.

47. Eleanor C. Parsons, *Thacher's. Island of the Twin Lights*. (Canaan, N.H.: Phoenix Publishing Co., 1985), 65 for Thacher's fog signal; LHBAR, 1867, 6 for replacement of Thacher's fog signal, West Quoddy fog signal and perplexity about the subject.

48. Joseph Henry, "Report of the Operations of the Light-House Board Relative to Fog-Signals", LHBAR, 1874, 86-87 and 101 for experiments and Duane's involvement; John O. Sands, "The U. S. Light-House Board: Progress through Process", *American Neptune*, Summer 1987, 176-178 for Henry's experiments.

49. *Portsmouth Chronicle*, 28 February 1878 for warning against plac   i   n   g Daboll fog signal in old tower; New Hampshire Lighthouse clipping file, NARG26 for installation; *Portsmouth Chronicle*, 12 October 1877 for dulcet tones of Daboll horn, 2 January 1878 for range; 1 March 1878 for woman's observation.

50. *Portsmouth Chronicle,* 26 February 1878 for dangerous situation at Whale's Back; New Hampshire Lighthouse clipping file, for appropriation.

51. *Portsmouth Chronicle*, 14 May, 2 August, 5 September and 27 November 1878 for new foghorn tower, smashed castings, need for first-class Daboll horn, problems landing at lighthouse.

Chapter XII: Nineteenth and Twentieth Century Lighthouse Keepers

1. LHBAR, 1872, 475 ff.

2. *Report of a Tour of Inspection of European Light-House Establishments, Made in 1873 by Major George Elliot,* 43rd Cong., 1st sess., 1874, S.Ex. Doc.54, 176-178, includes considerable detail about the arrangements for Scottish lightkeepers.

3. *Portsmouth Evening Daily Times,* 29 May 1873.

4. Registers of Lighthouse Keepers.

5. Putnam, 40.

6. Registers of Lighthouse Keepers.

7. Ibid.

8. Putnam, 238.

9. Johnson, 104-105; Wayne Wheeler, "The Keeper's New Clothes," *The Keepers Log,* Summer 1985, 11-13.

10. Johnson, 104-105; Wayne Wheeler, "The Keeper's New Clothes," *The Keepers Log,* Summer 1985, pp. 11-13.

11. Hawthorne, 208.

12. Celia Thaxter, *Poems,* 102-105.

13. Marriage notice of Caleb Gould and Sarah Williams, 25 July 1853. Gould became keeper before the Light-House Board instituted paid assistant keepers in the mid-1850s, and we might fit Gould and his wife to this poem if we could determine whether he died at the island in 1854. George Bowden became keeper on June 2, 1854. The board's Registers of Lighthouse Keepers contain the notation "removed," "resigned," "declined," "transferred," or, occasionally, "deceased" next to names on the roster, but there is no none beside Gould's. "Deceased" appears beside the name of keeper George Wallace (whose death at the island was reported in the *Portsmouth Chronicle* of 11 October 1861) and also beside the names of Benjamin Bridges (July 16, 1863) and Paschal Fernald (July 10, 1885).

14. Morgan Willis, telephone conversation with the author, January 1988.

15. *Portsmouth Journal*, 28 December 1868; *Portsmouth Daily Chronicle*, 19 December 1867 for Mary Amee's death of consumption.

16. *The Daily Evening Times* (Portsmouth), 1 and 2 April 1868

17. *The Daily Evening Times*, 2 April 1868

18. Ibid.

19. *Portsmouth Morning Chronicle*, 30 and 31 March 1868.

20. *Registers of Keepers.*

21. *Portmsouth Journal*, 24 June 1871 for keeper Barr's drowning.

22. Ibid.; Marriage records, City Clerk's Office, Portsmouth, NH for Barr's 12 Sept 1862 marriage to Lucy A. Watkins of Portsmouth. Barr was native of Philadelphia; *Registers of Keepers* for Frederick Barr, assistant.

23. *Portsmouth Weekly Chronicle*, 1 March 1856 for letter from Miller to his uncle, about whaling, visit to Hawaii; *Portsmouth Chronicle*, 1 Dec 1874 for more on Miller.

24. *Portsmouth Journal* 28 Nov 1874 for Miller's appointment.

25. "Our Foreign Correspondent," *Portsmouth Chronicle*, 8 Dec 1874.

26. *Portsmouth Chronicle*, 13 July 1875 for spoof of keeper's prowess.

27. *Portsmouth Chronicle*, 4 December 1875 for regulations and cats.

28. *Portsmouth Chronicle*, 4 Dec 1874.

29. *Portsmouth Chronicle*, 4 Dec 1874 and 11 Dec 1875 for Oceanic hotel construction.

30. *Portsmouth Chronicle* 13 Dec 1875 for Oceanic fire.

31. *Portsmouth Chronicle*, 16 Dec 1875 for Half-Way Rock.

32. Annie Lee Hobbs, January 18, 1876 letter published in *The Nursery*, reprinted in Edward Rowe Snow, *Famous Lighthouses of America* New York: Dodd, Mead & Co., 1955), 35-36.

33. Stillman Hobbs, grand-nephew of Edwin Hobbs, and Helen Hobbs, Hampton, New Hampshire, telephone interview with the author, 16 March 1988.(Hereafter Hobbs interview.)

34. Hobbs interview.

35. Hobbs interview.

36. Hobbs interview. The journal kept by Edwin Hobbs, no longer owned by the family, has not been located.

37. Annie Lee Hobbs.

38. Hobbs interview.

39. *Portsmouth Chronicle*, 24 October 1873 for visitors to White Island; "General Instructions to All Light-Keepers," Document No. 131, U. S. Treasury Department, 1881, 8: The regulation that "Keepers must not make any charge, nor receive any fee, for admitting visitors to light-houses" may have been instituted earlier, and was doubtless a response to an existing practice.

40. *Portsmouth Herald*, 29 July 1899 for visitors to towers permitted only between 2 and 4 P.M.

41. "Exit Exodus," *Portsmouth Chronicle*, 1 September 1876.

42. *Portsmouth Chronicle,* 22 March 1877 for keepers' house.

43. *Portsmouth Chronicle,* 15 August 1879 for Annie's accident.

44. *Portsmouth Chronicle,* 22 and 23 April 1880 for Grogran replacing Hobbs.

45. *Portsmouth Chronicle,* 4 July 1896 for Hobbs's suicide attempt; Hobbs interview.

46. Journal of the Light-House Board, Vol. 8, 1878–1881, NARG26, 225-227.

47. Margaret Grover Carr Scrapbook, Portsmouth Athenæum, Undated, unidentified newspaper clipping for Grogan's career at sea.

48. *Portsmouth Chronicle*, 15 July 1892 for Grogran's dog.

49. "General Instructions to All Light-Keepers, 1881, 6. for assistance to shipwrecked.; *Portsmouth Chronicle*, 30 December 1889 for Grogan helping out.

50. *Portsmouth Chronicle,* 6 October 1882.

51. Robert Sterling, *Lighthouses of the Maine Coast and the Men Who Keep Them.* (Brattleboro, Vermont: Stephen Day Press, 1935), 54

52. Ibid., 60-61 for night watch, dizzying spiral staircase.

53. *Portsmouth* (Herald?), 15 December 1900 for swaying and shuddering of lighthouse; Sterling, 60 for no place to sit, except box, etc.

54. First District Lighthouse Clipping File, contains references to the 1888 and 1902 cable installations at Boon Island; Sterling, for birds, salt caking lantern glass.

55. *Portsmouth Chronicle*, 22 January 1890 for Burke, getting birds mounted; *Portsmouth Herald*, 31 December 1910 for black ducks for Thanksgiving.

56. Sterling, 59-60 for soil for gardens; *Portsmouth Herald*, 9 November 1900. For four years, the Light-House Board and the Navy experimented with the use of carrier pigeons for communication with ships at sea. In 1897 pigeon cotes were established at six Navy Yards, including the one at Portsmouth, and at several offshore lighthouses. Boon Island was apparently one of them. James Dolph, "The Shipyard

Pigeon Cote," in *The Periscope* (Portsmouth Naval Shipyard) , 11 August 11, 1989, vol. 46, no. 21

57. *Portsmouth Journal,* 12 September 1885.

58. *Portsmouth Herald*, 29 June 1899 for Williams's tales.

59. Sterling, 56 for *Gold Hunter;* William O. Thomson, *Solitary Vigils at Boon Island.* (Kennebunk, Maine: By author, 'Scapes Me, distributor, 2000), 33-34 for rescue of the *Gold Hunter's* crew, quoting an interview of William C. Wiliams's son Charles by Eileen Wood.

60. *Portsmouth Daily Chronicle,* 28 December 1892.

61. Beulah Allen Quinn, interview with the author, Rockport, Maine, 15 September 1986; Alicia Rouverel, "Three Lights Lived: Profile of Beulah Quinn," *Island Journal*, Vol. 3, 1986, 55.

62. Beulah Quinn interview.

63. Ibid.

64. William O. Thomson, *Solitary Vigils at Boon Island,* 2000, 30-31.

65. Ibid.

66. Sterling, 61.

67. Beulah Quinn interview.

68. *Portsmouth Herald,* 19 March 1909 for Card's retirement at eighty-five.

69. Letters from District Inspectors and Engineers, vol. 502 (First District, July 1880–30 June 1881), 536.

70. "Charles E. Blunt," typescript record of Corps of Engineers appointments. U.S. Army Corps of Engineers Office of History, Alexandria, Virginia, courtesy of Michael J. Brodhead, historian.

71. Portsmouth Harbor Light Station Clipping File, NARG26.

72. *Portsmouth Herald,* 21 July 1931 for Brackett Lewis obituary.

73. *Portsmouth Chronicle*, 6 December 1888 about hens and hog.

74. *Portsmouth Chronicle*, 17 May 1893 for daughter's party.

75. Clifford Shattuck, *The Nubble. Cape Neddick Lightstation, York Maine.*(Freeport, Maine: The Bond Wheelwright Company, 1979), 26 for daughter Hattie's marriage.

76. "General Instructions to All Light-Keepers," 1902, 7; Sterling, 61.

77. Sterling, 61.

78. *Portsmouth Daily Evening Times*, 10 April 1875 for Leander White's ordeal in Boon Island boat.

79. *Portsmouth Chronicle*, 2 and 11 May 1885 for Leavitt overturning.

80. *LHBAR, 1889-1890*, 303; Sterling, 59 about the Williamses overturning.

81. *Portsmouth Daily Chronicle,* 26 June 1891 for Barbers's overtuning.

Chapter XIII: The Light-House Board, and Harbor and River Improvements

1. Winslow, *"Do Your Job!",* 247.

2. *Portsmouth Chronicle,* 12 October 1904.

3. *Portsmouth Chronicle,* 22 May 1889.

4. *Portsmouth Chronicle,* 10 May 1898.

5. *Portsmouth Chronicle*, 10 May and 10 June 1898 for cruisers offshore, lights and bells extinguished for war duration, lifesavers called back to duty; Winslow, *"Do Your Job!"* 60-67 for the *Lilac* laying buoys for mine sites, etc.

6. *Portsmouth Chronicle,* 9 June 1898 for telephone cable-laying.

7. *Portsmouth Chronicle*, 12 July 1898 for story about fire and rockets at Boon I; Dolph, "The Shipyard Pigeon Cote."

8. Peterson, 36; LHBAR, 1909, 61 for need to replace the *Myrtle;* 60th Cong., 1st sess., 1908, S. Rep.18 and 19, CS5218, for bill for nine new tenders.

9. LHBAR, 1867, 5; 1871, 6, 1877, 13 for tenders, buoy depots. Holland, *America's Lighthouses,* 206 shows a photograph taken around 1888 identified as the buoy depot at the Portsmouth Navy Yard. Such a depot is not listed in Light-House Board reports for this period, but there was one in the Fifth Lighthouse District at Portsmouth, Virginia, referred to in LHBAR 1884, 52 and 1903, 207.

10. Peterson, 34; *Portsmouth Chronicle,* 5 August 1882 for the *Fern.*

11. Peterson, 60; *Portsmouth Herald*, 14 August 1901 for the *Armeria; Merchant Vessels of the United States,* 1911, 445 shows the *Armeria* by then stationed in Alaska.

12. LHBAR,1889, 42 for need to replace the *Iris.*

13. Peterson, 20; LHBAR 1889, 45-46.

14. Peterson, 20; LHBAR 1889, 45-46.

15. *Portsmouth Daily Chronicle,* 28 December 1892 for the *Lilac* in Portsmouth Harbor. LHBAR, 1897, 45-46 for the *Lilac's* service.

16. Peterson, 64.

17. "Goodbye Geranium," *Portsmouth Herald*, 21 December 1909; 60th Con., 1st sess., 1908, S. Rep. 17, CS5218, for bill for replacement of the *Geranium.*

18. Peterson, 51.

19. *Portsmouth Chronicle*, 5 February 1880 for Whale's Back foghorn problems, storm.

20. LHBAR,1880,13 for removal of old tower, davits; *Portsmouth Chronicle*, 27 March 1880 for plans to remove old tower and 15 September 1880 for covered walkway.

21. *Portsmouth Chronicle*, 14, 21 June, 1 July 1882 for painting fog tower, death of John Lewis.

22. *Portsmouth Chronicle*, 11 January 1884 for storm damage at Whale's Back

23. LHBAR, 1889, 37-38. for 1888 storm damage and repairs at Whale's Back.

24. George Putnam, Commissioner of the Bureau of Lighthouses, letter to Oliver Frisbee of Portsmouth 18 October 1916 described the change of the optic. First District Lighthouse Clipping File, NARG26.

25. *Portsmouth Chronicle*, 3 May 1899 for notice from Washington re new fog signal.

26. First Lighthouse District Clipping File, NARG26 about first-class foghorn, 1902; LHBAR 1898-1907 for hours in operation, fuel consumed; *Portsmouth Herald* 5 August 1907 for burst water tank.

27. Dorothy M. Moulton, "Whaleback Light," *New Hampshire Profiles*, June 1957, 23-25. for foghorn, heat at Whale's Back.

28. Boon Island Lighthouse Clipping File, NARG26 for oil house, 1887.

29. Boon Island Lighthouse Clipping File for 1889 repairs.

30. Ibid., for 1902 repairs; *Portsmouth Chronicle*, 15 December 1900 for Charles Williams on storm, vibrations of tower.

31. Holland, 88. This lighthouse, two and a half miles offshore from Millbridge, Maine, is only slightly less tall then Boon Island. Holland writes that during heavy winter storms in 1886, the top of the tower swayed back and forth.

32. *Portsmouth Chronicle,* 5 December 1888 for storm of 25 and 26 November.

33. Ibid.

34. Ibid., 9 May 1889 and 15 February 1890 for repairs at Boon Island.

35. LHBAR 1889, 37 for alterations to Boon Island house.

36. Boon Island Clipping File, NARG26,1891 and 1902 entries for need for new keeper's house (1891), telephone connection (1902).

37. Boon Island Clipping File. For new keeper's house, 1904; *Ports-mouth Herald,* 19 October 1904 for Williams's report on.

38. Boon Island Clipping File, 1901 and 1909 entries; *Portsmouth Herald,* 18 June 1908, 21 April and 3 August 1910 for proposed foghorn, Williams's opposition to.

39. *List of Lights, Buoys and Day Marks in the First Light-House District,* 1909, 129 for Boon Island ledge whistling buoy. By the 1920s a whistle buoy with a flashing white light was in place off the ledge. *Buoy List Maine and New Hampshire First Lighthouse District.* (Washington: Department of Commerce Lighthouse Service, 1923), 61.

40. *List of Lights, Buoys and Day Marks in the First Light-House District.* 1909, 129 gives color of Boon Island lighthouse as white.

41. *Portsmouth Chronicle,* 5 December 1888 and 9 May 1889 for storm damage at White Island and repairs; White Island Clipping File, NARG26, for 1902 telephone between house and lighthouse.

42. LHBAR 1889,39 for rebuilding bridge.

43. Portsmouth Harbor Lighthouse Clipping File, NARG 26 for oil house; *Portsmouth Chronicle,* 27 February 1896 for bell.

44. Letters from Light House Board Secretaries to Engineers and Inspectors, December 29, 1894-July 3, 1897, 362, 370. NARG26; copies of National Archives documents, NH Parks and Recreation Department, Concord, NH, refer to the second moving of the house to make way for Battery Hackleman.

45. Cape Neddick Lighthouse Clipping File, NARG26.

46. LHBAR, 1889,.37 for enlarging boathouse, extending boat slip, rebuilding steps to house.

47. Cape Neddick Lighthouse Clipping File.

48. *Portsmouth Chronicle,* 11 and 19 November and 11 December 1889, 15 February 1890 for spindle at Anderson's Rock, changes to buoys, Half-Way Rock and Noble's Island; Half-Way Rock buoy carried away and replacement Feb 1890; also Frost's Point breakwater light.

49. LHBAR for the years 1888-1907 were used for Whale's Back foghorn statistics; Putnam, 226-227 for hours of fog along different coasts.

50. *Portsmouth Chronicle,* 5 April 1882 for sound of buoy; Johnson, 66-67 for illustration of Courtenay bell buoy; LHBAR 1882, 7 for date of placement Boon Island Ledge buoy.

51. *Portsmouth Chronicle*, 21 July , 11 August, 1882 and 7 May 1883 for placement and replacement of Courtenay fog whistle with bell buoy; Johnson, 67-68 for problems with summer folks, description of fog bell.

52. *Portsmouth Chronicle*, 4 March and 14 April 1884, the latter quoting the *Newburyport Herald* about solution to whistle with bell, fisherman-tourist problem; "List of Lights, Buoys, and Day-Marks in the First Light-House District 1909," 134 showing Kitt's bellboy still there; *Portsmouth Herald*, 23 Jan 1911 for projected replacement by the *Myrtle* of bell buoy with whistling buoy.

53. *Portsmouth Chronicle*, 6 February 1896, for White Island whistling buoy; *Portsmouth Herald*, 16 December 1905 and 11 February 1907 for planned bell at White I and discontinuation of White I ledge bell.

54. *Portsmouth Journal*, 17 December 1887 for electric light, Commercial Wharf; *Portsmouth Daily Chronicle*, 5 January 1889 for complaints about, wish to return to gas lamp.

55. LHBAR, 1906, 488 for act of 1882 mandating bridge lights; *Portsmouth Herald*, 22 November 1907 for stolen bridge lights.

56. Lighthouse Letters re Henderson's point—get citation

57. Johnson, 47-49; Putnam, 165 for post lights.

58. *Portsmouth Chronicle*, 25 September 1893 for Henderson's post light; Registers of Lighthouse Keepers for Pruitt, Wetzel and Stone as keepers.

59. Naish, 32, 38 for early range lights. *Portsmouth Chronicle*, 18 May 1894;First District Lighthouse Clipping File, gives 10 April 1894 as date of the establishment of the second light to create range lights.

60. *American Coast Pilot*, 1800, 39 and 1804, 140-141 for Plum Island lights for range lights. Even before post lights were used on the Mississippi River, two single reflector lamps, each hoisted on its own pole, were in use as range lights at least by 1850 at two south Atlantic coast islands close to harbor entrances. One such set was used on Sullivan's island to mark the course into Charleston Harbor. *Report of the general superintendent of the light-house establishment,* 1850, 8 for Sullivan's and Morris Island pole lights.

61. Registers of Lighthouse Keepers for Becker's appointment and pay. The *Portsmouth Chronicle,* 30 May 1896, noted his appointment and that he had begun his duties on May 25. August 1988 interview with Frederick S. White of New Castle, NH about Becker. Fabius Becker, of this family, was one of the earliest keepers of the ill-fated iron frame Minot's Light, but had left before its destruction in an April storm in 1851; *Portsmouth Herald*, 4 September 1903 for oil house, Jerry's Point.

62. *Portsmouth Herald*, 25 February,1909. *Annual Report of the United States Life-Saving Service, 1908-1909.* (Washington, D.C.: Government Printing Office, 1909),146 for rescue of Becker from breakwater.

63. Registers of Lighthouse keepers for A. B. White's appointment.

64. *Portsmouth Daily Chronicle,* 18 December 1882 for citizens' committee on closing Navy Yards; 22 May 1882 for Board of Trade report on port activity.

65. Whitehouse and Beaudoin, 47–48 for dredging Cocheco.

66. *Portsmouth Chronicle,* 24 June 1896 described the buoys and their distances from various landmarks.

67. *Report of the Chief of Engineers, U. S. Army, U. S. War Department Annual Report.* Washington, D.C.: U.S. Government Printing Office, 1879, Vol. 2, Part 1, 262–263 for 1878 survey and recommendations; 1880–1885 engineer's reports describe work done over these years.

68. *Report of the Chief of Engineers, U. S. Army, U. S. War Department Annual Report,* Vol. 2, Part 1, 1882, 506–507 for Thom's Little Harbor recommendation and cost estimate.

69. *Report of the Chief of Engineers, U. S. Army, U. S. War Department Annual Report,* Vol. 2, Part 1, Appendix A, 422–473 for Blunt's report, and 479 for his letter to General Newton.

70. *Report of the Chief of Engineers on preliminary examination of Little Harbor, at Portsmouth, N.H.* 48th Cong., 2nd sess., 1886, H. Ex. Doc. 91, for letters in support of Little Harbor project.

71. "Report of the Chief of Engineers, U. S. Army" in *U. S. War Department Annual Report,* 1887, 468-471, states that the project was adopted based on Colonel Thom's recommendation.

72. District Engineers were frequently reassigned, usually every two or three years. "Report of the Chief of Engineers, U. S. Army" in *U. S. War Department Annual Reports,* 1886–1905 contain yearly reports on the progress of the Little Harbor project.

73. "Report of the Chief of Engineers, U. S. Army" *U. S. War Department Annual Report,* 1902, 851 for 1901 statistics.

74. Peter E. Randall, *"There Are No Victors Here": A Local Perspective on the Treaty of Portsmouth.* (Portsmouth, N.H.: The Portsmouth Marine Society, Peter E. Randall, Publisher, 1985), 67.

75. *Portsmouth Herald,* 18 July 1932 and 22 June 1933 for Roosevelt's visits to Little Harbor.

76. Timothy P. Sullivan, "The Portsmouth Navy Yard, the New Dry Dock, and Henderson's Point," *Granite Monthly,* vol. 36, no. 2, February 1904, 77; Winslow, *"Do Your Job!",* 80 for removal of Henderson's Point.

77. First Light-House District clipping file, NARG26, for oil house; *Registers of Lighthouse Keepers,* for Stone; James Dolph, historian at the Portsmouth Naval Shipyard, located the lightkeeper's house, which still exists as Navy Quarters "A" for officers. It is within sight of its former location and has been vinyl-sided, with a gambrel-roofed addition above the original shed, and enclosed one-story porches on two sides.

78. Among the battleships of the Great White Fleet that spent time at the Navy yard were the U.S.S. *Wisconsin* and the second U.S.S. *Maine. Portsmouth Herald,* 9 March and 14 May 1909; Winslow, *"Do Your Job!",* 247 for navy yard personnel.

79. *Portsmouth Herald,* 5 February 1910 on dismal failure of Little Harbor as a refuge harbor.

80. *Report of the Chief of Engineers, U. S. Army, U. S. War Department Annual Report.* Washington: U. S. Government Printing Office, 1891, 614-615 for Pepperrell's Cove.

81. *Portsmouth Herald,* 7 January 1909; "Report of the Chief of Engineers, U. S. Army," 1910-1916, for dredging and blasting in Pepperrell's Cove.

82. Ibid.

83. Ibid., 1902-1904, 1910-1916 for Isles of Shoals breakwaters.

84. Ernest Holmes, "The Sea Ports of Europe," in the *Portsmouth Herald,* 6 January 1909 for *Titanic* reference.

85. 61st Cong., 3rd sess., 1910, H. Doc. 1086, CS 5904, 8, for commandant's statement; 3-11 for district engineer Lieutenant George Zinn's report; 10-11 for coal, shipping and rail rates.

86. Ibid.

87. *Portsmouth Herald* 22 June 1910 for masters preference for Boston.

88. *Examination of Portsmouth Harbor.* 61st Cong., 3rd sess., 1910, H. Doc. 1086, CS 5964, 5, for 1882 dam proposal.

89. Ibid., 8.

90. *Portsmouth Herald* 22 and 23 June 1910 for hearing on dam project;*Portsmouth Herald* 12 April 1910 for barge for Piscataqua Navigation Co.; 27 July 1916 for Consolidation Coal Co. purchase of steamer, plans for more); 7 October 1931 for concern about losing contract for Lowell coal.

91. Whitehouse and Beaudoin, 189-194 for March 1896 Dover flood.

92. "Report of the Chief of Engineers, U.S. Army," 1890, 450, for York Harbor project.

93. 61st Cong., 3rd sess., 1910, H. Doc. 301; *Portsmouth Herald,* 8 August, 20 September, and 24 October 1930; 31 March, 29 December 1934;19 June 1935; 30 January 1936; 25 May 1937; 5 August, 28 September, 20 October 1938; 25 April 1939 on Rye Harbor. The history of Rye Harbor is fully described in *Just Rye Harbor,* by Thomas C. Clarke and Rosemary F. Clarke. Portsmouth, N.H.: Portsmouth Marine Society, Peter E. Randall Publisher, 2005.

94. LHBAR, 1909, 61–62 for the *Myrtle*'s work; *List of Lights, Buoys and Day-Marks in the First Light-House District,* 1909, 129-135 for aids to navigation; *Portsmouth Herald,* 20 *November* 1909 for Hicks Rock approval. An iron spindle thirty-five feet high, surmounted by a sphere, was installed on the rock instead of a stone monument in January 1911, according to the *Portsmouth Herald,* 14 January 1911.

95. George Weiss, *The Lighthouse Service. Its History, Activities and Organization.* Institute for Government Research Service Monographs of the United States Government, No. 40. (Baltimore: The Johns Hopkins Press, 1926), 16-17, 19 for Navy takeover attempts and statistics.

96. *To establish the Bureau of Lighthouses.* 61st Cong., 2nd sess., January 1910, H. Report 224, 2-3 for Taft address to Congress; Weiss, 19, for problems with the board; John S. Conway, *The United States Lighthouse Service.* (Washington, D.C.: Department of Commerce, 1923), 111 lists chairmen of the Light-House Board; also Putnam, 45-46.

Chapter XIV: The Bureau of Lighthouses 1910–1939

1. *Portsmouth Herald,* 23 July 1910.

2. Winslow, *"Do Your Job!",* 247, for shipyard civilian employee statistics.

3. *Portsmouth Herald,* 8 April 1927 for shipments of Nova Scotia gypsumand 12 August, 1929 for Labrador shells to the poultry feet plant.

4. George R. Putnam, *Sentinel of the Coasts. The Life of a Lighthouse Engineer.* (New York: W. W. Norton & Company, 1937).

5. Ibid.

6. Ibid.; "Lighthouse Service Bulletin," (Washington, D.C.: U.S. Department of Commerce, vol. 4, no. 67, July 1, 1935), 209–11 for Putnam's retirement, accomplishments.

7. *Portsmouth Herald*, 23 July 1910 for Fahs, transfer of engineers from Boston to Portland; "Lighthouse Service Bulletin," No. 43, July 1, 1933, 156 for death and career of Carl Sherman, District. Superintendent; Sterling, 29 for Charles Brush.

8. *Portland* [Maine] *Telegram*, 25 March 1928 for retirement of Royal Luther.

9. *Portsmouth Herald*, 14 November and 27 December 1910, for desired improvements to help at night and in fog.

10. *Portsmouth Herald,* 23 January 1911.

11. Ibid., 4 February 1911 for new red light at Fort Constitution., i. o. v. lamp; Kenneth Sutton-Jones, *Pharos. The Lighthouse Yesterday Today and Tomorrow.* (Salisbury, England: Michael Russell, 1985),106.

12. Putnam, 187.

13. Constance Small, *The Lighthouse Keeper's Wife* (Orono, Maine: The University of Maine Press, 1986), 63–64 for i.o.v. lamp and lighting process. "Report of the Commissioner of Lighthouses for the Fiscal Year Ending 30 June 1914," in *Reports of the Department of Commerce.* Washington, D. C.: Government Printing Office (hereafter ARCL), 508 indicates all local lights furnished with i.o.v. lamps.

14. George Putnam to Oliver Frisbee, letter of 18 October 1914 about new Whale's Back Fresnel lens and characteristic, Whale's Back Clipping File; Description of Whaleback Light Station, May 1, 1935. Typed form, First District Lighthouse Files, NARG26; Sutton-Jones, 106 for mercury float.

15. *Portsmouth Chronicle,* 25 August 1894.

16. Wayne Wheeler, "The History of Fog Signals—Part II," *The Keeper's Log*, Fall 1990, 11 for the sounds of sirens and typhons.

17. *Portsmouth Herald*, 30 October 1911 reported Sherman's reassurances about the fog siren.

18. *Portsmouth Herald*, 23 December 1911, 15 January, 15 June 1912 ; Putnam, 230–231; Buoy List, Maine and New Hampshire, 1923, 62.

19. *Portsmouth Herald* 18 January 1932; "Description of Isles of Shoals Light Station" Department of Commerce, corrected to May 1, 1935, 7.

20. Peterson, 85–86; *Merchant Vessels of the United States,* 1911, 445; 1914, 464; 1922, 565; 1927, 954-5; Sterling, 68–9 for lighthouse tenders.

21. Sterling, 68–9 for Faulkingham, tenders; Peterson, 57 for *Zizania,* a steel-hulled tender built in 1888 and brought into the first district in 1912, where she served until 1924. *Portsmouth Herald*, 6, 7 August, 10,

11. September, 9 October 1931 for sinking and salvage of the *Shrub.*

22. ARCL, 1914, 530 for rescues.

23. Ibid., 23 January 1911 for Kitt's Rock whistler, etc. in Harbor.

24. Sutton-Jones, 135–137 for Dalen's work; Putnam, *Lighthouses and Lightships,* 215–236 for buoys; Undated newspaper clipping (probably Portland) and *Portsmouth Herald*, 2 February 1916 for replacement of gas buoy at Boon I. Ledge.

25. *Portsmouth Herald* , 22 January and 2 June 1915 for Goat I. acetylene buoy, Pumpkin I. flasher.

26. "List of Lights, Buoys, and Daymarks in the First Light-house District 1909" at the Maine Historical Society, Portland, ME (title page missing), 8-9 for 1906 and 1909

enactments on private lights; LHBAR, 1906, 488 for law regarding river lights, difficulty of enforcing; *Portsmouth Herald*, 24 May 1913 for theft of bridge light.

27. *Portsmouth Herald*, 23 April and 19 May 1915 for sites for upriver buoys and their placement.

28. Robert A. Whitehouse in a telephone interview with the author 18 October 1989 recalled that a few of the brickyards were still in operation as late as the 1920s but that bricks were no longer sent out by water.

29. *Scientific American*, 6 May 1916, 464 urges antisubmarine nets; Conway, 6–8 for lighthouse service during World War I.

30. Conway, 6-8; during World War II antisubmarine nets were placed at the entrance to Portsmouth Harbor; Shattuck, 40–42, 77 for Nubble and telephone hookup to mainland.

31. Shattuck, 40-41; *Portsmouth Herald* 4 December 1933 on James Burke, Navy.

32. William Washburn Nutting, *The Cinderellas of the Fleet* (Jersey City, N.J.: The Standard Motor Construction Co., 1920), 88 and *Portsmouth Herald* 4 August 1917 for sub-chasers patrolling; Winslow, *"Do Your Job!"*, 113-114 for U-boat destroying a Gloucester schooner after setting its crew off in dories, July 22, 1918.

33. *Merchant Vessels of the United States,* 1919,527; 1920,537 for radio equipment on tenders.

34. Conway, 93 on pensions.

35. *Portsmouth Herald,* 5 December 1922 for closing of river traffic during placement of draw span of new bridge.

36. Ibid., 5 July and 17 August 1923 for rules for draw openings, and opening of bridge to traffic; 10 October 1919 for hearing re 24-hour on-demand opening requests.

37. Putnam, *Sentinel of the Coasts,* 200–206 for radiobeacons.

38. Ibid.

39. Wheeler, "The History of Fog Signals—Part II", 13

40. *Portsmouth Herald* 10 March 1931 for removal of red sector at White Island.

41. Ibid., 26 December 1931 for change to white light at Portsmouth. Harbor; "Description of Portsmouth Harbor Light Station Corrected to May 1, 1935," 5-6 for change to electric light, green shade; *Portsmouth Herald*, 22 May 1931 for plans to electrify Boon Island.

42. "Science Ends Hero Role", *Portsmouth Herald,* 6 November 1925.

43. Ibid., 20 June 1928, 16 and 20 May 1933 for automated lights in New York Harbor and efforts to forestall closure of Fort Constitution lighthouse.

44. Ibid., 21 July 1933 ; Small, 208 for 1948 takeover of light by Coast Guard.

45. Conway, 92; Philmore B. Wass, *Lighthouse in My Life.* (Camden, Maine: Down East Books, 1987), 232, on itinerant teacher at Libby Island lighthouse station.

46. Eva Philbrook, "My Memories of Boon Island," handwritten reminiscence in the collection of the Kittery Naval and Historical Museum, Kittery, Maine; Banks, 362, lists Harry Smith as successor to Mitchell Blackwood as Boon Island head keeper October 23, 1916 to April 30, 1920. If Eva Philbrick's recollection is correct, his would have been the family with fifteen children. "Her's Was 'Longest' Classroom," undated newspaper clipping, probably Portland, Maine, ca. 1959. Collection of Kittery Naval and Historical Museum, Kittery, Maine for Lilla Severance. Wass,

231-2, writes of a slightly later itinerant teacher at Libby Island lighthouses, Mrs. Vera Sargent, but it is not known whether she taught at Boon Island. Wass also referred to a full-time teacher at Libby Island for the year 1925-6.

47. www.flyingsanta.org/HistoryOrigins.html.

48. Snow, 129.

49. The Registers of Lighthouse Keepers for the years after 1912 were destroyed by a fire at the Records Center in St. Louis, Missouri, and the Portsmouth city directories stopped listing their names by 1910. Reconstructing the rosters of keepers at each lighthouse is a somewhat hit-or-miss proposition, depending on articles and brief news items in newspapers, accounts in books on local history and reminiscences by wives, children, grandchildren and sometimes great-grandchildren of lightkeepers.

50. *Portsmouth Herald,* 30 September 1912 for James Burke's career and appointment to the Nubble lighthouse.

51. *Portsmouth Chronicle*, 28 November and 2 December 1889 for Burke and the *City of Ellsworth.*

52. *Portsmouth Herald*, 23, 27 January, 1 February 1911.

53. *Portsmouth Herald,* 30 September 1912; William O.Thomson, *Nubble Light. Cape Neddick Light Station.* (Kennebunk ME: By author, 'Scapes Me, distributor, 2000), 14; Shattuck, 27-28.

54. Shattuck, 28-41 for Burke's daughter Lucy's reminiscence.

55. ARCL, 1914, 532 and 1915, 618 for Burke's rescues.

56. *Portsmouth Herald,* 30 September 1912; Shattuck, 41-42 for WWI.

57. Registers of Lighthouse Keepers; *Portsmouth Herald,* 5 August 1907.

58. *Portsmouth Herald*, 24 July 1911 for rescue and 21 June 1921 for Walter Amee retirement.

59. Registers of Lighthouse Keepers.

60. Ibid.

61. Justine Flint, "Whales-Back, One of the Most Picturesque Lighthouses on the Coast," *Portsmouth Herald,* 12 August 1939.

62. Ibid.; Florence Zuckerman, "Historic Fort Point Light," *Portsmouth Herald,* 6 April 1944.

63. *Portsmouth Herald,* 20 October 1941 for retirement of Henry Cuskley.

64. Ibid.; Sterling, 32–33.

65. Sterling, 33–34.

66. Helen St. John, "Keepers of Little Harbor Lights," *Portsmouth Herald,* 20 November 1983.

67. Ibid., 4 November 1938 for storm signals at New Castle; "Coastal Warning Display Signals," http://weather.gov/om/marine/cwd.htm; Small, 204.

68. Herman Ingalls obituary notice, 1965 typescript. Collection of Prudence Heard, granddaughter of Herman Ingalls, Yarmouth, Maine.

69. Herman Ingalls record of employment with the U.S. Lighthouse Service, Printed form with typed entries. Collection of Prudence Heard.

70. Ibid.

71. *Machias Valley News-Observer*, 16 September 1959. Obituary notice reproduced in Marjorie Sprague Pinkham, *Starboard Creek from The Tides of Time,* (Machiasport, Maine: Self-published, undated, ca. 2000), 31.

72. Pinkham, 32-34.

73. Herman Ingalls Service Records. National Archives and Records Administration: Civilian Personnel Records, St. Louis, Missouri. Copies in possession of Marjorie Sprague Pinkham, Machiasport, Maine.

74. Herman Ingalls typescript obituary notice.

75. "Lighthouse Service Bulletin," June 1, 1935.

76. Ibid., August 1, 1935.

77. *Portsmouth Herald*, 1 May and 27 June 1939.

78. Ibid.

79. Robert Erwin Johnson, *Guardians of the Sea. History of the United States Coast Guard 1915 to the Present.* Annapolis, Maryland: Naval Institute Press, 1987, 162-163.

80. *Portsmouth Herald*, 27 June 1939.

81. Robert Erwin Johnson, 163-164.

82. Ibid., 164.

83. Gary E. Powell to Herbert C. Bonner, 2 February 1949. Herbert C. Bonner Papers, University of North Carolina. Chapel Hill, Southern Historical Collection. Cited in Robert Erwin Johnson, 164.

84. Florence Zuckerman, "History of Fort Point Light," *Portsmouth Herald,* 6 April 1944; Small, 176, 197.

85. Herman Ingalls Service Records.

86. *Portsmouth Herald*, 3 April 1940. Ingalls's expertise was valued, however, and after his retirement he was invited to Coast Guard headquarters in Washington to provide his advice. During World War II he was employed at the Bath Iron Works where he ran sea trials of many of the destroyers built there. Herman Ingalls Obituary Notice.

Chapter XV: Afterword

1. The *Portsmouth Herald*, 4 and 5 December 1945, describes a horrendous storm, with winds exceeding the great 1938 hurricane, demolishing a keeper's house and outbuildings and stranding the keeper in charge, his wife and two year old son, and two other Coast Guard men. Food was dropped onto the island by a helicopter; when the seas abated a boat from Wood Island Coast Guard station was able to land. A little more than two years later, another storm left the keepers unable to get ashore for provisions. *Portsmouth Herald* 10 and 11 February 1947. In 1978 a giant February storm put lighthouse keepers all along the coast in danger. Helicopter pads installed at both Boon Island and White Island were used to evacuate the crews of these stations, in which four and five feet of water were reported in the houses there. *Portsmouth Herald* 7 February 1978.

2. *Portsmouth Herald,* 29 August 1934 and 10 April 1935. For auctioning of lighthouses and lighthouse reservations.

3. Noble, 179.

4. *Portsmouth Herald*, 13 September 1962.

5. Noble, 179.

Bibliography

Adams, Henry. *The Life of Albert Gallatin.* Philadelphia: J. B. Lippincott & Co., 1880.

Adamson, Hans Christian. *Keepers of the Lights.* New York: Greenberg Publisher, 1935.

Albee, John. *New Castle, Historic and Picturesque.* Facsimile reprint of 1884 publication. Hampton, N.H.: Peter E. Randall, 1974.

Alexander, Karen. "Charting the Piscataqua," in W. Jeffrey Bolster, ed. *Cross-Grained and Wily Waters. A Guide to the Piscataqua Maritime Region.* Portsmouth, N. H.: Peter E. Randall Publisher, 2002.

American State Papers, Miscellaneous Volume One. Washington, D.C.: Gales andSeaton, 1834.

——. *Commerce and Navigation, Volumes One and Two.* Washington, D.C.: Gales and Seaton,1834.

——.*Documents, Legislative and Executive, 1815–1823, Volume Two.* Washington, D.C.: Gales and Seaton, 1835.

Annals of Congress. 11th Congress, 3rd Session. Washington, D.C.: Gales and Seaton, 1853.

——. 19th Congress, 3rd Session. Washington, D. C.: Gales and Seaton, 1829.

The Annual Cyclopaedia. New York: D. Appleton & Co., 1880.

Annual Report of the United States Life-Saving Service, 1908-1909. (Washington, D.C.: Government Printing Office, 1909.

Appleton's Cyclopaedia of American Biography. New York: D. Appleton & Co., 1887.

Appleton's Dictionary of Machines Mechanics, Engine-work and Engineering. New York: D. Appleton & Company, 1852.

Bachand, Robert G. *Northeast Lights.* Norwalk, Conn.: Sea Sports Publications, 1989.

——. "Whalesback Lighthouse." *The Keeper's Log,* vol. 9, no. 2, Winter 1993.

Banks, Charles Edward. *History of York, Maine.* Boston: Calkins Press, 1935.

Bauer, K. Jack. "Samuel Francis Du Pont: Aristocratic Professional," in James

C. Bradford, ed., *Captains of the Old Steam Navy.* Annapolis, Maryland: Naval Institute Press, 1986.

Beers, Henry P. *A History of the U.S. Topographical Engineers, 1818-1863.* www.topogs.org/history2.htm.

Bell, Kensill. *Always Ready.* New York: Dodd, Mead & Company, 1931.

Benes, Peter, ed. *New England Prospect: Maps, Place Names and the Historical Landscape.* Boston: The Dublin Seminar for New England Folklife Annual Proceedings, 1980.

Belknap, Jeremy. G. T. Lord, ed. *Belknap's New Hampshire. An Account of the State in 1792.* A facsimile edition of vol. 3 of *The History of New Hampshire.* Hampton, N.H.: Peter E. Randall, 1973.

Bell, Charles H. *The Bench and Bar of New Hampshire.* Boston and New York: Houghton Mifflin and Company, 1894.

Bickford, Charlene Bangs and Helen E. Veit, editors. *Legislative Histories,* vol. 5. Boston and London: Johns Hopkins University Press, 1986.

A Biographical Directory of the United States Customs Service 1771-1989. 2 vols. Information Services Division Office of Logistics Management, compiler. Washington, D.C.: Comptroller's Office, United States Customs Service, 1984,1986.

Blunt, Edmund March. *The American Coast Pilot.* Newburyport, Mass.: Edmund M. Blunt,1796, 1798, 1800, 1804, 1809.

———. *The American Coast Pilot.* New York: Edmund M. Blunt, 1812, 1815.

Blunt, Edmund and George W. Blunt. *The American Coast Pilot.* New York: E.and G. W. Blunt, 1827,1833, 1837, 1841,1847, 1850,1857.

Boyd, David, compiler. *History of the U. S. Navy Yard, Portsmouth, N. H.,*1930.

Bradford, Gershom. *The Mariner's Dictionary.* New York: Weathervane Books, 1952.

Bragdon, Lester MacKenzie and John E. Frost. *Vital Records of York, Maine.* Camden, Maine: Picton Press, n.d.

Brewster, Charles W. *Rambles About Portsmouth.* First series. Portsmouth, N.H.: C. W. Brewster, 1859.

———. *Rambles About Portsmouth.* Second series. Portsmouth, N.H.: Lewis Brewster, 1869.

Brighton, Raymond A. *Clippers of the Port of Portsmouth and the Men Who Built Them.* Portsmouth, N.H.: The Portsmouth Marine Society, Peter E. Randall Publisher, 1986.

———. *Tall Ships of the Piscataqua 1830-1877.* Portsmouth, N.H.: The Portsmouth Marine Society, Peter E. Randall Publisher, 1989.

———. *They Came to Fish.* Portsmouth, N.H.: Randall/Winebaum Enter-prises, 1979.

———. *Port of Portsmouth Ships and the Cotton Trade.* Portsmouth, N.H.: Portsmouth Marine Society, Peter E. Randall Publisher, 1986.

Bruce, Robert V. *The Launching of American Science, 1846-1876.* New York: Alfred A. Knopf, 1987.

Buoy List: Maine and New Hampshire. First Lighthouse District. Washington, D.C.: Department of Commerce Lighthouse Service, Government Printing Office, 1923.

Butler, Joyce. "Rising Like a Phoenix: Commerce in Southern Maine, 1775-1830," in Laura Fecych Sprague, editor, *Agreeable Situations: Society,*

Commerce, and Art in Southern Maine, 1780-1830. Kennebunk, Maine: Brick Store Museum, 1987.

Callum, George W. *Biographical Register of the Officers and Graduates of the U. S. Military Academy at West Point, N. Y.* Boston and New York: Houghton Mifflin and Company, 1891.

Candee, Richard M. "William and John Godsoe," in Peter Benes, ed., *New England Prospect: Maps, Place Names and the Historical Landscape.* Boston: The Dublin Seminar for New England Folklife Annual Proceedings, 1980.

Chadwick, John W. "White Island Light-House," reprinted from *Harper's Magazine. Portsmouth Chronicle,* 17 September 1874.

Chipman, Willis. "The Life and Times of Major Samuel Holland, Surveyor General, 1764-1801." *Papers and Records of the Ontario Historical Society,* vol. 21 (1924).

Clark, Charles E., *The Eastern Frontier.* Hanover, N.H. and London. University Press of New England, 1983.

Clifford, J. Candace and Mary Louise Clifford, *Maine Lighthouses. Documentaion of Their Past.* Alexandria, Virginia: Cypress Communications, 2005.

"Coastal Warning Display Signals." http://weather.gov/om/marine/cwd.htm

Cole, Donald B. *Jacksonian Democracy in New Hampshire, 1800-1851.* Cambridge, Mass.: Harvard University Press, 1970.

Conway, John S., compiler. *The U. S. Lighthouse Service.* Washington, D.C.: U.S. Department of Commerce, 1923.

Correspondence of the Treasury Secretary with Customs Collectors, 1789-1833, Record Group 26, National Archives, Washington, D.C., Microfilm M178, Roll 25.

Correspondence Concerning Keepers and Assistants, 1821-1902. Record Group 26, National Archives. Washington, D. C.

Cumming, William P. "The Colonial Charting of the Massachusetts Coast."

Frederick S. Allis, et al. *Seafaring in Colonial Massachusetts.* Boston: The Colonial Society of Massachusetts, 1980.

Daniell, Jere. "Frontier and Constitution: Why Grafton County Delegates Voted 10 to 1 for Ratification. *Historical New Hampshire,* vol. 45, no. 3., Fall, 1990.

Deane, John. *A Narrative of the Shipwreck of the Nottingham Galley in Her Voyage from England to Boston.* Reprint of the fifth, 1762 edition, Portland, Maine: The Provincial Press, 1968.

de Kerchove, Rene. *International Maritime Dictionary.* 2nd edition. New York: Van Nostrand Reinhold Company, 1961.

Dennett, Betsey. Letter to Alice Dennett, May, 1841. Armistead Dennett Collection, Kittery, Maine.

Dennett, Mark. "Daily Journal ..." Manuscript. Maine Historical Society, Portland, Maine.

———."Sketches of Life." Manuscript. Armistead Dennett Collection, Kittery, Maine.

Dictionary of American Biography. New York: Charles Scribner's Sons, 1959.

Dolph, James. "The Shipyard Pigeon Cote." *The Periscope,* vol. 46, no. 21, 11 August 1989. Portsmouth Naval Shipyard.

Elliot, Major George. *Report of a Tour of Inspection of European Light-House Establishments, Made in 1873.* 43rd Cong., 1st sess., 1874, S. Exec. Doc. 54.

Emery, William H. *The Salters of Portsmouth, New Hampshire.* New Bedford, Mass.,1936.

Evans, G. N. D. *Uncommon Obdurate: The Several Public Careers of J. F. W. DesBarres.* Salem, Mass. and Toronto: Peabody Museum of Salem and University of Toronto Press, 1969.

Evans, Stephen H. *The United States Coast Guard 1790-1915.* Annapolis, Maryland: The United States Naval Institute, 1949.

Fazio, Michael, "Bemjamin Latrobe's Designs for a Lighthouse at the Mouth of the Mississippi River." *Journal of the Society of Architectural Historians,* vol. 48, no. 3 (September 1989).

Fentress, Walter H. *Centennial History of the Navy Yard at Portsmouth, N.H.* Portsmouth, N.H.: O. M. Knight, 1876.

Fischer, Julian D. "Shipbuilding in Colonial Portsmouth: The Raleigh." *Historical New Hampshire*, vol. 42, no. 1, Spring 1987.

Flint, Justine. "Whales-Back, One of the Most Picturesque Lighthouses on the Coast." *Portsmouth Herald,* 12 August 1939.

Flint, Willard. Untitled, unpaged typescript on the history of U. S. lightships. Coast Guard Academy Library, New London, Conn.

Foss, Gerald D. "DesBarres Atlantic Neptune." *The Trestle Board.* Ports-mouth, N.H.: St. John's Lodge. January 1969.

———. "Hopley Yeaton and the Revenue Marine." *The Trestle Board.* Portsmouth, N.H.: St. John's Lodge. August 1965 and May 1975.

Fraser, Robert. "Scituate Lighthouse," *The Keeper's Log,* vol. 3, no. 2. Winter 1987.

Frost, John E. "York (Maine) Record Book." Typescript, 1943. Old York Historical Society, York, Maine.

Garvin, James L. "Academic Architecture and the Building Trades in the Piscataqua Region of New Hampshire and Maine, 1715-1815." Ph.D. diss., Boston University, 1983.

Gayle, Margot and David W. Look. *Metals in America's Historic Buildings.* Washington, D.C.: U. S. Department of the Interior, Heritage Conservation and Recreation Service, Technical Preservation Services Division, 1980.

"General Instructions to All Light-Keepers," Document No. 131, U. S. Treasury Department, 1881 and U.S. Department of Commerce, 1902.

Gleason, Sarah. *Kindly Lights: A History of the Lighthouses of Southern New England.* Boston, Mass.: The Beacon Press, 1991.

Grover, Eliphalet. "Logg." Manuscript, 1825-1839. Collection Old York Historical Society, York, Maine

Hague, Douglas B. and Rosemary Christie. *Lighthouses, Their Architecture, History and Archaeology.* Llandysed, Wales: Gomer Press, 1985.

Hall, Christopher, compiler. *Boston Architects and Builders compiled from the Boston Directory 1789–1846.* Cambridge, Mass.: Massachusetts Committee for the Preservation of Architectural Records, 1989.

Hawthorne, Nathaniel. *Passages from the American Notebooks of Nath-aniel Hawthorne.* Boston, Mass.: Houghton Mifflin and Company, 1880.

Hayward, Arthur. *Colonial and Early American Lighting.* New York: Dover
    Publications, Inc., 1962 reprint edition of the second, 1927 Little,
    Brown edition.
A History of Enforcement in the United States Customs Service 1789-1875. San
    Francisco: Department of the Treasury, 1998.
Hitchings, Sinclair, "Guarding the New England Coast: The Naval Career of
    Cyprian Southack." Frederick S. Allis, et al. *Seafaring in Colonial Mass-
    achusetts.* Boston: The Colonial Society of Massachusetts, 1980.
Holland, Francis Ross, Jr. *America's Lighthouses. An Illustrated History.* New
    York: Dover Publications, 1988.
———. *Great American Lighthouses.* Washington, D.C.: The Preservation
    Press, 1989.
Jenness, John Scribner. *The Isles of Shoals: An Historical Sketch.* Boston:
    Riverside Press, 1873.
Johnson, Arnold Burgess. "Lighthouse Establishment, The United States," in
    The Annual Cyclopaedia, 1880, vol. 5, 430. Typed copy of the entry in the
    author's possession, kindness of Rita F. Conant.
———. *The Modern Lighthouse Service.* Washington, D.C.: U.S. Government
    Printing Office, 1890.
Johnson, Paul Forsythe. *Steam and the Sea.* Salem, Mass.: Peabody Museum
    of Salem, 1983.
Johnson, Robert Erwin. *Guardians of the Sea. History of the United States
    Coast Guard 1915 to the Present.* Annapolis, Maryland: Naval Institute
    Press, 1987.
King, Irving H. *The Coast Guard Under Sail: The U.S. Revenue Cutter Service,
    1789-1865.* Annapolis, Maryland: Naval Institute Press, 1989.
Kobbe, Gustav. "Life on the South Shoal Lightship." *The Century,* vol. 42, no.
    69, August 1891.
Lacy, Harriet. "A. Postscript: Fort William and Mary Becomes Fort Constitution."
    Historical New Hampshire, vol. 29, no. 4, Winter 1974.
Laighton, Oscar. *Ninety Years at the Isles of Shoals.* Andover, Mass.: The
    Andover Press, 1929.
Laighton, Thomas B. Journal, 1839-1840, 1846-185?. Barbara Durant Collec-
    tion, Portsmouth Athenæum.
Lanman, Charles. *Dictionary of the United States Congress.* Philadelphia: J. B.
    Lippincot & Co., 1859.
*Laws of New Hampshire, including public and private acts and resolves ...*10
    volumes. By the State, 1904-1922.
Lewis, Isaiah William Penn. *Report of I. W. P. Lewis, Civil Engineer.* 27th Cong.,
    3rd sess., 1843, H. Rep. 183. CS422.
Lewis, Winslow J. *Description of the Light Houses on the Coast of the United
    States.* Boston, Mass.: Thomas G. Bangs, printer [1817].
———. *Remarks on Lighthouses.* Unpaged manuscript, ca. 1820. Lighthouse
    Letters, Box 17e, National Archives Record Group 26.
———. *A Review of the Report of I. W. P. Lewis on the State of the Light Houses
    on the Coasts of Maine and Massachusetts ...*Boston, Mass.: Tuttle and
    Dennett, 1843.
Lighthouse Clipping Files, Boon Island, Cape Neddick, Portsmouth Harbor,
    Whale's Back and White Island lighthouses. Record Group 26, National

Archives, Washington, D.C.

Lighthouse Deeds and Contracts. Record Group 26, National Archives, Washington, D.C.

Lighthouse Letters, National Archives Record Group 26, National Archives, Washington, D. C.

Lighthouse Service Bulletin. U.S. Bureau of Lighthouses. Vol. 4, Nos. 1-72, 1930-1935.

"List of Light-Houses, Lighted Beacons, and Floating Lights, of the Atlantic, Gulf, and Pacific Coasts of the United States." Washington, D.C.: Government Printing Office, 1862.

"List of Lights and Fog Signals on the Atlantic and Gulf Coast of the United States Corrected to June 30, 1903." Washington, D.C.: Government Printing Office, 1903.

Logs of the U. S. Navy Yard, Kittery, Maine. Portsmouth Naval Shipyard Archives, Portsmouth, N.H.

Machemer, Grace. "Headquartered at Piscataqua: Samuel Holland's Coastal and Inland Surveys, 1770-1774." *Historical New Hampshire*, Volume 57, Nos. 1 and 2, Spring/Summer 2002.

Mahan, D. H. *An Elementary Course of Civil Engineering for the Use of the Cadets of the U. S. Military Academy.* Second edition. New York: Wiley and Putnam, 1838.

Meloon, Ivan, compiler. "Correspondence with Washington. Lighthouse, Fort, Coast Guard." Undated typescript. Collection of Ports-mouth Athenæum.

Merchant Vessels of the United States. Washington, D.C.: Government Printing Office, various years.

Moody, Edward C. *Handbook History of the Town of York.* York, Maine: The York Publishing Company (ca. 1914).

Morgan, William James, et al., editors. *The Autobiography of Rear Admiral Charles Wilkes.* Washington, D.C.: Naval History Division, Department of the Navy, 1978.

Moulton, Dorothy M. "Whaleback Light." *New Hampshire Profiles*, June 1957.

Naish, John. *Seamarks, Their History and Development.* London: Stanford Maritime, 1985.

Nelson, George A., compiler. "Early U. S. Customs Records and History, Portsmouth, N. H." 6 vols. Bound typescripts. Collection of Ports-mouth Athenæum, Portsmouth, N. H.

New England Historical and Genealogical Register. Boston, Mass.: New England Historic and Genealogical Society, various dates.

New Hampshire Documents in the British Archives, Volume 14.

New Hampshire Lighthouse Contract File. National Archives Record Group 26.

New Hampshire Records of the Council, Book 7. New Hampshire Division of Archives and Records and Records Management, Concord, N.H.

New Hampshire State Papers. Nathaniel Bouton, compiler and editor. Concord, N.H.: various printers and dates.

New Hampshire Treasury Papers, Box 9. New Hampshire Division of Archives and Records Management. Concord, N.H.

Noble, Dennis L., *Lighthouses and Keepers. The U.S. Lighthouse Service and Its*

Legacy. Annapolis, Maryland: Naval Institute Press, 1976.

Nutting, William Washburn. *The Cinderellas of the Fleet.* Jersey City, N.J.: The Standard Motor Construction Co., 1920.

Parker, Benjamin Franklin, *History of Wolfeborough, N.H.* By the Town, 1901.

Parkman, Aubrey. *Army Engineers in New England: The Military and Civil Work of the Corps of Engineers in New England 1775-1975.* Waltham, Mass.: U. S. Army Corps of Engineers, New England Division, 1978.

Parsons, Charles L. "The Capture of Fort William and Mary." The William and Mary Committee of the New Hampshire American Revolution Bicentennial Commission, Reprint from Proceedings of the New Hampshire Historical Society, vol. 4, with additions of letters from New Castle selectmen and Governor Wentworth.

Parsons, Eleanor C. *Thacher's. Island of the Twin Lights.* Canaan, N.H.: Phoenix Publishing Co., 1985.

Parsons, Langdon B. *History of the Town of Rye, New Hampshire.* Concord, N.H.: Rumford Printing Co., 1947.

Patterson, Adoniram J., "Historical Address," in *Centennial Anniversary of the Planting of Universalism in Portsmouth, N. H.* Portsmouth: Wm. A. Plaisted, printer, 1874.

Penfold, P. A., editor. *Maps and Plans in the Public Record Office. 2. America and West Indies.* London: Her Majesty's Stationery Office.

Perry, Captain M. C. *Communication.* 25th Cong., 2nd sess., 1838, S. Doc. 159.

———*Light-Houses of Great Britain and France,* 26th Cong., 1st sess., 1840, S. Doc. 619

Peterson, Douglas. *U. S. Lighthouse Service Tenders 1840-1939.* Anna-polis and Trappe, Maryland: Eastwind Publishing, 2000.

Pierson, William H., Jr. *American Buildings and Their Architects. The Colonial and Neo-Classical Styles.* New York: Anchor Books, 1976.

Pinkham, Marjorie Sprague. *Starboard Creek from the Tides of Time.* Machiasport, Maine: By author, ca. 2000.

Pitch, Anthony S. "The Burning of Washington." White House Historical Association website: www.whitehousehistory.org.

"Port of Piscataqua Colonial Customs Records 1770-1775, Portsmouth N.H." Bound, unpaged facsimile. Collection of Portsmouth Athen-æum, Portsmouth, N. H.

Portsmouth City Directories.

Portsmouth Tax Lists and Accounts, Portsmouth, N. H. City Hall.

Portsmouth Tax Records, Portsmouth, N.H. Public Library.

Potter, Chandler E. *The Military History of the State of New Hampshire 1621-1861.* Baltimore, Maryland: Genealogical Publishing Co., Inc., 1972.

Preble, George H. *History of the United States Navy-Yard, Portsmouth, N. H.* Washington, D.C.: Government Printing Office, 1892.

Prince, Carl E. *The Federalists and the Origins of the U. S. Civil Service.* New York: New York University Press, 1977.

Putnam, George R. *Lighthouses and Lightships of the United States.* Boston, Mass.: Houghton Mifflin and Company, 1917.

———. *Sentinels of the Coasts: The Log of a Lighthouse Engineer.* New York: W. W. Norton & Company, Inc., 1937.

Quilici, Ronald H. "A Voyage to Antigua: A Social and Economic Study of the Maritime Activities of Colonial Portsmouth, New Hampshire." M. A. thesis, Department of History, University of New Hampshire, 1973.

————. "The Portsmouth Marine Society: Social Diversity in a Colonial Maritime Community." *Historical New Hampshire*, vol. 30, no. 2, Summer 1975.

Quinn, William. *Shipwrecks Around Maine*. Orleans, Mass.: Lower Cape Publishing Co., 1983.

Randall, Peter E. and Mary Ellen Burke, editors. *Gosport Remembered: The Last Village at the Isles of Shoals*. Portsmouth, N.H.: Ports-mouth Marine Society, Peter E. Randall, Publisher, 1997), 121.

Randall, Peter E. *"There Are No Victors Here": A Local Perspective on the Treaty of Portsmouth*. Portsmouth, N.H.: The Portsmouth Marine Society, Peter E. Randall, Publisher, 1985.

A Record of the Services of the Commissioned Officers and Enlisted Men of Kittery and Eliot, Maine. Boston, Mass.: Alfred Mudge & Sons, Printers, 1901.

Record of Movements. Vessels of the United States Coast Guard, 1790–December 31, 1933. Washington, D.C.: United States Coast Guard, 1933.

Records of the Committee of Safety. New Hampshire Division of Archives and Records Management, Concord, N. H.

Records of the Council. New Hampshire Division of Archives and Records Management, Concord, N. H.

Rees, Abraham. *The Cyclopaedia; or Universal Dictionary of Arts, Science, and Literature*. First American edition, 42 vols. of text and 6 of plates. Philadelphia: Samuel F. Bradford and Murray, Fairman and Co., 1806-1822.

Registers of Lighthouse Keepers and Assistant Keepers, 1845-1912. National Archives and Records Administration microfilm publication M1373, roll 1.

Register of Officers and Agents, Civil, Military, and Naval, in the Service of the United States. 1833, 1834, 1838. Place and publisher vary; Washington, D. C.: Government Printing Office, 1853–1871.

Report of the Chief of Engineers, U. S. Army. U. S. War Department Annual Report. Washington, D.C.: U. S. Government Printing Office, 1878-1916.

Report of the Commissioner of Lighthouses. Report of the Department of Commerce. Washington, D.C.: Government Printing Office, various years.

Report of the Light-House Board. Report of the Secretary of the Treasury. Washington, D.C.: Government Printing Office, 1853-1910.

Ristow, Walter W. *American Maps and Mapmakers: Commercial Cartography in the Nineteenth Century*. Detroit, Michigan:1986.

Rockingham County Probate Dockets. Rockingham County Registry of Deeds and Probate, Brentwood, N.H.

Rouverel, Alice. "Three Lights Lived: Profile of Beulah Quinn." *Island Journal*, vol. 3, 1986.

Rowe, William H. *The Maritime History of Maine: Three Centuries of Shipbuilding and Seafaring*. Freeport, Maine: The Bond Wheelwright Company, 1966.

Rutledge, Lyman. *The Isles of Shoals in Lore and Legend*. Boston, Mass.: The Star Island Corportation, 1971.

Sabine, Lorenzo. *Biographical Sketches of Loyalists of the American Revolution*. 2 volumes. Boston, Mass.: Little, Brown and Company, 1864.

The Sailor's Magazine and Naval Journal, December 1838 and January 1839.

Saltonstall, William G. *Ports of Piscataqua.* Cambridge, Mass. Harvard University Press, 1941.

Sands, John O. "The U. S. Light House Board: Progress through Process." *American Neptune,* vol. 47, no. 3, Summer 1987.

Schlesinger, Arthur, Jr. *The Age of Jackson.* Boston: Little Brown and Company, 1946.

Schubert, Frank N., ed. *March to South Pass: Lieutenant William B. Franklin's Journal of the Kearney Expedition of 1845.* Washington, D.C.: Historical Division Office of Administrative Services, Office of the Chief of Engineers, 1979.

———. *The Nation Builders: A Sesquicentennial History of the Corps of Topographical Engineers.* Fort Belvoir, Virginia: Office of History, United States Army Corps of Engineers, 1988.

Sganzin, M. L. *An Elementary Course in Civil Engineering.* Third edition. Boston, Mass.: Hilliard, Gray & Co., 1836.

Shallatt, Todd, "Building Waterways, 1802-1861: Science and the United States Army in Early Public Works." *Technology and Culture,* vol. 31, no. 1, January 1990.

Shattuck, Clifford. *The Nubble: Cape Neddick Lightstation, York, Maine.* Freeport, Maine: The Cumberland Press, Inc., 1979.

Small, Constance. *The Lighthouse Keeper's Wife.* Orono, Maine: The University of Maine Press, 1986.

Smith, John. *A Description of New England, 1616.* Boston: William Veazie, n. d.

Smith, Horatio D. and Elliot Snow, editors. *Early History of the United States Revenue Marine Service, 1789–1849.* A Coast Guard Bicentennial Publication, Washington, D.C., 1989.

Snell, Mark A. *From First to Last: The Life of Major General William B. Franklin.* New York: Fordham University Press, 2002.

Snow, Edward Rowe. *Lighthouses of New England.* New York: Dodd, Mead and Company, 1973.

Spinney, Franklin O. "An Ingenious Yankee Craftsman." *The Magazine Antiques,* vol. 44, September 1943.

Standeven, Hazel, compiler. "Brown-Duncan Genealogy," Typescript, 1981. Collection of New Castle, N.H. Public Library.

Stephan, Sharon Pavia. *One Woman's Work: The Visual Art of Celia Laighton Thaxter.* Portsmouth, N.H.: Peter E. Randall Publisher, 2001.

St. John, Helen. "Keepers of Little Harbor Lights." *Portsmouth Herald,* 20 November 1983.

Sterling, Robert. *Lighthouses of the Maine Coast and the Men Who Keep Them.* Brattleboro, Vermont: Stephen Day Press, 1935.

Stevenson, D. Alan. *The World's Lighthouses before 1820.* London: Oxford University Press, 1959.

Sullivan, Timothy P. "The Portsmouth Navy Yard, the New Dry Dock, and Henderson's Point." *Granite Monthly,* vol. 36, no. 2, February 1904.

Sutton-Jones, Kenneth. *Pharos: The Lighthouse Yesterday Today and Tomor-

row. Salisbury, England: Michael Russell, Ltd., 1985.

Tallman, Louise, compiler. "Families of Gosport." Typescript, unpaged. Collection of Portsmouth Athenæum.

Thaxter, Celia. *Among the Isles of Shoals*. Boston: James R. Osgood & Co., 1873.

———. *An Island Garden*. Boston: Houghton Mifflin and Company, 1894.

———. *Poems*. Boston: Houghton Mifflin and Company, 19th edition, 1893.

Thaxter, Rosamond. *Sandpiper: The Life and Letters of Celia Thaxter*. Reprint of a 1963 publication. Hampton, N.H.: Peter E.. Randall, 1982.

Thompson, William O. *Nubble Light: Cape Neddick Light Station*. Kennebunk, Maine: 'Scapes Me Distributor, 2000.

———. *Nubble Light. York Beach Maine*. By author, 1996.

———. *Solitary Vigils at Boon Island*. Kennebunk, Maine: 'Scapes Me Distributor, 2000.

Tolles, Bryant F., Jr. with Carolyn K. Tolles. *New Hampshire Architecture: An Illustrated Guide*. Hanover, N.H.: University Press of New England, 1979.

Tullock, Thomas L. "Presidential Appointments in Portsmouth." *Granite Monthly*, vol. 6, no. 4., January 1886.

U. S. Bureau of Lighthouses. *Annual Report*. Washington, D.C.: Government Printing Office, various dates.

U.S. Congress, House of Representatives. *Petition of William Palmer and Daniel Haselton*. 22nd Cong., 2nd sess., 1832, H. Rep. 343, CS 226.

———. *Relief of Daniel Hazleton and William Palmer*. 22nd Cong ., 2nd sess., 1833, H. Rep. 74, CS 236.

———. *Statement of Contracts authorized in 1834*. 23rd Cong., 2nd sess., 1835, H. Doc. 161, CS 274.

———. *Lighthouses. Fifth Auditor on Execution of Act of July 7, 1838*. 25th Cong., 3rd sess., 1838-39, H. Doc. 24, CS 345.

———. *Report of I. W. P. Lewis, Civil Engineer*. 27th Cong., 3rd sess., 1843, H. Doc.183, CS 422.

———. *Condition of the Light-houses on the Eastern coast*. 27th Cong., 3rd sess., 1843, H. Rep. 282, CS 428.

———. *Fifth Auditor's report relative to light-houses and lights, January 19, 1844*. 28th Cong., 1st sess.,1844, H. Doc. 62, CS 441.

———. *Light-house establishment*. 30th Cong., 1st sess., 1847, H. Ex. Doc. 27, CS 516.

———. *Report of the general superintendent of the light-house establishment*. 31st Cong., 2nd sess, 1850, H. Ex. Doc. 14, CS 598.

———. *A communication from the Fifth Auditor of the Treasury reporting the light-house system of the United States, in reply to a report made to Congress by the Light-House board*. 32nd Cong., 1st sess., 1852. H. Ex.Doc. 88.,CS 644.

———. *Report of the Chief of Engineers on preliminary examination of Little Harbor, at Portsmouth, N.H.* 48th Cong., 2nd sess., 1886, H. Ex..Doc. 91, CS 2302

———. *To establish the Bureau of lighthouses*. 61st Cong., 2nd sess., 1910, H. Rep. 224, CS 5591.

―――. 61st Cong., 3rd sess., 1910, H. Doc. 301.

―――. *Examination of Portsmouth Harbor.* 61st Cong., 3rd sess., 1910, H. Doc. 1086, CS 5904.

U.S. Congress, Senate. *Communication* from Capt. M. C. Perry. 25th Cong., 2nd sess., 1838, S. Doc. 159, CS 316.

―――. *Documents on the light-house establishment of the United States.* 25th Cong., 2nd sess., 1838, S. Doc. 258, CS 316.

―――. *Light-Houses of Great Britain and France,* report by Capt. M. C. Perry. 26th Cong., 1st sess., 1840, S. Doc. 619, CS 361.

―――. *Report of the Secretary of the Treasury on Improvements to the Light-house system and collateral aids to navigation.* 29th Cong., 1st sess., 1846, S. Doc. 488, CS 478.

―――. *Report of the Officers Constituting the Light-House Board.* 32rd Cong., 1st sess., 1852, S. Ex. Doc. 28, CS 617.

―――. *Report of the Light-House Board. Report of the Secretary of the Treasury,* 35th Cong., 2nd sess.,1858, S. Ex. Doc. 2, CS 979.

―――. *Report of a Tour of Inspection of European Light-House Establishment made in 1873 by Major George Elliot,* 43rd Cong., 1st sess., 1874, S. Ex. Doc. 54, CS 1581.

―――. *Lighthouse tender for first district inspector.* 60th Cong., 1st sess., 1908, S. Rep. 18. CS 5218.

―――. *Lighthouse tender for first and second district engineer.* 60th Cong., 1st sess., 1908, S. Rep 19, CS 5218.

U.S. Light-House Board, *Annual Report.* Washington, D.C.: Government Printing Office, various dates, 1852–1909.

U.S. Light-House Board Records. Record Group 26, National Archives, Washington, D.C.: Indexes to Minutes of the Light-House Board.

―――: Journals of the Light-House Board.

―――: Letters to District Engineers.

―――: Minutes of the Proceedings of the Light-House Board.

―――: Register of Letters Received from the Engineer of the First Lighthouse District, E42, vols. 114, 115.

Updike, Richard W. " Winslow Lewis and the Lighthouses." *American Neptune,* vol. 28, no. 1, 1968.

Ure, Andrew. *A Dictionary of Arts, Manufactures, and Mines.* London: Orne, Brown, Green & Longmans, 1840.

Wall, Edward. "Abraham Prescott: Bass Viol Maker." *Historical New Hampshire,* vol. 42, no. 3, Summer 1987.

Weiss, George. *The Lighthouse Service: Its History, Activities and Organization.* Baltimore, Maryland: The Johns Hopkins Press, 1926.

Wentworth, John. Letter Book, vol. 3. Transcript. New Hampshire Division of Archives and Records Management, Concord, N. H.

Wheeler, Wayne. "The Keeper's New Clothes." *The Keeper's Log,* Summer 1985.

―――. "The History of Fog Signals—Part II." *The Keeper's Log,* Fall 1990.

―――. "A Lighthouse for Bell Rock." *The Keeper's Log,* Summer 1988.

Whitehouse, Robert A. and Cathleeen C. Beaudoin. *Port of Dover: Two Centuries of Shipping on the Cochecho.* Portsmouth, N.H.: The Portsmouth

Marine Society, Peter E. Randall Publisher, 1988.

Whitehouse, B. T., collector, "Dover Cotton Factory No. 1." Pamphlet. Dover, N.H., Public Library.

Wilderson, Paul. "Protagonist of Prudence: A Biography of John Wentworth, the King's Last Governor of New Hampshire." Ph.D. diss. University of New Hampshire, 1977.

———."The Raids on Fort William and Mary: Some New Evidence." *Historical New Hampshire*, vol. 30, no. 3, Fall 1975.

Willard, John Ware, *Simon Willard and His Clocks.* New York: Dover Publications, Inc., 1968.

Winslow, Richard E. III. *"Do Your Job!" An Illustrated Bicentennial History of the Portsmouth Naval Shipyard, 1800-2000.* Portsmouth, N.H.: The Portsmouth Marine Society, Peter E. Randall Publisher, 2000.

———. *"Wealth and Honor": Portsmouth During the Golden Age of Privateering, 1775-1815.* Portsmouth, N.H.: The Portsmouth Marine Society, Peter E. Randall Publisher, 1988.

Willey, Benjamin G. *Incidents in White Mountain History.* Boston: Nathan-iel Noyes, 1856.

Witney, Dudley. *The Lighthouse.* Boston: New York Graphic Society, 1975. Reprint edition, New York: Arch Cape Press, 1989.

York County Deeds, York County Registry of Deeds, Alfred, Maine.

Zimmer, Edward. "The Architectural Career of Alexander Parris (1780-1852)" PhD. diss., Boston University, 1984.

Newspapers

Eastern Argus (Portland, Maine)
Machias Valley News-Observer (Machias, Maine)
New-Hampshire Gazette (Portsmouth, N. H.)
The Oracle (also *The Oracle of the Day*) (Portsmouth, N. H.)
Portsmouth Evening Times
Portsmouth Herald.
Portsmouth Journal of Literature and Politics.
Portsmouth Morning Chronicle.

Index

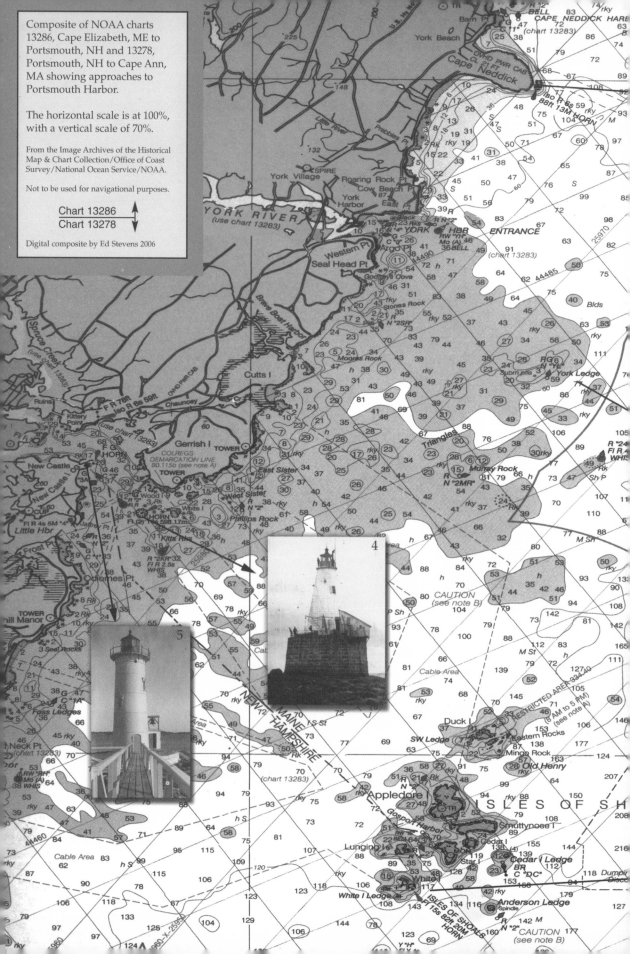

Composite of NOAA charts 13286, Cape Elizabeth, ME to Portsmouth, NH and 13278, Portsmouth, NH to Cape Ann, MA showing approaches to Portsmouth Harbor.

The horizontal scale is at 100%, with a vertical scale of 70%.

From the Image Archives of the Historical Map & Chart Collection/Office of Coast Survey/National Ocean Service/NOAA.

Not to be used for navigational purposes.

Chart 13286
Chart 13278

Digital composite by Ed Stevens 2006